STALIN
as
Military Commander

STALIN

as
Military Commander

Albert Seaton

Praeger Publishers
New York

Published in the United States of America in 1976
by Praeger Publishers, Inc.
111 Fourth Avenue, New York, N.Y. 10003

© 1975 in London, England, by Albert Seaton
All rights reserved

Library of Congress Catalog Card Number: 75-37026
ISBN 0-275-22960-2

Printed in the United States of America

Contents

Maps

Acknowledgments

Gratitude is expressed to the authors and publishers for kind permission to quote from the following books: *The Turn of the Tide 1939–1943* by Arthur Bryant – Collins, London; *Delo Vsei Zhizni* by Marshal of the Soviet Union A. M. Vasilevsky – Izdatel'stvo Politicheskoi Literatury, Moscow; *General'nyi Shtab v Gody Voiny (Kniga Vtoraia)* by General of the Army S. M. Shtemenko – Voennoe Izdatel'stvo Ministerstva Oborony SSSR, Moscow: and to the Imperial War Museum for permission to reproduce the photographs of Marshals of the Soviet Union Zhukov and Konev, and to the Radio Times Hulton Picture Library for the use of the 1920 photograph of the cavalry army military council.

Notes on Sources and Style

Since there is sufficient Russian printed matter available on Stalin as a military commissar and commander to form the basis of a work covering several volumes, the problem in writing this book has been to condense, in narrative form and within a limit of 100,000 words, the dictator's military activities over a period of 35 years. Moreover, since this book is intended for the general reader as well as for the Russian and military specialist, it has been necessary to include some background information covering Russian history, the Imperial Russian Army and the Red Army which followed it. Limitations of space have precluded comment or assessment by the author, and this is, in any case, unnecessary, since the material is for the most part self-explanatory. The substance of this book has been extracted from a much fuller monograph.

Before the Second World War, information, other than that contained in the Soviet encyclopedia contributions, the *Grazhdan-skaia Voina* and the popular *Stalin i Krasnaia Armiia*, certainly existed concerning Stalin's military activities from 1918 to 1920; but it was sparse and difficult to get. By 1938 Stalin had already been accorded great fame as a military leader and theorist, at least by Soviet authors, so much so that historians outside Russia tended to turn to Trotsky's writings as a palliative. But Trotsky's works, valuable though they are as commentaries, are based on recollections committed to paper many years after the event; and Trotsky, even in maturity, was still fascinated by a turn of phrase, by words rather than by their accuracy or import. Trotsky has supported his descriptions of Stalin by a skilful use of what has now become

9

known as *The Trotsky Papers,* copies of official records removed by him from the Soviet archives prior to his banishment. *The Trotsky Papers,* although authentic, are by themselves unsuitable for a biography on Stalin since their subject matter is Trotsky, and they represent in any case merely a random selection of documents. Trotsky's account of the part played by Stalin in the Civil and Polish Wars is therefore largely uncorroborated, and his chronology – even such factual detail as the military appointments held by Stalin during the period – is contrary not only to the information contained in the fourth volume of Stalin's *Sochineniia* published in 1947, but also to that in the successive issues of Lenin's *Polnoe Sobranie Sochinenii* and in the *Leninskii Sbornik*.

Much new light has been thrown on the Soviet High Command and the course of Red Army operations during the Civil and Polish Wars from 1918 to 1920, by the publication in Moscow during the late sixties and early seventies of a mass of official documents, edited and annotated by Soviet archivists, comprising correspondence, military appreciations and orders, and teleprinter traffic. This is particularly informative on the roles played by Lenin, Trotsky and Stalin *vis à vis* those of their military specialists, and does much to discredit the versions given by both Trotsky and Stalin. It can of course be proved that numbers of important documents are missing from the published Moscow collections, but this does not necessarily detract from their value for they have impeccable communist origins and represent an authoritative though not a definitive source of great importance.

Few Soviet documents have yet been published covering the period of the Second World War and, if the Moscow academic press is to be believed, few Soviet historians are permitted unrestricted access to the official archives. In Stalin's lifetime the work of military historians was too superficial to throw much light on the true nature of the military leadership during this period. Indeed, one of the most revealing publications of the time was probably the 1950 *Stalin – Kratkaia Biografiia* (which, according to Khrushchev, was edited personally by the dictator), since this unwittingly shows how Stalin misunderstood German strategic aims between 1941 and 1943. After Stalin's death, and particularly during Khrushchev's ascendancy, a number of detailed official histories of the Second World War appeared, together with a flood of military studies, war memoirs and reminiscences. Khrushchev was mainly responsible for the denunciation of the Stalin personality cult and for the exposure of some of Stalin's crimes against humanity, the party and the state, and he decried Stalin's military ability and caused Soviet historians to do the same. Yet within a short space of time a second Tsaritsyn group of generals began to laud Khrushchev's military genius, and this was only stifled with Khrushchev's removal from power. For the next few years the Soviet military press was uncertain and lacked its earlier uniformity of pattern. Condemnation of Stalin continued, but by degrees criticism became more moderate, and on some aspects, notably the repressions, muted. For Khrushchev bequeathed to the new Soviet régime a number of problems, among them that of publicly reconciling Stalin's excesses with the infallibility of Lenin and the Communist Party. From 1968 onwards increasingly frequent mention has been made of Brezhnev's role in the Second World War, relatively modest though this was. But whereas Khrushchev has been relegated to obscurity, it is impossible to do this to Stalin; so the dictator continues to dominate, in literature as in life, the 30 years of the history of the Soviet Union following Lenin's death.

The Soviet generals who were once close to Stalin are sensitive about their reputations, and their accounts are, not unnaturally, sometimes coloured by animosity, jealousy and prejudice: but all are informative. Some of the Soviet military studies are particularly well written and admirably produced. Much of the content of the more important historical works of the post-Stalin era is probably true, but it is certainly not the whole truth, for, of that part which can be verified, some is palpably false. Yet from this great wealth of Soviet evidence there emerges an unequivocal picture of Stalin as a military commander in the Second World War, whether written by an admirer or by an enemy, under Khrushchev or under Brezhnev. Even the silences are eloquent – *Tacent quia periculum metuunt : etiamsi tacent, satis dicunt.*

Of the memoirs of those officers who worked directly under Stalin, Zhukov's *Vospominaniia i Razmyshleniia* is full and instructive but lacks clarity and consistency; Vasilevsky's *Delo Vsei Zhizni* on the other hand provides a particularly informative, well-ordered and balanced account; Shtemenko's two volumes on the

General'nyi Shtab is a well-presented work of great value, by one who remains Stalin's ardent admirer. Of the front commanders who were close to Stalin, Rokossovsky's *Soldatskii Dolg*, Meretskov's *Na Sluzhbe Narodu*, Bagramian's *Gorod-Voin na Dnepre* and *Tak Nachinalas' Voina* all give an insight into Stalin's mentality and military capabilities; in addition Konev, Golikov, Tiulenev and Khozin have written memoirs or contributed to the Soviet military press. The front commanders Eremenko and Malinovsky belonged to the new Tsaritsyn group and were once protégés of Khrushchev, as was the tank commander Rotmistrov, and this is apparent in their writings. Some of the chiefs of staff and army commanders, such as Leliushenko, met Stalin frequently; many others, Batov and Moskalenko among them, did not see the dictator until late in, or after, the war, but he frequently spoke to them on the telephone during the course of operations. The artillery, air and naval chiefs, Voronov, Novikov and Kuznetsov, and the armament officials and designers Vannikov, Iakovlev, Emelianov and Grabin are authors of most informative accounts. All these reminiscences, and a score of others, have been used in compiling this work, and have been compared with each other (bearing in mind the origin and date of publication), and with western and German evidence. Whenever available, original Russian language works have been used in preference to translations.

Notwithstanding the restriction of space, a brief description of the Soviet state and military teleprint, telephone and radio system has been included, because its failure was partly responsible for the defeat of the Red Army in 1920 and again in 1941. The communication system is, in any case, part of the Soviet High Command.

In transliterating Russian words the Library of Congress method has been followed except that *y* has been used instead of *ii* for the endings of Russian surnames and the designations of tsarist regiments. There are unavoidable inconsistencies in the spelling of some proper names, particularly in quotation. Geographical names are shown in accordance with *The Times Atlas* current between the two world wars even though this does not necessarily follow the Library of Congress method or the spelling used on modern Russian maps. Surnames have been shown without initials (except on first mention to distinguish between two of the same name), and without titles or ranks. These can be found by reference to the index.

Because this book contains a great amount of factual material hitherto unpublished outside the Soviet Union, it has been thought necessary to annotate the text to show sources for the benefit of the historian and specialist; the source references have, of necessity, been much abbreviated and should be used in conjunction with the bibliography. The general reader can happily ignore the note numeration. Only six general maps are included since it is obviously impracticable to produce campaign maps to illustrate a text which covers so wide a field.

An appendix has been included at the end of the book in the form of short notes describing the organization and the terminology of the Russian and the Red Armies, for the benefit of the general reader who is unacquainted with this subject. Such readers may find it convenient to read the appendix before embarking on the main body of the book.

All dates are in accordance with the Julian calendar until 21 February 1918 and thereafter in the new style of the Gregorian calendar.

Foreword

The subject of this book covers a very wide field and the work could not have been completed without the assistance of a large number of people. To all of them I express my gratitude.

I should like in particular to thank my readers: Professor Dr Alexander Fischer of the Johann Wolfgang Goethe University, Frankfurt; Mr Jeremy Newton of Queen's College, Oxford; Mr Michael Parrish of Indiana University; and Professor Dr Peter Scheibert of the Philipps University, Marburg.

I am most grateful to the Governing Body and the librarians of St Antony's College, Oxford, for the use of their resources. My warm hearted thanks go, too, to the Librarian and staff of the School of Slavonic and East European Studies, London University, and to the Chief Librarian and the Librarian in charge of the Library's Historical Section of the British Ministry of Defence Library (Central and Army), for their generous loan of Russian, German and English printed material.

In addition I thankfully acknowledge the assistance of government departments, learned organizations, libraries and many people in England, Germany and the United States. In particular: the Keeper of the Public Records, London; the Director and the staff of the Bundes-Militärarchiv, Freiburg; the Librarian and staff of the Slavonic Section of the Bodleian Library; the Soviet Studies Centre and the Librarian and staff of the RMA, Sandhurst; the Librarian and staff of the Institute of Contemporary History and Wiener Library; and the Librarian and staff of the Royal United Services Institute for Defence Studies.

I am particularly grateful to: Professor Dr Andreas Hillgruber of Cologne University for his advice on reading; Dr David Kahn, formerly of St Antony's College, for information concerning cryptography; Mr B. Stagg of *The Post Office Electrical Engineers' Journal* for his technical comment on line systems; and Major J. K. Zieleznik MC and the staff of the Post Office Telecommunications Museum for their interest in, and advice on, telegraph equipment in use in the Soviet Union between 1918 and 1945, and for their kindness in setting up and operating Hughes and Baudôt teleprinter circuits, entirely for the benefit of this study.

Lastly I should like to thank my wife who has typed and retyped the script many times and, over the years, has shared with me the arduous research.

I
Tsaritsyn

Stalin was born at Gori in 1879, the son of a Georgian cobbler named Vissarion Djugashvili. In 1894 he entered the theological seminary in Tiflis, where, in cloistered seclusion, the monks attempted to instil into the future atheist, regicide and revolutionary, a reverence for God, the tsar and the church. Five years later he was expelled and became a professional revolutionary and a Bolshevik.

From 1902 onwards the young Djugashvili was imprisoned no fewer than six times. A fellow prisoner by name of Vereshchak described Djugashvili as a rude and unpleasing speaker with an outstanding memory, crude and lacking in principle, having little educational background or culture, with 'an aptitude for striking secretly by the hands of others while remaining in the background himself'.[1] Extracts of Vereshchak's account considered to be sufficiently laudatory to Stalin were later to be published in *Pravda*.[2]

The February 1917 revolution had caught the Bolsheviks by surprise and many of them were abroad or in Siberia. Djugashvili, who had taken the name of Stalin, had been exiled in 1913 for revolutionary activities; this had not exempted him, however, from military call-up in December 1916, but he had been returned to Achinsk, presumably as medically unfit due to obstetrical palsy, a birth injury to his left arm.[3] Stalin was among the first to arrive in Petrograd.

On 10 October 1917 the Central Committee of the Bolshevik Party resolved on armed insurrection against the *bourgeois* Provisional Government, Stalin voting with Lenin in favour of the motion. A bureau of seven members was set up to undertake on the spot policy decisions on behalf of the Central Committee, these being Lenin, Trotsky, Zinov'ev, Kamenev, Stalin, Sokol'nikov and Bubnov, and a few days later a party 'military centre' was created consisting of Sverdlov, Stalin, Bubnov, Uritsky and Dzerzhinsky.[4]

Trotsky, a Bolshevik and Central Committee member of only a few weeks' standing, had, however, already formed, on 12 October, a revolutionary military committee, an unofficial body within the Petrograd Soviet, which, under the guise of defending the revolution, was to organize the Bolshevik *coup*. This committee had 66 members, all Bolsheviks except for 14 Left Socialist Revolutionaries and four anarchists. Lenin had intended that the five members of the party 'military centre' should form a part of the Petrograd Soviet revolutionary military committee, but, said Trotsky, they did not do so, although four of the five 'sometimes undertook some military work'.[5] The fifth, Stalin, 'kept away altogether'. For, according to Trotsky, the 'military centre' was merely a paper organization; and Stalin, whom he once described as 'not devoid of courage but merely preferring to expend it economically', wanted to face both ways and remain uncommitted.[6] Stalin, for his part, did not deny that the insurrection had been entrusted to the revolutionary military committee of the Petrograd Soviet, but insisted that this committee was carrying out the decisions of the Central Committee, the moving spirit of which was the party 'military centre' headed by Stalin himself.[7]

The Bolsheviks had promised peace and land to the peasant and independence to the minorities; they had singled out the officer as the class-enemy of the soldier. The old army, recruited mainly from Russian and minority peasantry, disintegrated in a flood of desertion. Many officers went into hiding or began to make their way to the Ukraine or to the territory of the Don Cossacks, the most powerful and most conservative of the Cossack hosts, which, even under the tsars, had preserved a measure of autonomy; for during November it became clear that neither the *ataman* of the Don Cossacks, nor the Ukrainian nationalists, would recognize the authority of the Bolshevik centre. A number of generals, Alekseev and Denikin among them, escaped and set off south-eastwards,

SOUTHERN RUSSIA

0   200
Miles

Vyazma

Smolensk
Yukhnov

Orsha

Borisov

• Bialystok   • MINSK   Mogilev

BELORUSSIA

• WARSAW   Rogachev   Bryansk

POLAND   • Brest-Litovsk

PRIPET MARSHES

• Lublin   R. Pripet   Mozyr   Gomel

R. Dnieper

R. Desna

Konotop

• Lvov   Priluki   Romny

KIEV

• Fastov   Lokhvitsa

Berdichev   Skvir

Belaya   Poltava
Tserkov

U K R A I N E

Kremenchug

• Uman

Ekaterinoslav
(Dnepropetrovsk)

Zaporozhe

R. Dniester   Nikopol

• Iasi
Kishinev

Odessa   R. Dnieper

RUMANIA   Taurida
Perekop

Sea of
Azov

R. Danube

C R I M E A

Sevastopol
Yalta

Black   Sea

joining the throng of the aristocracy, the wealthy, the educated and the conservative, towards what they hoped would be the security of the established order. The Don was to prove the Vendée of the Russian revolution. _____

The main government organ of the new Bolshevik régime was the Council of People's Commissars (*Sovnarkom*), theoretically responsible to the Soviet and its executive the *Vtsik*; in fact the real source of power lay in Lenin and the executive of the Central Committee, later to be named the Politburo, consisting of Lenin, Trotsky, Sverdlov and Stalin. Sverdlov and Stalin were little known outside party circles, both being behind the scenes political organizers; Stalin was, however, still in the ascendency, even Trotsky admitting that Lenin was steadily 'advancing' him.[8] With Sverdlov's premature death in 1919 it was inevitable that Stalin must come into collision with Trotsky.

On 4 March 1918, immediately after the signing of the Treaty of Brest-Litovsk with the Central Powers, a Higher Military Council (VVS) was formed. Trotsky became the first Commissar for Military Affairs and, on 18 March, the Chairman of the VVS and Collegium, the other members being the Bolsheviks Podvoisky, Mekhonoshin, Skliansky, Antonov-Ovseenko and the former naval officers Al'tfater and Berens. Bonch-Bruevich, a former general of the Litovsky Guard Regiment, joined the VVS as its military director. In fact Bonch-Bruevich was responsible only for defence against the Central Powers, as all interior fronts were directed by a special department transferred from Moscow Military District to the Commissariat when it moved from Petrograd to the new capital on 10 March.[9] The military direction remained confused, particularly since orders were issued not only by these two operational bodies, but also by numerous other directorates, some newly created as part of the Red Army and some taken over from the old imperial army. Not until 8 May were these reorganized as a single executive body, the All-Russian Main Staff, with the former general Stogov (who in October deserted to the Whites) and the commissars Egorov and Bessonov at its head. Even this rationalization failed to provide the necessary centralized control.

The infant Soviet state was threatened by counter-revolutionary forces and Trotsky soon appreciated the urgent need to re-employ former tsarist officers in the Red Army. The most experienced of the officers were of course those of the pre-war cadres. Some regular officers in the ministries, the larger headquarters and the defensive screens in West Russia, had already become part of the Bolshevik military organization without a break in their service. Others, already demobilized, Shaposhnikov among them, wrote in and volunteered.[10] Some, like Littauer, were courteously invited to return, and permitted to decline.[11] Those who entered the Red Army came from a wide variety of tsarist regiments, the general staff and the foot guards being well represented, but there were comparatively few from the guard cavalry or cavalry of the line. The cadre officers' motives for joining either the Reds or the Whites were probably personal and varied, for there are no apparent grounds to suggest that they were based on divisions of wealth or social origin. Contrary to popular belief, in Russia and elsewhere, the regular officers did not form an exclusive society drawn from the nobility (which in any case was merely a bureaucratic caste), for they came principally from the *petite bourgeoisie* and the *razno-chinets*, the landless intelligentsia.[12] This was largely true also of the officers of the cavalry of the line, most of whom, for all their foppish manners, had neither property nor means other than their army pay.[13]

The pre-war cadre officers filled the principal command and staff appointments in the Red Army, except in the cavalry. The regular officers were, however, in the minority, for large numbers of former emergency officers were recruited for the formations and units. The experience and standard of efficiency of the wartime officer appears to have varied widely, for most of them came from the tsarist reserve of sub-ensigns or *praporshchiki*, men who originally had no experience or training as officers but who, by virtue of their education, were regarded as officer potential. Some had become efficient commanders and some were loyal to the tsar. Others, less patriotic, less able or less politically conscious, went into the tsarist service armed with little but egalitarian sentiments which turned them into poor officers, for, as Knox, the head of the British military mission, said, they hated military life and were too lazy or too lacking in character to enforce discipline or trouble themselves about their men.[14] This new type of officer, according to Trotsky, 'could not even make up his mind to sock the soldier on the jaw'.[15]

Other sub-ensigns made good revolutionaries, for some had already been convicted of subversion prior to 1917; others were a cross-section of the politically active intelligentsia, reflecting the views of Socialist Revolutionaries or Social Democrats, out of sympathy with the monarchy, patriotic ideals or the imperial armed forces. Numbers of these *praporshchiki* later became marshals of the Soviet Union.

The recruiting of former officers was soon put on to a compulsory basis and all were required to register. According to Denikin those who did so, if they did not later pass over to the Whites, were eventually 'exterminated or sucked down into the Bolshevik mire wherein human depravity and real tragedy found oblivion'.[16] Trotsky regarded 'the idealistic officer' as an insignificant minority, 'the rest who remained with us being without principles or energy to go over to the Whites'. Lenin, although he later admitted that the Red Army could not have been created without the former officers, said that he was going to 'make use of our enemy – compel those who are opponents of communism to build it'.[17] Many may have joined through fear, for, on 29 July, Trotsky ordered that any who refused to serve should be sent to concentration camps, and, on 30 September, commanded the arrest of families of those who had deserted to the Whites; Lenin elaborated this further by directing 'shooting for evasion of mobilization' and the taking of hostages from the families of officers and the *bourgeoisie* as a safeguard against desertion and treason.[18] Officers and their families were murdered. Some of those who did register for service were immediately thrown into concentration camps or Cheka cells from which they were brought out from time to time for examination or torture. Some died; some rotted away in forced labour camps; some passed via the Cheka into the Red Army. Yet, during 1918, more than 22,000 former officers volunteered or were mobilized into the Red Army and between 1918 and 1920 this figure rose to 48,000.[19]

The use of political commissars in the armed forces to supervise the commanders was not, of course, a Bolshevik innovation; Napoleon had revolutionary commissars accredited to his Army in Italy; Kerensky's Provisional Government had used them since the previous summer. But the replacement of Kerensky's commissars by Bolsheviks and Left Socialist Revolutionaries appears to have been done in a haphazard manner, and it was not until after Trotsky had taken office that an attempt was made to remove from the regional soviets and local partisan organizations the control of military affairs and the appointment of commanders and commissars.

The election of commanders by the troops had been short lived, and the dictatorship of the proletariat was eventually applied by the dissolution of all soldiers' elected committees, replaced in name, but not in substance, by the Bolshevik revolutionary military councils at all front and army headquarters. Although the title of these councils was in harmony with the spirit of popular revolution, in fact they consisted of the military commander, not necessarily a former officer, and one or two political members nominated from the centre and usually approved by the Politburo. None of course was elected, and all members were jointly accountable for their actions to their superior headquarters. Commissars were eventually appointed down to regiments.

By the early summer of 1918 the military situation was developing unfavourably for the Bolsheviks. A Czecho-Slovak corps had gained control of the Trans-Siberian railway and formed, together with the Ural and Orenburg Cossacks, the nucleus of the new White Siberian Front, which, moving westwards, took Ufa and Simbirsk and, on 6 August, the Tatar city of Kazan where the imperial reserves of gold were stored.

The Don and Kuban Cossacks had at first not been unfriendly towards Bolshevism, since they assumed that the Cossack territories would be permitted to become completely autonomous republics. For this reason the arrival on the Don of the thousands of former Russian officers and other anti-Bolsheviks was an embarrassment to the *ataman*. The presence of a Volunteer Army of 4,000 aristocrats, officials, schoolboys, and officers who had elected to serve in the ranks, was indeed so unwelcome that it was prevailed upon to move south where the Kuban Cossacks, who were of Ukrainian stock, had already suffered from the arrogance and depredations of the mainly Russian city soviets. There the Volunteer Army began to recruit both Kuban Cossacks and Circassians. In spite of their lack of weapons they soon showed that they were of high fighting quality, and began to destroy, one by one, the Bolshevik strongholds in Caucasia. Their effectiveness was based largely on their mobility.

The indigenous Don Cossack herdsman and farmer had little affinity with the Great Russian except in language; he could have had nothing in common with the openly hostile Red Guards arriving from the northern industrial areas. The *ataman,* Krasnov, encouraged by the Austro-German occupation of the Ukraine which sealed his west flank from Bolshevik foray, eventually roused his host and began to expel the Red forces. From 8 May German troops occupied Rostov, Bataisk, and the Taman peninsula across the Kerch straits, together with part of the Donets Basin. Krasnov exchanged his grain with the Germans for captured stocks of Russian weapons, preparatory to re-equipping the Don host and its traditional ally the Kalmyk.[20]

Bolshevik Russia, though it still stretched from the Arctic to the Caucasus, was being rapidly compressed from west and east. Much of the southern part of this narrowing funnel was the territory of the Don Cossacks, reaching eastwards from the Ukraine border almost as far as Tsaritsyn. When Rostov was lost and Kazan threatened, the Moscow government had to rely on the railroad, which ran south-eastwards across the Don Cossack territories through Tsaritsyn and then on to Tikhoryetsk and Stavropol, for its communication with the Caspian, the Caucasus and the Black Sea littoral. The Don, the Caspian and the Caucasus had become of primary importance to the economy of European Russia, following the loss of the rich agricultural and industrial Ukraine to the Central Powers.

The Soviet State was threatened by extinction and all measures were geared to the fight for survival. Lenin himself remained in the capital and had sent members of the Politburo and Central Committee as party and personal representatives to the threatened sectors. Trotsky boarded the train which was to become his travelling headquarters for many months ahead, a train so heavy that it needed two locomotives to draw it, equipped with offices, library, printing press, radio and telegraph station, carrying its own motor vehicles and an armed escort, dressed in black leather uniforms to make them look, as Trotsky said, more imposing.

On 29 May 1918 a telegram had been received in Moscow from the Soviet North Caucasus Military District, describing the unsatisfactory military situation there, and calling attention to the importance of Tsaritsyn as a base and as a river and railway communication centre.[21] A further report came from Ordzhonikidze, Lenin's Commissar Extraordinary, critical of the conditions in Tsaritsyn and of the flabbiness of the officials. Since the situation called for resolute measures, Lenin instructed Stalin, on 29 May, to go to Tsaritsyn to organize, in a civilian capacity, the food deliveries to Moscow and Petrograd. He was then to move on to the naval base of Novorossisk and to the Transcaucasus.[22]

Stalin arrived by train in Tsaritsyn on 6 June 1918, with two armoured cars and an escort of 400 Red Guards. As a member of the Politburo and Central Committee, the representative of both party and government, he had plenipotentiary powers, except in the field of military operations.

On 7 June Stalin reported to Lenin the 'bacchanalia of profiteering and speculation' in Tsaritsyn; he had abolished the many committees and appointed his own commissars, and he was going to declare 'a grain week'. The rest of the telegram concerned the uncertain news from the Caucasus, the latter-day published version concealing that Stalin was, at the time, ignorant that German troops had occupied Bataisk.[23] On 13 June Lenin ordered Stalin 'or Shliapnikov', to go to Novorossisk immediately to forestall the seizing of that base by the Germans. Four days later Lenin again demanded action.[24] Shliapnikov then went to Ekaterinodar to meet the naval delegates, who carried out the sinkings of the Black Sea Fleet on 19 June.

The Bolshevik troops in the south were under the command of the North Caucasus Military District, with its headquarters at Tsaritsyn; the military council consisted of Snesarev, a former general from 1 Ekaterinoslavsky Grenadier Regiment, and Zedin, a naval rating and old Bolshevik. Snesarev was theoretically responsible for the area of the Don, Kuban, Black Sea, Stavropol and Daghestan, stretching from the Voronezh *guberniia* southwards for 1,000 miles down to the Turkish border. In reality, however, the northern part of the district was Don Cossack territory, while much of that to the south-west was in the hands of the Kuban Cossack host and the Volunteer Army; in Caucasia, both Armenia and Azerbaijan had declared themselves independent, while Georgia had become a German protectorate; only in the country of the Terek Cossacks did the Bolsheviks have a decisive numerical advantage.[25] The number of Red Guards in Caucasia, estimated at 100,000, was in fact unknown, but in any case Snesarev's and Zedin's control over them was largely nominal since the Bolshevik troops and the Red Guards acknowledged prior allegiance to their own semi-independent soviet republics. The Red Army strength in the land-bridge between the Don and Volga was increasing rapidly, however, with the arrival of armed bands and refugees, calling themselves 3 and 5 Ukrainian Armies, who were retiring, under German and Ukrainian nationalist pressure, eastwards towards the haven of industrial Tsaritsyn.

On 14 June Snesarev divided his district into the Khoper, Tsaritsyn and Kuban Groups, each of only 1,000 men or so, and appointed one Krachovsky to the command of the Tsaritsyn Group.[26] Nine days later, either at the bidding of the VVS or at Stalin's prompting, he replaced Krachovsky by Voroshilov, an old Bolshevik well known to Lenin and Stalin, the new Group Voroshilov incorporating Krachovsky's command and 3 and 5 Ukrainian Armies.[27] Voroshilov had no previous military experience, for since 1914 he had been employed in what was, presumably, a reserved occupation, the ordnance factory in Tsaritsyn, where 'he cloaked his activities as a political agitator under the cover of leading the workers' choir'.[28] A 1917 photograph shows him as a diminutive and clerkly figure, dwarfed by 11 burly soldiers, the only civilian member of the military section of the Lugansk Soviet.[29]

On 25 June the railway from Central Russia through Tsaritsyn to the Black Sea and the Transcaucasus was cut near Tikhoryetsk by a northern detachment of Alekseev's Volunteer Army, thus separating Kalnin's Group Kuban from Voroshilov's Group Tsaritsyn.[30] Since the telegraph was also destroyed, the only southern communication link remaining to the Bolsheviks in Tsaritsyn were the pony messengers who had to run the gauntlet of Volunteer Army and Don Cossack patrols. The middle Volga shipping route was shortly to be stopped up by the White forces advancing from Siberia, leaving only the two railroads Tsaritsyn–Tula and Kamyshin–Tambov connecting Moscow with the Caspian. Supplies from Caucasia and Trans-Caspia had to be brought in by water and offloaded at the Tsaritsyn or Kamyshin riverports for railing inland.

Stalin wrote to Lenin on 7 July telling him that the railway to the south was still blocked and, if only the military specialists (he called them *sapozhniki* synonymous with blockheads in tsarist Russia) had not been sleeping, the line would not have been cut. Stalin insisted that the deteriorating situation demanded the presence of a plenipotentiary with military powers, and suggested that he himself might be appointed. He asked for an immediate answer on the direct line.[31]

Three days later Stalin penned an angry letter to Lenin, intemperate even by the uninhibited Bolshevik standards of the time, complaining of Trotsky's high-handed action in ignoring Snesarev and Zedin. Trotsky, said Stalin, had, without reference to Tsaritsyn, dealt directly with the Don, Kuban and Stavropol military organization. Lenin should hammer (*vdolbite*) into Trotsky's head that he should not make appointments without consulting the people on the spot. This outburst was coupled with an abrupt demand for aircraft, armoured cars and six-inch guns, 'without which the Tsaritsyn Front will not remain in being'.

> To get things done I must have full military powers. I have already written to you about this but have received no answer. Very well. In that case I will, without formality, root out those commanders and commissars who are ruining everything. I am obliged to do this in the common interest and, in any case, the lack of a chit from Trotsky will not stop me.[32]

The next day Stalin sent another telegram, impatient to the point of rudeness, complaining about the dilatoriness of the Tsaritsyn headquarters and the military specialists. He had, he told Lenin, already assumed full military responsibility and he was removing commanders and officials as he thought fit.[33]

As a result of this correspondence Stalin was officially appointed on 19 July as the chairman of the military council of the North Caucasus Military District, with Minin, a Bolshevik writer and mayor of Tsaritsyn, as the second political member. Zedin was transferred to the Volga flotilla. On 22 July Stalin and Minin signed Tsaritsyn Order No. 1 giving notice that they comprised the new military council 'together with such military commanders as they might appoint'.[34] Snesarev was not a signatory.

Trotsky has made light of Stalin's military activity in the south and has said 'that he headed only one of twenty armies', that is to say Voroshilov's Group Tsaritsyn.[35] This version has been generally accepted in the west.[36] Yet, on 24 July, Trotsky signed an order detailing the responsibilities of the North Caucasus Military District, reaffirming that it was to command not merely Group Tsaritsyn but all military and partisan activity from the borders of Voronezh to Baku. Stalin's angry outburst a fortnight earlier had presumably struck home, for Trotsky's signal was most deferential to the new chairman.[37]

Budenny, a Don *inogorodnii* uitlander and former sergeant of 18 Seversky Dragoons, was second in command of *vakhmistr* Dumenko's 1 Socialist Cavalry Regiment when he attended a political mass meeting near Tsaritsyn. Stalin, described by Budenny as 'a swarthy, thin man of medium height', was present there, and from this encounter began the life-long association between the two men.[38]

Snesarev signed his last order at Tsaritsyn on 16 July and was put on a train for Moscow. From 22 July onwards orders were issued daily over the signature of the military council, mostly concerned with the defence of the city of Tsaritsyn, mobilizing the 1896 and 1897 classes and covering such tactical detail as the movement of a Serb battalion, together with a company of the Peasant Regiment, an artillery section and eight machine-guns. On 26 and again on 29 July, the military council was pleading to the VVS for help, asking for an attack from the Voronezh *raion* on the enemy's northern flank to take the pressure away from Tsaritsyn; for unless help was forthcoming the North Caucasus Military District would be lost 'with consequences so vital to Russia'.[39]

Stalin said that he travelled widely in the region of Tsaritsyn, but apparently not into Caucasia or the Don Cossack territory. Voroshilov, who commanded only the Group Tsaritsyn, began to accompany Stalin on his tours. At the beginning of August, at Stalin's suggestion to the VVS, Voroshilov's name was added to the district military council. Henceforth orders lost their tsarist general staff format and took on the appearance of minutes of a political meeting, for Stalin appears to have conducted military affairs much as he wished. Or, as Voroshilov expressed it, 'a group of old Bolsheviks and revolutionary workers rallied round Comrade Stalin and, in place of the helpless staff, a Red, Bolshevik stonghold grew up in the south'.[40]

Stalin had described the military specialists to Lenin as 'psychologically unfitted . . . in general they feel themselves to be strangers, guests'; and he spoke the truth. For numbers of officers had been shot, and many of his specialists, including those newly dispatched from Moscow, were guests of the Cheka. Voroshilov has quoted with approval the account of Nosovich, a former colonel appointed in May by Trotsky as chief of staff to the district:

Stalin's order was brief. 'Shoot them!' . . . a large number of officers, some belonging to the [counter-revolutionary] organization while others were merely suspected of being accomplices, were seized by the Cheka and immediately shot without trial.

Nosovich described Stalin's attitude to Trotsky's orders from the centre:

Trotsky . . . sent a telegram that the headquarter military staff must be left alone to get on with their work. Stalin wrote across the telegram a categorical and significant order 'Take no notice'.[41]

Of the three principal military specialists on the district headquarters, Nosovich, arrested by Voroshilov, fled to the Whites; another was shot.[42] Stalin made no secret of his views in his letters to Lenin, for, on 4 August, he wrote of 'the inertia of the former commander [Snesarev] and the conspiracy of certain persons brought in by him' and he gave himself the credit for the 'timely removal of the so-called specialists'.[43] Over 30 years later Stalin was still congratulating himself on 'ruthlessly breaking down the resistance of the counter-revolutionary military experts appointed and supported by Trotsky'.[44]

With the removal of the specialists, Stalin's council was military only in name. Minin, the writer, was the regional representative. Voroshilov, described by Trotsky as 'a hearty and impudent fellow, not overly intellectual but shrewd and unscrupulous', was himself dependent on the advice of the non-commissioned officers,

comrades like Dumenko and Budenny, and on that of the remaining
military specialist, a former captain Sokolov. Trotsky subsequently
characterized Voroshilov as 'a military know-nothing, half-
guerilla, half-party man hanging on to his job for dear life . . . very
indulgent with the chiefs of his divisions'. But Trotsky liked the
ring of these words and applied them to other of his enemies, and
his latter-day account is not always supported by what he said at
the time. For on 27 October 1918 Trotsky praised Voroshilov as 'a
conscientious worker with a pretty firm hand (*dovol'no tverdaia
ruka*) over his indisciplined subordinates'; and of Voroshilov's
military specialist, whom Trotsky subsequently described as a
weak and pliant alcoholic unlikely to expose Voroshilov's ignorance,
Trotsky wrote 'he is an able worker with an excellent understanding of the organization of 10 Army'.[45] The North Caucasus
Military District had no designated military commander, but as
Stalin was a political figure of almost unlimited power, described
in the 1957 *Grazhdanskaia Voina* as bringing to the councils 'his
enormous experience of party work and of the revolutionary
struggle', Stalin decided military as well as political problems.[46]
It is doubtful whether anyone in Tsaritsyn would have contradicted him.

On 4 August Stalin told Lenin that Cossack partisans upstream
of Tsaritsyn were attempting to block the link with Kamyshin and
had already cut the Tsaritsyn-Moscow railway. Troops would be
thinned out from Tsaritsyn to thrust up the Don to the Khoper
river, clearing the railway and disorganizing the enemy rear areas.
This would take all his efforts. Matters did not stand well in the
Caucasus, said Stalin, where there was widespread fighting against
the Kuban and Terek Cossacks. The Group Kuban was apparently
in the process of final disintegration – 'I say "apparently" because
reliable intelligence about Kalnin has been impossible to get'.[47]
Stalin's fears were justified for, a fortnight before, Kalnin's headquarters had been overrun; the deputy commander, a former
colonel of the general staff, had committed suicide together with
his wife rather than fall into the hands of the Whites, while the bare-
headed Kalnin, a Latvian old Bolshevik, was last seen running for
his life down the railway track.[48]

Voroshilov's popular account has described Tsaritsyn as
threatened from the east by Astrakhan and Ural Cossacks, from the

west by Don Cossacks, while the Volunteer Army stood near at hand at Kotelnikovo. In reality the only threat to Tsaritsyn during the summer of 1918 came from Krasnov. The terrible atrocities of the Red Guards on Don Cossack soil had caused an uprising on the middle Don and the Khoper, and had enabled the *ataman* to mobilize ten classes, so raising the military strength of the host to 40,000 men. But Krasnov was unable to deploy the whole of this force against Tsaritsyn, for much of the Cossack territory was still in turmoil and he was also waging war against the Bolshevik forces in the Voronezh *guberniia*.

The Don Cossack, although ethnically Great Russian, had, over the centuries, acquired a passion for liberty, free speech and for meetings. Although he had more dash and initiative, he lacked the discipline and stamina of the Russian from the north. His loyalty lay with the host and he suffered from Cossack sickness, the reluctance to leave his paternal *stanitsa*; he co-operated only grudgingly with the *khokhol*, the Ukrainian Kuban Cossack. The Don Cossack excelled as a scout and raider, a lancer and swordsman; he was a dangerous adversary in close combat, a *beau sabreur* unfitted by temperament, military organization or training to fight pitched battles.[49] The Don Cossack's lack of dismounted troops and infantry experience resulted in a defective command and a serious fault in the structure of Krasnov's force, for the predominantly mounted element, supported only by horse artillery three-inch guns, could not hold ground. These military and personal deficiencies resulted, in Denikin's words, in extraordinary fluctuations – from lightning success to total collapse.[50]

At the end of July a Don Cossack force under Mamontov drove in Voroshilov's levies west of the Don near the Chir bridge, and crossed the shallow and slow moving river. Raiding patrols came whooping eastwards over the steppe, penetrating almost to the city outskirts, while others, under Fitskhelaurov, struck north towards Kamyshin. If Budenny is to be believed, the Red armoured trains and cavalry were used offensively, the fighting taking the form of forced marches and scattered raids, the struggle being fierce and pitiless, wounded and prisoners being done to death by both sides.

On 11 August Stalin, Minin and Voroshilov signed an order covering the shortening of the front and regrouping, all commanders being ordered to form independent companies directly under their own command 'for the struggle against deserters', a euphemism for the shooting down of broken units. Two days later Stalin declared a state of siege throughout the *guberniia*, and, on 14 August, the *bourgeoisie* were mobilized to dig the defensive trench works around the city. On 15 August the poet Minin sent a graphic and staccato telegram to Lenin:

> Varying fortunes . . . our forces took *stanitsa* Voroponov capturing seven machine-guns . . . order in the town . . . send every cartridge cartridge cartridge [*sic*] . . . Tsaritsyn key to southeast and source of corn . . . demands urgent help.[51]

Stalin continued to concern himself with minor detail, although his orders for 16 August, besides appointing Shchadenko as a military commissar, showed an unexpected interest in Zhloba's Steel Division in the North Caucasus Republic, for he nominated Zhloba, a former miner, as 'the representative in the south of the military council'. On 22 August an order signed by 'the military council', no names being given, presumably in case it should fall into White hands, was sent by overland messenger to Sorokin, a former Kuban Cossack medical assistant who, following the routing of Kalnin's headquarters, commanded the Red troops in the area between Kotelnikovo and Vladikavkaz. Sorokin was ordered to instruct Zhloba to report to Tsaritsyn in person.[52] The messenger did not, however, reach Sorokin until 2 September. Meanwhile the danger to Tsaritsyn had receded, for Mamontov had broken off his attacks and fallen back 40 miles to the west. By early September Voroshilov was able to reoccupy and restore the positions on the bank of the Don.

On 31 August two dispatches were sent to the capital. The first was a cheerful and friendly personal letter to Lenin, following the unsuccessful attempt on the party leader's life, in which Stalin said that the Cossack enemy was finally breaking up. He asked that Artem should be directed to send some light torpedo-boats and two submarines down the Volga to the Caspian, which area, Stalin assured Lenin, was to be had for the asking, leading 'without doubt' to the freeing of Baku, Turkestan and the North Caucasus. Subsequent events failed to justify this optimism. The second was the telegram to Sverdlov, signed by both Stalin and Voroshilov, congratulating on his escape, 'the greatest revolutionary in the world, the tried leader and mentor of the proletariat, Comrade Lenin' and urging him to reply 'to this low-down attempt from round the corner, by the organizing of a public, massive, systematic terror against the *bourgeoisie* and its agents'.[53]

On 6 September, Stalin sent a telegram as *Narkom,* for he was the only signatory, detailing a number of localities reoccupied, and ending once again on a buoyant note 'the enemy is crushed and withdraws beyond the Don'.[54] This, too, was premature.

During the first weeks of July the Central Committee decided that the outcome of the revolution 'lies on the Volga and the Urals' and by the end of the month Lenin was to add 'that its fate rests on one map'.[55] The military situation continued to worsen during August, the Bolshevik weakness lying in the lack of a proper machinery for centralized military control, a defect pointed out in a paper by Egorov urging the appointment of a supreme military commander. Egorov's suggestions were accepted by Lenin and Trotsky, and the former colonel Vatsetis was appointed Commander-in-Chief.[56] The VVS was abolished, its functions being assumed by a Revolutionary Military Council of the Republic (RVSR) set up on 2 September, consisting of Trotsky as chairman, Vatsetis, Danishevsky, Kobozev, Mekhonoshin, Raskol'nikov, Rozengolts and Smirnov; later Aralov, Podvoisky, Skliansky and Iurenev were added. All, except Vatsetis, were Bolsheviks. The executive of the RVSR was the *shtab,* known from 11 October as the *polevoi shtab* (field headquarters). Vatsetis's post as the Commander of the East Front was taken by S. S. Kamenev, a former general staff officer and colonel of 30 Poltava Regiment. From this time onwards the Red Army began to be organized in established military fashion, further fronts being formed and the many screens, groups and detachments being concentrated into armies; these did not have a corps organization and at first consisted of only a few thousand men.

On 18 September a new South Front was created to replace the North Caucasus Military District and Stalin was appointed as chairman of its military council, the other political member being Minin, with Voroshilov as the district deputy military commander, all three retaining in addition their appointments on the military council of Group Voroshilov (later 10 Army) in Tsaritsyn.[57] On 28 September Stalin presided over what he called the first meeting of the council, to reorganize, on paper at least, the Red forces on the Don and in the Caucasus into the four groupings of 8 (Voronezh), 9 (Povorinsk), 10 (Tsaritsyn), 11 (Vladikavkaz) and 12 (Terek) Armies.[58]

Meanwhile, on or about 13 September, an unknown military specialist at Balashov wrote a paper on the proposed tasks and organization of the new South Front. The writer viewed the operations against Alekseev as separate from those against Krasnov and he was critical of the way the battle against Krasnov was being fought, for there was little co-ordination between the forces at Tsaritsyn and those north of the Don bend. Krasnov could only be destroyed, thought the writer, if a single command were to be set up in the area of the north Don directing the operations of 9 Army facing south, and 10 Army facing west, the junction point between the two being at Kamyshin. The writer suggested that Egorov should take command of 9 Army – which he later did; Voroshilov, however, was apparently unknown to, or little regarded by, the writer, for he believed the command of 10 Army to be vacant.[59] This paper may have influenced Trotsky in his decision to order the move of the South Front headquarters to Kozlov, a railway town about 400 miles north of Tsaritsyn. Shortly afterwards he appointed to the South Front a military specialist commander, a former general of artillery and chief of staff of the Rumanian Front, named Sytin. Sytin went to Kozlov while the other members of the military council remained at Tsaritsyn.

On 22 September Sytin complained to Vatsetis about the difficulty of working with Tsaritsyn since he received no replies to his signals; two days later he protested once more when he became aware that Stalin, Minin and Voroshilov had, without consulting him, issued an order to Sorokin covering the task and organization of the troops in the North Caucasus.[60] Vatsetis had the order cancelled.

Meanwhile Krasnov's Don Cossack cavalry had begun their second offensive and were again driving Voroshilov's troops eastwards. On 27 September Stalin's council, in a state of alarm, sent another order to Sorokin, commanding him to send Zhloba's

Steel Division, at that time 400 miles away, post-haste to Tsaritsyn; and, to give the order fitting legality, they instructed the former captain Sokolov to append his name to the ladder of signatures. That same night the council sent a situation report to the RVSR, written in Stalin's inimitable style:

> Situation deteriorating from 20 September. *Ataman* Krasnov has thrown twenty regiments, mostly horsed, against our front with some elements of Alekseev's Volunteer Army. Front broken . . . Something could still be done from the north sector of the South Front, but this sector is absolutely supine (*vialyi*) and the commander Sytin, in some stange way, is not interested in the matter . . . moreover, to our repeated enquiries as to the situation on the north sector he has, up to now, made no reply.

The signal ended in another demand for a large quantity of munitions, including 30,000 three-line Russian rifles, 150 Maxims and 50 three-inch guns, adding that 'unless this minimum is delivered immediately we shall have to retire to the left bank of the Volga'.[61] The RVSR instructed Sytin to go to Stalin, armed with a written brief detailing his functions and accompanied by the RVSR member Mekhonoshin, a former Bolshevik student. On 30 September, the day after his visit, and as soon as he had got away from Tsaritsyn, Sytin telegraphed his report to the centre. The South Front military council had met at 2200 hours the previous night, Stalin, Mekhonoshin, Sytin, Minin and Voroshilov being present. Minin, not Stalin, took the chair. Sytin pointed out that Tsaritsyn was to the flank, even to the rear, of operations, remote from the centre and relying on a single railway line through Saratov, often out of action for days on end because of storm damage. He and Mekhonoshin wanted the headquarters to be at Kozlov or Balashov. Minin and Stalin insisted on Tsaritsyn. There was disagreement, too, as to the competence of the council to nominate military commanders and conduct operations, and Stalin, Minin and Voroshilov passed their own resolution 'finding themselves unable to recognize Sytin's full jurisdiction (*polnaia vlast'*) or the legality of his brief'.[62]

Trotsky has described his difficulties with the Tsaritsyn group that summer; 'in the early autumn Voroshilov began to disregard the orders from his superior South Front Headquarters, leaving unanswered its questions and ignoring its rebukes'. Trotsky said that he fumed against Voroshilov and he blamed Stalin for over-leniency in failing to make him carry out orders. It never entered Trotsky's head, so he subsequently said, that Stalin was the actual instigator of Voroshilov's insubordination, for Stalin, busy at work behind the scenes, 'bore himself so that at any moment, he would be able to jump back, his skirts clear'. This is Trotsky's explanation of what Rotmistrov called the weakness of the Central Committee 'in tolerating a conflict wherein Stalin and Voroshilov ignored the requirements of the RVSR'.[63] But Trotsky's inability to discern what was afoot in Tsaritsyn was due to his own deficiencies and his attempt to keep abreast of military operations from a moving train. As soon as a High Command was brought into being with professionally trained commanders, it was inevitable that Stalin would be found out. For a study of the teleprinter traffic between the RVSR and Tsaritsyn indicates that Vatsetis and Sytin had no doubt where the responsibility lay.

Stalin associated himself with the activity of only one of his armies – that in Tsaritsyn – for he, too, lacked professional guidance. Trotsky, for his part, appears to have forgotten, or has concealed, that the military council of 10 Army also formed, with the addition of Sytin, the military council of the South Front. According to an account published during Stalin's lifetime, the military council of the South Front was empowered to select its own front headquarters' location, and, in the event of Sytin not proving suitable, to recommend his replacement within a week.[64] In the event, it was Stalin who was replaced.

The Latvian colonel Vatsetis was not one of those military specialists described by Stalin as 'strangers or guests' with the Red Army. He identified himself with the revolution, although he might have been a little less confident if he had seen Lenin's draft of 30 August (afterwards amended) containing the random and wanton suggestion that Vatsetis should be shot *pour encourager les autres*.[65] Vatsetis's sympathies were presumably those of a minority separatist, since he was not a Bolshevik and was to remain outside the Communist Party until the day he was liquidated in 1938. He was probably a man of mediocre ability – said to be better with troops than on the staff – for he had failed to qualify for the general staff on completing the 1909 course at the General Staff Academy. At the time of the revolution he commanded, at the age of 44, 5 Zemgalsky Latvian Rifle Regiment. Trotsky called him 'stubborn, cranky and capricious'.

The South Front continued to be commanded by two military councils, with Sytin and Mekhonoshin at Kozlov, and Stalin, Minin and Voroshilov at Tsaritsyn. On 2 October Stalin and Minin signed a signal to the RVSR, with personal copies to Lenin, Sverdlov and Vatsetis, but not to Sytin:

> Situation on South Front unsteady due to lack of armament and the failure to send submarines. With munitions we could have cleared the Povorino railway, driven back the Cossacks and sent detachments to Baku and Astrakhan. Since the RVSR has not given us what we requested, we feel it necessary to put the following questions:
>
> 1. Do you consider it necessary to hold the south?
> 2. If yes, can you provide the means?
> 3. If you cannot supply, should we not make a timely withdrawal to prevent the front disintegrating?
> 4. If you do not think it necessary to hold the south, then say so outright.[66]

A second, more temperate, signal the same day emphasized that the need was for weapons, clothes and supplies, not for men who were to be had in plenty since they could draw on the Don *inogorodnie* and the populations of the North Caucasus.[67]

The Central Committee sat on 2 October to consider the insubordination of party workers to the decisions of the centre; on that day Sverdlov telegraphed Tsaritsyn chiding the council and reminding it that all decrees of the RVSR were binding on the fronts.[68] Vatsetis's replies were more direct. His first signal of 3 October to Tsaritsyn was a categorical order that there was to be no regrouping of any units without the approval of Sytin. The second summarized the situation as it was seen in Arzamas:

> It is noted by your telegrams that Sytin did not take part in the meetings of the military council. . . . You have centred your main attention on the Tsaritsyn sector at the expense of

others. . . . It has been proposed repeatedly that you should move from Tsaritsyn to Kozlov in order to join its commander, but up to now . . . you have continued to operate independently. Such a disregard of orders. . . . I consider to be intolerable . . .[69]

That same day Vatsetis appealed to Trotsky, who was then at Tambov, against 'Stalin's order No. 118 which must be cancelled', for Stalin's actions, said Vatsetis, were disrupting all the Commander-in-Chief's plans.[70] Stalin and Voroshilov, in their turn, so Stalin said, sent a telegram to Lenin demanding that the Central Committee should examine the actions of Trotsky, which threatened the destruction of the South Front.[71] On 4 October Trotsky signalled Sverdlov, with a copy to Lenin, insisting on Stalin's recall; and unless Voroshilov and Minin submitted to the orders of Sytin, Trotsky proposed to commit them for trial, for as long as Stalin and Minin remained in Tsaritsyn they were, according to the constitution of the RVSR, merely members of the military council of 10 Army.[72] Lenin supported Trotsky, and Stalin was removed from the South Front appointment. Stalin was recalled to Moscow on 6 October, returning to Tsaritsyn five days later, to remain there until 19 October when he finally gave up his additional post as the political member with 10 Army. Trotsky reconstituted the South Front council on 5 October and Voroshilov and Minin were excluded. Yet although Lenin had sided with Trotsky, Stalin had not fallen from grace, and the party leader went to some pains to emphasize this publicly by appointing him on 8 October to the membership of the RVSR and returning him to Tsaritsyn to conclude his business.

Meanwhile the raids and counter-raids continued on the Don–Volga land-bridge, and Stalin and his council signed their daily operation orders, often concerning only the movement of a cavalry squadron or an infantry battalion. The broad situation was well summed up, however, in a report prepared by Vatsetis for Lenin and Sverdlov and dated 7 October. Vatsetis put Krasnov's Don Cossack strength at no higher than 11 cavalry and two and a half infantry divisions, the latter being made up of dismounted cavalry and peasant levies; these were opposed by Iakir's 8 Army on the line of the Khoper, Egorov's 9 Army between the Khoper and Kamyshin, and Voroshilov's 10 Army covering Tsaritsyn. The

Volunteer Army, which Vatsetis estimated at 80,000 strong, was not immediately involved in the fighting since it was still in the Caucasus.[73]

The pressure against Tsaritsyn became increasingly acute and Vatsetis allocated his few available reserves, mainly reliable Latvian regiments, to Sytin. On or about 8 October Vatsetis himself visited Kozlov. By 15 October the situation inside Tsaritsyn was critical and Stalin, Minin and Voroshilov were thoroughly alarmed, for they sent a constant flow of telegrams to Lenin, Vatsetis and Sytin, appealing for help. Vatsetis's reply that same day was characteristically robust:

> From today's telegrams direct to me I see that the defence of Tsaritsyn has been brought by you to a catastrophic state. . . . You alone are responsible for the chaotic situation. . . . In view of the serious state of Tsaritsyn I am now sending reserves there. . . . Under no circumstances is Tsaritsyn to be given up.

Vatsetis followed by a signal to Sytin: 'I agree entirely with your decision to go over to the offensive but I beg you to push home the attack with such vigour and purpose that it really deals effectively with the Cossack troops operating against Tsaritsyn'.[74] Meanwhile Lenin and Sverdlov were demanding from Vatsetis the most urgent measures for the relief of the city.

At nightfall on 15 October, Minin was telegraphing Sytin in gloomy terms, saying that the evacuation of Tsaritsyn had begun and that there was a great need of everything 'which you have promised but have not sent'. On the following night at 2200 hours Minin spoke to Sytin once more, saying that the position was very bad and would have been worse if Zhloba's Steel Division, consisting of eight infantry and two cavalry regiments, had not arrived the previous night with its artillery. The division had gone straight into action and had already inflicted 1,500 casualties on the enemy. If it had not been for this division, said Minin, it was possible that Tsaritsyn might have been lost the next day. Vatsetis should be told that the position was worsening every hour.[75]

There is still much difference of opinion in present day Soviet military literature regarding the responsibility for the movement of Zhloba's division out of the North Caucasus. It is said that Zhloba left on the long march even before receiving Stalin's order dated 27 September, which he may have done, since it is over 300 miles in a direct line from Stavropol to Tsaritsyn. Because of this action Zhloba was outlawed as a deserter by a 12 October decree of the RVS of the North Caucasus Republic, for Armavir and Stavropol fell to the Volunteer Army shortly afterwards.[76] Zhloba's surprise attack into the rear of the Cossack forces barely 12 miles from the centre of Tsaritsyn, saved the city for the moment. But the fighting continued during the remainder of October and early November, until Cossack troops were drawn away northwards to face 8 and 9 Armies. By then other Red Army levies had been moved by Vatsetis into Tsaritsyn from Kamyshin, Astrakhan, Saratov, Nizhnii Novgorod and Moscow.

Tsaritsyn was saved, according to Voroshilov, 'by Stalin's indomitable will to victory, in spite of the almost hopeless situation'. At a later date Tsaritsyn was to be renamed as Stalingrad in honour of its defender.

On 23 October Stalin joined Lenin in Moscow and showed himself to be co-operative and almost contrite; for he much desired, he told Lenin, to work closely together with Trotsky, and he agreed to fit in with Sytin and Mekhonoshin on the South Front military council. Lenin telegraphed Stalin's case to Trotsky that same night.[77] Stalin did not return to the South Front, however, for shortly afterwards came the sudden collapse of the Central Powers, followed, on 13 November, by the Moscow repudiation of the Treaty of Brest–Litovsk. Civil war broke out in the Ukraine between the forces of the German puppet *hetman* Skoropadsky, Ukrainian nationalists, Bolsheviks, greens (armed deserters), anarchists and banditry.

On 17 November Stalin was appointed to the Ukraine Front in the area of Kursk, which had been given the mission of reoccupying the Ukraine, the other members of the military council being Antonov-Ovseenko and Zatonsky.[78] Troops were allocated to the new front by Vatsetis, and five military specialists joined it from Kozlov, together with Voroshilov, Shchadenko and 20 party workers from 10 Army 'who were placed at Comrade Stalin's disposal'.[79] Their tasks appear to have been political as well as military for, according to the 1 December issue of *Zhizn' Nat-*

sional'nostei, Voroshilov and Sergeev (Artem) had arrived in Kursk as members of 'the provisional government of the Ukraine'.[80] The Kursk group began operations near Kharkov but it appears to have achieved little while Stalin was with it. But the party workers continued to complain to Stalin, even after he had returned to Moscow, about Vatsetis's 'wrongful acts and omissions', his lack of interest in the Ukraine and his sabotaging of their work.[81]

On 30 November, Lenin appointed Stalin, together with Trotsky, Sverdlov, Krasin, Nevsky and Briukhanov, to the newly formed Council of Defence which sat under Lenin's chairmanship to co-ordinate and control all measures for the prosecution of the war. A latter-day Trotsky said that Stalin did little there, merely regarding its membership as an additional title; a much older Stalin was to style himself as the deputy chairman of that council.

2

From Perm to Rostov

Towards the end of 1918 the right wing of Kolchak's White forces in Siberia began a westwards offensive, scattering Lashevich's 3 Army and taking the city of Perm together with 30,000 prisoners and a great store of booty. Although the axis of this offensive was in the general direction of Moscow, it was also intended to link up with the Archangel White troops to the north of Kotlas, about 500 miles away.

In the second week of December 1918, Lenin, much alarmed, had sent two telegrams to Trotsky's train, telling him 'to put pressure on Vatsetis' to reinforce the Urals.[1] A week later he described to Trotsky 'the catastrophic state of 3 Army and its drunkenness'. Lashevich, an old Bolshevik and former sergeant, was 'drinking and in no fit state to restore order'. Lenin had considered sending Stalin there, and he asked Trotsky to telegraph his opinion and go to the East Front himself. Trotsky did not go but he signalled his agreement that Stalin should journey to Perm and 'restore order, purge the commissar personnel and severely punish the offenders'.[2] On the first day of the New Year, Stalin, together with the Pole Dzerzhinsky, the head of the Cheka, set out to investigate.

On 5 January Stalin sent a preliminary report to Lenin in his own handwriting, emphasizing the material weakness of 3 Army; it had been reduced from 30,000 to 11,000 men, and reinforcements were urgently required. For the units sent by Vatsetis, said Stalin, were so unreliable that they were even hostile to the Bolshevik cause. It was *absolutely* essential to *rush* three *completely* reliable regiments to the area (Stalin's italics): otherwise 'Vyatka is threatened with the fate of Perm'.[3] In reply Lenin told Stalin to remain with 3 Army and to signal his proposals by priority cipher.[4] Eight days later Stalin sent a further dispatch, giving some of the causes of the defeat. The language and content were to the point, Stalin blaming exhaustion, lack of reserves, mismanagement on the part of the army commander, the isolation of the commanders from the troops and the instability of the rear; for, said Stalin, the Soviet and party organizations behind the front were hopelessly incompetent. Stalin condemned 'the downright criminal (*prestupnyi*) method' of directing operations by the RVSR in sowing confusion with contradictory orders.[5] In acknowledgement Lenin authorized Stalin to take all necessary measures on the spot.[6]

Stalin's and Dzerzhinsky's final report, signed in Moscow on 31 January, was a comprehensive work, the result of a detailed investigation into operational, tactical and administrative matters. Stalin paraphrased Kamenev's evidence in this fashion:

A directive was received [from the RVSR] saying that 2 Army . . . was to be ready for another assignment on another front, without saying where this was likely to be. In these circumstances 2 Army could not be committed in case it might be impossible to extricate it. . . . Then suddenly Shorin, the Commander of 2 Army, was called to Serpukhov, thus paralysing 2 Army (things being what they were), and a further five days were lost. At Serpukhov, Kostiaev [a former engineer and general staff officer] . . . merely wanted to know whether Shorin had belonged to the general staff – which he had not . . . Kostiaev said that he 'would think about it'.[7]

The report continued, in Stalin's own words:

Gusev . . . the front political member . . . received three telegrams in succession, each giving a different main axis for the East Front. . . . One may easily judge how light-hearted are the attitudes of the RVSR and the Commander-in-Chief to their own directives.

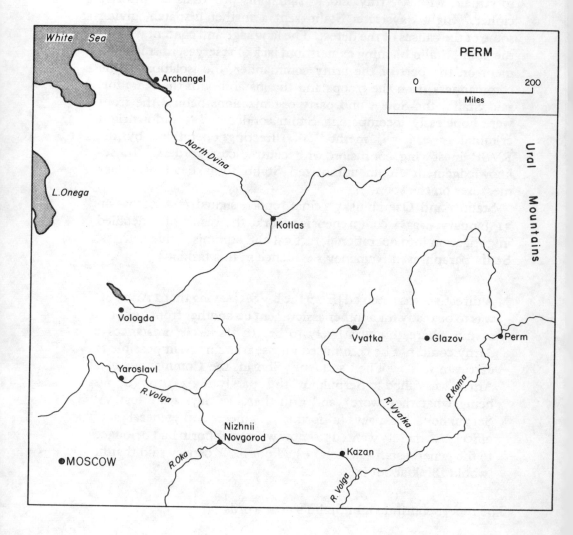

Nor did Stalin spare 3 Army:

> The military council consists of two: Lashevich, who com-
> mands; as for the other, Trifonov [the political member], I have
> not succeeded in ascertaining what his role or function is . . . it
> looks as if he does nothing . . . the headquarters is entirely
> divorced from the scene of operations, having no liaison officers
> at the divisions or brigades to watch and inform . . . and army
> headquarters is satisfied with formal written (and often impre-
> cise) reports. The army is completely in the hands of subordinate
> formations, the commanders of which behave like feudal princes
> . . . lack of centralized control and the everlasting screams of
> protest about the weakness of junction points and boundaries.
> And it is a fact that while 3 Army was shedding its blood the
> neighbouring 2 Army was marking time and doing nothing for
> a fortnight.

Stalin had something of the quartermaster-general about him in
his insistence on statistics – a trait out of keeping with the military
methods of the time, for it was part of the Russian character to
make grandiose plans without first ascertaining whether the means
were available to carry them out. Stalin set out his figures in
pedantic detail, noting that 3 Army had lost 248 of its 571 machine-
guns, and, between August and December, had received 13,153
men, 3,388 bayonets, 134 machine-guns, 22 guns and 977 horses;
holdings and losses of warlike materials were listed; butter, fats,
aluminium and steel rails, were similarly itemized by weight,
length or cubic capacity.[3]

Voroshilov's panegyric has made bold claims for Stalin's three
week stay in Perm.[9] But his version is contrary to both White and
British contemporary accounts and is not supported in modern
Soviet works.[10]

In March Stalin was present during the Eighth Party Congress,
where one of the main points discussed was the future organization
of the High Command and the Red Army. Many of the delegates
arriving from the fronts were seething with anger against Trotsky,
but Trotsky himself did not attend. Although Stalin had instigated
the resistance of the Tsaritsyn group only six months before, and
continued, in private, to denounce the military specialists and the

RVSR, he did not publicly identify himself with what was to become known as 'the military opposition'. So when the absent Trotsky came under attack 'for his dictatorial manners, for his scornful attitude to the front workers and his unwillingness to listen to them, for his adoration of the specialists, and for his torrent of ill-considered telegrams sent over the heads of commanders and staffs, changing directives and causing endless confusion', Stalin spoke with Lenin against the opposition, prominent among whom were Voroshilov and Minin.[11]

At the closed session, on 21 March 1919, Lenin refuted the contention that a feudal army was being raised based on serfdom and a system of rank, and that the *Narkomvoen* and RVSR duplicated each other; and Lenin defended Trotsky against the charge of not carrying out the policy of the Central Committee. Lenin pointed out that 'the Politburo decides all questions of strategy and the movement of reserves, discussing these questions almost daily'.

> We have of course . . . made our mistakes. . . When Stalin carried out his Tsaritsyn shootings I thought . . . that the shootings were wrong. Those documents which Comrade Voroshilov has quoted to illustrate the mass heroism of 10 Army – and in part of Comrade Voroshilov himself – disclose our mistakes. . . . There were disagreements between Stalin and myself . . . but there was no question that the policy of the Central Committee was carried out by the military.

Lenin continued:

> Comrade Voroshilov has said that we had no military specialists at Tsaritsyn and we had 60,000 losses. But that is dreadful . . . and to say 'We managed without specialists' – is *that* really defending the party line?[12]

In May 1919 the Red forces were driven out of Latvia, while, further to the south, Vilna had been taken by the Poles, who then began to force the Bolsheviks eastwards. On 13 May Rodzianko's 5,000 strong White Russian corps crossed into Russia and was redesignated as the North-West Army, under the overall command of Iudenich, the White Commander-in-Chief Baltic. When Rodzianko began his march on Petrograd, he was opposed by part of 7 Soviet Army, which, although it totalled 15,000 men and 160 guns, was extended over a 400 mile front and was already under attack by White Finnish forces.

Trotsky took no part in repulsing this offensive, but he did play an important role in October of the same year when Iudenich made his second march on the former capital. Iudenich got closer to Petrograd in October than he did in the previous June, but whether this justifies Trotsky's description of Iudenich's first campaign as 'passing practically unnoticed by the party', is to be questioned.[13] Rodzianko's success was in fact rapid and by taking deserting Red Army units into his ranks he increased his numbers three-fold, Soviet historians putting the White strength at over 15,500 men.[14] On 12 June the Bolshevik garrisons of the coastal forts of Krasnaia Gorka and Seraia Loshad', in the Red rear, mutinied and declared for Rodzianko.

On 17 May Lenin had sent Stalin to Petrograd with plenipotentiary powers to organize the defence in the north-west. Four days later Petrograd was declared to be 'one of the most important fronts', and on 10 June the Central Committee formally resolved that the Petrograd front was 'the most important front of the republic'.[15]

Lenin had always followed the course of day-to-day military operations closely and, since Trotsky was rarely in the capital, dealt directly with the RVSR. Skliansky, as its secretary, had the duty of relaying to him daily, sometimes hourly, the most important military developments, together with requests for decisions.[16] An ageing Stalin once said that Lenin had had no military knowledge and had confessed to being too old to learn, so he had encouraged his younger colleagues, Stalin among them, to study military affairs and act in his stead.[17] Stalin's assertion is contradicted by the volume of evidence available. Trotsky, on the other hand, maintained that Lenin 'remained in Moscow with all the threads concentrated in his hands', giving judgement on military questions 'which were new to all of us' on the basis of information which came, for the most part, from party representatives with the fronts.[18] Lenin lent a ready ear to complaints against the RVSR made verbally or by ciphered telegram, and his lack of military knowledge

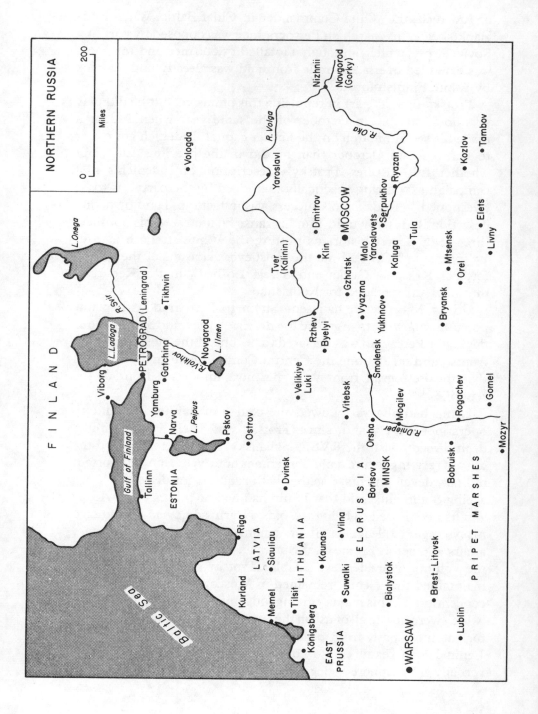

NORTHERN RUSSIA

0   200
Miles

did not inhibit him from controlling the RVSR and interfering
with the lower echelons, sending a daily stream of notes and signals
to Skliansky, Trotsky and the front councils, in emphatic and often
violent terms, urging, chiding and threatening. He was constantly
'surprised', 'alarmed' or 'shocked' at the lack of information from,
or success of, the fronts, describing the conduct of his close party
colleagues as 'monstrous' and 'criminal'.

On 20 May Lenin sent a telegram to Stalin at the Smolny,
'trusting that the general mobilization of Petersburgers will result
in offensive operations and not just sitting about in barracks'.[19]
On 27 May he warned Stalin that the rapid White advance obliged
him to assume treachery; a few days later Lenin dispatched the
following signal:

> It is said (1) that the Petersburg units are more demoralized than
> the reinforcements from the provinces which deteriorate under
> their influence (2) that in spite of their numbers they are not fit
> for the offensive (3) that the military have already decided on
> evacuation (4) that the Commander of 7 Army [Remezov] is not
> at his post but has turned himself into Zinov'ev's adjutant.
> Inform me of the position in cipher.[20]

On 2 June Lenin was again instructing Stalin to keep him informed
of developments; the next day he was demanding from Stalin an
early, strong and decisive offensive.[21] On 8 June Lenin ordered the
emergency transfer of troops to Petrograd from other fronts; two
days later he was berating Skliansky for being misled by someone
'playing down the disaster' at Petrograd, Lenin calling Skliansky's
tardiness 'an act of treason'.[22] Meanwhile the defence of Petrograd
had been removed from the control of the RVSR and placed directly
under the Committee of Defence and the Central Committee,
Stalin becoming 'the Extraordinary Commissioner in command of
the Petrograd area and other regions of the West Front'.[23]

On arrival in Petrograd Stalin had held a meeting with Vatsetis,
and Nadezhny and Remezov, the commanders respectively of the
West Front and 7 Army. On 20 May he was at the headquarters of
the West Front at Staraya Russa, then going on to Gatchina and
Kronstadt. On 9 June Stalin signalled Lenin to say that he was

siting his second line of defence on the old Peterhof-Gatchina fortifications once used against Kerensky; he wanted further reinforcements and he complained yet again about the unreliability of those already dispatched by the All-Russian Main Staff.[24] On 16 June, the two coastal forts were reoccupied by Bolshevik troops, Stalin, so he said, personally directing the attack on Krasnaia Gorka 'from the firing line'.[25] That day Stalin sent the telegram described by Trotsky as 'overbrimming with provocative braggadocio'. 'The naval specialists assure me,' said Stalin, 'that the capture of Krasnaia Gorka from the sea counters all naval science. I can only deplore this so-called science. Its swift capture was due to the rudest interference in the operations by me. . . .' On the telegram Lenin wrote 'But Krasnaia Gorka was taken from the land!'.[26] Among the West Front directives is one, dated 14 June, requiring the fleet to concentrate against Krasnaia Gorka, and the guns of Kronstadt to bombard it from a range of 15 miles; from this it would seem that Stalin was not the only director of operations.[27]

Voroshilov's cartographic account of Rodzianko's repulse shows a large red banner marked 'Stalin' flying over the Smolny, while 7 Army near Gatchina deployed 6 and 2 Rifle Divisions in defence of Petrograd. Success, denoted by the broad red arrows, went to 6 Division.[28] Again the military directives throw a different light on the affair. On 14 June the headquarters of West Front had moved to Smolensk, and Nadezhny, a tsarist corps commander originally from 14 Georgian Grenadier Regiment, would appear to have been directing the Petrograd battle from there, strengthening 7 Army by removing formations from his other armies. On 17 June he had a teleprint conversation with Remezov (a former general staff officer from 117 Yaroslavsky Regiment) and suggested that 7 Army should envelop Rodzianko from the south by thrusting on Veimarn or Yamburg. Remezov replied that he had already drawn up his plan and proposed to make his envelopment closer than that suggested by Nadezhny, deploying eleven regiments in the south and six regiments (of 6 and 19 Rifle Divisions) in the north between the main road and the coast. Meanwhile 7 Rifle Division would be held in reserve in the area of Gatchina. Nadezhny was not content with Remezov's plan, which resembled, he said, a frontal attack (*lobovoi udar*), much of it through wood and swamp. He wanted

7 Army to adopt the West Front solution and commit the newly arriving reserves further to the south.[29] Remezov had, therefore, elements of five rifle divisions in this sector, and some of these appear to have been converted to the 1918 establishment of nine regiments to the division. Whatever was finally settled, the main attack certainly did not come, as Voroshilov said, from 6 Rifle Division on the extreme right against the Gulf of Finland.

At the time of Stalin's arrival in Petrograd 6 Rifle Division covered the main south-west approaches to the city, and this formation appears to have captured his attention. Stalin's reports to Lenin were in the first person, for he had apparently begun to regard Remezov and Nadezhny as interlopers. The Commissioner continued to stress the lack of support from Moscow, for on 22 June he signalled Lenin 'our attack began yesterday, although we have not received the promised reinforcement . . . our offensive goes well . . . we have secured the line Kernovo–Kaskovo [in front of 6 Division] and have taken prisoners and two or more [*sic*] guns'. He ended 'send quickly two million cartridges at my disposal for 6 Division'.[30]

Some of Stalin's political and military assessments at this time were Lenin's views, relayed back to the capital. Lenin had suggested treason and Stalin had not been slow to unearth it. A search of the foreign consulates had brought to light what Stalin claimed to be a counter-revolutionary conspiracy, and the Cheka began to work on and embroider the evidence. Trotsky believed that Stalin's revelations were inspired by hostility to himself, a not improbable hypothesis; yet the Cheka's quarry appears to have been the RVSR, military specialists in general and perhaps those who had offended Stalin. For, according to Stalin, it was evident that the All-Russian Main Staff and the field headquarters of the RVSR, headed, Stalin reminded Lenin, by Kostiaev, 'were all working for the Whites'; he conjectured that both organizations were responsible for certain mass desertions, which he named. He added a goad, so clumsily worded as to be offensive: 'The whole question now is that the Central Committee should summon up the courage to draw the proper conclusions – but has the Central Committee sufficient character and resolution?'.[31]

At the beginning of June Okulov, the political member with the West Front, had complained to the Central Committee about

Stalin, saying 'that 7 Army is being divorced from the West Front and is receiving reinforcements and equipment through parallel lines of supply'. Okulov wanted 7 Army either returned to the West Front or put directly under the RVSR. Lenin asked for Stalin's views.[32] This complaint by Okulov, an old Bolshevik who was hostile to the Tsaritsyn group, drew from Stalin the reply that it was his 'profound conviction that Nadezhny is not a commander, or capable of commanding, and will finally wreck the West Front', while 'party workers such as Okulov who urge the military specialists against our commissars . . . are harmful and demoralize the vital core of our army'.[33] The Central Committee acceded to Stalin's demand that Okulov be removed.

Trotsky subsequently charged Stalin and Voroshilov with 'merging both of Iudenich's campaigns into one so that the famous defence of Petrograd is represented as Stalin's handiwork'.[34] In fact Stalin took no credit for the October battle but merely repaid Trotsky in his own coin, by ignoring operations other than those in which he was personally involved. Stalinists have since improved on these methods by imputing to both Trotsky and Zinov'ev plans 'to let the enemy into Petrograd'.[35]

On 5 July, following the repulse of Rodzianko, Stalin was appointed as the political member of the West Front military council, together with a new commander, Gittis, who was, in due course, to replace Nadezhny. From 9 July to 26 September Stalin was at Smolensk.

On 18 July Stalin sent a personal telegram to Lenin outlining the position as he saw it on the Polish sector. The situation in the area of Minsk was poor; at Dvinsk – no better; at Lubents it was even worse. The Red units were in tatters and the enemy would not wait. Stalin believed that the front could do much, however, if Lenin would give it one suitable division. But he feared, he said, that Lenin would not do so, and then later, in a month's time, three divisions would not be enough. It was no use standing where they were; therefore they had decided to attack, scraping up and sticking together units as they went. Something might come of it. Stalin ended by condemning 'the military commander [Nadezhny], who is no use, for he only ruins everything'.[36] Stalin's brave intentions were not realized, however, for the enemy began his own offensive. By 1 August Lenin, fearful for Petrograd, was again harrying Stalin, ending; 'Ought you not personally to be taking heroic measures there?'.[37]

By 11 August Stalin had returned to his well-worn theme, describing the situation to Lenin in gloomy terms and heaping reproaches on the military centre. The Polish enemy was prising loose 16 Army so that the flanking armies would have to close up to stop him, using not one army but the whole front. It was apparent, he said, that the West Front was in the same position as the East Front the previous year, 'when Vatsetis and Kostiaev needlessly messed up operations'. He had already warned Lenin that the West Front was a ramshackle affair (*loskutnyi dvor*) which needed immediate reserves. Stalin ended: 'Now decide yourself; will you let us have a division . . . or will you allow the enemy to destroy the already crumbling 16 Army; but decide immediately, for each hour is precious'.[38]

Kamenev, the Commander of the East Front, was easy to get on with, and the political members Smilga, Lashevich and Gusev, spoke highly of him. Gusev lived *en famille* with the Kamenevs. Trotsky and Vatsetis, however, were hostile to Kamenev, and Kamenev's daughter has described a Trotsky visit to Simbirsk, when, dressed in black from head to toe, armed with a parabellum pistol and accompanied by a retinue, he burst into Kamenev's office, shouting threats in a highly excited state.[39] Vatsetis did not want the East Front to pursue Kolchak beyond the line of the Urals. Kamenev was in favour of doing so. Trotsky supported the Commander-in-Chief and, on 5 May, at Vatsetis's urging he summarily dismissed Kamenev, sending him on indefinite leave.

Having been advised by Gusev to put his case to Skliansky, Kamenev set out for Moscow where he lived with his family in a railway coach at the Kazan terminus. Meanwhile the East Front military council protested to Lenin against Kamenev's removal. Lenin interviewed Kamenev on 15 May, requiring from him a briefing, and then told him to return to his old command.[40]

Trotsky knew nothing of this – he was not aware of Kamenev's whereabouts, and he first heard of the reappointment on 21 May, Lenin explaining that he had reinstated Kamenev 'as a consequence of the signal' from Smilga, Gusev and Lashevich.[41] Trotsky was losing influence with Lenin, possibly because his military judgement was being called into question; his conduct had alienated military as well as political workers, and Vatsetis's personality had served to sharpen this conflict, for his correspondence shows him as an arrogant pedant. Lenin, having sided with Kamenev against Trotsky and Vatsetis, privately told Smilga, Lashevich and Gusev to let him have, by ciphered telegram, details of any future disagreements between Kamenev and Vatsetis.[42]

On 6 June Kamenev prepared a plan for the continuation of the advance into Siberia; Vatsetis vetoed it. The military council of the East Front protested to Lenin, and Smilga and Gusev were called to Moscow for consultation. On 14 June a meeting of six members of the Central Committee was held in Petrograd, at which Stalin was present, and a plenary meeting followed in Moscow the next day. These meetings sided against Vatsetis and, in consequence, Trotsky, according to Gusev, 'exasperated by his setback in the Central Committee vented his rage on the East Front'.

Matters finally came to a head at the Central Committee meeting of 3 July, for everyone voted against Vatsetis. Trotsky stormed out and wanted to resign all his offices, an offer which was declined. It was decided that Kamenev should be appointed as Commander-in-Chief, bringing in Lebedev, a former general staff officer of the Moskovsky Guard Regiment, who was Kamenev's chief of staff, to replace Kostiaev. The RVSR was to be reconstituted to include only Trotsky, Skliansky, Rykov, Kamenev, Smilga and Gusev, a council consisting largely of former members of the East Front, who were not kindly disposed towards Trotsky.[43] Trotsky, smarting under his reverse, remained for the rest of the summer with the South Front at Kozlov, his absence and estrangement from the RVSR serving, in Kamenev's view, to bring the organization closer under Lenin's control.

Stalin supported Smilga and Gusev against Vatsetis. A few days later his ally Dzerzhinsky brought to light the results of a Cheka investigation, implicating Vatsetis in suspected treason.[44] Vatsetis was arrested, subsequently released, and then, since the Central Committee felt itself to be in his debt, appointed to an academic post as an instructor.

Although Kolchak and Iudenich had retreated and the authority of the White government in Archangel was on the wane, a new and greater threat was looming in the south. The British had prevailed upon Krasnov to resign as *ataman* of the Don Cossacks, because the White generals refused to co-operate with him; as Alekseev was dead, Denikin had taken over the supreme command of all the White and Cossack forces, and was already receiving British support in weapons and supplies.

Denikin's force consisted of three armies: on the right, Wrangel's Caucasians on the Manych; in the centre, Sidorin's Don Cossacks in the Don bend; and on the left, Mai-Maevsky's Volunteer Army to the north of Rostov. The White strength in the south rose between May and October 1919 from 64,000 to 160,000 men.[45] Opposing Denikin was Egor'ev's South Front, stretching from the middle Dnieper to the lower Volga, and consisting, from west to east, of 14, 13, 8, 9 and 10 Armies, totalling in July about 178,000 men.[46] Denikin's principal aim, so he said, was to strike north and take Moscow, but in fact his formations fanned out across the Ukraine and South Russia, apparently intent on recovering territory and material resources and on protecting the Ukraine from the Poles. By the middle of August the larger part of the Ukraine had been taken, including the cities of Kharkov and Belgorod; in the east Wrangel had advanced beyond Tsaritsyn, nearly half-way to Saratov. The momentum of the offensive showed no signs of falling off.

Denikin's rapid successes caused a split in the views of the Bolshevik Government and its military command, a conflict of ideas which continued to be ventilated in the world press generations after the event. Expressed in simple terms, it was whether to counter-attack Denikin in the flank, on an axis running roughly from east to west, or in the centre by a thrust running from north to south. The east-west axis from the lower Volga to Rostov was aimed at overrunning the territories of the Don Cossacks, Denikin's principal supporters; but this advance had to be made over the open steppe with few roads and rail links, against an implacable enemy. When put to the test of battle it failed. The main axis was then changed to the north-south direction down the Donets Basin, traversing an industrial area inhabited by workers whose sympathies lay with the communists. This virtually destroyed

Denikin's forces. Subsequently, both Trotsky and Stalin claimed to be the author of the victorious plan, imputing to the other the unsuccessful course of action.[47]

Trotsky has used documents in an attempt to prove that the successful plan, based on a shrewd appreciation of geographical, economic and political factors, was his own, and he has convinced both Souvarine and Deutscher that this was so.[48] Yet all that can in fact be deduced with certainty from his papers is that Vatsetis and Kamenev disagreed on the strategy to be adopted by the East Front.

On 27 July Trotsky, who was with the South Front, reported to Moscow that its commander Egor'ev considered 'Kamenev's plan of operations *incorrect*' (Trotsky's italics); Trotsky suggested that Egor'ev be replaced by someone 'who acknowledges the operational authority of Kamenev and agrees with his plan', almost intimating that such a commander might be hard to find.[49] In his writings Trotsky discusses this incident, immediately following his description of the disagreement on the axis to be used against Denikin, so that the reader might assume by this juxtaposition that the Egor'ev affair was part of the same controversy. Yet an examination of the correspondence between Kamenev and Egor'ev indicates that the disagreement was based on entirely different objections.

Egor'ev, a former general of artillery, had sent to Kamenev on 24 July a detailed appreciation fully accepting Kamenev's first strategic plan, to strike the main blow on the east-west axis across the Don Steppe. The Don Cossack population admittedly, said Egor'ev, would not take kindly to Soviet power, and the rail communications were more plentiful west of the line Voronezh-Rostov than to the east; but there were numerous roads and earth tracks over the plain, excellent for summer use, and the *balki* gullies and rivers were no obstacle; on the Don itself there were fordable shallows every eight versts. It was true, continued Egor'ev, that the steppe could be used to advantage by the Cossack cavalry, but it also gave excellent fields of fire to the Red motorized machine-guns. Egor'ev did bring to Kamenev's notice the possibility that Denikin might counter-manoeuvre by striking due northwards from Kharkov; he imagined that Kamenev had taken this contingency into consideration and held reserves to deal with it, for Egor'ev's troops there, 'Ukrainian formations in a chaotic state

[14 Army commanded by Voroshilov], would be unable to stop it'.[50]

The next day, however, Egor'ev received a further teleprinted order from Kamenev, altering the original concept, in that 14 Army was required not merely to pin the enemy opposing it but was to advance southwards and secure such far-flung objectives as Kharkov and Ekaterinoslav, this being additional to the main blow to be struck westwards across the Don Steppe. Egor'ev's angry reply of 25 July demanded that Kamenev should change his orders or find a new commander for the South Front.[51]

Trotsky was determined to disagree with Kamenev, and his signals met with a sharp rebuttal from Lenin and the Central Committee.[52] The plan which Trotsky later claimed as his own would appear to have been based on an imprecise paper, written by Vatsetis on 22 June 1919, in which geographical, economic or political considerations were not mentioned. Vatsetis came to a conclusion, not a logical deduction to be drawn from his preamble, that the decisive blow against Denikin should be made 'by 8, 13 and 14 Armies of the South Front striking due south' while '10 and 9 Armies maintained pressure from the Volga to the Don to restrict the enemy withdrawal'.[53] This was the Vatsetis plan, the authorship of which appears to have been subsequently assumed by Trotsky.

The first Kamenev plan was based on the immediate use of those reserves made available by the south flank of the East Front, since these could be quickly transferred to 10 and 9 Armies in the area of the lower Volga north of Tsaritsyn. These two armies, which formed a single group under the command of Shorin, were to make the main thrust in mid-August, westwards across the Don Steppe.[54] The Central Committee had accepted this concept in preference to that of Vatsetis, because the plan reflected the position of Red Army troops on the ground and because Lenin was opposed to delaying a counter-offensive while extensive redeployment took place.[55]

Shorin's August offensive was successful only insofar as it made some ground towards Tsaritsyn and the line of the Khoper. The South Front's subsidiary pressure by 8 and 13 Armies, forming a group under the former general Selivachev, failed entirely, since it was attacked by Denikin on 12 August; 8, 13 and 14 Armies of the South Front were herded off to the north. In the west, Kiev fell to the Whites at the end of August and Kursk was lost shortly afterwards. By the beginning of October the Volunteer Army stood at Orel, Voronezh having been taken by Sidorin's Cossacks. A raiding force of about 8,000 Don Cossack cavalry under Mamontov broke deep into the Bolshevik rear, seizing Tambov on 18 August and then Kozlov, the headquarters of South Front, forcing Trotsky to flee for his life.[56]

Denikin's advance on Moscow and the bitter resistance of the Don Cossacks raised serious doubts in Kamenev's mind regarding his own strategy; for at some time between 21 and 26 September he wrote an undated appreciation which attempted to justify his earlier choice of the main east-west axis from the lower Volga flank. It was still necessary as a primary task, he believed, to separate Denikin from the Cossacks who were his main support; but he now wondered whether this could not be done by making political concessions to the Cossack peoples. If the Shorin offensive from the Volga were to be continued, the enemy 'might penetrate even further to the north'; and it was easier to reinforce the area south of Moscow with formations railed from the West Front, than to send them to far-away Tsaritsyn. So he offered the Central Committee the alternative of concentrating all reserves to the south of Moscow, primarily as a defensive measure. Political, economic and geographical factors were not even hinted by Kamenev.[57]

Lenin and the Central Committee, after considering this document, ordered Kamenev 'not to consider himself bound by his former recommendations, or by any previous decisions of the Central Committee', and they gave him 'full powers as a military specialist to take what measures he thought fit'.[58] This instruction would appear to reveal the extent to which the Central Committee relied on Kamenev's judgement, and tends to support Denikin's contemptuous dismissal of the generalship of Trotsky 'and other commissars' as being 'at first quite fictitious'.[59]

Where Stalin stood during this dispute is easier to determine. Between 3 July and 9 September 1919 he voted with Lenin against Trotsky and in support of Kamenev. By the second half of September when Kamenev changed his mind, Stalin as well as Trotsky would have known the contents of the Commander-in-Chief's new appreciation.

Following the two plenary sessions of the Central Committee on 21 and 26 September decreeing that 'the best workers and commanders should be sent to the south, the South Front being the main front of the republic', it was decided on 27 September to reinforce the southern approaches to Moscow. On this day, too, the South Front was split, throwing off Shorin's group which was redesignated as a new South-East Front. Egorov, a former lieutenant-colonel of 132 Bendersky Regiment commissioned in 1905 from the Kazan military school, replaced Egor'ev at the South Front. Trotsky had been present with the South Front during a long period of defeat, and the Central Committee decided to move Stalin there. By mid-October the South Front stood at 119,000 troops and 600 guns while Shorin's South-East Front mustered 58,000 men and 285 guns.[60]

Stalin did not arrive at the South Front headquarters at Sergievskoe until 3 October, where he found Trotsky well esconced. Both of them went to Moscow to attend a Politburo meeting on 15 October, during which it was decided that Trotsky should go to Petrograd, which was again threatened by Iudenich.[61] Stalin, according to his *Kratkaia Biografiia*, then set to work 'rooting out Trotsky's placemen', and he 'scrapped the old criminal plan' replacing it by one of his own 'which was a stroke of strategic genius'.[62]

At about this time Stalin was supposed to have written the letter to Lenin, sneering at the obstinacy of Kamenev for adhering to the plan to attack Denikin from the east. It was necessary right away, said Stalin, 'to throw over this discredited plan and launch an attack on Rostov from the Voronezh area by way of Kharkov and the Donets Basin'. He then marshalled a number of pertinent political, economic and military factors in favour of his newly found strategy – a friendly population, coal and good communications; and he ended his otherwise logical and well-reasoned letter with an emotional flourish:

Without this change of strategy my work . . . will be pointless, criminal and superfluous, giving me the right, indeed making it my duty, to go anywhere, even to the devil. . . .[63]

This letter was originally published in *Pravda* in 1929 and was undated, an omission noted by Souvarine. There are a number of doubts as to its timing, relevance and purpose, particularly since subsequent Stalinist accounts dated the letter as 15 October and placed its authorship at Serpukhov.

It is certain that Stalin attended the Politburo meeting in Moscow on 15 October. Serpukhov is on the railway 70 miles south of Moscow, and Stalin might have returned to Serpukhov the same day. But Stalin does not appear to have been a signatory to the front orders of 14, 15 or 16 October.[64] The concentration of Red Army formations immediately south of the capital was already well under way when, on 15 October, the Politburo meeting, attended by Stalin, had decided to switch the South-East Front to the defensive and so release more troops for the protection of Moscow. Moreover, the opening words of Stalin's letter '*two months ago* the Commander-in-Chief raised no objection to an offensive through the Donets Basin' give some ground for believing that the missive, whatever the true form of its content, was written nearer the middle of November.

Why Stalin should have written this letter at all, even in November, may be partially explained by the jealousy which existed between the fronts over the allocation of resources. Smilga, Shorin's political member, wrote to the Central Committee on 3 November insisting that the South-East Front remained 'the main and decisive theatre'.[65] Meanwhile Stalin and Egorov were keeping up a constant pressure on Kamenev for reinforcements, on 29 October demanding 83,000, and hinting on 12 November that they might have to withdraw if they did not get them.[66] Between 5 and 12 November Stalin countered Smilga by sending to the Central Committee two angry and discourteous demands for reinforcements, together with an ultimatum that 'either Gusev and the headquarters of the Commander-in-Chief should go, or the military council of South Front should be replaced'. For this demand Stalin was rebuked by the 14 November session of the Politburo.[67]

Voroshilov's account describing Stalin as the architect of the strategy which crushed Denikin is at variance with the documentary evidence which indicates that there were three strategic plans, the first belonging to Vatsetis and the other two to Kamenev. Stalin may indeed have written his complaint to Lenin elaborating on the advantages, which were by then self-evident, of a strategy based on the main blow being made by his own South Front; but he probably did this when his battle was almost won, between 12 and 14 November, in order to forestall the reinforcement of the rival South-East Front. By subsequently antedating the letter by about a month Stalin attempted to endow himself with strategic foresight.

Rotmistrov, writing at the time of Khrushchev's ascendancy, has said that Kamenev's first and unsuccessful plan 'corresponded with the conditions of the political and military situation and the grouping of the forces of the South Front at the time', and that 'the final strategic plan of the main thrust from the area of Orel and Voronezh was not determined personally by Stalin, as was put out in military literature during the time of the Stalin personality cult, but was worked out collectively between the Central Committee and the military command, the object being to defeat those enemy forces south of Moscow. . . .'[68] On the basis of the documentary evidence so far made available, Rotmistrov's conclusions are not improbable.

Stalin remained at the South Front, redesignated on 10 January 1920 as the South-West Front, from 3 October 1919 until 23 March 1920, and it was his subsequent boast that during this period when Denikin was finally defeated, victory was achieved 'without the presence of Comrade Trotsky'. Nor did Trotsky visit the front during this time.

Among the documents of this period of the South Front offensive are a number of operational directives, signed by Egorov and Stalin. It is impossible to estimate Stalin's personal contribution. On occasion he took action on his own account, for, on 25 October, he was on the teleprinter to Ordzhonikidze, the political member with 14 Army, discussing the temporary loss of Kromsk. Stalin told Ordzhonikidze 'to fight – it was simply a question of fighting (*ibo rech' idet ob istreblenii*) for Kromsk could easily be regained. Under no circumstances,' continued Stalin, 'should counter-attacking regiments be committed to battle piecemeal, but the enemy should be smashed by one massive concentration on a single predetermined axis'.[69] Stalin did not hesitate to bring to Lenin's attention trivial matters, such as the unauthorized drawing of equipment by other formations, what Stalin called 'the plundering of South Front's engineer stores at the Ryazan dump', demanding that the culprit, Kornev, 'be made answerable for his actions'.[70] Whatever his military value, Stalin, together with Trotsky, on 27 November was awarded the Order of the Red Banner, according to Stalin's own citation, 'for his services in the defence of Petrograd and for his self-sacrificing work at the South Front'.

Budenny's cavalry, by then part of the South Front, included a number of commanders who subsequently occupied senior posts during the Second World War, among them Voroshilov, Shchadenko, Kulik, Timoshenko, Apanasenko, Tiulenev, Meretskov, Kharitonov, Kostenko, Khrulev, Cherevichenko, Lopatin and Leliushenko. None of them was a former cavalry officer. Budenny himself was an extended-service equitation instructor, well decorated for bravery, a man of limited education who appears to have been a difficult subordinate; like Voroshilov, he was a shrewd intriguer. Budenny pressed Stalin and Kalinin to expand his cavalry corps and he recommended that a cavalry army should be formed by uniting his own 1 Cavalry Corps and Dumenko's 1 Composite Cavalry Corps, with Budenny himself as army commander. According to Voroshilov, Stalin 'recognized the power of massed cavalry, although the past could provide no precedent for such an original experiment as the formation of a cavalry army. . . .'[71] Trotsky, according to Stalin, opposed the idea.[72] Budenny's proposal was not acted upon, however, for his corps of three cavalry divisions, together with its infantry formations, numbering in all only 9,200 men and 26 guns, was merely redesignated, on 19 November, as a cavalry army. It had no corps organization, but, since it had been raised to the status of army, it was provided with a military council, the newly joining political members being Voroshilov and Shchadenko.[73] The renaming of a cavalry corps as a cavalry army is still regarded in Soviet military literature as 'a new phenomenon of the military art'.[74]

After a 40-day advance Budenny reached the Sea of Azov on 7 January 1920, splitting the enemy between the Crimea and the Caucasus. Three days later Egorov's South Front was redesignated as the South-West Front, and it became responsible for operations against the Crimea. That same day Shorin's South-East Front took over Budenny's 1 Cavalry Army and Sokol'nikov's 8 Army, to add to its own three armies, and, on 16 January, it was renamed the Caucasus Front.

Stalin was in the forward area only once during the South Front advance.[75] According to Trotsky, Stalin was incapable of 'appearing under the open sky before a regiment' or of 'appealing to the hearts of soldiers and commanders' by a personal address.[76] Yet Trotsky was not necessarily a reliable judge for, although he rated highly his own ability to address troops, impressing this on Lenin and on the Russian and foreign press, in the company of soldiers he himself appeared, according to Budenny, as a foreign and rather ludicrous figure, ignorant of traditional military procedures and with so little understanding of the intelligence and education of the rank and file that his address gave rise to angry and audible mutterings among the men.[77] A reliable non-communist witness, present on such an occasion, has described how the soldiers found Trotsky's harangue incomprehensible and irritating.[78]

Stalin retained his own personal connections with the former Tsaritsyn group transferred to the Caucasus Front. Budenny and Voroshilov had earned a name among the Whites for cruelty and atrocity, and stories of the cavalry army's indiscipline and drunkenness had reached Lenin's ears. It was unpopular, too, with other Red commanders and staffs. Budenny, Voroshilov and Shchadenko looked about for allies, sending letters and telegrams to Lenin, Stalin, and even Trotsky; they begged Stalin to intercede for them and to present their most humble greetings to Vladimir Il'ich. Budenny wanted to be rid of Shorin and Sokol'nikov; he would have liked to expand his command and he still coveted Dumenko's cavalry corps. On 3 February, according to Budenny, Stalin was on the direct line to Ordzhonikidze, the newly appointed political member for the Caucasus Front, saying that he had arranged to have Shorin and Sokol'nikov dismissed shortly 'for adopting an attitude of mistrust and enmity towards the cavalry army'. Stalin continued: 'I am completely convinced that your new *Komfront* [designate Tukhachevsky] should . . . use the right flank to some purpose, and put Dumenko's corps into the cavalry army . . . for flank operations'.[79] It was soon brought home to Tukhachevsky, a 26 year old former second-lieutenant of the Semenovsky Guard Regiment, who, according to the version accredited to Ordzhonikidze, 'was ill-disposed to the cavalry army and to Budenny in particular', that Budenny, Voroshilov and Shchadenko had a powerful ally.

Shorin had been commissioned in 1892, he was neither staff trained nor qualified, and in 1914, at the age of 44, he was a captain. As a Red front commander he suffered a severe check at the beginning of February 1920 when the Cossacks rallied temporarily and defeated Budenny's and Dumenko's cavalry. On 3 February Lenin and Trotsky jointly signed a telegram to Stalin appointing him to the Caucasus Front – in addition to the posts he already held – and instructed him to transfer troops from the South-West Front after first journeying out to see Shorin. Stalin replied sharply that it was his profound conviction that journeys by individuals were not needed; what was wanted was 'the transfer of cavalry reserves – the South-West Front being without them'. He continued, 'Budenny and Ordzhonikidze consider . . . Shorin the reason for our failures. I am not entirely well and ask the Central Committee not to insist on the journey'.[80]

Lenin did not insist. On 19 February Stalin telegraphed the Politburo expressing his disagreement with an order from Kamenev withdrawing formations from 'the Ukrainian Army of Labour'; on this telegram Lenin wrote 'he is just cavilling, the Commander-in-Chief is absolutely right'.[81] The next day Lenin signed a telegram, written in Lebedev's handwriting, instructing Stalin to speed up the transfer of troops to the Caucasus Front. Stalin's reply to Lenin, dated 20 February, said that he was not clear why the matter should be Stalin's responsibility since the reinforcement of the Caucasus Front was entirely the concern of the RVSR, the members of which according to his information were in good health, and not that of Stalin, who was overburdened with work anyway. This brought a mild reproof from Lenin.[82] These documents, including Lenin's reply, have since been published in Moscow, except, apparently, Stalin's 20 February signal. Instead, Stalin is said to have replied that same day – possibly in answer to the reproof – 'you may be assured that everything possible will be done'.[83]

Stalin, however, regarded his work as finished. He had, for the time being, lost interest in military matters and he wanted to return to the capital. Even the Polish capture of Mozyr was of little concern to him. Finally, on 23 March, he set out for Moscow and severed his connection with the South-West Front.

3
Poland

The Polish relationship with Denikin had been cool since Warsaw feared that the Whites, if victorious, would be unlikely to permit Polish troops to remain on Belorussian or Ukrainian soil. Warsaw feared and distrusted the Bolsheviks. The Polish aim was to push its own frontiers eastwards, and their armies in Belorussia continued to edge towards Smolensk, reaching, by January 1920, the area of Polotsk and Borisov. In the south Warsaw intended to weaken its powerful and troublesome neighbour by detaching from it, as part of the process of self-determination, its subject Ukrainian peoples.

Before April 1919 Lenin had favoured war with Poland, but the threat from the south forced him to advocate peace; indeed, from the Trotsky-Markhlevsky correspondence it can be deduced that there was a secret understanding between Warsaw and Moscow.[1] But no sooner had Denikin been defeated than Trotsky began to threaten, in *L'Internationale Communiste,* to overrun Poland. Warsaw, for its part, had been evasive to Bolshevik requests for an armistice, and Lenin came to the conclusion that a new Polish offensive was to be expected.[2] Yet Russia needed peace with Poland for, although most of Caucasia was in Red hands by the end of March 1920, there had been a new build up of White forces in the Crimea under Wrangel, Denikin's successor, where 20,000 men of the Volunteer Army and 10,000 Cossacks were being reorganized and re-equipped.

On 25 April three Polish armies attacked the Soviet South-West Front, which had 12 and 14 Armies deployed facing west, and 13

65

Army to the south opposite the Crimea. By May the Poles were in Kiev and over the Dnieper.

The Russo–Polish War of 1920 was fought in two theatres, separated by the great barrier of the Pripet Marshes, nearly 300 miles in length from east to west. The Soviet High Command decided as a preliminary measure to draw off the Polish pressure against the South-West Front by attacking in the north in Belorussia, and Gittis was replaced by Tukhachevsky in command of the West Front. The offensive would then be taken up by Egorov's South-West Front. The military situation was somewhat altered, however, when on 25 May Wrangel launched an attack against 13 Army, capturing 8,000 prisoners and occupying the rich Taurida littoral to the north of the Crimea. The Central Committee concluded that Egorov, even when joined by Budenny's 1 Cavalry Army, would not be strong enough to defeat both Wrangel and the Poles in the Ukraine. Priority was to be given to driving out the Polish invaders and, as the South-West Front objected to this decision, the Central Committee on 26 May detailed Stalin to rejoin the front. He arrived at Kharkov by special train the next day.

On 29 May Stalin sent a personal signal to Lenin saying that he had visited the Crimean area, 'the situation there giving rise to great anxiety', and had had the Commander of 13 Army, a Latvian former colonel Pauka, replaced. Stalin had a number of requirements, mostly of a trivial military nature; Lenin, in a ciphered reproof, told him 'to address all military communications to Trotsky as well'.[3]

Egorov's offensive against the Poles, beginning on 26 May, was at first unsuccessful, and Stalin asked for a further two divisions to be allocated to the South-West Front. On 2 June Lenin replied, explaining that Tukhachevsky, too, was in difficulties; he reminded Stalin that the South-West Front was bound by the Politburo decision not to attack in the Crimea for the time being.[4] Stalin's unreferenced reply to Lenin of the same day read:

I understand your telegram to signify that the Central Committee refuses the two divisions, notwithstanding my warning; it has therefore released me from responsibility for the undesirable consequences which will probably result. Well, so be it. I recall the decision of the Poliburo, but Wrangel is disregarding that decision. . . .[5]

The following day, Stalin requested the Politburo to secure a cease-fire with Wrangel; should this be impossible, he asked for permission to attack the Crimea. Stalin wanted 'a quick and clear answer'; the Poles, he said, would not wait. On this signal Lenin noted, 'This is pure Utopia'.[6] Stalin had not yet given up, for on 4 June he told Lenin that he had 'just found some information from various sources' that Wrangel planned to envelop Odessa on 10 June.[7] He failed, however, to convince Lenin, and the Politburo adhered to its original decision.

On 2 June Kamenev instructed the South-West Front that the cavalry army should break through towards Belaya Tserkov–Fastov–Skvir to outflank the enemy grouping at Kiev from the south; Egorov and Stalin conformed in an order to Budenny the next day, giving the line as Novo Fastov–Pustarovka.[8] It was this order which was later described by Voroshilov to the Eighteenth Party Congress as 'the child of Stalin's military genius'.

On 4 June Stalin had a teleprinter conversation with Kamenev querying the role of the cavalry army. Stalin's message was formal and polite, but military terminology was not Stalin's forte at that time, for he became uncertain, even diffident. Kamenev's replies, though no less polite, showed signs of impatience. But he had, he said, discussed all this with Egorov two days before. Stalin assured Kamenev that Egorov was by his side and that he was talking with Egorov's agreement. Could Budenny first take Berdichev 'before turning to the right – for that would suit us very well?'.[9] The outcome appears to have been an exercise in deceit intended to impress the party leader with Stalin's sagacity, for he wrote that same day to Lenin, saying what was untrue, that he had 'altered the old [*Glavkom* and *Komfront*] plan . . . to a new, less deep and more realistic envelopment in the *raion* Fastov'.[10]

Budenny's four cavalry divisions attacked on 5 June; a week later all the Polish forces south of the Pripet were withdrawing rapidly westwards to escape encirclement. In Belorussia Tukhachevsky's West Front launched a new offensive on 4 July. Once again the Polish enemy began to retreat. By the end of the month the Red Army entered north Poland where, at Bialystok, the so-called

Provisional Polish Government was set up under the chairmanship of Dzerzhinsky. By the first week in August Tukhachevsky's
four armies were lining the Vistula and stretching more than 100
miles to the west of Warsaw.

Kamenev visited Smolensk on 22 July and confirmed Tukhachevsky's plan. Warsaw was to be outflanked from the north and
west and taken by 12 August. The great Lublin gap on the left
between Tukhachevsky and the Pripet Marshes, which now lay
much to the east, was to be covered by the Mozyr group of only
5,000 men. Basing its course of action on the optimistic appraisal
received from Kamenev, the South-West Front suggested on 22
July that its own front axis should be moved from Lublin further
to the south through Lvov. Kamenev agreed the next day and the
new front orders were issued over Egorov's and Stalin's signatures
and a copy was sent to Kamenev.[11] Budenny subsequently said
that Egorov told him that the West Front was already victorious
and did not need the cavalry army's close support.[12]

During July Stalin had reported to Lenin and Kamenev further
losses by 13 Army in operations against Wrangel.[13] Wrangel had
also made landings across the Sea of Azov and, on 29 July, a White
raiding force of 5,000 men crossed the Kerch Straits into the
Kuban.

Tukhachevsky had apparently persuaded Kamenev that the
West Front should eventually command all the armies fighting the
Poles, with the reservation that this should not be done until the
armies had left the Pripet behind them. On 28 July Kamenev told
Egorov that 12 Army, 'and then perhaps 14 Army', would be
transferred to the West Front, and Trotsky, in his minute to the
Politburo on 2 August, said that the South-West and West Fronts
were to be merged.[14] But in Trotsky's view Wrangel was such a
threat 'that Comrade Stalin should be charged with forming a
new [front] military council with Egorov or Frunze as commander,
by agreement between the Commander-in-Chief and Stalin'.
Lenin told Stalin that day that the Politburo had discussed the
reorganization of the fronts in order that Stalin should be able to
devote himself entirely to the problem of Wrangel. The Wrangel
threat, said Lenin, was becoming so enormous that inside the
Central Committee a tendency was growing to make peace with
Poland straightaway. Lenin wanted Stalin's views. On 3 August,

Kamenev issued the premature order uniting the West and South-West Fronts.

Meanwhile Stalin had sent off his reply to Lenin. How the fronts should be split was not, said Stalin, the business of the Politburo, which should not concern itself with details. He blamed Kamenev, and he said that he could not help pointing out that Soviet diplomacy sometimes wrecked, most successfully, the results of Soviet military victories. Lenin, taken aback by this reply, asked for clarification.[15]

On 3 August, a calmer Stalin described the organizational problems involved:

> The decree of the Central Committee . . . is not clear in the parts concerning 'the forming' of the South Front military council and the joining 'of the South-West and West Fronts' . . . it is necessary to point out that it is not merely a question of joining up two fronts but more particularly one of sorting out and reallocating headquarters, command machinery and resources.

Stalin went on to explain that the handing over of the armies to the West Front would also involve the transfer of commitments to that front, commitments for which Stalin's old South-West (or new South) Front would no longer be responsible. For:

> The South-West Front is not being broken up and shared out but will remain intact, with a view to . . . renaming as the new South Front, while those armies transferred from the South-West to the West Front would be maintained where they are at present by arrangements made by the headquarters of West Front.[16]

This reply seems to have mollified, even impressed, Lenin, for he asked for Stalin's military appreciation of the Lvov and Crimean sectors to place before the plenum of the Central Committee, 'for on your views may depend the weightiest political decisions'. Stalin answered that Lvov would be taken 'after some delay'; Poland, he thought, was becoming enfeebled; Wrangel would be defeated in the near future – by the beginning of the autumn if the Commander-in-Chief would send cavalry.[17] The plenum of the Central Com-

mittee accepted Stalin's recommendations in its protocol No. 35/5.
Yet it is doubtful whether the Politburo and RVSR really understood the implications of Stalin's signal of 3 August, since they
apparently took no action to follow it up.

On 4 August Egorov and Stalin signed a directive to 1 Cavalry
and 12 Armies ordering them to establish their own communications with the West Front in Minsk through the Mozyr group. On 6
August Kamenev sent a warning order to the South-West and
West Fronts, saying that 14 Army, in addition to 1 Cavalry and 12
Armies, was to be transferred to Tukhachevsky; the West Front
was to establish its own signal link with 14 Army.[18] There, for the
moment, the matter was left.

Meanwhile the cavalry army had exhausted itself in attacking
towards Lvov and, on 4 August, its council, Budenny, Voroshilov
and Minin, signalled Egorov and Kamenev that they had, on their
own responsibility, gone over to the defensive. Kamenev replied
on 6 August transferring 1 Cavalry Army to reserve 'for a rest,
pending a new assignment'; Egorov and Stalin acted on Kamenev's
directive and ordered 1 Cavalry Army into *front* reserve from 2359
hours on 8 August.[19]

On 7 August Tukhachevsky signalled Kamenev saying that he
was unwilling to accept the three armies from his neighbour without 'four points first being met', among which were the transfer of
all supply installations and the signal organization serving those
armies, and the establishing near the South-West Front field
headquarters of an 'operative point' or signal centre to maintain
telegraph communication with the three armies, until a direct link
could be established between them and Minsk; to set up this direct
link, said Tukhachevsky, might take from 10–14 days.[20] According
to Budenny's uncorroborated account, Kamenev told Tukhachevsky that the immediate transfer of the armies did not appear
necessary.[21] The South-West Front, in its reply to Kamenev,
could not accept Tukhachevsky's four points, as they would lead to
the breakdown in the command of the new South Front. Instead,
it suggested that the transfer of the armies should be timed to
coincide with the establishing of an operative point, 'using the
West Front's own equipment – for the South-West has none'.[22]
The signal was signed by both Egorov and Stalin, but the wording
and style were Stalin's.

On 10 August Voroshilov learned from Egorov that the cavalry
army would be transferred to the West Front, but that while it
remained subordinate to the South-West Front it should hold
itself in readiness to attack Lvov. This conversation was apparently
unpleasing to Budenny and Voroshilov, for, according to Budenny,
they sent a telegram direct to Moscow asking Kamenev to take the
cavalry army into GHQ reserve.[23] Meanwhile they reported information to the South-West Front, gleaned from Timoshenko's
skirmishers, that the enemy in the area of Lvov was thinning out
and sending troops northwards.

Lenin had come to the conclusion that Polish resistance was near
its end. On 11 August he sent a hasty signal to Stalin announcing a
victory which would be even greater if Wrangel could be smashed.
He told Stalin to do his utmost, no matter what, to seize the whole
of the Crimea with an immediate offensive. Everything depended
on it.[24]

The politicians appear to have been at variance with the military.
In the early hours of 11 August Kamenev told Tukhachevsky that
the West Front's centre of gravity was too far to the north of Warsaw; 1 Cavalry and 12 Armies might be brought in, he thought, to
fill the gap near Lublin in the south. At three o'clock that same
morning the RVSR sent a signal, signed by Kamenev, Klim and
Shaposhnikov, to the South-West Front, ordering 'the timely
breaking-off of the Lvov operation', and directed 'as large a force
as possible towards Lublin . . . to assist Tukhachevsky's left flank'.
Command of 12 and 1 Cavalry Armies should be transferred as
quickly as possible to the West Front. Kamenev ended this
strangely worded order with, 'I ask for your conclusions in this
matter'. Nine hours later the Commander-in-Chief, believing that
the Poles were in full retreat, sent another signal, timed at 1305
hours 11 August, urging 12 Army to begin its advance on Lublin
immediately.[25]

There is no apparent reason why Kamenev's two telegrams
should not have been deciphered by the early afternoon of 11
August, since teleprinter messages over the Baudôt and Hughes
telegraph were received instantaneously at their destinations as
they were being typed in Moscow. If they had in fact been speedily
deciphered, Stalin might have dismissed them as being out of date
and irrelevant, for the battle for Warsaw appeared to have been

won, and Lenin's pressing personal signal had demanded the immediate reduction of Wrangel. Moreover the South-West Front had an interest in retaining the cavalry army and, according to Budenny, 'Stalin and Egorov were counting on using it against the Crimea'.[26]

On 12 August 1 Cavalry Army was ordered by the South-West Front to take Lvov. Budenny, writing in 1965, described the order as irregular since, again according to his uncorroborated account, the army was in GHQ reserve; yet this objection had not in truth prevented him from making the necessary offensive preparations on 11 August, the previous day.[27] The South-West Front continued to ignore, or act in ignorance of, the contents of Kamenev's two signals of 11 August, and, on 12 August, it addressed an untimed telegram to Kamenev, following up Lenin's signal of the previous day, and suggested that 1 Cavalry Army should be withdrawn to Proskurov, still in front reserve, where it would be available for use against the Crimea.[28]

This last message stirred Kamenev to issue clear orders, timed at 0310 hours on 13 August and countersigned by Kursky and Lebedev. Both 12 and 1 Cavalry Armies were to come under the command of the West Front from midday on 14 August. The West Front was to establish a command and signals centre at Kiev, but until this was done Tukhachevsky was to transmit his orders through the South-West Front signal network. The terms of this order could brook no delay and the South-West Front had either to comply or refuse. On 13 August Stalin telegraphed to the Commander-in-Chief, again an untimed signal, saying that the two RVSR telegrams of 11 August had 'just been received and deciphered – cause of delay to be investigated'. Stalin continued: 'The armies of the South-West Front are engaged in clearing the area of Lvov . . . a change . . . I consider to be impossible'.[29] Yet, as Budenny noted, on 12 August, the same day as Stalin had committed the cavalry army to battle, the South-West Front had suggested to Kamenev that the cavalry army should be railed off towards the Crimea. The ease of disengagement apparently depended on the direction in which the cavalry army was to be sent.

Egorov, however, felt compelled to comply with Kamenev's order, for the demands from the centre were being reinforced by threats, presumably from Trotsky. Stalin angrily refused to sign the draft: instead, he sent a telegram to the RVSR, full of reproaches. Kamenev's last order, he said, was completely ruining the South-West Front. Berzin, the second political member, feared to append his signature when a Politburo member had refused to do so. He asked Trotsky for instructions and was told in forceful terms to sign the order immediately. A faithful repetition of Kamenev's last order was issued at six o'clock in the evening of 13 August, signed by Egorov, Berzin and the former engineer officer Petin, merely transferring the command of the two armies to Tukhachevsky.[30] No action was taken by the South-West Front on Kamenev's signals of 11 August, laying down the new axes and tasks for these armies; and so the cavalry army continued to fight for Lvov.

On the evening of 15 August Tukhachevsky sent an order to Budenny telling him to quit Lvov and proceed to Vladimir-Volynsky; the order was countersigned by Butkevich, the commissar for the front headquarters, and was therefore valid. But, during the transmitting through the South-West Front signal network, Butkevich's signature was somewhere omitted, enabling Budenny to refer the order back to Minsk, the next evening, for authentication.[31] Technically Budenny was justified in doing so, although he should at the same time have put in hand preparations to disengage. In fact, military orders not bearing a commissar's countersignature were not infrequent, Vatsetis and Kamenev being common offenders, and in practice these orders were normally acted upon.

Tukhachevsky had begun his offensive on Warsaw three days before, making a steady but slow advance against bitter resistance when, on 16 August, his left flanking army and the Mozyr Group were shattered by a Polish striking force concentrated in the Lublin gap. In attempting to outflank the Poles from the north-west, three of Tukhachevsky's armies had been enveloped from the south-east. On 17 August Tukhachevsky sent another signal to Budenny. That same day Kamenev told Tukhachevsky by teleprint that no action had yet been taken by Budenny to regroup his army 'because of some very unpleasant events'; 'and', continued Kamenev, 'there is no surety that regrouping will start tomorrow since the cavalry army received your directive with only one signature'.[32] Tukhachevsky's answer clearly showed his amazement and concern.

The Central Committee recalled Stalin from the South-West Front on 17 August, after his refusal to sign the front order, Lenin remarking, according to Trotsky, 'Stalin again caught in the act'. Budenny, Voroshilov and Minin continued to disobey the orders which they received from the West Front on 16, 17 and 19 August. Instead, Budenny sent two long signals to the West Front exaggerating the enemy strength he claimed to be pinning and setting out the reasons why he could not move. Egorov continued to side with Budenny, and, even as late as 21 August, he had a teleprinter conversation with Tukhachevsky, begging that the cavalry army be allowed to complete the capture of Lvov.[33]

At the Politburo meeting of 19 August, attended by Stalin, the members were still not aware that the West Front was about to be crushed. Lenin's attention was rivetted on Wrangel, and Stalin and Kamenev were bickering about cavalry for the Crimea. After 'having heard the military reports of Comrades Trotsky and Stalin' the Politburo decided that the Crimea should be regarded as the main front and that Timoshenko's cavalry division should be diverted from Budenny to 13 Army.[34]

With the virtual destruction of Tukhachevsky's West Front, Poland won the war. Lenin declined to allocate blame for what he called 'this military defeat', and was content that the analysis should be left to future historians. But Lenin's personal intervention had not been limited to his signal to Stalin on 11 August, for the next day he had been enthusiastic about Stalin's proposal to move the cavalry army against Wrangel, and had thought that Tukhachevsky could procure the help he needed simply 'by calling up all the adults' in his area.[35] Lenin's political and military judgement was not without fault.

Current Soviet military literature usually ignores the existence of Trotsky, attributing actions initiated by him to his deputy Skliansky. According to his public utterances at the time, Trotsky does not appear to have been so averse to the Polish adventure as he subsequently maintained. During the campaign he was subordinate to Lenin's military control and was obliged to conform to the methods of Kamenev's organization within the RVSR. Whatever he might have said later, Trotsky's papers show that at

the time he had, like Lenin, a high opinion of Stalin's ability as a
military organizer for, on 11 May 1920, anxious about the cavalry
army, he had considered it essential that Stalin should go there and
put it aright. A latter-day Trotsky considered Stalin's strange
behaviour with the South-West Front to have been the manifestation of a vainglorious desire to take Lvov at the time when
Tukhachevsky was taking Warsaw. This may have been the case.
But Trotsky was not reluctant to pass judgement, even when he
was not in possession of the facts or was confused by them. For
Trotsky has made no mention of Lenin's interference and he has
translated the Berzin incident to Egorov's South Front in 1919; nor
could he distinguish R. I. Berzin from Ia. A. Berzin.[36]

At the time, it was accepted in Red Army circles that one of the
principal reasons for the Russian defeat was the delay in the
movement of the cavalry army into the Lublin gap. Tukhachevsky
tactfully touched on this point during his 1923 lectures to the
Moscow Military Academy.[37] Shaposhnikov thought that it was a
war that should have been won.[38] By 1929, however, Egorov made
a half-hearted attempt to deny 'the legend of the disastrous role
of the South-West Front', and by 1935 Rabinovich's history concluded that Trotsky's 'basically incorrect directive' forced 1
Cavalry Army to abandon the capture of Lvov. Later, at the
Eighteenth Party Congress, Voroshilov described Trotsky's
orders as treasonable. But by 1963 Todorsky's eulogy of Tukhachevsky ascribed the fault to the South-West Front, 'principally
of its political member J. V. Stalin'; Rotmistrov and other writers
under Khrushchev supported this opinion.[39] Stalin himself of
course had no compunction, even as early as the Tenth Party
Congress in March 1921, in blaming Smilga and Shvarts, the
political member and chief of staff of the West Front, for exercising
an unduly optimistic influence over Tukhachevsky, a view which
Budenny was still ventilating in 1965.

The Soviet High Command and field organization had been
unsatisfactory in that the South-West Front was responsible for
operations in both Galicia and the Crimea. Because of the Pripet
barrier, two separate fronts were certainly required in the west, but
with a closer co-ordination than that exercised by Kamenev. Nor
does Shaposhnikov escape censure for the drafting of the directive
of 11 August. On reaching the Bug, the West and South-West

Fronts could have been merged, but only if the signal and supply facilities had permitted it. Whether Tukhachevsky could in fact have commanded seven armies and several independent corps over a 300 mile front is doubtful, and whether the transfer of armies should have been made at the crucial moment when the outcome of the war was about to be decided, is certainly to be questioned. Lacking reliable long range radio and telephone equipment, the RVSR in the area of Moscow was too removed to co-ordinate the two fronts.

Lenin's system of military control was defective in that Kamenev, although he enjoyed Lenin's support, was unable to overcome the indiscipline of members of the Central Committee forming part of the military councils of the fronts. Few men were more ruthless than Lenin; once, hearing of the lack of productivity in the Omsk engine sheds, he said he was 'surprised that Smirnov did not punish, by shooting, the sabotage of the railway workers'; on another occasion he approved the paying of a bounty of 100,000 rubles for each Polish priest or landowner hanged.[40] Yet Lenin was very indulgent with his closest associates, particularly with Stalin.

The Tsaritsyn group, apparently abetted by Egorov, continued to resist the orders from the West Front, even after Stalin's departure, this giving some indication of the lack of authority of the centre. Budenny himself had a long record of indiscipline. In tsarist days he had, as a sergeant, knocked down his sergeant-major in front of his troop and, on his own admission, had forced his men to give false evidence that the sergeant-major had been kicked by a horse. When Wrangel had taken Tsaritsyn in 1919, Budenny had refused to call off his corps counter-attack on the pretext that the verbal cancellation had been given only by the 10 Army political member, the military specialist not being present; many years afterwards he recounted – with evident pleasure – how he had told the commissar to 'clear off'.

The extent to which Stalin's refusal or delay in the carrying out of orders was indirectly responsible for the defeat of the West Front and the consequent loss of the Russo-Polish War is a question which can only be examined by considering the Russo-Polish War as a whole. Many other factors contributed to the defeat: political misjudgement, military misdirection, poor training and organization, indiscipline in the West as well as the South-West Front, over-confident and inexpert commanders and inadequate signal communications. It seems probable, however, that if 1 Cavalry and 12 Armies had moved off to the north when ordered to do so, Tukhachevsky might have been saved from so overwhelming a defeat.

4
Towards the Greatest Army

After the death of Sverdlov, the Politburo had consisted of Lenin, Trotsky, Stalin, L. V. Kamenev and Bukharin, later increased to seven members by the addition of Zinov'ev and Tomsky. But it was Stalin who began to assume a plurality of functions. As a member of the subordinate *Orgburo*, he alone was concerned with the detail of the party machinery, besides being the commissar of *Rabkrin*, a body formed at Lenin's suggestion to inspect all branches of the government administration. Stalin was, moreover, the Politburo representative of the GPU (after it had absorbed the Cheka in 1922). Then, on 3 April 1922, he was appointed, again on Lenin's initiative, as General Secretary to the Central Committee, a newly created post which was to prove the most influential in the party and, by extension, in the government. Stalin became the executive for all the main party appointments and was to assume a directing role in the Central Control Commission, an inquisitorial body parallel to *Rabkrin*. The new General Secretary appointed and advanced those members who best served his, as well as party, interests.

Bazhanov, who had been selected in 1923 as Stalin's personal secretary and as secretary of the Politburo, has told how Lenin admired Stalin for his fist, not for his brain, and he quoted Lenin as once saying 'we don't need an intelligent man there – let us send Stalin'. Lenin, said Bazhanov, was unwilling to share his power with anyone, and he could not have been ignorant of the effect of centralizing so many activities under the hand of one man. But the party leader considered that Stalin, Molotov and Mikhailov, the three party secretaries, were entirely loyal to him, and that

Stalin was the obvious choice for the many key posts since he was unlikely to be a rival on account of his poor education.[1]

Bazhanov portrayed Stalin as a rough Caucasian, lacking in originality, with little understanding of politics, economics or finance, who read virtually nothing beyond 10–15 documents a year, a poor and boring speaker with a deliberate, dry and humourless style. Stalin's main characteristics were cunning, malevolence, political ambition and a pathological desire for power; he entrusted to no man his inner thoughts and was strangely out of place in a land where everyone talked too much. When he spoke he used words to conceal his thoughts; one could not know by his words whether he had thoughts or not. He was sly, the simple down-to-earth mentality of the peasant taking the place of intelligence. He had neither the critical faculty of the philosopher nor the dispassionate mentality of the sage, yet he was independent and obstinate. Stalin never generalized – he was not capable of it – for he had to have concrete facts. Given a question, he had an eye only for the practical solution; he solved positive, uncomplicated problems logically and with perspicacity, and he had the good sense to leave alone anything which was beyond his powers.[2] Stalin was vindictive, said Bazhanov, and the forgiveness of a slight was foreign to his nature. If it was in his interest he would sell anyone. Scornful of friendship and displaying an unbelievable cynicism in his personal relationships, he was treacherous and credited others with his own dark motives. He respected only those who stood up to him, though this would not save them. To Bazhanov is owed the well known description of Stalin living in the servants' quarters of the Kremlin eking out the existence of a state employee; in the presence of his family he maintained a contemptuous silence. He was not interested in money, possessions, sport or women, and art, music and literature meant nothing to him. The legend of the decisive Stalin was untrue, Bazhanov said, for he had seldom seen so mistrustful and cautious a man.[3] His dialectic was based on a constantly reiterated demand for facts.[4]

When Lenin was on his sickbed Kamenev, Zinov'ev and Stalin together formed the conspiratorial *troika* against Trotsky, rehearsing their parts prior to the meetings of the Politburo. Only Stalin greeted Trotsky cordially, shaking him warmly by the hand. While the Politburo was in discussion, Stalin would leave his chair, walking up and down the room with his waddling gait, his hands clasped behind his back, puffing at his pipe, a description to be repeated countlessly over the next 30 years. Stalin would make no comment until the discussion was finished, and then would summarize the majority view as if it originated from himself – and this was the decision usually adopted. Later, when his ascendancy was assured, he disdained to do even this, but merely left Bukharin to do the talking. Stalin rarely interrupted, but when he did so, his intervention was decisive and the other members hastened to agree with him.[5]

Bazhanov thought that Trotsky towered intellectually over Stalin and Zinov'ev, as a man who liked to shine but who attached more importance to the form than to the content, and was more concerned in how he spoke than in what he said – more of an actor than a politician, for politics were for him a stage.[6] Molotov and Voroshilov were steadily coming to the fore during these early years. Bazhanov saw Molotov as Stalin's creature, a stutterer and slow-thinker who never had an opinion of his own, but an industrious and thorough worker withal; and Voroshilov was 'quite a man, full of himself', yet in reality only Stalin's pliant puppet; Dzerzhinsky was an emotional, excitable neuropath; Budenny was ignorant and limited, a man without pretensions who, said Bazhanov, when asked by his subordinate for direction on a particularly important military question, replied 'Do what you want. My speciality is to sabre them down'.[7]

At some time after Lenin had returned to his office, he became aware of a situation similar to that which had faced Plekhanov 20 years before, except that Stalin had assumed the role of the young Lenin. Stalin tried to isolate the party leader from events, for that December he struck, somewhat prematurely, at Krupskaia, Lenin's link with the outside world, using, so it is said, vile abuse and threats, and promising to have her expelled from the party by his own Central Control Commission.[8]

Lenin had already recorded in his testament his fears concerning the concentration of so much power in the hands of the General Secretary and, on 5 March 1923, having heard of the Krupskaia incident, he wrote to Stalin that he had no intention of forgetting what was done against him. Four days later Lenin had his third and final stroke. The party at large knew nothing of these dissensions.

At one time Trotsky had professed to believe that the new Red Army should be based on a territorial militia, a part-time army centred on the industrial areas, drawing only a proportion of its troops, mainly private soldiers, from the agricultural periphery. Commanders were to come not from the regular army but from industrial management, the trade unions and the shop floor.[9] This concept found no support from his own military specialist staffs and little from the party ranks.[10]

Frunze, Voroshilov and Gusev pressed for the unified doctrine presented in Frunze's Ukrainian theses, to identify the Red Army with the new social system. But Trotsky denied that the Bolsheviks had invented a new concept of waging war, reminding his listeners that the White troops had been inferior in numbers but superior in military skill, and that the use of cavalry and manoeuvre was not a Red Army innovation but had been learned from Mamontov's Cossacks. War, he said, was a practical art, a skill, a trade; and to learn it, one did not have to be a Marxist, for the military specialists did it well enough. Meanwhile he advised the doctrinaire writers to confine themselves to the mundane but no less necessary tasks of teaching the soldier to shoot, oil his rifle and grease his boots.[11] Although this talk came strangely from the advocate of a militia to be officered by factory managers, Trotsky could be clear-sighted in criticism of his opponents' proposals. In the following year, in his condemnation of functionarism in the army, he said that according to Red Army history there were only heroes in its ranks, that every soldier burned with a desire to fight and that the enemy was always superior in numbers. This censure is still pertinent to much Soviet literature today.

Trotsky's remaining allies were being detached from him, Skliansky to be replaced by Frunze and Antonov-Ovseenko giving way to Bubnov. Muralov, the Commander of Moscow Military District, was replaced by Voroshilov. In June 1923 the Central Control Commission set up a military inquiry and its report was an indictment of Trotsky.[12] On 11 March 1924, as part of a far-reaching reorganization, the post of Commander-in-Chief was abolished and the Red Army High Command, though it still retained its tsarist pattern, was broken down into a central staff, an inspectorate and separate directorates (*upravleniia*) for each of the armed forces, all subordinate to the RVS. Frunze became the chief of staff with Tukhachevsky and Shaposhnikov as his assistants. Finally, in January 1925, Trotsky was replaced as Commissar for Military and Naval Affairs by Frunze.[13] The party disagreements concerning the cadre and militia systems were settled by a compromise whereby the Red Army was to be made up of both cadre and territorial divisions, so that by 1 October 1925 the new Red Army numbered twenty-five regular cadre and thirty-six territorial militia divisions.[14]

Frunze's championship of the military commander and one man command (*edinonachalie*) brought him under suspicion, if Bazhanov is to be believed, of wishing to bind the Red Army to himself. By the direction of the Central Committee, Frunze was forced, against his wish, to undergo minor surgery for an ulcer, and he died under the operation. His wife committed suicide immediately afterwards. Voroshilov felt obliged, or was directed, to write an apologia in *Pravda* defending the Central Committee decision.[15] Voroshilov then became the new Commissar for Military and Naval Affairs, an appointment which he was to hold until 1940. By July 1926, when Trotsky and Zinov'ev had been removed from the Politburo, the Red Army already belonged to Stalin.

Stalin's earlier writings give little guidance as to his military or indeed his political philosophy, for he preferred to rule through others, concealing the nature and extent of his power not only from the outside world but also from the population of the Soviet Union. Unlike Lenin, he was never the chairman of his own committees. It is true that the dictator sometimes posed, particularly abroad, as a moderate, subjected to extremist pressures from a hard-line element within the Politburo and party. Radek, however, put the situation in perspective when he said, in what was assumed at the time to be an inspired leak, that Litvinov only represented the man above him, a man endowed with a firm will who was hard, cautious and distrustful.[16]

In a speech made in 1925 to a plenary session of the Central Committee, Stalin, prefacing each argument with the word 'fact', had opposed the conversion of the whole of the Red Army to a militia. In the event of war, the Soviet Union could rely, he thought, only on its own might and not on foreign revolutionary movements.[17] In the main, however, Stalin appears to have used Voroshilov as his spokesman on military matters; and, according to Barmine, Voroshilov consulted Stalin on the smallest detail.[18] Voroshilov welcomed Russo-German military co-operation and was to extol the creation of a Soviet industrial armaments base.[19] Foreign weapons were bought for trials and research, and arms experts were hired on contract from abroad. State industrialization and the several five year plans, the effect of which was described by Chamberlin as early as 1934 as 'a vast undertaking with new industrial growth in the Urals and Western Siberia stretching from Magnitogorsk to Berezniky, 1,200 to 2,000 miles away from the western frontier', were to have a profound effect on military re-equipping.[20]

Von Manstein, during official liaison visits to the Soviet Union in 1931 and 1932, had talks with the principal Red Army commanders. Voroshilov seemed 'a not unsympathetic personality, but more of a politician than a soldier'; Budenny was *ein primitiver Haudegen*, entirely natural and uninhibited in his coarseness, and, unlike other senior commanders, was careless of the presence of commissars or secret police. Tukhachevsky gave the impression of being clever and devious, and was enthusiastic about Russo-German co-operation, insofar, said von Manstein, as this meant taking everything and giving as little as possible in return. The Germans also met Egorov, newly appointed Chief of the *Shtab RKKA*, but the elegant French speaking actress introduced to them as his wife made more impression than did Egorov. The visitors did not fail to notice that the woman presented to them in Kiev as Tukhachevsky's wife, was not she who had been introduced as Tukhachevskaia at an earlier reception in Moscow.[21]

It has been said that the Red Army military theory of this period was based on that of the imperial Russian school of the early twentieth century.[22] That there was a connection could hardly have been otherwise, for the revolutionaries relied on the teachings of Svechin and Novitsky, two former generals of artillery in the Bolshevik service, and their contemporaries, some of whom had been military theorists under Nicholas II. Sokolovsky lays a special emphasis on this continuity and considers that 'Russian military theory of the early twentieth century . . . far surpassed that of other countries'.[23] Such a chauvinistic view would have found no support from Shaposhnikov, who attended the 1909 course of the General Staff Academy; for there was, according to him, no national Russian doctrine, but 'just complete disorder in strategy and tactics' which was eventually dispelled by the use of direct translations from works by German military writers, so that Russian professors and students became disciples of the German precept 'with its crude insistence on the offensive'.[24] This German doctrine was carried forward into the twenties and the thirties. In 1931, Köstring, the German military attaché, reported that German influence could be seen in all aspects of the Red Army, and that 'German views and methods go through theirs like a red thread'.[25]

In tsarist times interest had also been shown in French military thought, and the Red Army continued to take note of French organization and methods. Tukhachevsky, who had had no staff training and little military service in the tsarist army, gave von Manstein the impression in 1931 that he was French oriented. Stalin, too, had a high opinion of the fighting ability of the French Army.[26]

At the beginning of the thirties the concept of 'the battle in depth' became popular, this being applied to both the offensive and defensive phases of operations, in the strategic as well as the operative field, Voroshilov stressing in 1931 that future war would be waged on the territory of the attacking enemy. Three years later Stalin adopted the slogan that the Red Army must be stronger than any possible combination against it, and drove the point home in his address to the Red Army Academy when he emphasized the need to cut the production of consumer goods in favour of armament and the needs of heavy industry.[27]

Until 1934 there were two committees responsible for defence, the Defence Commission headed by Molotov and formed within the Council of the People's Commissars (SNK), and Voroshilov's Revolutionary Military Council (RVS) which was part of the People's Commissariat for Military and Naval Affairs. Since these two committees tended to duplicate each other, the RVS was disbanded in June 1934, three months after the collegiate (military council) principle had been done away with at district and independent army level and Voroshilov's commissariat had been renamed the Commissariat for Defence (NKO). In September 1935 the *Shtab RKKA*, still headed by Egorov, became the Red Army general staff. In April 1937, the Defence Commission was reformed as a Committee of Defence, Molotov remaining as chairman, and it included among its members Stalin as well as Voroshilov. Eleven months later the RVS was revived as the Main Military Council RKKA consisting of Voroshilov as chairman and Stalin as one of its members. A similar council dealt with matters for the Soviet Navy, but Stalin did not sit on the naval council.

In view of the resurgence and rearmament of Germany, Moscow had decided in 1935 gradually to convert the Red Army from its mixed cadre territorial organization to a standing regular army based on a two year conscription period, so that by January 1938 only 35 of the existing 106 divisions should remain on a militia basis. The 1933 standing army strength of 885,000 was to be increased to 1,513,000 in the same period.[28] At the end of 1935 many of the former tsarist officer designations had been taken into use once more, and the constitution of the following year made service obligatory for all the population, irrespective of race, religion, social origin or former class.

In May 1937 the military commissars were restored to a level of command equality with the commanders, and the old system of military councils was reintroduced at military districts, fleets and independent ground armies.[29] This tightening of political control coincided with the purge of the army and the fleet. In August 1936 Zinov'ev, L. V. Kamenev and five other party leaders had been put on trial and executed; in January 1937 the principal defendants in a second major trial were Radek, Piatokov, Muralov, Serebriakov and Sokol'nikov. The arrest and shooting of Tukhachevsky, Iakir, Uborevich, Eideman, Kork, Primakov and Putna was followed by the massive purge which, during the next two years, cost the Red Army three of its five marshals, all the heads of districts and the deputy commissars for defence, the chief of the political directorate (PUR) and tens of thousands of its commanders. There appears to have been no clear design for the arrests which covered the whole spectrum of Soviet life, and it is impossible to establish even a general pattern within the armed forces. It is certain, however, that Shchadenko and Mekhlis, the new head of the PUR, were responsible for many of the military casualties, particularly in the Ukraine and the Far East.

When Kuznetsov assumed his duties as People's Commissar for

the Navy, in place of the purged Smirnov, he said that 'in his ignorance' he took all important naval questions to Molotov, who was chairman both of the Council of People's Commissars and of the Committee of Defence. Molotov, however, merely referred him to Stalin. Stalin, according to Kuznetsov, devoted much attention to all naval affairs, and no one ventured to act without his approval.[30] Kuznetsov's account is supported by Hilger, who was part of the German Ambassador's staff. Hilger considered that Molotov had no creative mind or personal initiative, for he kept strictly to the rules laid down for him by Stalin. At meetings, Stalin, who held no government post, would ask Molotov to take the chair and it was one of the rules of the game when important issues were at stake, said Hilger, that Molotov would decline. Stalin's manner was simple and unpretentious, but the paternal benevolence used to disarm Germans would turn into icy coldness when he rapped out short orders to People's Commissars. Hilger had, he said, noted the submissive attitude of Shaposhnikov, successor to the purged Egorov as Chief of General Staff, when Stalin was in conversation with him. Hilger was, however, surprised by the assurance with which Stalin made decisions on a wide variety of subjects, and in particular by the extent of his technical knowledge when he chaired a meeting of German and Russian naval experts, discussing the ordnance specifications of the turrets for a cruiser which Germany was delivering to the Soviet Union. Without Stalin's express permission it was impossible to obtain any Soviet agreement.[31]

The Main Military Council RKKA appears to have been conducted in much the same way. Its chairman, Voroshilov, preferred to deal with people rather than with intricate military problems, but in any case the onus of decision did not rest with him. Meretskov, who acted as the council secretary, has described how the council met two or three times a week; Stalin often attended but whether he did or not, the minutes were forwarded to his office in the form of recommendations, to approve or reject as he thought fit. Stalin was, according to the secretary, well informed about the military commanders and on army life in general, and he would frequently have supper with the council and senior district staffs and continue his talks into the night.[32]

The designer Grabin has said that Stalin took a close interest in artillery development, for he attended the artillery proving trials in 1935, together with Molotov and Voroshilov, and questioned the staff on the characteristics and performance of the guns. He was particularly interested in the F22 project for a new 76 mm gun, and he directed the designers to criticize each other's inventions. The F22 was accepted for further development. But some time later Grabin was called to a Kremlin meeting, chaired by Molotov; Stalin said nothing, merely walked up and down. An artillery engineer, unknown to Grabin, then read a paper describing how the F22 had failed its test, and until the artillery engineer had begun to speak, Grabin had no idea of the business to be discussed.[33] In 1937 Voronov, as head of the artillery, had held firmly to his own view on the acceptability of the 1936 pattern 76 mm gun, behaviour which was described, even in 1969, as courageous. In this particular instance, so said Voronov, Stalin accepted his criticism, saying that it was better to listen to the user, 'for guns, unlike soap, could not be melted down again should they prove to be useless'.[34]

Soviet writers are agreed that Stalin took a personal and directing role in the development of army equipment.[35] Indeed, according to Zhukov, no single pattern of armament could be adopted or discarded without Stalin's approval, 'a measure which certainly cramped the initiative of the Commissar for Defence'.[36] Notwithstanding the practical nature of Stalin's direction, his knowledge was probably uneven, to be expected in one who had received no military training or scientific instruction. Vannikov, the Commissar for Armament, has told how, in early 1941, Stalin had favoured the 107 mm gun as the main armament for tanks and he had surprised Vannikov when he said that it was a good weapon 'for he knew it from the Civil War'.[37] Vannikov was undoubtedly right in advocating the 85 mm anti-aircraft gun for the purpose; yet Stalin, perhaps fortuitously, was not entirely wrong. For the 1910 pattern 107 mm gun, with the 1930 recoil modification, was still in service in 1940, and, although it was designed as a field gun, its anti-tank performance was much superior to any other weapon in service.[38] An incident similar to that recounted by Vannikov occurred later that year when Stalin told Hopkins, who was not always a reliable source on military technicalities, that he needed a million or more American rifles but not the ammunition since, 'if the calibre was the same as that used by the Red Army, he had plenty'.[39]

Vannikov complained that a sudden idea or casual comment often settled an issue, and Kuznetsov confirmed that it was easier to talk to Stalin alone than in committee, where a decision, sometimes rashly given, was final. Emelianov, a metallurgist, has illustrated this in his description of a 1939 meeting in Stalin's office in the early hours of the morning, to discuss one Nikolaev's paper on double-skinned tank armour, a proposal which had already been judged as valueless by Emelianov. Nikolaev described his armour as 'active instead of passive, for in being destroyed it protects'. This catchword, said Emelianov, fascinated Stalin and appeared to convince him. Stalin asked Nikolaev what had been the reactions of 'the representatives of industry'. When Nikolaev replied, using Emelianov's own words, 'that there are no miracles in this world', the dictator became angry, wanting to know *who* had said this. Nikolaev, confused, and trying to protect Emelianov, said he could not remember. '*Such* people should be remembered', Stalin replied. Emelianov, who described himself as sick with fear, sat silent, although he knew that the experiment must fail.

In 1940, Emelianov attended another meeting to discuss the use of cast instead of pressed and welded turrets for the T34 tank. Stalin wanted to know the tactical, as opposed to the technical, advantages. When Emelianov asked permission to speak Stalin rounded on him, with, 'What are you, a military man?'. Undeterred, Emelianov provided the required answer, but since he unwittingly addressed the dictator using his forename and patronymic instead of 'Comrade Stalin', he earned in thanks a scowl. Stalin turned back to the designer and the generals. 'How would the centre of gravity be changed by the new turret?' and, 'What was the difference in load on the front axle?'. The designer's reply of 'slight' angered him, for slight, he said, was not an engineering term. Emelianov again knew the answer, but his upraised hand was ignored. The proposal was rejected as inadequately prepared and Stalin ordered a new commission to handle it, the members to be the armoured general Fedorenko and 'him', Stalin pointed to Akopov, and 'him', with a jerk of the thumb towards Emelianov.[40]

Vershinin said in 1948 that Stalin alone made the final decisions in aircraft development, and this is supported by the air designer

Iakovlev's account written in 1966.[41] In 1940 Iakovlev was sent to Germany to inspect and purchase military aircraft, cabling his recommendations direct to Stalin. Yet Stalin also sought opinions from outside his immediate circle of advisers, according to Iakovlev even accepting impractical plans sent direct and unsolicited by junior designers, simply because they caught his fancy.[42]

By the end of the second five year plan 15,000 tanks were with the army, the main armoured formation being the corps, each of 400 tanks. In 1939, following the experience of the fighting in Spain, it was concluded that the primary role of armour was to support infantry, and the large tank formations were broken up. In the air arm the air brigade comprised three squadrons and totalled about 100 aircraft; three brigades made an air corps, and two or more air corps formed an air army.[43] The average annual production of aircraft from 1935 to 1937 was 3,500, of which 1,200 were fighters and 500 bombers.[44]

In July 1938 fighting had broken out against the Japanese in the area of Lake Khasan and, in the following May, there began a series of actions near Khalkhin Gol. But it had already been accepted in Moscow that, in the event of general war, the Red Army Far Eastern and West European establishments could not be interdependent due to the impossibility of reinforcing one from the other.[45] So when, on 3 September 1939, von Ribbentrop invited the Soviet Union to occupy those Polish areas previously agreed by the secret protocol of the Russo-German Pact as the Soviet sphere of interest, action was delayed for a fortnight until the signing, on 16 September, of the truce with Japan. The Red Army was ordered across the Polish frontier the next day. The troops involved were four armies of Kovalev's Belorussian Military District and three armies of Timoshenko's Kiev Military District. Two weeks before, on 1 September, the conscription age had been lowered from 21 to 19 years of age, and the two additional age groups were called up during October and November. This was to increase the size of the Soviet armed forces to over 4,200,000 men.

At the end of June 1939 Stalin had ordered Meretskov, the Commander of the Leningrad Military District, to draw up plans for 'a counter-offensive blow against Finland', which had to be won within a space of three weeks. Meanwhile other planning groups were working independently on the same problem, each taking their separate solutions to Stalin. Eventually Meretskov's plan was accepted in preference to Shaposhnikov's, since the Chief of General Staff was inhibited by the conviction that the Finnish resistance would take several months to overcome.[46] Meretskov said that in making his own preparations he consulted directly with Stalin.

At the beginning of the four months' Finnish Winter War 20 Red Army divisions were deployed against 15 of the enemy, but poor leadership and inadequate training, the lack of a centralized field command and the exceptionally bitter weather resulted in heavy Red Army casualties and repeated failures.[47] Stalin was sensitive to foreign press comment on the poor quality of the Red Army and, fearing armed intervention by Sweden, France and Britain, he became irritated by the delays. Meretskov was repeatedly called back to Moscow to report, the last occasion being at the beginning of January when he was required to brief Stalin in the presence of Molotov, Voroshilov, Timoshenko and Voronov. On 7 January Stalin transformed Leningrad Military District into the North-West Front commanded by Timoshenko. Meanwhile Mekhlis had been sent to the area to dismiss, arrest and recommend the shooting of divisional commanders.[48] The final and successful offensive began on 11 February and lasted for four weeks; numbers of Red Army commanders who distinguished themselves were earmarked for promotion and important appointments, among them Timoshenko, Voronov, Meretskov, Pavlov and Kirponos.

At a meeting of the Main Military Council on 17 April 1940 Stalin said that it was necessary to bring the Red Army up to date, and that he believed that the cult of revolutionary tradition and the experience of the Civil War were proving to be obstacles to that aim.[49] On 8 May 1940 Timoshenko replaced Voroshilov as the Commissar for Defence. Generals' and admirals' ranks replaced the former revolutionary designations of *komarm, komkor* and *komdiv*, and the contemporary military press praised German military discipline of the First World War. On 12 August the single-command principle was reintroduced, the commissar again becoming subordinate to the commander and, by the disciplinary code of 12 October 1940, commanders became liable for court martial if, in cases of necessity, they did not use their personal arms to enforce obedience.[50]

During the summer of 1940 Meretskov became head of military training while Voronov was appointed as deputy to Kulik in the main artillery directorate (GAU). Pavlov, who had tank experience in Spain, took command of the Belorussian Military District, while Kirponos was given the Leningrad Military District. Zhukov was recalled from the Far East in May 1940, prior to taking command of the Kiev Military District, Stalin and the Politburo requiring from him a personal briefing on the Japanese Army, together with a report on Soviet strengths and weaknesses.[51]

By May 1940 the tank force had been broken down to 35 medium and four heavy tank brigades. In addition there were 98 tank battalions with the rifle and cavalry divisions, totalling in all about 13,000 armoured fighting vehicles.[52] Following the defeat of the French Army by a German force with an inferior number of tanks, the Red Army armour was hurriedly reorganized on the German pattern, the largest mobile formation being the mechanized corps consisting of two tank divisions and one motorized infantry division, in all over 1,000 tanks, of which 120 were heavy KV and 420 the new medium T34.[53] The Red Army command was still floundering, however, and there remained a wide difference of opinion as to the role of armour. Even Timoshenko and Meretskov were unable to find common ground.

During that summer Stalin continued to hold the late night military discussions in his *dacha*. According to Voronov, the dictator was rarely satisfied with second-hand briefings or reported opinion, and, in consequence, the Kremlin conferences and defence committees appear to have formed only part of the method by which he controlled the armed forces; he often saw Timoshenko, Voroshilov, Shaposhnikov, Budenny, Kulik, Meretskov and Golikov, the head of army intelligence (GUR), individually and privately in his own office. Beria, the head of the NKVD and secret police, Mekhlis and Shchadenko were other informants.

At one such meeting Stalin directed Shaposhnikov to write a general staff paper on the likely German plans to attack the Soviet Union, and this Shaposhnikov appreciation was presented, in the absence of its author, to the Politburo during September 1940.

Stalin would not agree, however, even on the premise and basis of the presentation, for Shaposhnikov had believed, rightly as it transpired, that the Germans would make their primary effort between the Pripet and the Baltic coast, the main force deploying north of the mouth of the San.[54] Stalin rejected this on economic grounds, for he considered that the underlying theme of German strategy must rest on seizing Ukrainian corn, Donets coal and Caucasian oil.

In August Stalin replaced Shaposhnikov by Meretskov as Chief of General Staff. According to what Shaposhnikov told Vasilevsky at the time, Stalin was pleasant and respectful (*uvazhitel'nyi*) when he gave Shaposhnikov his *congé*; Stalin said that the time had come 'to show the world that there had been a complete change in the military leadership since the Finnish War'; this might also, he thought, 'lessen international tension'.[55] Stalin privately told Meretskov that Shaposhnikov had been frequently unwell of late and that a younger man was needed.[56] Shaposhnikov remained a deputy commissar for defence and took over the responsibility for military engineering and fortifications.

Shaposhnikov's departure was, apparently, much regretted by the general staff. The son of a minor civil servant, he had been commissioned in 1903 into 1 Turkestan Rifles, qualifying at the General Staff Academy in 1910. He was a man of education, dry and reserved, and had, according to Vasilevsky, a keen and analytical brain, being outstanding in the operative sphere.[57] Golikov was impressed by what he described as Shaposhnikov's mental capacity and breadth of education, his mastery of both strategy and operations, his retentive memory and meticulous attention to detail, his clear thought and expression, his dignified bearing, and by his politeness and tact. He was, said Golikov, a man of discipline, integrity, modesty, benevolence, humanity and decency, an excellent speaker with an exceptional ability of getting things done on a personal plane. Yet he was exacting and demanding, in spite of his urbane and old-fashioned forms of address such as 'I beg you' and 'old fellow' (*golubchik*).[58] This opinion appears to have been generally shared by other members of the general staff, and by Knox, who knew him during the First World War.[59]

Meretskov was a child of the revolution who had entered the Red Army through the Red Guards. Largely self-educated, he was, according to Vasilevsky, a simpler and more expansive personality than Shaposhnikov, and was endowed with a marked sense of humour and much native cunning.[60] His writings show him to have been somewhat brash and insensitive. He had, according to Khrushchev, been arrested during the purges.

The first of Meretskov's war games was held in Belorussia in the late summer of 1940 and was conducted by Vatutin, then head of the operations department, since Stalin would not allow Timoshenko or Meretskov to go near the border for fear of provoking the Germans. The report was approved by Stalin.[61]

The second war game, held after the end of the annual conference on 29 December 1940, proved to be Meretskov's undoing. His address had given offence to Timoshenko and stirred some of his listeners to anger. Shortly afterwards all the participants received an unexpected summons to the Kremlin, where Stalin, members of the Politburo and the Main Military Council, wished to hear the conclusions. Meretskov was unable to summarize the salient points, and Stalin would not allow Vatutin to help him out. Stalin dismissed as propaganda the Soviet field regulations, quoted by Meretskov in working out the relative fire power of German and Red Army divisions, 'for here among ourselves we have to talk in terms of our real capabilities'. Future war, Stalin concluded, would be one of manoeuvre, and victory would go to the side which had the preponderance of tanks and motorized forces, a numerical superiority of two or three to one.[62] On 1 February 1941 Meretskov was replaced as Chief of General Staff by Zhukov.

Zhukov had been a tsarist non-commissioned officer in 10 Novgorodsky Dragoons and, like Meretskov, was self-educated. Although he had attended a senior commanders' course in 1929 he does not appear to have been staff trained or to have ever served in any staff appointment except as part of Budenny's cavalry inspectorate in 1930. Other than a short period as a deputy commander of the Belorussian Military District in 1938, the whole of his service in the Red Army had been in command of horse cavalry units and formations. At Khalkhin Gol in 1939, probably his first experience in commanding armour, only two tank and three motorized brigades were deployed. Zhukov apparently owed his appointment to Timoshenko, who asked Stalin for him. Zhukov's command at Kiev Military District was given to Kirponos.

By February 1941, therefore, most of the principal actors in the opening stages of the Russo-German War had already taken their places. Kirponos, Pavlov and F. I. Kuznetsov commanded the border districts. Timoshenko was the Commissar for Defence with Budenny as his first deputy, in charge of intendance, medical, veterinary and finance; Kulik was responsible for the GAU, the provision of all armament other than vehicles, and for chemical warfare; Rychagov headed the air force, part of the Red Army; Meretskov continued to be responsible for military training, and Shaposhnikov for engineering and fortifications; Zaporozhets was charged with political propaganda within the Red Army. All ranked as deputy commissars for defence but, other than Timoshenko, only Budenny, Kulik and Shaposhnikov were marshals of the Soviet Union. Shchadenko, who headed the main directorate for personnel and was shortly to take over the newly organized *Glavupraform*, was also a deputy commissar and held the army rank of Army Commissar 1st Class, equivalent to that of general; an important main directorate responsible directly to Timoshenko was that of armoured troops under Fedorenko. Zhukov was a deputy commissar and Chief of General Staff with Vatutin as his first deputy; Malandin was the head of the operations directorate with Vasilevsky as his first deputy; N. G. Kuznetsov was the Commissar for the Navy, Isakov being his chief of staff and Rogov heading the main directorate for naval political propaganda. Army Commissar 1st Class Mekhlis, the Commissar for State Control, remained with the PUR, independent of the Commissars for Defence and for the Navy.

During the late autumn of 1940, Zhdanov had told Admiral Kuznetsov that Germany and Britain were bogged down with the war in the west and that this gave the Soviet Union a chance to go about its business undisturbed. What this meant was revealed on 12 November, when Molotov relayed Stalin's territorial aspirations to von Ribbentrop.[63] The following February Zhdanov did not speak with the same assurance, but he continued to maintain that Germany was incapable of fighting a war on two fronts and he explained to Kuznetsov that the violations of Soviet air space, the intelligence preparations and the concentrations of German troops were merely 'precautionary measures on Hitler's part or a means of exerting psychological pressure'.[64]

On 20 March 1941, Golikov presented an intelligence appreciation to Stalin in which he set out the evidence of German activity in the border areas. But, according to Zhukov, Golikov's paper was nullified by its conclusions that a German attack was unlikely while the war was being fought in the west; Golikov professed to believe that the evidence in his paper originated from English or German intelligence services.[65] On 6 May Kuznetsov sent a similar memorandum to Stalin briefing him on information received from Vorontsov, the naval attaché in Berlin, about the imminence of war. He, too, added to the report his opinion that the information was false and fed to both the Soviet and German Governments by an outside agency.[66]

Stalin, presumably taking his precedents from the time of the German Empire and the period immediately after the First World War, appears to have entertained some strange notions as to the political power exercised by the German generals in the Third Reich. In September 1939 he had surprised Köstring by his question as to whether the German military leaders would obey Berlin's order to hand over occupied Polish territory to the Red Army. According to Khrushchev, Tiulenev and Voronov, his suspicion had ripened by the spring of 1941 into a conviction that the German military intelligence organization, manipulated by the generals, had an interest in fabricating evidence and staging provocations which would precipitate a war against the Soviet Union. He continued to persist in this belief after the invasion had taken place.[67]

During May and June Stalin, so Kuznetsov has said, became irritable and unnerved by the persistence of the intelligence reports concerning the imminence of war, and he brushed facts and arguments aside more and more abruptly. A pronouncement by Stalin, continued Kuznetsov, precluded any further discussion, it being unwise to express any other view, even privately to one's subordinates.[68] Zhukov's 1969 account criticizes Golikov and Kuznetsov for failing to add more honest conclusions to their reports. Yet at the time, according to Voronov, Zhukov did not stray a hair's breadth from Stalin's orders. Khrushchev's subsequent summing up of the situation was that any intelligence on Russo-German relations, however palatably presented, could only be forwarded to Stalin 'in fear and trepidation'.[69]

On 6 May Stalin publicly assumed the office of Chairman of the Council of People's Commissars, presumably to impress on Berlin the seriousness of the times. The significance was lost, however, on the German Ambassador, who associated the move with what he believed to be Molotov's decline.

In mid-March Timoshenko had asked Stalin for permission to bring the infantry divisions up to war establishment by calling up the reserves. Stalin agreed, apparently with some reluctance, but of the total of 303 infantry, tank and motorized divisions, 81 were said to be still in skeleton form.[70] Timoshenko and Zhukov pressed in vain, so Zhukov has said, for the raising of further mechanized corps.[71]

Stalin's actions were dictated, according to Zhukov, by the desire to avoid war and he appeared confident that he would succeed in doing so. Although Stalin considered hostilities improbable, he still believed that if Germany attacked the Soviet Union the main enemy thrust would be made in the Ukraine.[72] For this reason the weight of the Soviet defence was sited to the south of the Pripet Marshes; and, said Zhukov, 'as Stalin was the greatest authority for us all no one at that time doubted his judgement'. Neither Timoshenko nor the general staff had ever thought it possible, continued Zhukov, that the Germans would concentrate such powerful tank forces against the Soviet Union and launch them on the first day in such strategic depth.[73] Although the present day Soviet press blames Kulik, Shchadenko and Mekhlis for the siting of the bulk of the *matériel* so close to the frontier, Stalin must have given his agreement.[74] For stress was laid on linear defence, with Soviet territory being held inviolate, this forming the basis of the orders of 5 May demanding that the rifle formations should hold their ground, any enemy penetration being destroyed by the mechanized corps and air forces in reserve.

There are some apparent contradictions in Stalin's political and military actions at this time. According to Khrushchev, when Kirponos asked Stalin for permission to fortify the border as a defensive zone, the dictator forbade such action as a provocative act.[75] Yet, on 18 April, five days after the signing of the Soviet-Japanese Pact, Stalin felt sufficiently secure to menace the Reich, surprising though this may seem, for he directed Kirponos to close up his formations nearer to the frontier; this order, which had a

purely political significance, made no sense militarily and was described by Kirponos as 'passive defence'.[76] But the unexpectedly rapid overrunning of Yugo-Slavia and Greece by the Axis subdued Stalin once more.[77] In the purely military field Stalin had for many years abetted the theory of wars on enemy territory, wars which were to be won quickly with few Soviet casualties; and he had subscribed to the propaganda extolling the invincibility of the greatest army. Whether he really believed in Soviet superiority at arms is perhaps open to doubt for, according to Bagramian, who headed the operations directorate in the Kiev Military District, Zhukov said at that time 'that it was Stalin's opinion that the superiority of the *Wehrmacht* was such that at first the Red Army would be unable to hold the frontier areas, let alone contain the sector of the enemy main attack, for the Germans had both battle experience and greater technical ability'. Bagramian continued: 'I remember that this statement absolutely staggered us all (*chrezvychaino vsekh porazilo*) as if it were sedition'.[78]

In early June Maisky, the Soviet Ambassador in London, had been informed by the Foreign Office that an invasion of the Soviet Union was imminent.[79] In Moscow the diplomatic corps talked of little else.[80] Air and frontier violations were frequent, but Stalin had forbidden the firing on German aircraft in case Berlin should treat such incidents as a provocation.[81] On 14 June, Molotov is said to have rejected Kuznetsov's information showing the lack of German mercantile shipping in Soviet ports, with the remark that 'only a fool would attack Russia'.

On 13 June, Stalin had refused Timoshenko's request to bring the border districts to war readiness, but two days afterwards he agreed to the deployment, from 17 June, of the second echelon rifle divisions in the border areas. By 19 June the situation was sufficiently tense for Timoshenko, undoubtedly with Stalin's agreement, to order the move of the front headquarters in the border areas.[82] On Saturday 21 June a further telegram was received from Maisky and, at 2 p.m., Stalin himself telephoned Tiulenev, the Commander of Moscow Military District, ordering the anti-aircraft defences to be brought to combat readiness.[83] Timoshenko, Zhukov and Vatutin were summoned that evening to see Stalin, who was, according to Zhukov, clearly worried, for a German deserter was said to have brought news of the imminence of war. Stalin's reaction, which had already been telegraphed to Kiev Military District, was that the line-crosser 'has perhaps been sent by the German generals to provoke a conflict'. He declined to authorize the draft directive, brought by the Commissar for Defence, ordering the districts to war readiness, and would agree only that the districts be warned of the possibility of provocations; they were specifically ordered 'not to be incited'. Fortified border posts were to be occupied during the night and aircraft dispersed and camouflaged. The salient points of the order were dictated by Stalin to Zhukov who, together with Vatutin, then drafted the directive in the antechamber; it was taken back to Stalin, who first had it read aloud, before reading it himself; he made some alterations in his own hand, and then gave the signal to Timoshenko to sign. Because the message went out as a text and not a code word it was not received by the field units until 0230 hours.[84] Timoshenko, the general staff and the headquarters of districts and lower formations remained at their posts all night.

The Soviet armies from the Baltic to the Black Sea had been clustered hard against the frontier since April, with the new and incomplete mechanized corps shared out between them. In the view of Halder, the German Chief of General Staff, the Red Army deployment made little military sense, and by May the OKH department of *Fremde Heere Ost* judged it to be merely a political demonstration of force.[85] The German High Command reasoned, quite rightly, that, if attacked, the Soviet formations would defend ground and so be unlikely to escape from the great seething cauldrons in which they would finally meet their end.

5
From Brest to Vyazma

The Commissar for the Navy had not been consulted on the developments immediately before the outbreak of war and it was not until 11 p.m. that Kuznetsov was sent for by the Commissar for Defence and told to bring the fleets to combat readiness. Meanwhile Zhukov continued to receive messages from the military districts reporting unusual activity on the other side of the border. At 30 minutes after midnight the situation report was telephoned to Stalin who asked whether the warning order had already been transmitted to the districts; the dictator then went to bed.

At 3.27 a.m. Oktiabr'sky, the Commander of the Black Sea Fleet, telephoned Zhukov from Sevastopol reporting the approach of unidentified aircraft from the sea, and he sought confirmation of the telephonic orders just received from Kuznetsov. Timoshenko agreed that the naval anti-aircraft defences should open fire and he continued the check and double check by telling Oktiabr'sky to report the latest situation to Kuznetsov. By the time Kuznetsov was called, Sevastopol was already under attack. When Kuznetsov tried to reach Stalin, Malenkov came on the line, irritable and disbelieving, then rang off quickly since he wanted confirmation direct from Sevastopol.[1] By 3.40 a.m. Zhukov received further reports of air raids from Klimovskikh and Purkaev, the chiefs of staff of the Belorussian and Kiev Military Districts, and was told by Timoshenko to telephone Stalin. When Zhukov made his report to the dictator, there followed a long silence and the only sound to be heard at the other end was that of breathing. Zhukov asked whether he had been understood. Still there was no answer.

99

Finally, Stalin instructed Zhukov to go to the Kremlin and tell his secretary Poskrebyshev to summon the Politburo.[2]

When, shortly after 4.30 a.m., Timoshenko and Zhukov were called in to the Politburo meeting, Stalin sat pale and silent, cradling an unlit pipe in his hands. Molotov returned from a meeting with the German Ambassador with the news of the Berlin declaration of war. According to Zhukov, Stalin sank in his chair, lost in thought.

Even after the formal declaration of war Stalin still appeared to believe that the attacks were a provocation on the part of the German generals. Directive No. 2, issued at 7.15 a.m., ordered the Red Army to destroy the enemy penetration, but to keep out of Germany and restrict air activity to a limit of 90 miles within enemy territory. Meanwhile the Politburo kept open the radio link with the German Foreign Ministry and asked Japan to mediate.[3]

When Tiulenev met Voroshilov early on 22 June he was taken aback by the former Commissar of Defence's first question, as to where the High Command was accommodated.[4] No plan had in fact been made for a joint command of the Commissariats of Defence and the Navy until Timoshenko sent a draft to Stalin that morning proposing the setting up of a High Command, with Stalin as the Commander-in-Chief. When Stalin signed the decree, twenty-four hours later, it had been redrafted. Stalin named Timoshenko as the Commander-in-Chief and established a General Headquarters of the High Command which consisted of a council of war with Timoshenko as chairman, and Stalin, Molotov, Voroshilov, Budenny, Zhukov and Kuznetsov as members.[5] Although this body took the somewhat grandiose title of *Stavka,* with its imperial echoes, it was, in fact, merely a committee, without a separate secretariat or staff, and had nothing in common with the organization of the last tsarist *Stavka* at Mogilev which, in February 1917, consisted of three chancelleries and 16 directorates (*upravleniia*) employing 250 officers and officials. Stalin's first *Stavka* had merely an institute of permanent advisers which included Vatutin, Voznesensky, Voronov, Zhdanov, Zhigarev, Kulik, Meretskov and Mikoian.[6]

Although Timoshenko had been nominated as chairman, he was not, according to Zhukov, empowered to take any decisions of importance, and Stalin continued to write his ministers' directives. On the evening of 22 June 1941 Stalin had drafted the Commissar of Defence Directive No. 3 and ordered that Zhukov's name be affixed to it, although the Chief of General Staff was at that time 600 miles away at Tarnopol and unaware of its contents.[7] At a later date Zhukov took the blame for the order.

On the first day of war the border military districts had been converted to fronts. Stalin followed the example of Lenin at the beginning of the Civil War, sending his own personal representatives from the Politburo and the Central Committee to the fronts and armies, Zhdanov to the North, Khrushchev to the South-West and Voroshilov to the West Fronts; in due course nearly all the professional military commissars filling the appointments of political members of front military councils were replaced by Stalin's close associates. Personal military representatives followed, for Zhukov was already in the Ukraine and Shaposhnikov and Kulik were sent to Belorussia. Budenny took over the command of the Reserve Front, and Tiulenev the new South Front based on the former Odessa Military District. The South-West and South Fronts outnumbered the invaders to the south of the Pripet, and, because they escaped the full weight of the German air attack, Kirponos and Tiulenev managed to retain a tenuous and intermittent control over their troops. Elsewhere between the Pripet and the Baltic the Soviet communication system was largely destroyed by enemy air attack and saboteurs.

In 1941 the Soviet government and military communications system was based almost in its entirety on the use of line. In the capital the state telephone served both the civil and the military, this being additional to a separate Kremlin telephone for party and government leaders. The main Union system, controlled by the Commissariat of Communications (NKS), was based on a line network which ran out radially from Moscow to the republic and region capitals, each of which in turn had a separate spider based on the *oblast'* centre. The connections relied on one circuit, or more usually, on one wire, and there were few alternative or bypass systems. Trunk cable was not in use in the Soviet Union at that time. Most of the lines were suspended aerially on poles running alongside the railway tracks and main roads, where they were particularly vulnerable to air and saboteur attack. The reliability and capacity of the line was not high and a break in a single connection might cause a communications black-out over a considerable area.

Telegraph was widely used over this line system, and although the Wheatstone morse-typing automatic instrument and the Hughes letter-typing machine were still in service, reliance was placed on the Baudôt telegraph printer, which could work duplex on four or six channels over a single circuit. Accord or isochronism had to be maintained between the dispatching and receiving machines, but the training of telegraphists was a simple matter as the keyboard had only five keys. The Baudôt was the mainstay of the Soviet governmental, civil and military communications, and Stalin had such faith in it, being convinced that it was secure from interception, that he marked his own signals 'for transmission only by Baudôt' and required that the general staff did the same. Shaposhnikov would wait patiently for hours for a Baudôt link to transmit urgent and important telegrams, refusing to use morse facilities which were available. In fact Baudôt could be intercepted if the receiving equipment had access to the line; although Baudôt had great capacity it was only as reliable as the line system it used.[8]

Shortly before the war a separate communication network had been introduced throughout the Soviet Union for a limited number of subscribers, this being known as high frequency (*vysokochastotnyi*) line, popularly called *V Ch* or *V Ch NKVD*. This system, which had been used commercially in the USA since 1917 and in the United Kingdom since 1934, was based on line using a carrier frequency from 6.3 to 28.5 kilohertz, and was used for both voice and telegraph. It had important technical advantages over the normal state telephone system, one being that the transmissions above the 15–20 kilohertz frequencies were beyond audio range and therefore secure against aural interception unless equipment was available to translate the carrier wave. Frequencies were changed from time to time and lines were duplicated to provide alternatives in case of failure. The system was manned by the NKVD. Although *V Ch* terminals were allocated to the Red Army shortly after the war started, eventually being taken into use by all front and army headquarters, there were so few available in 1941 that military commanders had to travel great distances to the nearest *V Ch* telephone when required to talk to Stalin. Stalin had his own signal centre, equipped with *V Ch* and Baudôt, in the Kremlin room adjoining his secretary Poskrebyshev's office.

The Commissariat of Defence had accepted that the line system operated by the NKS would provide the basis of the military signal service at both strategic and operative level. Only in wartime would the Red Army take over line operation, construction and maintenance, and the troops for this would be found by the conscription of NKS personnel. Peresypkin, the Commissar for Communications, became overnight a deputy commissar for defence and head of a new military signals main directorate, in addition to his other posts. In June he was made a colonel and in December a lieutenant-general. Other NKS administrators and engineers were similarly inducted and given appropriate army ranks.

The scale of provision of command radio was meagre and its range so limited that it was regarded of little significance. The general staff had a number of RAF, RAT, 11 AK and 12 AK stations, and the RSB(40) was the basic set between divisions and armies; the divisions used the 6 PK, 5 AK and 71 TK radio. The Red Army started the war with only two radio codes. At divisional level and below a two digit system was used, known in Russian as the PT 39A; behind the divisions, messages were transmitted in five digit code taken from block list tables. But the system became complicated and, in the forward areas, largely unworkable when further codes were superimposed for formation and unit designations, names and co-ordinates, with the result that commanders avoided using it.[9] According to the German intercept service, Russian call signs and frequencies were changed every three hours.

The breakdown of the signal communications to the north of the Pripet left Kuznetsov's and Pavlov's formations paralysed. Kuznetsov, like Kirponos in the south, was lucky, however, in that he was assailed by only one panzer group which attempted, in vain, to pin him against the coast. Yet his armies fell back in such disorder that it was 18 days before the general staff in Moscow could get a situation report from them.[10] Pavlov was less fortunate, for his three armies were deployed forward close to the frontier in the great Bialystok salient, inside what was in effect a gaping German mouth. On 27 June Hoth's and Guderian's panzer groups met near Minsk encircling the main element of the West Front. It may have been at this time that Stalin, hearing of these defeats, thought that the end had come and gave way to hysteria, saying that 'all Lenin has created is lost for ever'; he then ceased to do anything 'for a long time'; Khrushchev's version, strangely reminiscent of Ivan IV, said that Stalin returned to the helm of state only after a deputation had pleaded with him to do so.[11] Zhukov has denied that this happened; but, whether it did or not, Stalin's inactivity could have hardly lasted more than a day or two for, according to other accounts, he was in control of the Soviet war machine on 26, 29 and 30 June.

According to Voronov, Stalin was unable to assess the scope of the war or estimate the effect of time, space and the relation of forces.[12] Stalin's Directive No. 3 issued on the night of 22 June ordering the South-West Front to take Lublin, 50 miles inside the *General Gouvernement* of Poland, by 24 June, was greeted with incredulity by both Purkaev and Bagramian.[13] The North-West and West Fronts were similarly directed to make a concentric attack on the Suwalki salient of East Prussia. At the West Front, Boldin, Pavlov's deputy, remonstrated that it was impossible to carry out the order.[14] The South-West Front, instead of attacking, was already retreating when Malandin, in a direct wire conversation on 26 June, forbade – in Stalin's name – any further withdrawal.[15]

That day Stalin had telephoned Zhukov at Tarnopol telling him that the enemy was nearing Minsk, that Pavlov was in a state of confusion, Shaposhnikov was ill and Kulik had disappeared. Zhukov was to return to Moscow immediately. Late that evening Zhukov was ushered into Stalin's office, where Timoshenko and Vatutin were stiffly at attention, their faces pale and drawn and their eyes red from lack of sleep. The generals could do little except suggest that a rearward defence line be occupied by two armies behind the line Polotsk-Mozyr, which was about to be prepared and occupied by the four armies of Budenny's Reserve Front. On 27 June Zhukov sent a Baudôt order to Minsk, rambling in its content and full of generalities and promises of glory.[16] If Stalin did seek seclusion, this was probably the day on which he did so.

On 29 June, after Minsk had fallen, Stalin appeared twice in Timoshenko's office and, in Zhukov's words, 'on both occasions

reacted extremely harshly (*kraine rezko*)'. The next day, on 30
June, Stalin instructed Zhukov to summon Pavlov to Moscow.

It would appear that the decision to remove Pavlov had been
taken on or before 28 June, for on that night Timoshenko had
interviewed Eremenko in Moscow and appointed him as the
Commander of the West Front. It may be indicative of Stalin's
absence that Eremenko was not seen by the dictator. Malandin
was to take over the duties of front chief of staff. Together Eremenko
and Malandin arrived at the West Front command post the next
morning and presented Pavlov with the written order removing
him from his command, establishing a precedent frequently used
by Stalin for the dismissal or arrest of high ranking officers.[17]
Starinov, who was present, has described how the exhausted
Pavlov at first showed relief at his release from responsibility,
supposing that Stalin's punishment would not go beyond dismissal.[18] Pavlov was, however, arrested together with Klimovskikh, the chief of staff, Klich and Grigor'ev, the heads of artillery
and signals, and Korobkov, the Commander of 4 Army. These
luckless generals 'were brought to trial on the proposal of the
military council of West Front [Eremenko and Malandin]', and
although Zhukov does not say so, they were shot.

During Stalin's lifetime Pavlov was held responsible not only
for the destruction of the West Front but also for the decision
taken in November 1939 to break up the large tank formations. In
Khrushchev's time the fault was said to be Stalin's, in that the
West Front was deployed close to the border, against Shaposhnikov's advice, Zhukov being censured 'for his unwillingness to
withstand Stalin's pressures'.[19] Zhukov excused himself by blaming Voroshilov.[20] At the time, according to one senior officer, the
generals did not believe the sensational announcement of the
treachery within the West Front, although they did fear that this
might herald a new purge. What Shtemenko has since called 'the
inexplicable change round of commanders' unnerved the general
staff. The commissars there were not slow in making their suspicious presence felt, accusing a general staff colonel, engaged on a
routine marking up of enemy dispositions on a battle map, of
exaggeration and panic-spreading.[21] The Pavlov *affaire* did much
to shake the confidence of the troops and the people in its commanders. It was a pattern which was not to be repeated, for there-

after during the war the disappearance and subsequent fate of unlucky or incompetent commanders remained a state secret.

The commissars now came in for preferment. In a decree of the Presidium of the Supreme Soviet of 16 July, signed by Kalinin, the former powers of the military commissars, no longer to be known as political deputies, were restored, these powers being defined as 'similar to those which they had during the Civil War against the foreign interventionists'. The need for the change was explained by 'the transition from peace to war'.[22] By a directive of 29 June, grave measures, that is to say shooting, had been announced against rumour-mongers, panic-spreaders and cowards.

On 30 June Kuznetsov and his political member Dibrova were replaced by Sobennikov and Bogatkin in command of the North-West Front, Vatutin being sent from the general staff as the chief of staff. Eremenko's West Front no longer existed, for all fighting ceased in the Bialystok pocket on 3 July and five days later 290,000 Soviet prisoners, including several corps and divisional commanders, were in German hands together with 2,500 captured or knocked out tanks and 1,500 guns.[23]

A State Committee of Defence (GKO) had been brought into being on 30 June, this being responsible for all the wider aspects of the war, political, economic and military, its functions being similar to those of Lenin's Council of Defence of the Civil War. It originally consisted of Stalin, Molotov, Malenkov, Voroshilov and Beria, and its orders, in the form of numbered GOKO resolutions, were supreme, being enacted by the Council of People's Commissars through the machinery of the commissariats.[24] The *Stavka* continued as the main directing organ for military matters but, on 10 July, it was reformed with Stalin as its chairman, and Molotov, Timoshenko, Budenny, Voroshilov, Shaposhnikov and Zhukov as members, and was renamed the *Stavka* of the Supreme Command. On 19 July Stalin nominated himself as People's Commissar for Defence and, on 8 August, he became the Supreme Commander of the Armed Forces of the USSR, his military committee taking the name of *Stavka* of the Supreme High Command (VGK). The fact that Stalin was the Commander-in-Chief was concealed, however, from the Soviet Union and the outside world, and orders of the day and public announcements signed by the dictator described him as the Commissar for Defence. Only after Stalingrad did he admit to being the Supreme Commander.[25]

On 1 July Timoshenko had been given the command of a new West Front, reconstituted from the recently arrived armies of Budenny's Reserve Front and the remnants of Eremenko's force, Eremenko and Budenny being appointed as Timoshenko's deputies. Bulganin became the political member of the military council, Malandin remaining as chief of staff until 21 July when he was replaced by Shaposhnikov. Reserves in depth were collected for a Reserve Front under Bogdanov of six armies, and a Moscow Front under Artem'ev of three armies covering the outskirts of the capital.[26] On 4 July, by GOKO decree No. 10, 270,000 citizens of Moscow city and *oblast'* were mobilized to form 25 divisions of the people's military reserve (*narodnogo opolcheniia*), another description borrowed from the tsarist empire.

On 10 July Stalin had decided to establish three theatres (*napravleniia*) each controlling two or more fronts. Timoshenko's West Front became the West Theatre, controlling the West, Reserve and Moscow Fronts and F. I. Kuznetsov's Central Front consisting of two armies detached from the left wing of the West Front. Budenny, together with Khrushchev, took command of the South-West Theatre, commanding Kirponos's South-West and Tiulenev's (later Riabyshev's) South Fronts and Oktiabr'sky's Black Sea Fleet. Voroshilov and Zhdanov formed the North-West Theatre comprising Popov's North and Sobennikov's North-West Fronts and Tributs's Baltic and Golovko's North Fleets.[27] By a decree of 15 July, corps headquarters were temporarily abolished in order to economize in staffs. The great tank losses could not be readily replaced and the mechanized corps were disbanded, the remaining tank divisions, soon to become tank brigades, being allocated to rifle armies. For some time to come there could be no question of combating the panzer thrusts with massed armour.

On the German side there was only a short delay in launching the second stage of the offensive along the main Moscow highway, another great pincer movement starting from the area of Minsk and closing over 150 miles to the east. Timoshenko's West Front was soon broken open, and by 17 July Hoth and Guderian met east of Smolensk having entrapped a vast number of troops. By 5

August, the Germans recorded the taking there of 309,000 prisoners, 3,000 guns and 3,205 captured or knocked out tanks.[28] The total number of German tanks in action was barely over a 1,000.

Stalin was, as Zhukov put it, beside himself with rage at the Smolensk defeat. 'We generals', he said, 'felt the full weight of his anger'. Towards the end of July Poskrebyshev telephoned Zhukov and Timoshenko to go to a Politburo meeting in Stalin's *dacha*. No reason was given. Stalin wasted no time in preliminaries and told Timoshenko that the Politburo had decided to appoint Zhukov in his place. Timoshenko was silent. Zhukov has said that he spoke out in Timoshenko's defence, emphasizing the confidence which Timoshenko enjoyed among the troops and the unsettling effect of the frequent change of commanders. 'For Stalin', Zhukov tells his latter-day readers, 'was not always objective in his judgement of military leaders'.[29] Stalin put the question to the Politburo members and eventually Timoshenko was allowed to return to his post.

Hitler had always intended that Leningrad should be taken before Moscow, and very early on he had come to regard the seizure of the whole of the Ukraine, the Donets Basin and even Caucasia as having priority over an eastwards advance from Smolensk. His attention was fixed on the Crimea, the occupation of which would, he thought, enable German troops to invade the Caucasus by way of Kerch. On 30 July Hitler ordered von Bock's Army Group Centre to go over to the defensive and this was followed by the order of 12 August turning Hoth's panzer troops northwards towards Leningrad and Guderian's armour south into the Ukraine.[30] The great Smolensk battle of 1941 in which, according to Soviet accounts, the Red Army defenders are said to have defeated von Bock in his eastward march on Moscow, inflicting on the Hitlerite forces 250,000 casualties, did not take place.

Zhukov subsequently said that he himself became convinced, towards the end of July 1941, that the enemy's intention was to move southwards and strike at the flank and rear of the South-West Front in the Ukraine.[31] If this was indeed Zhukov's belief, it could have been based on nothing but surmise, for the German Army Commander-in-Chief, the Chief of General Staff and the three army group commanders were all agreed that the immediate objective should be Moscow; only Hitler was determined that the advance should be deflected south into the Ukraine. The arguments in favour of the Moscow offensive were still being presented in Rastenburg as late as 23 August.[32]

On 29 July Zhukov asked Stalin to receive him, so he said, to hear his appraisal of the situation. Stalin saw Zhukov in the presence of a hostile Mekhlis. Zhukov wanted to move a number of divisions from the Far East and evacuate the whole of the right bank Ukraine. When Zhukov recommended that Kiev should be given up Stalin became angry. Forty minutes later Zhukov had been relieved of his appointment and transferred to the command of the Reserve Front, and Shaposhnikov was on his way from the West Theatre to take over once more his old post as Chief of General Staff; this is Zhukov's version of how he came to be removed from his appointment, although the reasons given by him are unlikely to be the real ones. Vasilevsky and Shtemenko are silent on the matter. The naval staffs had found Zhukov difficult to work with and Khrulev intimates that he had already lost a measure of Stalin's confidence, at least in so far as staff and organizational matters were concerned.[33] Yet there is no doubt that Stalin still had great confidence in Zhukov's command ability.

On the evening of 30 July Hopkins, Roosevelt's personal representative, arrived in Moscow. It was arranged that, as a preliminary, Hopkins should talk to Iakovlev, of the main artillery directorate. But Hopkins found that no one dared give any information or offer an opinion on any subject, Iakovlev saying that he was not empowered to disclose 'whether the Soviet Union does or does not need equipment'. Any question as to the holdings of Soviet armament or its capabilities met with an evasive answer. Only Stalin could give any information; and Hopkins noted the awful fear with which any subordinate regarded his superior.[34] At the second meeting Stalin assured Hopkins that the Leningrad-Smolensk-Kiev line then held was 'more easy to defend than the original frontier'; he did not say that the Soviet withdrawal had been deliberate and part of Soviet strategy.

On 8 August, only three days after the Smolensk cauldron had been cleared, Guderian's panzer group had attacked Kuznetsov's Central Front between Mogilev and Gomel; two weeks later the front had been destroyed with the loss of a further 78,000 prisoners. This new German thrust was interpreted by Stalin and Shaposhnikov as an enveloping movement to outflank the West and the Reserve Fronts from the south, as part of a general advance on Moscow through Bryansk.[35] This was indeed what von Bock wanted to do, but the arguments with the Führer continued and meanwhile Guderian's troops marked time on the Desna awaiting the decision to march to the east or south.[36]

The destruction of the Central Front caused Zhukov, who was still a member of the *Stavka*, to send a signal to Stalin on 19 August warning him of the likelihood of a German thrust southwards to the rear of the South-West Front.[37] Zhukov advocated the concentrating of a force of ten infantry and four cavalry divisions with 1,000 tanks and 500 aircraft on the Desna athwart Guderian's route to the south, and suggested that the necessary forces could be found 'from the Far East, Moscow and the military districts of the interior'. This optimistic proposal, which disarmingly overcame all difficulties of time and space, evoked a polite but cool acknowledgement from Stalin and Shaposhnikov.

On 8 August Stalin had talked to Kirponos on the direct line, accusing him of 'light-heartedly being about to give up Kiev'.[38] On 14 August, while the Central Front was under attack, Stalin had created a new Bryansk Front under Eremenko, originally consisting of two hastily formed armies, concentrated, not south of the Desna, but to the flank covering Bryansk and the route to Moscow. Stalin and Shaposhnikov had produced their own plan, whereby Eremenko, together with the left wing of Zhukov's Reserve Front, was to attack due westwards. The offensive was to start at the end of August.[39]

Vasilevsky, by then head of the operations directorate and deputy chief of general staff, had not met Eremenko before he saw him in Stalin's presence at the time of his appointment to the Bryansk Front. Eremenko was known, however, to Stalin and members of the GKO. Stalin was friendly and solicitous, asking him about the battle on the West Front. Eremenko, who had once been a non-commissioned officer in the tsarist cavalry, conducted himself, said Vasilevsky, with great dignity, answering questions quick-wittedly and skilfully; he appeared confident and resourceful and told Stalin that the enemy was already losing his arrogance (*spes'*).

Eremenko said that he had no doubt that he would destroy Guderian in the next few days. According to Vasilevsky, Stalin was visibly impressed and, as Eremenko took his departure, he looked admiringly after him with the remark 'that is the sort of fellow we want in a tight corner'.[40]

When on 16 August Shaposhnikov hinted that it might be necessary to retire behind the Dnieper, Stalin was still full of Eremenko's praises. Zhukov, however, was uneasy about the fighting value of his left-hand neighbour, and when, on 23 August, he communicated his fears to Shaposhnikov, the Chief of General Staff told him that he, too, doubted whether Eremenko would be able to block the path of the German armour. On 25 August Stalin again cross-examined Eremenko by Baudôt and asked for an assurance of success, Eremenko replying 'I will smash this scoundrel Guderian without any doubt'.[41] Eremenko's offensive was to come to nothing, his armies, despite Stalin's messages of severe displeasure, retreating eastwards in disorder. Yet, a fortnight later, Stalin still appeared to be unaware of the extent of the Bryansk Front's defeat.

Guderian, having received final orders to move south, crossed the Desna on 2 September and began his rapid advance deep in the rear of the South-West Front. In the far south, the German Army Group South was to secure a bridgehead over the Dnieper at Kremenchug on 9 September, from which, three days later, von Kleist's panzer group was to strike northwards and join Guderian in the area of Romny and Lokhvitsa, these panzer thrusts cutting off about six Soviet armies to their west in the great bend of the river.

On 7 September the South-West Front reported the threatening situation to Budenny and Shaposhnikov. Shaposhnikov and Vasilevsky, so Vasilevsky has said, went to see Stalin, who reproached them for wanting to run away. Two days later, however, the dictator issued an order permitting the South-West Front to make a limited withdrawal to the Desna except that Kirponos was to continue to hold Kiev.[42]

Bagramian, a former tsarist *praporshchik* with the Armenian cavalry who was Kirponos's deputy chief of staff, has said that the front had been aware since 7 September of the threat from Guderian, and that this was foremost in their thoughts during the military council meeting held on the night of 10 September. The political members Burmistenko and Rykov were cautious. Tupikov, the chief of staff, recently the military attaché in Berlin, considered the threat to be so serious that he advised an immediate withdrawal to the River Psel, 180 miles to the east. Kirponos, too, was outspoken, and he regretted that Budenny was not allowed to decide any matter of importance without first seeking Stalin's permission.[43] Nor could Kirponos realign his own armies without prior *Stavka* approval. He had little faith in the academician Shaposhnikov, who would weigh up all the courses and present his evaluation without making a single concrete proposal, merely asking Stalin for orders. For Kirponos did not believe 'that this very competent officer of the old general staff could not see the mortal danger . . . he simply could not muster the courage to tell Comrade Stalin the whole truth'. Finally, the military council decided to send a telegram to Moscow asking for permission to withdraw troops from the Kiev area and prepare a general withdrawal to the line of the Psel. At 0200 hours that morning Shaposhnikov came on the direct line, speaking in the name of the *Stavka*, describing any withdrawal as premature, and not permitting any troops to be removed from the area of Kiev.[44]

Following an appeal from Kirponos, Budenny spoke to Shaposhnikov on the telephone but failed to move him. That same day, on 11 September, Budenny addressed a signal to Stalin protesting against Shaposhnikov's reply. Budenny thought that the enemy's intention was clear, a double envelopment from north and south, and that delay in withdrawing the South-West Front might result in the loss of troops and an enormous quantity of armament.[45] Budenny was thereupon relieved of his appointment, Khrushchev being permitted to remain, an indicator that the political member may not have been so loud or insistent in his requests for a withdrawal as he subsequently claimed. Budenny's successor was to be Timoshenko.

Zhukov, by tampering with the calendar, has given a somewhat different account. He was, he said, called from the Reserve Front to the Kremlin on 8 September and ordered to assume command of the Leningrad Front the next day, for the city had already been surrounded by the enemy. Stalin told him that 'we have also decided to replace the command of the South-West Theatre'.

Discussion took place as to whether the Kiev group should be withdrawn east of the Dnieper, and, Zhukov adds, Stalin consulted not only himself but also Shaposhnikov and Timoshenko.[46] This account is presumably intended to disarm censure of Stalin for arbitrarily rejecting advice and removing a commander who was in fact right, for Zhukov's version conveys the impression of a collective and well-considered decision which had no connection with Kirponos's and Budenny's signals of 11 September. Yet Zhukov's new dates are not attributable to a slip of the pen because his story continues in chronological sequence starting with his air flight to Leningrad, which he said he made on 9 September. If this meeting described by Zhukov took place at all, it would appear to have done so on Thursday 11 September shortly after Budenny's signal had been received in Moscow, for Zhukov was appointed to the Leningrad Front on that day. Fediuninsky, who accompanied Zhukov to Leningrad, has described taking off together from Vnukovo airport on the morning of 13 September, the same day that Timoshenko arrived in Poltava.[47] Kuznetsov was sent for by Stalin on 12 September and was told that Zhukov had been appointed to the Leningrad Front, the decision having been taken 'only yesterday'.[48]

Meanwhile, on 11 September, Stalin held a Baudôt teleprint conversation with the South-West Front military council. Stalin began by telling Kirponos that the South-West Front proposal to withdraw to the Psel seemed dangerous, and he would want a guarantee from the South-West Front that previous failures would not be repeated. The proposed withdrawal, said Stalin, would lead to encirclement, since the enemy was advancing, not only from the north in the area of Konotop, but also from Kremenchug in the south and from the west; these attacks would be stepped up as soon as the Red Army troops started to fall back again. The proposal to withdraw the South-West Front before the positions on the Psel were in fact prepared, was hazardous; a bold offensive against the north grouping in co-operation with the Bryansk Front was a prerequisite, without which a withdrawal could lead to catastrophe.

According to Bagramian, who was himself retelling Tupikov's account, Kirponos sat motionless studying the lengthening Baudôt ticker tape as Stalin talked on. The dictator appeared to be reasoning with himself. 'There might', said Stalin, 'be a way out'.

> *First*. Regroup the forces. . . . Make attacks against the Konotop grouping together with Eremenko. . . .
> *Second*. Prepare a defensive line on the Psel by withdrawing five or six divisions and a powerful artillery group facing north and west.
> *Third*. After the forces have been concentrated against Konotop . . . and after the Psel defensive line has been prepared . . . the evacuation of Kiev can begin . . . when Kiev is evacuated the east bank must be held secure.
> *Finally*. You must cease looking for rearward defensive lines . . . and must seek only ways of stopping, I repeat, stopping the enemy.

This *Stavka* order shows that the earlier disasters of Minsk, Smolensk and Uman had apparently left Stalin ignorant of the speed with which the German panzer leaders developed their encirclement operations. He was still pinning his hopes on Eremenko. Yet, even though this is taken into account, the directive is illogical and contradictory.

When the Baudôt tape stopped ticking, the military council of the South-West Front sat silent. Tupikov, who appeared dumbfounded, later confided to Bagramian that, when the second paragraph appeared, his hopes began to rise that the South-West Front could withdraw, but Stalin's closing words were shattering. Kirponos, pale and silent, turned to the other members for their views. Burmistenko said that they had no alternative but to remain; Rykov merely ran his hands through his hair. Stalin was waiting for an answer. Kirponos turned to the telegraphist and began to dictate the reply straight on to the machine. He was much unnerved by Stalin's Baudôt presence, for he denied that the proposal to withdraw had originated from him, but had, said Kirponos, 'been in response to requests from above'.

The Baudôt began to tick away once more as Stalin's reply was received. The request to withdraw *did* come from the South-West Front *and* Budenny, and to illustrate his point Stalin read out extracts from Budenny's signal of the same day. Shaposhnikov, said Stalin, was against a withdrawal, but Budenny and Kirponos were for it. Kiev was not to be given up nor were the bridges to be blown without *Stavka* approval. The substance of Bagramian's account is supported by Zhukov and by Vasilevsky.[49]

On 14 September Tupikov drafted and sent to Shaposhnikov his own signal, since Kirponos refused to sign it, placing the responsibility for the impending catastrophe on the Supreme Command and ending by forecasting disaster at the end of two days.[50] Stalin himself penned the reply branding Tupikov as a panic-monger, and handed the draft back to Shaposhnikov to sign.[51] On 15 September, the day that Guderian and von Kleist made contact, Stalin sent a signal to London asking for twenty-five to thirty British divisions to be transported to Archangel or to the southern regions of the USSR.[52]

On 16 September the encirclement of the South-West Front was complete, and two days later, as if to distract public and world attention from the area, a special NKO order announced the award of a newly introduced guards status to formations heroically defending the area of Smolensk.

Bagramian, who was on a visit to the theatre headquarters on 16 September, was told by Timoshenko that the theatre military council had decided to order the South-West Front to organize a break-out 'in anticipation that the Supreme Commander will allow the withdrawal to the Psel'. Bagramian was instructed to give Timoshenko's verbal orders to Kirponos. Bagramian subsequently said that he felt vaguely uncomfortable about not having a written directive, but he associated this with the security risk of being flown back into the pocket. That same afternoon he rejoined the South-West Front headquarters.

At first the front military council was in high spirits at the news of Timoshenko's order. But then Kirponos refused to act unless he received an order from Stalin or a written authority from Timoshenko, and no urging by the other members of the council could move him. On the evening of 16 September Kirponos sent a radio message to the Supreme Commander asking for instructions, adding that he, Kirponos, thought that withdrawal to the Psel River was the correct course.[53] Twenty-four hours later, at midnight on 17 September, a radio reply was sent by Shaposhnikov in the name of the *Stavka* authorizing the pulling back of troops from the Kiev area.[54] But no word was said about a front withdrawal out of the encirclement back to the Psel. Stalin appears to have washed his hands of the affair and left his subordinates to their own devices. In desperation, Kirponos ordered a general retirement; by then many of his forward formations were already outflanked and being broken up.

By 26 September the South-West Front had ceased to exist; the German count of prisoners and booty taken by both Army Groups Centre and South from the beginning of September amounted to 665,000 prisoners, 3,400 guns but only 800 tanks.[55] The four members of the military council of the South-West Front perished. The Soviet accounts of the circumstances of their fate have been contradictory.

Meanwhile Leningrad and the Soviet north-west had been under heavy attack and the Red Army troops had given ground. In consequence, on 23 August, Voroshilov's North-West Theatre was broken up. Kurochkin's North-West Front reverted to the direct control of Moscow and was joined by a *Stavka* commission, consisting of Bulganin, Mekhlis and Meretskov, to investigate its lack of success. Popov's North Front had been redesignated as the Leningrad Front and it gave up its responsibilities in the far north to a new Karelian Front under Frolov. When Zhukov arrived at the Smolny on 13 September, he gave a Moscow authority to a dejected Voroshilov, instructing him to hand over command. According to Bychevsky, Zhukov telegraphed to Vasilevsky in Moscow asking him to tell the Supreme Commander that he, Zhukov, proposed 'to conduct the defence more actively than his predecessor'.[56] It is not clear whether this referred to Popov or Voroshilov.

At about this time Stalin instructed Kuznetsov to send a telegraphed order to Tributs, the Commander of the Baltic Fleet, to carry out preparatory work for the scuttling of all warships, in case it should be necessary to abandon Leningrad. Kuznetsov, who apparently lived in fear that the NKVD was, at Stalin's direction, preparing a dossier of documents to incriminate him in charges of treason, blurted out almost involuntarily that he could not, as so important an order would have to come from the dictator himself. It was, thought Kuznetsov, apparent that Stalin did not want to sign this directive, for he then sent the admiral to Shaposh-nikov with orders to dispatch the telegram over their joint signa-tures. Shaposhnikov was aghast and refused point-blank. Eventu-ally Kuznetsov and the Chief of General Staff drafted an instruction for Stalin to sign. Nothing more was heard of it.[57]

On 5 September Hitler decided that his aim was already achieved, for the South-West Front was about to be destroyed and Leningrad could henceforth remain as a secondary theatre. The main strategic task now, he reasoned, was to go for Moscow before the onset of the bad weather.[58] Army Groups North and South were ordered to give up panzer and air formations to von Bock.

The West Front, commanded by Konev, was deployed due west of the capital astride the Smolensk-Vyazma road. Behind the West Front lay the Reserve Front, commanded by Budenny, only two of his six armies, those in the south linking the West to the Bryansk Front, being in contact with the enemy. Yet further to the south was Eremenko's Bryansk Front.

The German plan envisaged Hoth's panzer group attacking in a wide encircling sweep north of the Moscow road and joining up near Vyazma with the southern pincer formed by Hoepner's panzer group. Meanwhile Guderian was to outflank the Bryansk Front from the south and advance on Moscow by way of Orel and Tula. Guderian's offensive was to begin on 28 September and was to be taken up by the German troops further to the north on 2 October.

Konev, who had been a non-commissioned officer in the tsarist artillery and a military commissar until 1927, subsequently said that he informed Moscow of the imminence of an enemy offensive on 26 September. In reply he received a *Stavka* directive for-bidding any form of mobile defence.[59] Konev in his turn was obliged to veto his subordinate Rokossovsky's plan for a fighting withdrawal.[60] The strength of the West, Reserve and Bryansk Fronts was said to have totalled eighty-three divisions, in all 1,252,000 men, but only 820 tanks and 360 aircraft.[61]

Meanwhile in Moscow, on 28 September, Harriman and Beaverbrook had the first of three evening meetings with Stalin. The dictator was cordial and gave a review of the military situation as he wished it to be known to western powers. Stalin felt that British divisions might be sent to the Ukraine, but he dismissed

Beaverbrook's suggestion that British troops in Persia could be moved into the Caucasus, with the retort that 'there is no war in the Caucasus, but there is in the Ukraine'. Beaverbrook's proposal that strategic discussions should take place between the British and Red Army general staffs was rebuffed.[62]

At the meeting the next day Stalin was surly and hostile, abrupt and rude, restlessly walking about and smoking, making three telephone calls unconnected with the discussion and each time dialling the number himself. Beaverbrook believed that the dictator was under some intense strain; this may have been the case, although Guderian's probing attacks of 28 and 29 September had as yet been unsuccessful. Stalin showed little interest in western help. Deliberately offensive, he inferred that the Soviet Union was bearing the whole burden of the war and that the proffered aid was of little consequence. The following day Stalin performed the Pavlovian *volte-face* which was to be the common feature of the meetings with foreign statesmen and their envoys. He was all smiles, geniality and co-operation, and agreement was speedily reached, even though this represented hardly more than a readiness by Stalin to accept material assistance.

The only intelligence concerning the state of the Soviet armed forces was that which could be deduced from Stalin's requirements. He wanted tanks, aircraft, anti-aircraft and anti-tank guns, and raw materials, and since the dictator showed no interest in field branch artillery or small-arms it was assumed that the Soviet Union, in spite of its losses, still had plentiful stocks. Harriman noted that Stalin was the only man to deal with in foreign affairs and 'that dealing with others was almost a waste of time'. Ismay used the same words in describing the military sub-committee discussions with Soviet generals. Ismay noted Stalin's shrewd eyes, full of cunning; his handshake was flabby and he never looked one in the face. But he had great dignity and his personality was dominating; as he entered the room every Russian froze into silence and the hunted look in the eyes of the generals showed all too plainly the constant fear in which they lived. It was nauseating, said Ismay, to see brave men reduced to such servility.[63]

On 1 October Guderian had broken into open country in the Soviet rear and was on the move towards Orel, having turned the southern flank of the defence line. That night Leliushenko, a commander awaiting an appointment, was interviewed by Stalin and ordered to organize the defence of Mtsensk and Orel, taking with him a motor-cycle regiment, the only troops readily available in Moscow. At Tula, according to Leliushenko's account, he picked up some guns from the artillery school together with municipal buses as towing vehicles. He was in constant telephonic communication with Shaposhnikov who began to route to him, by road and rail, units and part formations, offering him *Katiusha* multiple-rocket batteries, provided that there was no risk of losing them to the enemy. 'But', added Shaposhnikov, 'take care of them, my dear fellow, otherwise you will answer for it with your head; so says the Supreme Commander'.[64] Shortly afterwards Leliushenko was joined by part of a tank brigade, which happened to be on rail flats, and his command grew rapidly from a motor-cycle regiment to that of two guards rifle divisions, two tank brigades, part of an airborne corps and a tactical support air group.[65] On 2 October Stalin sent Artem'ev, the Commander of Moscow Military District, to Tula to organize the defences there.

The main enemy offensive on the axis of the old Moscow highway at first went unnoticed, for the breakthrough was unreported by the West and the Reserve Fronts. So it came about that Moscow Military District knew of the penetration before the general staff in Moscow. Telegin, the political member of the military district council, has said that on the morning of 5 October he heard that Hoepner's tanks were in Yukhnov, as close to Moscow as Tula, and it was some hours before he could convince Shaposhnikov and Stalin of the truth of the reports.[66]

According to Rokossovsky, the army commanders of the West Front were poorly informed and controlled. Rokossovsky stayed in his original position unaware of developments elsewhere until, on the evening of 5 October, he received a signal from the West Front telling him to transfer all his divisions to the command of his neighbour and withdraw his army headquarters to Vyazma where, on 6 October, he would form a new force to counter-attack on Yukhnov, about fifty miles to the south-east. He was suspicious of the order and asked for it to be confirmed in writing. When he entered Vyazma, German troops were already there. Having escaped from encirclement and arrived at the West Front headquarters, he was to find Stalin's investigators, Voroshilov and

Molotov, already with Konev and Bulganin. Voroshilov was reluctant to believe that Rokossovsky had been ordered to leave his troops behind and the army commander was obliged to produce his written order. Konev and Bulganin appear to have suffered from a lapse of memory. Altogether it was, as Voroshilov said at the time, 'a strange affair'.[67]

If Budenny was aware of the extent of the German success he made no report to Stalin but dealt with the emergency in the only way he knew, by going forward into the battle area. Konev, for his part, remained unaware until 6 October that Hoth had broken his right flank and was rapidly approaching Vyazma from the north. The Vyazma encirclement of Konev's West and Budenny's Reserve Fronts resulted in the destruction of forty-five divisions and the loss of 673,000 prisoners.[68]

The primary cause of the defeat would appear to have been the *Stavka* directive of 27 September committing the troops to a rigid defence. Within the West Front the defence preparations and the command exercised by Konev could not have been of a high order, for an Army Group Centre war diary entry on 2 October said that 'all subordinate armies are agreed that the enemy has been surprised and has put up little resistance'.[69] Konev replied to criticism by pointing to his over-extended front and his lack of depth, and emphasized the inadequacy of his reserves; for this he subsequently blamed the *Stavka*. Yet a cogent reason why information and intelligence was not passed back to the *Stavka* would appear to have been that commanders feared to report reverses; for if they were in any way responsible they might be punished as traitors, and if they were merely reporting the failure of others they could be arrested as panic-spreaders. This happened to Sbytov, the head of the Moscow Military District air force, who was threatened by Abakumov with NKVD arrest for producing the air reconnaissance reports confirming that Hoepner's tanks were in Yuhknov.[70]

On 5 October Stalin held a leisurely Baudôt conversation with Zhukov in Leningrad. The Supreme Commander wanted Zhukov to come to Moscow the next day so that they might 'discuss action to be taken on the Reserve Front's left wing in the area of Yukhnov'.[71] The following day Stalin, obviously not yet aware of the encirclement at Vyazma, agreed to Zhukov's postponing his flight for yet another twenty-four hours. But during the course of that day German troops entered the city of Bryansk cutting off all signal communication with Eremenko, whose forces had been partially encircled, and news came from Cherevichenko's South Front of the envelopment of two Soviet armies near Osipenko against the Black Sea, eventually leading to a further loss of 106,000 prisoners. Konev was still unable or unwilling to give a coherent account of the battle situation on the West Front. That night Stalin ordered Zhukov to hand over the command of the Leningrad Front to Khozin and return at once to Moscow.

6
The Winter Campaign

The German winter offensive from October until December was launched along the whole of the eastern front from Leningrad to the Black Sea, having as its strategic objective the north-south line of Vologda-Stalingrad-Maikop, extending up to 300 miles to the east of Moscow.[1] During the first few days the weather had been generally dry, with favourable ground and air conditions giving the firm going and the clear skies and visibility needed for reconnaissance and air and artillery support. From about 7 October, however, heavy and continuous rain began to fall over the whole of the front.

When Zhukov arrived in Moscow on the night of 7 October, Stalin ordered him to go out to the West Front headquarters to investigate and report from there. Zhukov found the West Front military council, Konev, Bulganin and Sokolovsky, in session; the extent of the encirclement was known to them, but they had not told Stalin and they left this unpleasant task to Zhukov. As Zhukov subsequently judged the situation, the West Front 'might have averted the Vyazma disaster by the display of more energy and determination'. Zhukov moved off once more in search of the headquarters of the Reserve Front; when he found it, Mekhlis, the *Stavka* representative, was already there, but little information was to be gleaned from him except that it was feared that Budenny was captured. In Maloyaroslavets, already a deserted town, Zhukov came across Budenny, but he knew little except that two of his armies had been cut off. Zhukov went on towards Yukhnov to ascertain personally if the enemy was there, despite the fact that the Moscow air reconnaissance sorties had definitely confirmed, three days before, that panzer troops were in the town. Like other senior army commanders he was without mobile radio, and he reported his movements by detailing local units to phone messages to the general staff in Moscow.[2]

The GKO investigating commission already with the West Front, consisting of Voroshilov, Molotov and Malenkov, and attended by Vasilevsky, was not idle, and, according to Konev, Molotov dictated 'with the greatest of persistence' the manner in which the withdrawing troops should be redeployed.[3] On 10 October the commission recommended to Stalin that Zhukov should replace Konev and that the West Front be amalgamated with the Reserve Front. Budenny had been removed from his command on 8 October. The commission's recommendation was accepted by Stalin. New forces were rapidly concentrated and grouped into four armies to defend the western approaches to the capital, and, on 17 October, the *Stavka* ordered the detachment of the four northern armies of the West Front's right wing to form a new Kalinin Front under Konev. Three weeks later, on 10 November, the Bryansk Front was broken up. All fronts were then directly subordinated to Stalin and the *Stavka*, except that Timoshenko still had a co-ordinating responsibility for Cherevichenko's South Front.

On the south-west approach to the capital Leliushenko's hastily assembled force, aided by the rain, snow and the *rasputitsa,* the breaking up of the roads, had brought Guderian's force to a temporary halt at Mtsensk. When Leliushenko was recalled to the Kremlin on the night of the 11 October, to be given the command of a newly raised army, he felt that he had accomplished his mission in holding the enemy on the Zusha, the *ne plus ultra* line which Stalin had marked on the map. Leliushenko entered the dictator's conference room to find Stalin walking up and down in silence, while Shaposhnikov bent over the maps. Molotov opened the interview by turning to Leliushenko, looking at him severely and demanding, most unexpectedly, why the enemy had not been pushed back out of Orel. The surprised Leliushenko replied that he had so few troops available that, even if he had done so, the enemy would have outflanked him from north and south. Stalin stopped his walking for a moment, then nodded silently, which, said Leliushenko, was Molotov's cue to break off the interrogation with a wintry smile. Leliushenko had the feeling that this little scene had been discussed and rehearsed before his arrival.[4]

On 7 October *Pravda* had reported the giving up of the city of Vyazma 'after a glorious and heroic struggle', but the fact that the West and the Reserve Fronts had suffered an overwhelming defeat could not be concealed. There was panic and looting in the capital, and the diplomatic corps and a number of government commissariats were moved to Kuybyshev. Werth has described what he called 'the great skedaddle' and Birse, of the British Military Mission, has said that there was everywhere among the Muscovites a sense of defeat and impending calamity. Leaflets could be found strewn in public places, blaming the Soviet Government for the misfortunes.[5] When, on the night of 19 October, Artem'ev and Telegin, the military council of Moscow Military District, were ordered to attend a meeting of the GKO in Stalin's office, the atmosphere there was tense, and Stalin was nervous and irritable. Artem'ev, a NKVD general, suggested the proclamation of a state of siege. Stalin instructed Malenkov to draft a GOKO decree to this effect, there and then; but it proved, on being read aloud, to be verbose and so little to the dictator's liking that, according to Telegin, he became angry, 'rushed to Malenkov and snatched the papers from him'. The decree was then dictated by Stalin to Shcherbakov, the Moscow party secretary, 'and approved by all present'. The decree provided for 'the strengthening of controls, the setting up of military tribunals and the shooting on the spot' of real or suspected offenders.[6]

In the second half of October, the enemy advance fell off rapidly due to the exhaustion of his troops, the over-extended fronts, the bad weather and the difficult going conditions. The air situation, too, was gradually changing in favour of the Red Army since much of the *Luftwaffe* was being withdrawn. The defenders were falling back on their Moscow base, and reinforcements began to arrive at the fronts, the West Front alone receiving 100,000 men, 2,000 guns and 300 tanks by the first fortnight in November.[7] In late October, three reserve armies had been brought into being, and in November a further six armies were deployed in depth on a line from Onega to Astrakhan.[8] In Vasilevsky's opinion, the forming of these nine armies was one of the most important factors in deciding the outcome of the winter war.[9] In order to ensure that these armies could be moved forward, the Moscow railway complex and the main east-west lines from the interior were put under military control from 24 October.[10]

All the reserve formations were not formed from the *opolchenie,* however, for the forty or more divisions in the Far East were being steadily reduced, an attempt being made to conceal from Tokyo the decrease in the real fighting strength by a proliferation of formation headquarters, so that, where before there had only been an army, Apanasenko's Far East Front deployed four armies. Kovalev's Transbaikal Military District became a front, though it commanded but one army. By a NKO directive of 16 April 1941, three days after the signing of the Soviet-Japanese Pact, two rifle corps, two rifle divisions and two air brigades were moved to the west, and by the end of November 1941, the total troops ordered to Europe had increased to 17 regular divisions.[11] More were to follow after the attack on Pearl Harbour.

The organization and responsibilities of the Soviet general staff were in some respects similar to those of the tsarist general staff, except that the description 'general staff' was applied in tsarist times to the corps of staff officer graduates who served either in the body of the general staff at the capital or were accredited to formation staff vacancies. The Soviet general staff, however, comprised only the command and staff centre in the capital and, in 1939, was in fact called the general staff of the NKO. The Soviet general staff in Frunze Street thus approximated to what was once *der grosse Generalstab* in the Berlin Königsplatz. With the departure of Timoshenko at the beginning of July 1941, the general staff became independent of the Commissariat of Defence and directly subordinate to the newly formed *Stavka.* It took its orders only from Stalin.

When Zhukov quitted the general staff at the end of July it was in confusion, for not only had it been inadequately prepared for war, but its organization had been drained of its principal experienced members. On Stalin's orders, officers were dispatched from the general staff, as well as from the directorates of the Commissariat of Defence, to field formations or as members of the many investigating commissions, which he used as eyes and ears; for

Stalin believed that any officer of ability ought to be at the front. Sokolovsky and Malandin had gone to the West Theatre. Vatutin went to the North-West Front; Golikov left for London; Sharokhin, Kurasov and Kokorev, the chiefs of the theatre and sector operations departments, were appointed as chiefs of staff to fronts or armies. Zlobin, the new chief of the operations directorate, was replaced almost immediately by Vasilevsky.[12]

In July, by order of the GKO, the responsibility for rear services, signals and army organization were removed from the general staff, in order that it might concentrate its attention on strategic and operative matters.[13] The lot of the general staff was not, however, enviable, for Stalin held the general staff in low regard in the first few months of war and he constantly vented his anger on it. It was rarely consulted, and military decisions were usually taken above its head, it being used merely to transmit Stalin's orders.[14]

Stalin covered the widest range of subjects and demanded exhaustive information on any matter under discussion, occasionally asking the Chief of General Staff for comment, but more often than not deciding himself and, said Vasilevsky, giving out his orders without using a single superfluous word. He spared neither himself nor others. According to Vasilevsky, he was an excellent organizer and this organizing ability was eventually to play an enormous role in bringing strategic and operative plans to fruition. He alone found and allocated reinforcements and *matériel*. Yet, in the first year of war, continued Vasilevsky, Stalin 'made miscalculations, some of them grievous', for he was unjustifiably self-confident and presumptuous (*samonadeian*) and overrated his knowledge and ability in the military field. He often changed commanders without good reason, and his interference brought unsatisfactory results. He demanded that others should not be enslaved by old ideas and should learn by modern methods, but in the beginning he could not do this himself. His leadership, said Vasilevsky, was personal and arbitrary.[15]

Zhukov bore witness to Stalin's work in organizing strategic material and technical resources, and he has said that Stalin's real achievement during the winter of 1941 was the creation of carefully husbanded *Stavka* reserves, details of which he guarded from his front commanders. Both Zhukov and Shtemenko have described the dictator's capacity for work and for detail, his retentive memory

– he was never at a loss for a name and he never forgot a face – his gift for sifting essentials and factual data and his ability to uncover the weakness of others; they have told how he demanded clarity and exactitude and of his intolerance of verbosity, of his sternness, formality and reserve, broken by spiteful anger.[16] He was also fervent, impetuous and headstrong and, as Zhukov put it, 'if Stalin was already decided there would be no further argument – discussion ceased anyway as soon as Stalin supported one of the parties'.[17]

In Rotmistrov's judgement the main reason for the 1941 losses was Stalin's personality cult, 'for he concentrated in his own hands great powers, believing himself to be infallible in his ability to decide all questions, including military ones'. At this time he also appears to have had firm faith in his Old Guard supporters, and Rotmistrov has criticized the former Commissars of Defence and the tyranny and incompetence of those who enjoyed Stalin's confidence.[18] Although Rotmistrov names only Mekhlis, the censure would also appear to include Shchadenko, Beria, Voroshilov, Budenny and Kulik. In the autumn of 1941 Mekhlis and Shchadenko still worked hand in glove, and, as Gorbatov has recounted, could effect the arrest and imprisonment of senior army commanders.[19]

Stalin at first sought to improve the high command and general staff by innovation and experiment. In the winter of 1941, he came to believe that the senior officers of the general staff lacked combat experience and therefore authority in their relationship with the staffs of the fronts and armies; so he had commanders and chiefs of staff of armies posted to the general staff to head the theatre and sector departments. This was a failure because, as Shtemenko said, many of these warriors lacked staff training, and the others had lost the habit.[20] The morale of the general staff suffered, and its efficiency was criticized by the fronts and by the directorates of the Commissariat of Defence.[21]

The heads of the operations directorate, and the theatre and sector departments within the directorate, came into daily contact with the Supreme Commander since he preferred to deal directly on points of detail. It proved difficult to find officers of quality and stamina suitable for these onerous duties and, more particularly, satisfactory to Stalin, for if they met with his approval they were soon posted to the fronts. Vasilevsky, a former tsarist *Shtabs-kapitan* in 409 Novokhopersky Regiment, a man of ability and great lucidity in thought and expression, narrowly escaped being sent to Leningrad to help out Voroshilov. He remained heading the operations directorate from August 1941 until June 1942, being appointed deputy chief of general staff in March of that year. But because Stalin believed that a good staff officer was also a competent commander, Vasilevsky, when still head of the operations directorate, began, on Stalin's instructions, to spend most of his time in visits or attachments to the fronts, the day to day direction of the general staff being left in 1942 not to a general staff officer, but to Bokov, its political commissar, merely because Stalin had got used to his face. As Shtemenko said, the Supreme Commander asked no one's advice on this subject and apparently considered such a situation normal.[22]

In the first year of the war Shaposhnikov, inclining towards von Moltke's precedent and perhaps hoping to protect the operations directorate against Stalin's misuse of its staff, introduced the 'corps of officers of the general staff', the first time that the word *ofitser* had been used since the revolution. Their function was to keep the general staff informed of the actions of the commanders to whom they were attached.[23] Many commanders resented their presence as 'spies and overseers'.

The accommodation for the Soviet High Command was unsatisfactory since the work was shuffled backwards and forwards daily between the Kremlin, the Kuntsevo *dacha,* the 'far house' on the Dmitrov road, Frunze Street and later Kirov Street and other addresses in the capital. But, for lack of better, this peacetime accommodation continued to be used throughout the war. The German air raids on Moscow, which started at the end of July, made it necessary to move part of the general staff each night to the Kirovskaia underground station, no trains being allowed to stop there. The platform which served as a general office was screened from the rails by plywood partitions, a communications centre being installed in one corner and an office for Stalin in the other. Later the general staff was given a building in Kirov Street with an annexe set apart for the dictator.[24] After December 1941 the underground shelters were no longer used, but the general staff remained in Kirov Street; Stalin was usually to be found in the

1 Stalin in 1919 aged 39 years, successively Chief Commissar with the North Caucasus, South, Ukraine, Petrograd, South and South-West Fronts.

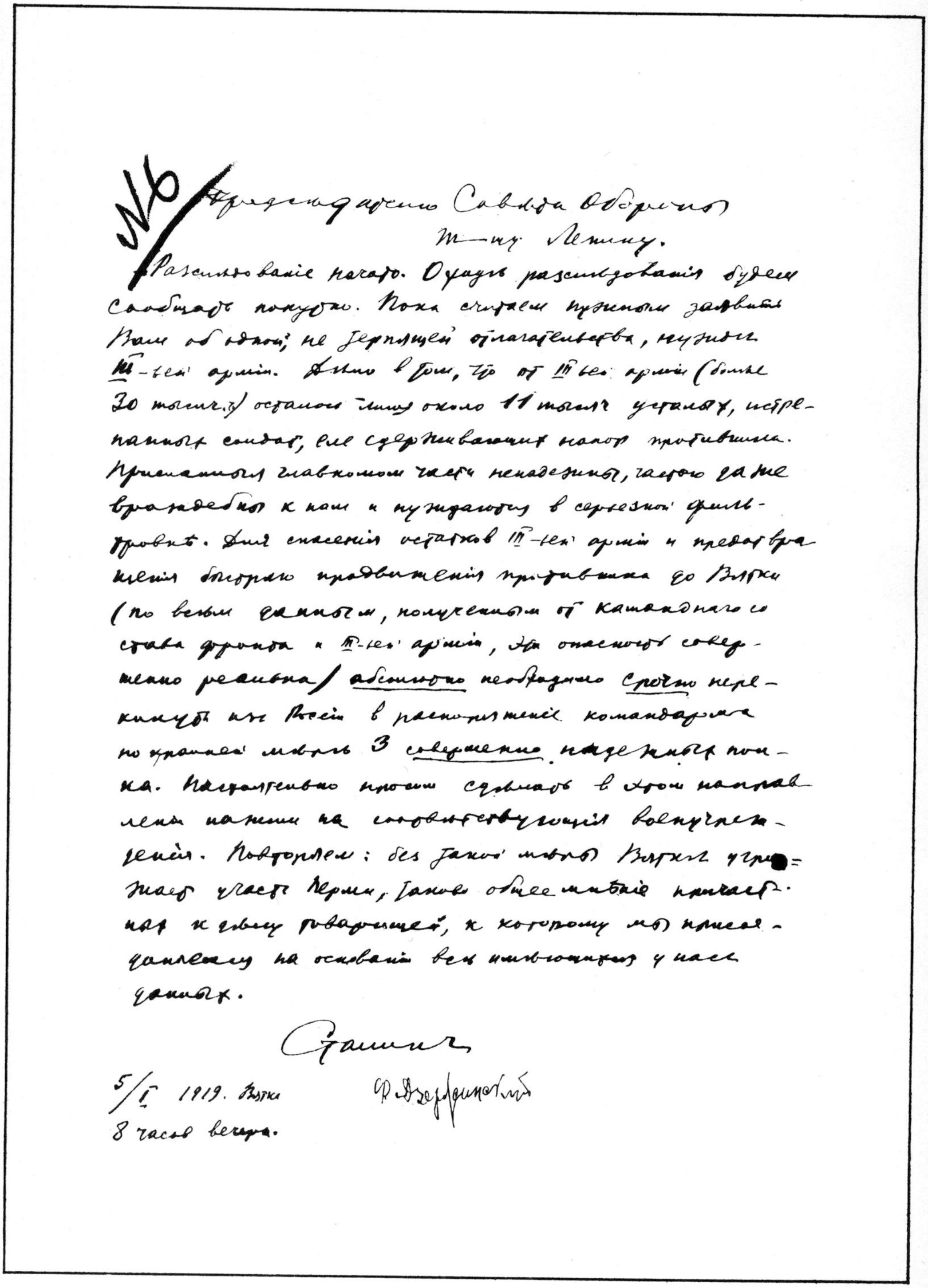

3 Vatsetis, a Latvian tsarist colonel and the first Red Army C in C from 1918–19. He was purged in 1938.

4 S. S. Kamenev *(right)* a tsarist colonel and Red Army C in C from 1919–24 (died 1936), together with his chief of staff Lebedev, a former tsarist major-general (died 1933).

5 Egorov, a tsarist colonel and Commander of the Red Army South
and South-West Fronts. From 1931 he was Chief of General Staff (purged 1939).

6 Tukhachevsky, a tsarist second-lieutenant and Commander of
the North Caucasus and West Fronts. From 1925 he was Chief of Staff of the
Red Army (purged 1937).

7 The cavalry army military council 1920, the commander Budenny flanked by his commissars, Voroshilov and Shchadenko.

8 *Above left.* Voroshilov, who had no military experience before 1918, was successively an army commander and commissar in the Civil War. From 1925–40 he was Commissar for Defence.

9 *Above right.* Mekhlis, formerly Stalin's secretary, until 1942 an Army Commissar 1st Class and head of the main political directorate of the armed forces.

10 *Below left.* Timoshenko, a Bessarabian Ukrainian and tsarist cavalry NCO, Commissar for Defence from 1940–41, and thereafter a theatre and front commander.

11 *Below right.* Budenny, a tsarist cavalry leader, later a theatre and front commander.

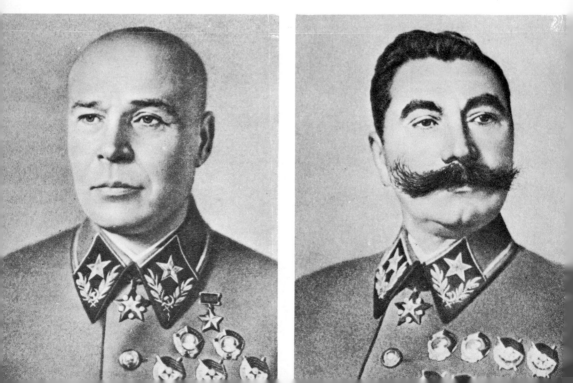

12 Stalin, c. 1941 aged 63 years, on becoming Chairman of the Council of Commissars, Commissar for Defence and the Supreme Commander.

13 *Above left*. Shaposhnikov, a tsarist colonel, who was Chief of General Staff from 1937–40 and again from 1941–42 (died 1945).

14 *Above right*. Zhukov, a tsarist cavalry NCO, who was Chief of General Staff from February to June 1941 and Deputy Supreme Commander from 1942–46.

15 *Below left*. Bagramian, an Armenian, a tsarist junior cavalry officer, later a Soviet front commander.

16 *Below right*. Tiulenev, a Red Army cavalry brigade leader who later commanded Soviet fronts.

17 *Above left*. Vatutin, who had entered the Red Army infantry in 1920, became deputy chief of general staff in 1941. From 1942 he was a front commander (killed 1944).

18 *Above right*. Golikov, who joined the Red Army in 1918, was for many years a commissar before becoming an infantry commander. In 1941 he headed military intelligence.

19 *Below left*. Eremenko, a tsarist cavalry NCO and Red Army cavalry corps commander, was an army and front commander from 1941–45.

20 *Below right*. Popov entered the Red Army infantry in 1920, eventually to become a mechanized corps leader. From 1941 he commanded successively fronts and armies.

21 The military council of the South-West Front, destroyed at Kiev in September 1941; from the left, the commander Kirponos, the commissar Burmistenko and the chief of staff Tupikov.

22 Stalin's aircraft designers *(from the left)*, Lavochkin, Tupolev, A. S. Iakovlev and A. I. Mikoian.

23 N. D. Iakovlev, the Deputy Chief of the Main Artillery Directorate (GAU) responsible to Stalin for combat equipment.

24 Admiral N. G. Kuznetsov, the Commissar for the Navy.

25 Rokossovsky, said to be of Polish-Russian parentage, was a tsarist cavalry NCO and Red cavalry corps commander, later imprisoned during the purges. From 1942 onwards he was a front commander.

26 Voronov joined the Red Army artillery in 1918, by 1937 becoming the Director of Artillery. From 1942–45 he commanded groups of fronts.

27 Shtemenko (*left*), head
of the operations directorate
together with Antonov, the
first deputy chief of general
staff.

28 Konev, a tsarist artillery
NCO and then a Red Army
commissar. In 1927 he
transferred to command
appointments and from 1941
onwards was a front
commander.

29 Purkaev, a Mordvin, was a tsarist junior officer of infantry who entered the Red Army in 1918. In 1939 he was military attaché in Berlin. Throughout the war he commanded armies and fronts.

30 Rotmistrov entered the Red Army in 1919 becoming an instructor in mechanized warfare in 1935. In the war he was an armoured leader of note.

31 Leliushenko, a tsarist cavalry NCO and Red Army cavalry leader who qualified as a commissar in 1925. In 1933 he went to the armoured forces as a commander.

32 The military council of the Leningrad Front in 1943 showing its commander, Govorov, with Zhdanov, his commissar.

33 At 3 Belorussian Front July 1944; from the left, Makarov the commissar, Vasilevsky the Chief of General Staff, and Cherniakhovsky the front commander (killed 1945).

34 In the Far-East August 1945; Meretskov *(left)* commanding 1 Far East Front, Malinovsky commanding the Transbaikal Front and Vasilevsky, the C in C Far East.

Kremlin. The rump of the old signal centre continued a separate existence in providing a telegraph service for the Commissariat of Defence, while the main element served Stalin's Kremlin office and the general staff in Kirov Street.

Stalin took a close interest in military communications and many of his instructions bore the influence of his experience during the Civil War. In one directive he said he was averse to 'excessive reliance by commanders on the telephone, for they should do as the military did at the time of the imperialistic war', that is to say make fuller use of the teleprint telegraph. On 23 July the dictator signed a general signals directive to his field commanders, having, said Peresypkin, 'characteristically' altered the draft to emphasize once more the value of teleprint; he pointed out that all fronts and armies had been re-equipped with Baudôt taken from government and industry in the rear areas.[25] That September the Supreme Commander required that Baudôt terminals with an alternative line layout should be established between the general staff and the armies, bypassing the front headquarters, so that, in the event of signals failure, armies could be controlled from Moscow.

Stalin's working day began an hour or so before noon when he would himself dial the operations directorate for a briefing on what had happened during the night. According to Shtemenko, the answering officer would verbally describe the situation, using a ten yard long telephone lead as he walked from one battle map to the next, Stalin having a corresponding set of maps in his own office which were brought up to date every five days by Platonov. The most important fronts were dealt with first, fronts, armies and armoured formations being referred to by the names of their commanders, the lesser formations by their number and designation. Even though there were twenty or thirty armies in contact with the enemy, Stalin never allowed a single one to be passed over without mention. Occasionally, he would interrupt and dictate an order to be sent to a particular front and this was taken down verbally, read back to the dictator, and dispatched. The second briefing would be at about 1600 hours, sometimes by telephone but usually in the form of a written summary collated by Shaposhnikov; this also went to members of the Politburo and the government. Shortly before midnight the Chief of General Staff or his deputy, the head of the operations directorate, and the theatre or sector chiefs if required, would drive either to the Kremlin or to Kuntsevo with their maps and folders for the nightly report to Stalin and the Politburo or GKO. The heads of main arms and services, usually Voronov, Fedorenko, Novikov, Vorob'ev, Iakovlev and Khrulev, might be in attendance.

Stalin's study and conference room, which was entered through Poskrebyshev's office and the cubby-hole occupied by the chief of the dictator's NKVD bodyguard, has been frequently described by its many visitors; the vaulted ceiling and light oak panelling, the portraits of Suvorov and Kutuzov, Marx and Engels; the long table with the Politburo members sitting against the wall facing the military; Stalin's desk near the death-mask of Lenin under a glass case, and the globe. Stalin would walk up and down, his hands behind his back, smoking his pipe and listening to the reports of operations over the last twenty-four hours. After the reports came the draft directives, which were signed by Stalin and counter-signed by the Chief of General Staff or his deputy or by one other member of the *Stavka*. Less important orders were agreed by Stalin and signed by Shaposhnikov or Vasilevsky after the conclud-ing words 'by order of the *Stavka*'; a distribution copy was sent to Stalin. Directives and orders were often formulated on the spot at Stalin's dictation, many of them being handed untyped to Poskrebyshev's signal centre for immediate transmission to the fronts. Stalin dealt personally with proposals for the promotion, decoration and appointment of senior officers. These nightly meetings often lasted until three or four in the morning.[26]

In the first few months of the war the claims of the field com-manders had been optimistic; their failures they had tried to conceal. As the true situation emerged, Shaposhnikov had borne the weight of Stalin's rage, usually in silence. Some angry scenes were caused by nothing more serious than the late rendition of a front situation report, and, when he could, Shaposhnikov apparently attempted to protect his subordinates.[27] According to Voronov, Stalin wanted to know everything, but his commanders and staff feared to tell him the truth; Iakovlev, the aircraft designer, on the other hand, considered that Stalin was more angry at failure to report than with the lack of success reported.[28]

On 17 October Shaposhnikov and the general staff were evacuated from Moscow, Vasilevsky and Shtemenko remaining as Stalin's immediate assistants.[29] Shaposhnikov, however, soon returned to Moscow until he became ill at the end of November, when he handed his duties over to Vasilevsky. Vasilevsky, like Shaposhnikov, was a man of education, culture and tact, and of charm and modesty; he was also circumspect in his relationship with Stalin and the party. He was of a different stamp from Zhukov, who, like Timoshenko, had much of the cavalry non-commissioned officer about him, being particularly blunt and outspoken, offensively so to his subordinates, according to his colleagues. Belov and Rokossovsky would have their readers believe that Zhukov was capable of speaking sharply even to Stalin; but this is scarcely to be credited, for western observers noted how subdued Zhukov was in the presence of his political masters.[30]

Stalin's mentality was devious, for in October 1941 Voronov proposed to him that a reserve of 160 guns should be formed into ten artillery batteries to thicken up Moscow's anti-tank defences. Stalin pondered aloud, and wished that he had twice as many. Finally he agreed to the ten new units but, to Voronov's surprise, suggested that they should be called regiments. For, said Stalin, this would ensure that 'proper attention would be paid to the units'; and, as for the commanders, 'commander of an artillery regiment – that had a proper ring to it – not only a divisional commander but even a corps commander would have to take notice of him!'. Stalin pointed out to the doubting Voronov, that many infantry divisions had been reduced by casualties to shells, with a fighting strength of less than a regiment, but they still remained on the order of battle as divisions, these numerous cadres swelling the totals of the formations said to be in action on the Russo-German front. When, ten days later, the new artillery regiments had been formed, Voronov suggested to Stalin that the general staff should allocate them. The Supreme Commander, he said, looked at him in surprise, asking, 'Who there could do it?'. Stalin thereupon himself deployed the regiments from his reading of the map.[31]

Zhukov has said that no master plan existed for the winter counter-offensive, and Vasilevsky has confirmed that there was no thought in Moscow of a military initiative until the beginning of November when the German attacks had died down. Events made this impossible, however, for it soon became apparent that the Germans intended to resume the offensive.[32]

On 13 November Stalin telephoned Zhukov, instructing him to mount pre-emptive attacks on the German flanks according to a plan which he and Shaposhnikov had thought out, and so disorganize the enemy's preparations. When Zhukov objected that he could not spare a man for the purpose, Stalin became angry and ordered him to 'consider the matter as settled'. Stalin then spoke to Bulganin to tell him that both he and Zhukov had got too big for their boots (*zaznalis'*). The attacks were mounted as ordered, with little time for preparation, and both Zhukov and Rokossovsky confirm that they failed.[33]

The new enemy offensive, which had as its primary aim the taking of Moscow, began on 15 November, when the wet weather had given way to cold. The German troops on the Nara were to pin the Soviet West Front, while Hoepner's and Reinhardt's panzer groups outflanked the capital from the north and Guderian came up from the south. When Reinhardt struck his main blow north of Moscow, Khomenko's 30 Army on Konev's left wing was routed. That the blame lay with the *Stavka* did not save Khomenko, for at Stalin's order he was immediately relieved by Leliushenko, who had been briefed personally by the dictator. Leliushenko's arrival was Khomenko's first intimation that he had been dismissed.[34] In the next ten days Reinhardt and Hoepner moved forward fifty miles almost to the northern outskirts of the capital; then, like Guderian in the area of Tula, they could do no more, and they waited impatiently for von Kluge to begin his offensive from the Nara, due west of the city.

During the last ten days in November Stalin became increasingly agitated, and, on or about 30 November, occurred the Dedovo-Dedovsk incident when Stalin, under the mistaken impression that the town of Dedovsk, only twenty miles west from the Kremlin, had fallen, 'lost no time in expressing his anger' and ordered Zhukov, together with Rokossovsky and Govorov, both army commanders, to go to Dedovo and supervise an attack by a rifle company and two tanks to retake the locality. Stalin was deaf to entreaties that it would be ill-advised to leave the front headquarters at such a time, and became furious when told there had been confusion in place names. The three generals had to go to Dedovo.[35]

Rokossovsky, a former tsarist non-commissioned officer of 5 Kargopolsky Dragoons, at one time, prior to his three years imprisonment during the purges, a cavalry corps leader and Zhukov's senior commander, has said that Zhukov, too, was very nervous during this period. If Rokossovsky is to be believed, Zhukov forfeited much of the respect of his army commanders because of his impetuosity and lack of self-control and his distrust of his subordinates.[36] The Istra incident which occurred at this time, while of no great consequence in itself, has subsequently attracted much attention in the Soviet military press. Rokossovsky wanted to fall back a few miles and use the Istra as an obstacle, and, as Zhukov disagreed, Rokossovsky appealed to Shaposhnikov, who gave his assent. Rokossovsky reasoned that since the Chief of General Staff rarely assumed any direct responsibility, then Shaposhnikov would have told Stalin of the change. He was surprised, therefore, when Zhukov shortly afterwards countermanded Shaposhnikov's agreement.[37] Although some western commentators have assumed that Zhukov dared to oppose Stalin's will, it is more probable that Zhukov had first taken his complaint to Stalin; and it is in character that Stalin would, with the intention of reaffirming his confidence in the front commander, have told Zhukov to issue his own order.[38] A day or two afterwards Stalin, who, as Anders said, on occasion liked to play the role of *bon papa*, had a telephone conversation with Rokossovsky 'in a kindly and fatherly voice'. Rokossovsky judged that the Supreme Commander merely wanted to express his trust in the army as well as the front commander.[39]

On 29 November, Zhukov had telephoned Stalin asking for two further armies from the *Stavka* reserve in order to destroy the enemy panzer penetrations to the north and south of the capital before they should be reinforced. Stalin, according to Zhukov, listened attentively but was doubtful whether von Bock might still hold a reserve. But when Zhukov assured him that the enemy was exhausted, Stalin said that he would first talk to the general staff.[40] Later that day Zhukov was informed that three armies would be released to him, but that plans as to their use would be required in Moscow on the morrow. This, said Zhukov, was the seed of the winter counter-offensive which was to throw the enemy back 200 miles. A few hours later, at dawn on 30 November, Stalin telephoned asking whether the whole of the West Front could not go over to the offensive. Zhukov pleaded lack of resources, but, as an alternative, suggested that the offensive might be extended beyond the flanks of the West Front. This, however, had been done the day before, for a newly confident Timoshenko had already driven the enemy out of Rostov, and his proposal to use his right wing against von Bock's flank was readily accepted by Stalin. Zhukov gave his own plan to Vasilevsky on 30 November, requesting that he should lay it before the Supreme Commander quickly. It was agreed without amendment that day.[41]

At 0330 hours on 1 December, Stalin and Vasilevsky signed the directive to the Kalinin Front, the Supreme Commander telling Konev that he was dissatisfied with his conduct of the battle; Konev was to concentrate his forces and strike along new axes. Later that day Konev told Vasilevsky that such an offensive was impossible in view of his depleted strength and lack of tanks. Vasilevsky countered by quoting back the strength returns furnished by the Kalinin Front. Was not Konev aware of the successes at Rostov. It was necessary to strike now, said Vasilevsky, for any delay might be fatal.[42] The earlier West Front defeats had presumably undermined Konev's confidence, and Stalin became concerned at his lack of determination. On 4 December Vasilevsky arrived at the Kalinin Front, personally to ensure that Konev gave out his orders in the spirit of the directive. Eight days later Shaposhnikov was well again and both he and Vasilevsky were present when Stalin spoke on the direct line to Konev, demanding that he cease his hairsplitting tactics (*krokhoborskuiu taktiku*).[43]

Zhukov's plan concerned itself only with the West Front and the three recently allocated armies. Cherevichenko, the hero of Rostov, took command of Timoshenko's right flank, forming a new Bryansk Front on 18 December, and began to envelop the German Army Group Centre from the south. Konev's Kalinin Front moved forward, cautiously at first, supported by Kurochkin's North-West Front, Purkaev's and Eremenko's armies outflanking the enemy from the north and penetrating westwards almost as far as Smolensk and Vitebsk.

The success of the Moscow battle, which involved four fronts, was at one time popularly attributed to Zhukov. Rotmistrov's 1963 study has said that the offensive originated from the plan forwarded by the military council of the West Front. Neither Stalin nor

Zhukov is mentioned by name.[44] Sokolovsky, who was a member of that council, writing in the following year does not make that claim, but he blames Stalin for interfering in the conduct of the front battle.[45] Zhukov's 1968 account, that the overall plan was drawn up by the general staff and Stalin in consultation with the front commanders, is substantially the same as that written by Vasilevsky in 1974. Whatever the truth of the matter, there can be little doubt that Stalin remained in overall military control, and that neither he nor Timoshenko ever needed prompting to undertake offensive operations.

On 2 December 1941 Anders, a former Polish officer of the tsarist army only recently released from the NKVD Lubianka prison, was, together with Sikorski, received in audience by Stalin. Anders's description of Stalin differs little from that recorded by other western observers, his eyes black, cold and dull, wrinkled into a smile which seemed only skin-deep, the salesman's joviality, the quiet deliberate tones and the pronounced Caucasian accent, and 'the unmistakable atmosphere of power about him'. Anders noted the subservience shown to Stalin, particularly by the obsequious Molotov 'with his quick offer of a light every time Stalin drew out a cigarette, more like a lackey than a colleague'. At this meeting, Stalin, when asked concerning the fate of 4,000 missing Polish officers, replied, imperturbably according to Anders, that 'they must have escaped to Manchuria'.[46]

A fortnight later when Eden visited Moscow, Japan had attacked the American and British dependencies in the Pacific, and Hitler had declared war on the United States. Stalin showed none of the nervousness and strain apparent during the previous September, and Eden found him 'a quiet dictator in his manner'. He sympathized with Eden on Britain's defeats in the Pacific, saying that 'we, too, have had our difficult periods'. Stalin was particularly interested in Japanese air power and told a sceptical Eden that his military advisers believed 'but were not absolutely certain' that Germany had given Japan 1,500 aircraft together with pilots. If the German aircraft had not been transferred to Japan, said Stalin, where had they gone. For the last six weeks he had noticed a considerable decrease in German air power on the Russian front and he did not believe the aircraft had gone to Libya.

Stalin gave Eden a *resumé* of the military situation as it appeared to him on 16 December. Putting the best gloss that he could on the earlier Russian defeats, the extent of which had never been admitted either at home or abroad, the dictator said, quite falsely, that the war policy of the Soviet Union had hitherto been that of a fighting retreat so as to wear down the German forces. By now, the enemy was tired and ill-clad, having made no preparation for a winter campaign, whereas on the Soviet side the new formations arriving at the front had enabled the Red Army to counter-attack. Counter-attacks, said Stalin, had gradually developed into counter-offensives, and he would 'try and carry this on all through the winter'. He had, he thought, two months in hand before the Germans could organize a counter blow; it was difficult to say how far the Red Army would be able to move forward, but that would be its aim until the spring. The Red Army had air superiority continued Stalin, but not a great one, and needed tanks, 'especially Valentines which have been found to be much better for winter use'. In the south the position was quite satisfactory. The secret of the recent successes was the opportune arrival of fresh reinforcements; 'the German Army was not so strong after all, in spite of its enormous reputation'.[47]

On 17 December Stalin asked that the talks either be postponed for a day or else held after midnight as 'he had a conference of generals'. Timoshenko and his staff were in Moscow and this meeting probably centred around the formation of the new Volkhov and Bryansk Fronts, and the directive issued on 18 December concerning a fresh offensive in the north-west. On 19 December Eden was driven out to Klin, which had been reoccupied only four days before, and sat down to lunch next to 'the Russian general who had described to us the battle'. Eden believed him to be a major-general 'on the staff of an army'. It was in fact Leliushenko. At the banquet on the final day of the meeting Stalin was clearly embarrassed at the spectacle of a somewhat drunk Timoshenko. Yet, when the Ribbentrop-Molotov pact was discussed, he showed no shame, said Eden, in brazenly giving Molotov the discredit for it.[48]

In the south the situation was, as Stalin had told Eden, satisfactory, for the enemy Army Group South, ordered to secure the line Stalingrad-Maikop, had overreached itself in trying to enter the

Caucasus and had been forced back from Rostov to the line of the Mius.

In the north, near Leningrad, von Leeb's Army Group North had moved north-eastwards preparatory to joining up with the Finns on the Svir. Tikhvin fell on 8 November and the defending Red Army troops began to disintegrate. The rear of 7 Independent Soviet Army, facing north against the Finns, was threatened, and its commander Meretskov telephoned the *Stavka*, presumably Poskrebyshev, for Meretskov said that 'there and then Stalin came on the phone'; having heard Meretskov's report, the dictator ordered him to hand his army over to his deputy and take over the command of the routed troops facing von Leeb.[49] Stalin told Meretskov he could give him no reinforcements, but authorized him to use the three armies in the area as the situation demanded. By 11 November the energetic and jovial Meretskov had already organized the first counter-attack and this steadily built up into an offensive. On 9 December, Meretskov's troops entered Tikhvin.

Two days later Meretskov was summoned to the general staff in Moscow and told by Vasilevsky that he was to form a new front headquarters, the Volkhov Front, interposed between the Leningrad and North-West Fronts. The following day Meretskov was called to the Kremlin where he found Stalin and Shaposhnikov, together with Khozin and Zhdanov from the Leningrad Front, grouped round a map of the Leningrad-Volkhov area. The task was to plan an offensive which was intended to link up by land with Leningrad.[50]

In addition to the four armies already allocated to him, Meretskov wanted to take over yet another from the Leningrad Front; Khozin and Zhdanov objected. Stalin listened to the argument and finally sided with Khozin; 'if that is best for Leningrad, let it be that way'.

The main difficulty that was to bedevil the new offensive was that of timing, because Meretskov still awaited the arrival of his troops. Meretskov has said that he was given no time to prepare his offensive, but was goaded into the attack as soon as he had arrived back on the Volkhov; he has cited the *Stavka* directive of 17 December and 'one in the clearest terms' on 24 December. 'On top of that' continued Meretskov, 'Mekhlis arrived as the *Stavka* representative to speed up operations'. Consequently Meretskov had been obliged from 20 December onwards to make fruitless and costly tactical attacks before the main offensive was launched. Voronov, one of the few to earn Meretskov's thanks, came to assist in artillery matters, but, by the first week in January, the attacks by the two armies already in place were dying out and the other two reserve armies were not yet assembled. On 10 January Meretskov was still not ready, and he subsequently said that he needed, in fact, another fifteen to twenty days to complete his concentration.

On 11 January Stalin and Vasilevsky had a direct wire conversation with Meretskov in which they stated that 'according to the information available to them' the Volkhov Front was not ready, and they suggested that the offensive be postponed to ensure success. Meretskov has admitted that he grasped 'at the additional two days offered', still knowing that he could never be prepared in time. Then, on the eve of the offensive, the divisional commanders of a shock army, the main striking force, complained to Meretskov that their army commander did not know what he was about. Meretskov reported the facts to the *Stavka,* and Stalin had the commander replaced immediately. The offensive, born of these inauspicious beginnings, failed. The *Stavka* accused the front military council of turpitude and indecision and Voroshilov, as Stalin's representative, arrived for a tour of inspection of the armies, returning once more with Malenkov and Novikov as part of a GKO investigating committee.

According to a Soviet reviewer of Meretskov's memoirs 'the Volkhov Front did not have the courage to tell Stalin the true state of affairs before or after the offensive was launched'. This may indeed have been the case, but this criticism must also have applied to Mekhlis, Voroshilov, Voronov, Vasilevsky, Khrulev and Novikov who went there in turn. However this may be, Stalin afterwards put the blame on Meretskov, saying 'the offensive has been hurried without preparation and has set people laughing; if you remember, I proposed that you delay the attack, but you refused and now you reap the fruits of your rashness'.[51]

Stalin may indeed have used these admonitory words to Meretskov; whether he would have agreed to a delay of three weeks is another matter. For, on 5 January, Zhukov had been called to a

GKO meeting where Shaposhnikov had outlined the plan for a massive counter-offensive from Leningrad to the Black Sea, and this included the lifting of the Leningrad blockade and the re-occupying of the Donets Basin and the Crimea, all to be done in the shortest time possible. Stalin summarized the presentation by saying that the enemy was in confusion and unprepared for winter warfare; the need for offensive action was immediate. He asked if anyone had anything to say.

Zhukov has said that he spoke against a general offensive on the grounds that this might starve his own West Front of troops and material and put its advance at risk; his address, he said, was obviously unwelcome to Stalin who interjected a number of critical remarks. Voznesensky, Chairman of the Economic Council of the Defence Industry, supported Zhukov on the grounds of the general shortage of equipment. Stalin retorted by saying that he had talked to Timoshenko, who was all for the offensive. 'We must', said Stalin, 'finish the Germans off quickly so that they will not be able to come back in the spring'. This was the cue for Malenkov and Beria to take the floor and attack Voznesensky. In Zhukov's opinion, which was reinforced by what he afterwards heard from Shaposhnikov, the immediate and general offensive was Stalin's brain-child and was not initiated by the general staff.[52] Zhukov could see no reason why he had been told to attend since discussion was superfluous, and he came to the conclusion that it had been Stalin's intention merely 'to put pressure on the military'; in this case himself. Vasilevsky has said that on 10 January, on Stalin's initiative, a directive was sent to all fronts concerning the coming offensive 'which was going to drive the aggressor out of the country'.[53]

Stalin continued to act as the co-ordinator of the fronts immediately to the west of Moscow. On 16 December he had, against Zhukov's wishes, transferred Leliushenko's army back to Konev. On 19 January Zhukov was told to transfer a shock army to the *Stavka* reserve from whence it was to go to Kurochkin. When Zhukov and Sokolovsky appealed to the general staff against the order, they were informed that the decision was that of the Supreme Commander. Zhukov telephoned Stalin, only to be told that he was to send the army back 'without any more argument'; when Zhukov attempted to continue the conversation Stalin replaced the receiver. By the end of February the West Front had already outrun its logistic support and resources; the enemy had regrouped and was counter-attacking strongly, enveloping Soviet armies one after the other. But, said Zhukov, the appeals of the front for a respite so that the position might be consolidated were ignored by Stalin, who constantly repeated his self-formulated principle of offensive action: 'Attack! If you have no results today, you will tomorrow; even if you achieve nothing except the pinning of the enemy, the result will be felt elsewhere'. Yet by his harsh measures, continued Zhukov, Stalin achieved the well-nigh impossible; he was attentive to advice but he made his own decisions, decisions which, in Zhukov's opinion, did not always correspond to the demands of the situation.[54]

Stalin's simple philosophy has been criticized in the six volume history, published under Khrushchev, for over-optimism and dispersal of effort. The troops, it said, were thrown into battle piecemeal without proper preparation and with inadequate tank or artillery support. But the main charge levelled against Stalin concerned the allocation of the nine reserve armies; of these, three went to the West and two to the Volkhov Front, and one each to the Kalinin, Bryansk, North-West and South-West Fronts; if most had gone to the West Front, Army Group Centre might have been destroyed.[55]

The gains made by the Red Army in the north and south, measured in territory, were admittedly small and, in the south at least, transitory. Kozlov's Transcaucasus Front in the Kuban crossed the Kerch straits on 26 December and established a bridge-head in the Crimea, so enabling the besieged Sevastopol garrison to hold out for a further few months. In the Ukraine Timoshenko, once more a theatre commander, used the left wing of Kostenko's South-West Front and the right wing of Malinovsky's South Front in an offensive which, starting on 18 January, achieved an eighty mile wide breakthrough in the area of Izyum, penetrating sixty miles into the enemy rear in eighty days and threatening the supply artery to Stalino. In the north von Leeb had fallen back, his left flank still being under pressure from Meretskov's Volkhov Front, when his right flank was unexpectedly assailed on 7 January by Kurochkin's North-West Front. By 8 February Kurochkin had encircled a German force of 90,000 men at Demyansk. Over the whole of the eastern front there was a nervousness and tension never experienced before by the German command.

Hitler's intention had been to occupy the line Vologda-Stalingrad-Maikop that winter. Yet, throughout the course of the further three and a half years' fighting, the Germans did not succeed in advancing beyond the line on which they had halted in the spring of 1942, roughly in the area Leningrad-Velikiye Luki-Spas Demensk. Only in the Ukraine were Axis troops to resume the advance in the great summer offensive.

Khozin, the Commander of the Leningrad Front, had complained, during a teleprint conversation with Moscow, that the efforts of the Leningrad and Volkhov Fronts so lacked co-ordination that the enemy could easily parry their blows in turn. He urged, so he has since said, that the *Stavka* should exercise a more centralized control over both fronts, so directing their efforts and reserves in the decisive sectors. Meretskov has imputed to Khozin less disinterested motives. Khozin was called to Moscow on 21 April to report to Stalin and the GKO, Shaposhnikov and Vasilevsky being present. Having heard Khozin's address, Stalin proposed that the Leningrad and Volkhov Fronts be merged into a single front, this proposal, according to Khozin, surprising not only himself but all the others present. The decision, as Khozin admitted, subsequently proved to be a bad one, 'but at that moment no one could think of any objections, and indeed, in view of the colossal authority which Stalin wielded, hardly anyone could in fact object'.[56]

The directive covering the reorganization and the disbandment of the Volkhov Front was signed that night and the front was downgraded to the status of a group under Khozin's Leningrad Front. Meretskov learned on 23 April, he said to his 'utter surprise', that he was to be transferred to the West Front firstly as a deputy commander and then to command an army. The Leningrad Front, however, could provide no remedies and, in Khozin's words, 'the situation instead of improving steadily worsened'. The armies, he said, were worn out, with formations sixty or seventy per cent short of establishment; tank brigades had no tanks and the artillery no ammunition. On 8 June Meretskov received a telephone call from Moscow informing him that the Volkhov Front was to be reconstituted with himself as the front commander.

Meretskov has recounted, with satisfaction, his version of the GKO meeting which took place in the second week in June. Stalin summed up the situation by saying that '*we* committed a grave error in joining the two fronts' and that Khozin had seriously mismanaged things. Meretskov, together with Vasilevsky, was to go to the Volkhov and bring out Vlasov's encircled shock army no matter what the cost, even if it had to abandon heavy weapons and equipment.[57] As for Khozin, he lost the advancement and subsequent fame which went to Govorov, the former artillery officer of the White Guards, who, on 3 June, relieved him as the Commander of the Leningrad Front.

7
Further Defeats

The German Führer had abandoned his intention of resuming the offensive on Moscow and had decided to occupy Caucasia in the summer of 1942; he intended to get to the Volga, but the taking of Stalingrad was unimportant, except that every effort was to be made to reach the city 'or at least control the area by the fire of heavy weapons' so that the Soviet Union could no longer use it as an industrial or communications centre.[1] The campaign was to open by a thrust in the north from the area of Kursk, striking due east towards Voronezh. The German motorized forces were then to change direction south-eastwards, moving rapidly along the right bank of the Don and enveloping the South-West Front from the rear. In order to conceal the direction of the offensive, Keitel, the head of the OKW, had issued a directive, on 12 February, for an intelligence cover plan to disseminate false information that the next German offensive was to be directed on Moscow.

In the spring of 1942 Stalin and the Red Army general staff believed that the seizure of Moscow would be the main enemy strategic object, and, according to Vasilevsky, 'the majority of the front commanders thought so too'. It was considered that any enemy offensive in the Ukraine was likely to have as its aim not the occupation of Caucasia, but the envelopment from the south of both the West Front and Moscow. Shaposhnikov urged Stalin to go over to the strategic defensive in order to accumulate reserves, so that the expected enemy offensive could be met with a counter blow.[2] Stalin accepted Shaposhnikov's proposals in principle, but it transpired that the dictator's interpretation of 'active defence' was a series of major offensives at Demyansk, the Crimea, Kharkov, Kursk, Smolensk and Leningrad. Meanwhile the strategic reserves were held in the areas of Tula, Voronezh, Stalingrad and Saratov, so that, as Vasilevsky said, 'looking at the plan critically, one must say that we intended both to attack and defend'.

That March Shaposhnikov received from Timoshenko a request for additional forces for a grand offensive to be made by the Bryansk, South-West and South Fronts with the aim of clearing the enemy from the Ukraine as far west as Kiev. Although the general staff begged the Supreme Commander not to agree, Stalin sanctioned as much of Timoshenko's offensive plan as could be undertaken with his own resources.[3] At the end of the month, at a GKO planning conference, Shaposhnikov attempted to decry the merits of Timoshenko's proposal, but he was silenced by Stalin, who asked whether they should idle and allow the enemy to attack first. It was necessary, said Stalin, to strike a number of blows over a wide front.[4] Timoshenko spoke in favour of his plan and Voroshilov agreed with him. Zhukov supported Shaposhnikov in general terms but adhered to his own view that there should be one offensive, that by his own West Front. Shaposhnikov took no further part in the discussion. Vasilevsky shared Shaposhnikov's opinion and he subsequently condemned Stalin's strategy as a frittering of strength and effort. He later commented: 'Many might rightly censure the general staff for failing to tell Stalin the negative consequences of his plans, but would only do so if they did not know the difficult conditions under which the general staff had to work'. The only comfort which Vasilevsky could draw was that these errors were fully taken into account a year later at Kursk.[5]

Timoshenko intended to use the larger part of two fronts to attack out of the Izyum bulge, a salient surrounded on three sides by the enemy. Notwithstanding Shaposhnikov's opinion that 'an offensive mounted from an operative bag (*iz operativnogo meshka*) was attended by great risks', Timoshenko assured Stalin that it would be successful. The dictator thereupon ruled that the South-West Theatre offensive was 'an internal matter in which the general staff should not interfere'.[6]

Zhukov agreed both with Stalin and with the general staff that the main German thrust would be from Orel and Kursk, the enemy then wheeling in a north-easterly direction behind Moscow, and that the Bryansk Front, newly under Golikov's command, was holding a key sector. Increased tank production had made possible once more the raising of large armoured formations, and Golikov had been heavily reinforced; in addition, a new 5 Tank Army under Liziukov, part of the *Stavka* reserve, was concentrated behind the Bryansk Front. Stalin had refused to allow Golikov to support Timoshenko's offensive, and, on 24 April, he ordered Golikov to move his main forces further north to the Orel area where they would be closer to the capital.[7]

Timoshenko's offensive began on 12 May, Kostenko's South-West Front attacking out of the salient northwards on Kharkov.[8] Hitler had already ordered operation *Fridericus I* to be mounted on 18 May, having as its aim the destruction of the Izyum bulge.

At first Timoshenko's operation was most successful and this caused Stalin to make some bitter comment on the worthlessness of the general staff.[9] Hitler countered the Soviet offensive by bringing *Fridericus I* forward and, on 17 May, von Kleist's panzer army began its attack on the south face of the salient, cutting through Malinovsky's South Front and making rapid progress into Kostenko's rear, so that the Izyum bulge, held by part of two fronts, was in immediate danger of encirclement. What Shaposhnikov had forecast was about to come to pass.

On the evening of 17 May Vasilevsky suggested to Stalin that part of Kostenko's attacking force be turned round to assist Malinovsky in its rear. Timoshenko, however, told Stalin that the situation was under control. Although Khrushchev has said that he warned Stalin on 17 May of the danger, it would appear that this really occurred late on 18 May. Stalin would not agree to break off the attacks on Kharkov; Khrushchev then spoke to Vasilevsky, at about 1800 hours that day, and pleaded with him to intercede with Stalin; but Vasilevsky declined, telling Khrushchev that he had more than once attempted, in the face of Timoshenko's and Khrushchev's opposition, to dissuade Stalin from the operation and from maintaining the Kharkov attacks; Khrushchev must now deal directly with the Supreme Commander himself.[10] When Khrushchev telephoned the Kuntsevo *dacha* Stalin refused to speak to him but suffered the conversation to be conducted through Malenkov, at the end of which he directed that everything should remain as it was.[11] Khrushchev criticized Stalin only after his death.[12] Timoshenko subsequently tried to place the responsibility for the Kharkov defeat on Kharitonov.[13]

Against a German loss of 20,000 men, the Red Army casualties in prisoners alone totalled 214,000, in addition to 1,200 tanks and 2,000 guns. Kostenko and a number of army commanders were said to have been among the killed and the South-West Front had ceased to exist. The South-West Theatre was downgraded to a front. With this defeat the Soviet Union had lost all strategic initiative.

Kharkov was not the only defeat suffered by the Red Army during the Stalin offensives. In March the dictator had sent Mekhlis to Kerch as the *Stavka* representative to Kozlov's Crimea Front. Stalin had confidence in Mekhlis, trusting him, according to Meretskov, 'because he reported everything and concealed nothing'; Meretskov, himself not distinguished for urbanity or tact, described Mekhlis as 'suspicious, rude, curt, obstinate and rigid'. Shortly after arriving in the Crimea, Mekhlis had replaced Tolbukhin, the front chief of staff, by Vechny; and, according to Shtemenko, 'true to his usual practice, instead of helping he began capriciously to shuffle around (*peretasovyvat'*) other senior commanders and staff'.[14] The Crimea Front neither began its own offensive nor deployed defensively to meet that of the enemy. Finally, on 8 May, the German blow fell and Kozlov's troops began to disintegrate.

On that day Mekhlis sent a telegram to Stalin commencing with the words, 'this is not the time to complain, but I must report, so that the *Stavka* will know the front commander for what he is'; Mekhlis placed the responsibility for the unreadiness for battle on Kozlov's shoulders. Stalin, however, dispatched what Shtemenko called 'a no less remarkable reply'. Stalin thought Mekhlis's position, 'as a mere observer without responsibility, strange . . . and very comfortable', reminding him that as a *Stavka* representative he was answerable for failures, and was in duty bound to rectify mistakes on the spot. If, continued Stalin, Mekhlis had confined himself to passive criticism, so much the worse for him. 'You demand that we replace Kozlov by somebody like Hindenburg, but you must know that we have no Hindenburgs in reserve'.[15]

Two days later, at 0300 hours on 10 May, Stalin is said to have ordered Kozlov to withdraw immediately, and, at 2350 hours the next day, he instructed Budenny to go to the Crimea and compel Kozlov to disengage.[16] By then, however, the Crimea Front had been routed and, against German casualties totalling 7,500 men, Kozlov lost 170,000 in prisoners alone, 1,100 guns, 250 tanks and 300 aircraft. A month later Sevastopol fell with a loss of a further 90,000 prisoners. For this failure Mekhlis was recalled, degraded in rank and replaced as head of the main political directorate by Shcherbakov. Kozlov, two army commanders and other more junior commanders were removed, losing rank or being otherwise punished. Budenny's North Caucasus Theatre was redesignated as a front.

Elsewhere the Leningrad, North-West and West Front offensives gained no real advantage; the enemy Demyansk salient still held and Army Group Centre began to make limited attacks to pinch out the salients near Vyazma and Byelyi defended by Zhukov's West Front. These resulted in the loss of a further 70,000 Red Army men as prisoners.

On 19 June a German light plane, carrying the luckless Major Reichel bearing plans for von Bock's summer offensive into the Ukraine, lost its way in bad weather and was brought down on Soviet territory. Details of the plans were hurriedly transmitted to Moscow. When, the next day, Stalin and Vasilevsky asked on the direct line for the South-West Front's evaluation of the documents, Timoshenko replied that he had no reason to doubt their authenticity. Stalin, however, was not convinced, and in a short telegraphed instruction he told Timoshenko to keep the incident secret, for he himself believed that the captured order covered only part of the German plan.[17]

On the morning of 28 June the left wing of von Bock's Army Group South drove a great gap between the Bryansk and the South-West Fronts and moved rapidly towards Voronezh, which von Bock was to take if he should so please, provided that it did not delay the departure of the motorized force south-eastwards to the lower Don bend.[18] Von Bock, however, became nervous about Golikov's tank strength and allowed himself to be drawn into the heavy fighting. Hitler subsequently blamed von Bock's delay at Voronezh for the failure of the whole Stalingrad campaign.

Stalin and the general staff had predicted that the enemy

thrusts would be made on the Orel-Tula and Kursk-Voronezh axes.[19] Von Bock's tank attacks into Voronezh reinforced the Moscow interpretation of the enemy's strategy, and, so that Timoshenko should keep this foremost in his mind, Stalin sent a message at 1605 hours on 2 July, through Vatutin, warning him that the penetration threatened the rear of the Bryansk Front as well as that of the South-West Front.[20] Since Golikov's front reserves had already been committed, Stalin put at his disposal two further armies together with Liziukov's tank army, with orders that it should attack, in conjunction with the tank corps already forming part of the front, on a north-south axis and envelop von Bock's left wing. Although Rotmistrov has said that Liziukov had only 400 tanks, Golikov, according to Vasilevsky, had a further 600, and, of the total, 800 were of modern T34 or KV type; this force was sufficient, Vasilevsky reckoned, 'to change the whole situation'.[21]

Golikov had been sent to Voronezh, probably on 2 July, leaving his deputy Chibisov at the Bryansk Front headquarters at Elets in control of the northern wing; Vasilevsky, appointed Chief of General Staff only a week before, arrived there on 3 July. According to Vasilevsky, 5 Tank Army was still without orders on 4 July. Vasilevsky took command himself and issued verbal instructions to Liziukov, Vasilevsky subsequently justifying his action by quoting Kazakov, the Bryansk Front chief of staff: 'the front commander was in Voronezh, the deputy commander Chibisov had only just arrived; in this situation the general staff representative took over control'.[22] The tank army offensive failed, according to Vasilevsky, 'because of lack of leadership and poor front support'. The tank army commander's account remained unwritten, for Liziukov was said to have died in the battle.

Rotmistrov, the commander of one of Liziukov's tank corps, has a different story. Rotmistrov's 7 Tank Corps had just arrived from Kalinin, and the other two tank corps were still sixty miles to the north. Vasilevsky decided to send 7 Tank Corps forward, presumably to establish contact, and he personally gave Rotmistrov preliminary orders. On 4 July Liziukov, 'after spending two hours with Vasilevsky', issued his own orders, but Rotmistrov had difficulty in understanding them because they had been framed by someone 'accustomed to command infantry and not tanks', that is to say by Vasilevsky, for Liziukov was an armoured leader. The other two tank corps did not go into action until 7 and 10 July. The offensive failed, Rotmistrov said, because the force was committed piecemeal without proper artillery and air support, and his 1963 account held Stalin and Vasilevsky responsible.[23]

Meanwhile, however, there was a further lack of harmony in the Soviet High Command. On 7 July, when Liziukov's tank battle was at its height, Stalin had recalled Vasilevsky to Moscow in order to split the armies of the Bryansk Front by interposing a new head-quarters to the south, Golikov and his staff becoming the nucleus of a new Voronezh Front headquarters. The old Bryansk Front headquarters remained in being, still under Chibisov.[24] Vasilevsky escaped censure for Liziukov's defeat, but Golikov and Chibisov suffered an immediate, if temporary, eclipse. According to Kazakov, Stalin had heard from the NKVD that 40 Army under Popov, who was frequently in Stalin's disfavour, was allowing the two NKVD regiments in Voronezh to bear the brunt of the fighting. Since Golikov was reluctant to give Stalin an assurance that Voronezh would be held, he was replaced on 14 July as the Commander of the Voronezh Front.[25] On the other hand, others, including Vasilev-sky, say that Golikov was directly relieved of his command *of the Bryansk Front* by Rokossovsky.

This point is relevant to Rokossovsky's description of his interview and appointment by Stalin, in the presence of the out-going front commander, whom Rokossovsky does not name. Stalin's views were contrary to those expressed two months before, when he censured Mekhlis for failing to interfere with the actions of the Crimea Front commander. The former Bryansk Front commander complained to Stalin that he thought that he was being removed from his post unjustly, because Vasilevsky had 'got in the way by interfering, holding conferences when it was necessary to act, and in general overriding the front commander'. Stalin retorted that 'the party and the government had entrusted the front to *you*, not to the *Stavka* representative'. Soviet military organization and functions were often what Stalin happened to say they were at the time. Stalin may have been talking to Golikov. Yet the quick-witted Golikov, who had been a military commissar for many years, had not scrupled formerly to complain directly to Stalin; and in any case Golikov had been at Voronezh. On the other hand the slow tempo of command activity, about which Vasilevsky complained, is more suggestive of Chibisov's Olympian calm; for Rokossovsky has described how Chibisov was wont to go his own unhurried way, cheerfully dispensing tea from his *samovar* in the most difficult and threatening situations. The lesson which Rokossovsky learned was to refer all disagreements, difficulties and reverses, however unpalatable, directly to Stalin by telephone.[26]

When the replacements for Golikov and Chibisov were being nominated, Vasilevsky, together with his deputy Vatutin, were attending Stalin in his Kremlin office. The first suggestion, Rokossovsky for the Bryansk Front, was immediately agreed; but Stalin rejected the list of candidates for the Voronezh Front. The long and thoughtful silence was broken by Vatutin who rose to his feet with the words, 'Comrade Stalin, nominate me to command the Voronezh Front'. Vatutin, a friend of Zhukov's, was not highly regarded by the dictator. The interruption surprised both Vasilevsky and Stalin who, in open amazement, said 'What, you!' (*Vas*), and sat frowning, lost in thought. 'What does Vasilevsky think?'. Vasilevsky supported Vatutin. After further reflection Stalin gave a grudging acquiescence. 'If Comrade Vasilevsky is satisfied with you, I will not oppose it'.[27] Vatutin, a lieutenant-general of infantry, who had entered the Red Army as a recruit in 1920, had held no commands other than a temporary group at the time of the Moscow battle; he had been Vasilevsky's immediate senior, both in appointment and rank, in 1940 and 1941.

Timoshenko's South-West and Malinovsky's South Fronts fell back rapidly to escape envelopment. The 1961 account says that the Soviet command, presumably the South-West Front of which Khrushchev formed part, 'skilfully combined the defence of natural features with a timely withdrawal'.[28] This description hardly accords with the panic felt at the time and Stalin's standstill order No. 227 of 28 July.

On 12 July a new Stalingrad Front had been raised from three reserve armies, together with two tank armies in the process of formation, absorbing also the remnants of the South-West Front. Timoshenko was given the new command, but, eleven days later, he was replaced by Gordov, Khrushchev remaining with the front military council. A large part of the Stalingrad Front was deployed on a narrow bridgehead on the right bank of the Don covering the approaches to Stalingrad, the area once defended by Voroshilov against Krasnov's Don Cossacks. On 23 July, the day that Gordov assumed his new post, the enemy began his offensive to destroy the bridgehead, preparatory to an advance to the Volga.

On 23 July Vasilevsky arrived in the bridgehead, having been told by Stalin to take control of operations, and there he ordered two separate counter-attacks, by one tank army on 25 July and by the second, two days afterwards; for this piecemeal employment of armour, though it totalled only 240 tanks, he was, two decades later, criticized in the Soviet military press. Stalin, or so Vasilevsky said in 1965, was reluctant to use tanks in this fashion, but on this occasion he did not interfere.[29] The counter-attacks failed and Gordov was driven over the Don, leaving behind him about 48,000 dead and prisoners, 270 tanks and 600 guns.

Further to the south the approach of Hoth's panzer army along the Kotelnikovo railway, over which Budenny had skirmished in 1918, posed a second threat to Stalingrad, for Hoth was already east of the Don. Gordov's Stalingrad Front stretched from its junction with Vatutin's Voronezh Front down to the Sarpa Lakes, a distance of over 450 miles. Stalin met the problem of the extended front and the exposed southern flank by interposing yet another headquarters there, and conjuring up new forces, in the first instance by cutting the Stalingrad Front in two.

In the early hours of 2 August the wounded and still lame Eremenko was brought from a Moscow hospital to the Kremlin, where a GKO meeting was in session, and Stalin appointed him as the commander of 'a front in the Stalingrad area'. At a second GKO meeting the following night, Eremenko, still decisive and confident in his manner, objected that he did not like the proposed inter-front boundary which was to run from Kalach-on-Don to the Tsaritsyn stream; since enemy attacks were usually directed along Soviet boundaries, the whole of Stalingrad, Eremenko felt, ought to be the responsibility of a single front. Stalin's irritable outburst, unexpected by Eremenko, surprised, so he believed, even the GKO members; the dictator said, with some emphasis, that the boundary would remain exactly as he had laid it down. The formations and resources were then divided between the two fronts, and Eremenko was appointed to the more southerly, the new South-East Front. The necessary directives were drafted in the light of the decisions taken and, said Eremenko, the changes were confirmed there and then by Stalin.[30]

On 4 August Eremenko took off from Moscow without a headquarters or staff, and the next day the South-East Front came into being, temporarily sharing the Stalingrad Front headquarters in the Tsaritsyn river gorge. Eremenko's account, published at the time of Khrushchev's ascendancy, recounts without inhibition the events which led to his establishing a close relationship with Khrushchev at Gordov's expense. Gordov appears to have been an excitable and difficult character. Konev considered him experienced but wilful and unbalanced; Rokossovsky called him an abusive (*maternyi*) commander. Zhukov was more tolerant of such a failing but told Stalin that Gordov did not get on well with people.[31] He was certainly on unsatisfactory terms with Khrushchev. Vasilevsky was sent to Stalingrad to suggest a solution.

Vasilevsky had come to disagree with Stalin's recent action in splitting the former Stalingrad Front and in siting the inter-front boundary in the city, and he apparently succeeded in passing on his doubts to Stalin; and, because Khrushchev had no confidence in Gordov, a compromise was arrived at whereby the front boundary remained temporarily where it was, but Eremenko was placed in the overall command of the two fronts, with Khrushchev acting as the political member for both military councils.

Eremenko has stressed his closeness to Khrushchev and, like some of his fellows during Khrushchev's ascendancy, was critical of both Stalin and Vasilevsky. Vasilevsky in his turn has recounted *verbatim* the Baudôt teleprint conversation of 9 August, in which Moscow asked Eremenko to comment on Stalin's proposal that Eremenko should command the two fronts, with Gordov and Golikov acting as his deputies. For Eremenko is said to have replied 'my answer is that no one is wiser than Stalin'.[32] The coupling of the two fronts under one commander was not to prove a success, for Eremenko lacked confidence in his subordinates. Instead of directing the battle through Gordov and Golikov he began to act as the field commander for both forces, passing orders direct to armies and holding consultations with the military councils and arms commanders of both fronts.[33]

As in the summer of 1918, the civil population of Stalingrad were digging field works to the west of the city, except that this time it was the proletariat not the *bourgeoisie* who had been conscribed. By 5 August Hoth had reached the outer defence ring, not thirty miles south-west of the city, and ten days later Paulus's 6 Army was preparing to cross the Don and come to Hoth's support. In the Caucasus, List's Army Group A had, on 5 August, taken Voroshilovsk (Stavropol), and Maikop fell immediately afterwards; by mid August German troops were in the old Kuban Cossack capital of Krasnodar (Ekaterinodar) and moving up the foothills of the Caucasus, hardly fifty miles from Novorossisk and the other Black Sea ports.

It was at this time that Churchill and his military staff arrived in Moscow to bring news to the dictator that there would be no second front in Western Europe that year.

8
Stalingrad and the Caucasus

On the evening of 12 August Churchill and Harriman, Roosevelt's representative, attended the meeting with Stalin, Molotov and Voroshilov, during which Stalin took issue at every point with a degree of bluntness amounting to insult, telling his allies that they could not win wars if they were afraid of the Germans and were unwilling to take risks. He did, nevertheless, show some interest in the proposed allied landings in French North Africa, and accurately predicted their political and strategic merit in that they would provoke French and Germans to fight each other, put Italy out of action and ensure Spain's neutrality.[1]

At the next meeting, on the night of 13 August, Churchill and Harriman were handed a long *aide-mémoire*, signed by Stalin, accusing his allies of failing to fulfil their undertaking of a second front in Europe in 1942. Stalin wanted an immediate landing of six to eight allied divisions on the Cherbourg peninsula.[2] When Harriman asked about plans for ferrying American aircraft across Siberia, Stalin curtly dismissed the question with 'wars are not won with plans'. Brooke recorded in his diary that night:

Stalin is a realist . . . facts only count . . . plans, hypotheses, future possibilities mean nothing to him, but he is ready to face facts, even when unpleasant.[3]

On the afternoon of 15 August Brooke, Wavell, Tedder and Jacob attended the Spiridinovka Street military conference with Voroshilov and Shaposhnikov, whom the British delegates believed

154

to be the Chief of General Staff. Brooke considered Voroshilov to be 'an attractive personality, a typically political general who owed his life to his wits', and believed that 'in the early days when Voroshilov commanded a battalion, Stalin was attached to his unit as the political commissar'. Voroshilov's military knowledge, thought Brooke, was painfully limited, and only the charming Shaposhnikov had a well-trained military brain. Shaposhnikov said little, most of the talking being left to Voroshilov, who, 'with his squat figure, round head, bluff manner and uncultured speech, seemed the typical Russian peasant'. Behind the friendly, pleasant, rather disarming and mischievous smile there lurked, Birse felt, the ruthless obedient-to-existing authority spirit to be found in the USSR, a view shared by Deane, who has described how the chummy and cherubic Voroshilov could drop the hard *peretsovka* drinking guise of the previous night's bacchanalia and, with the dawn, assume to order the cold or offensive demeanour so common to Soviet officials.[4] Voroshilov could not reveal the Soviet strength in Caucasia without first obtaining Stalin's permission, and the meeting, which Birse considered to be futile, appears to have been a political exercise, for Voroshilov had been instructed merely to press for a second front. Shaposhnikov and the twenty other Soviet generals attending the conference raised no points and answered no questions.

Over the whole visit Jacob had been impressed only with Stalin, with his complete self-possession and detachment and his cold and calculating mastery of the situation.[5]

On the final night, Birse met Stalin for the first time when he accompanied Churchill to the Kremlin. Much of Birse's description confirmed what was already widely known, Stalin's uncomfortable office, the limp handshake, the shifty glance usually directed to the ground, the unfamiliar Georgian accent and the foreign sounding Russian. When the time came to depart, Stalin invited the British Prime Minister to supper at his Kremlin apartment – Birse thought 'on the spur of the moment'; according to Stalin's daughter, however, she had been brought to the capital earlier in the day 'to be shown off to Churchill that night'.[6] Inside Stalin's flat Birse noted the same sparseness of furnishing, described many years before by Bazhanov. Later, Stalin surprised and impressed his visitors by his knowledge of Wellington's campaigns. Stalin might, as Birse imagined, have made a special study of the Napoleonic Wars; on the other hand, to judge by his daughter's account of the preparation, with 'the Commissariat for Foreign Affairs explaining the etiquette for dealing with foreigners', it is possible that the dictator's knowledge was based more on the reading of notes hurriedly prepared that day to provide him with table talk.

Meanwhile the real Chief of General Staff was on the Don when, on 23 August, Paulus's panzer troops crossed the river, reaching the west bank of the Volga by nightfall. On 23 and 24 August Stalingrad, which had up till then been turning out tanks, guns and other armament, was heavily bombed from the air and left a sea of flame. It was not until the night of 24 August, when the *V Ch* telephonic link had been re-established, that Vasilevsky spoke again to Stalin, and the unpleasant conversation remained forever in his memory for he was subjected to a torrent of what he has called 'painful, insulting and mostly undeserved abuse, directed not only at the Chief of General Staff but at all Red Army military commanders'. It was all that Vasilevsky could do, he said, to convince the Supreme Commander that the city was still in Soviet hands.[7]

At midday on 23 August, Eremenko received a radio message of exhortation from Stalin, telling him that 'the enemy forces involved are not large and you have sufficient resources to annihilate them; concentrate the air forces of both fronts; mobilize the armoured trains and bring them forward on the city loop line; lay smoke to confuse the enemy and strike home by night and by day, using every gun and rocket launcher that you have. Above all do not give way to panic. Have no fear of this impudent (*nakhal'nogo*) foe and do not lose faith in victory'. When this message was received, Stalingrad was alight from end to end, the asphalt roads were aflame, the telegraph poles were crackling like matchsticks, and the burning oil and petrol spreading across the surface of the Volga had set the river craft on fire; from the tractor works, German tanks could be seen immediately to the north, fighting it out with antiaircraft gun detachments.[8]

By 24 August the city itself had already lost its strategic and economic significance, except that Hitler by degrees became determined to take possession of it. Yet Stalin's instruction that day forbidding the evacuation or demolition of industrial equipment in Stalingrad, showed that the dictator was sensitive to giving up a locality which bore his name and which had contributed to his fame, and to the effect which he imagined this would have on the morale of the Soviet people.[9] Stalin sent a further directive to Vasilevsky, Eremenko and Malenkov in which he ordered that the German penetration should be destroyed without fail.[10]

Because of the serious situation at Stalingrad Zhukov had been withdrawn from the West Front on 27 August and appointed as Deputy Supreme Commander. From the time of Zhukov's arrival at Kamyshin at midday on 29 August, it would appear, contrary to what Eremenko has said, that Gordov's front was taken out of Eremenko's and Khrushchev's hands, henceforth being controlled directly from Moscow.[11]

Stalin had told Zhukov to begin a Stalingrad Front offensive using Moskalenko's army, with two more reinforcing *Stavka* armies being committed as they arrived; in addition Stalin held out a promise of further formations, although he would not allot 'the newly formed strategic reserves intended for later tasks'. When it became clear that Moskalenko could not be ready by 2 September, Zhukov postponed the attack for twenty-four hours, at the same time reporting the reasons to the Supreme Commander. Yet the attack, when launched, failed for lack of preparation and support. That same day, on 3 September, Zhukov received a teleprint, signed by Stalin, reminiscent of a Lenin missive in the Civil War, saying that Stalingrad might be lost that day or the next, and ordering all commanders 'to attack immediately – no delay permissible – any delay would be criminal'.[12]

When Zhukov telephoned Stalin to say that an offensive could be ordered the following morning, but only if it was to be made without artillery support, Stalin asked whether he (Zhukov) thought that the enemy would wait for the Deputy Supreme Commander to bestir himself. A compromise was eventually arrived at whereby Gordov would put off his attack until 5 September but would come to Eremenko's support earlier if Stalingrad should be directly threatened. The attack on 5 September was a failure, the Red Army men being driven back to their start line by fresh enemy forces being moved up from Gumrak. Stalin, however, was pleased with these meagre results and he told Zhukov 'to keep attacking and so divert the enemy from Stalingrad'. The fighting continued, Zhukov remaining with Gordov while Vasilevsky paid flying visits to Eremenko. 'Only once and with Stalin's permission', said Zhukov, did Eremenko and Khrushchev visit the Stalingrad Front to familiarize themselves, in Zhukov's presence, with the situation there.[13]

In the latter part of August Stalin called Rokossovsky and Vatutin to Moscow to discuss an offensive against Voronezh. Both wanted to play the main role. Stalin listened to their arguments and finally sided with Vatutin. 'But since Rokossovsky was finding life a little dull he had better come to Moscow'. Rokossovsky was named commander-designate of a new front which was to attack the Stalingrad enemy from Serafimovich in the northern Don flank, and the Bryansk Front was given to Reiter, at one time a tsarist regular officer. In the event, this plan came to nothing, because the troops earmarked for the operation were drawn into the Stalingrad fighting.[14] Towards the end of September, Rokossovsky was appointed by Stalin to take over the Stalingrad Front from Gordov. On 28 September, the Stalingrad Front was re-designated as the Don Front while Eremenko's South-East Front became the new Stalingrad Front. Both were directly subordinate to the *Stavka*.

The concept of a massive counter-offensive was born, according to Zhukov, in Stalin's office on 12 September. He and Vasilevsky had given their estimate of the additional formations needed for Stalingrad, and while Stalin began to study what Zhukov called 'his own map showing the detail and location of the *Stavka* reserves', the two generals moved away from his desk and began a whispered discussion saying that they would have to seek 'some other solution'. Zhukov was surprised that Stalin had such a keen ear, for the dictator looked up and asked, 'What other solution?'. He sent both back to the general staff to prepare outline proposals for other forms of a counter-offensive.[15]

Zhukov's and Vasilevsky's preliminary planning on 13 September was influenced by the long exposed Rumanian held flanks to the north and south of the German salient which stretched eastwards to the Volga, and by the absence of German mobile reserves. The decisive blows should be made, they thought, against the Rumanians, but these could not be mounted until Stalin's strategic reserves were ready, and this in its turn depended on the production of the tanks and vehicles needed to equip the reserve formations; November appeared to be the governing date.[16] That same night Vasilevsky and Zhukov explained their ideas to Stalin, who was alone. Stalin wondered whether a deep double envelopment was not too ambitious; would it not be better, he suggested, to keep it on the land-bridge between the Don and Volga. His advisers thought not, since this would be too close to Stalingrad, allowing the German armour to turn about and quickly engage the new Soviet thrusts; the envelopment should be made well inside the Don bend before the river froze over. Stalin ordered the planning to continue, but meanwhile no one else should know what had been discussed.

Neither Zhukov nor Vasilevsky has outlined any proposals they might have made concerning the battle still being fought in the far south by Tiulenev's Transcaucasus Front, which had absorbed both Malinovsky's South Front and Budenny's North Caucasus Front. The key to the Caucasus lay of course in the area between Stalingrad and Rostov. Yet it is doubtful whether such strategic factors received much consideration within the Soviet High Command that September. Zhukov has said that Stalin 'emphasized that the main task was to hold Stalingrad and prevent an enemy advance along the west bank of the Volga to Kamyshin'.[17] But this is only a half truth. In reality Stalin was obsessed by the conviction that Hitler's strategy was based on an advance northwards up the Volga. Five years after the war had ended and before the captured German archives had been investigated, the dictator was still stating that this was so, for the 1950 *Kratkaia Biografiia* contained the following paragraph:

Comrade Stalin promptly divined the plan of the German command. He saw that the idea was to create the impression that the seizure of the oil regions of Grozny and Baku was the major and not the subsidiary objective of the German summer offensive. He pointed out that in reality the main offensive was to envelop Moscow from the east, to cut it off from the areas of the Volga and the Urals, then to strike at Moscow, and in this way end the war in 1942.[18]

This misappreciation is no longer mentioned in Soviet war histories.

In the years immediately following the Second World War, Stalin was credited with personally planning the Stalingrad counter-offensive. In 1963 Rotmistrov rejected this, but dwelt on the part played by Khrushchev and Eremenko.[19] Khrushchev had his own story.[20] Eremenko, writing in the comforting warmth of Khrushchev's patronage, has said repeatedly that it was he who suggested to Stalin a double envelopment, meeting at Kalach-on-Don.[21] Vasilevsky has supported Zhukov.[22] The unravelling of Russian contemporary history is complicated not only by Soviet pretensions of infallibility, by prejudices and politics, but also by writers with revisionist tendencies, some of whom have seen Vatutin as the architect of victory. Zhukov, in denying this, has stressed that a number of fronts were involved together with 'concrete calculations of the availability of *matériel*'. This could be done only by Stalin and the general staff.[23]

On the enemy side, Hitler was not unaware of the course open to the Soviet High Command, for even as early as 16 August he had been concerned in case the Red Army should mount a counter-offensive against Germany's weak allies in the area of Serafimovich. His own bold style of planning and the Civil War map, which was said to have been brought to his notice, led him to believe that Stalin might repeat '*den russischen "Standard-Angriff" von 1920*', with Rostov as its strategic objective.[24] But Hitler had no idea of the strength in which such an offensive could be launched, nor did he take into account an envelopment from the area to the south of Stalingrad.[25]

The main Soviet blow was to be struck from the north by a newly formed South-West Front under Vatutin, interposed between the Don and the Voronezh Fronts, Vatutin handing over his former command of the Voronezh Front to Golikov.[26] Vatutin's force, concentrated in the Serafimovich and Kletskaya bridgeheads, was to begin the offensive against Dumitrescu's Rumanians, while, one day later, the left flank of Eremenko's Stalingrad Front, about thirty miles to the south of the city, was to attack a Rumanian corps holding the Axis southern flank; Eremenko would thrust northwards to meet Vatutin's armour in the area of Kalach-on-Don. A subsidiary offensive was to be made by the flanks of Rokossovsky's Don Front, aimed at pinning Paulus and putting a barrier between him and Dumitrescu. The operation was to be named *Uranus*.

During the second week in October the front military councils began work on their own plans, these being co-ordinated by Zhukov at the South-West Front and by Vasilevsky with the Stalingrad Front. On 7 November Zhukov gave a presentation to the GKO.[27] Four days later he was back at Serafimovich, where he came to the conclusion that the offensive would have to be delayed because of logistic problems and he signalled to Stalin the reasons. Stalin agreed, but raised a new factor in reminding Zhukov that the outcome of the battle must depend on a favourable air situation; if Novikov had any doubts then the offensive should be further postponed.[28]

Stalin apparently took a close and controlling interest in air force organization and reserves. In the early summer of 1942 all tactical air forces had been removed from the command of ground armies and had been concentrated under the fronts.[29] During that year the air forces of several fronts began to be used, together with the long range air force (ADD), in single co-ordinated blows, the commander of the VVS often being on the spot as the air representative of the *Stavka*; his duties were never defined in writing but were given to him on each occasion by Stalin. At the end of each day the *Stavka* air representative sent a personal report to Stalin outlining the results of the air operations, with a copy to the chief of staff of the VVS.[30]

Nikitin, a deputy commander of the VVS, has said that Stalin's air reserves were at first quite meagre. By June 1942, however, two fighter and one bomber air armies were in existence, each having from three to five air divisions and numbering from 200 to 300 aircraft. According to Nikitin, Stalin was carefully accumulating and equipping air corps of the *Stavka* reserve during 1942, 'daily noting in his own notebook' the deliveries from aircraft production; Stalin personally made the allocation of equipment to the air forces in the field and to those in reserve, and even during the difficult Stalingrad days the process of building up the air reserve continued. On 1 October 1942 Stalin was interesting himself in 'live-firing two-sided tactical air exercises' for the reserve air corps, prior to committing them to battle, requiring that Nikitin should personally brief him on the results.[31]

On the morning of 14 November Zhukov and Vasilevsky saw
Stalin again and made their reports; the dictator was satisfied, 'for
he listened attentively and did not interrupt even once'. They
then suggested to Stalin, so Zhukov has said, that a new offensive
should be mounted by Konev's West and Purkaev's Kalinin
Fronts in the area of the Rzhev salient, in order to prevent the
movement of enemy troops to the south, it being proposed that
Zhukov should prepare the offensive to the west of Moscow while
Vasilevsky should co-ordinate the Stalingrad operation.[32]

Zhukov's account of the events which led to the successful
counter-offensive conveys an impression of mutual respect between
superior and subordinate, and of close co-operation and goodwill
between the civil, military and political organizations. Yet it is
questionable whether this description corresponded with reality.

Lugansky has told how, in September 1942, Khriukin, the
Commander of 8 Air Army, was hurriedly summoned, together
with a number of his officers, to the South-East Front headquarters
at Stalingrad; they imagined that they were about to receive
decorations. Malenkov, Zhukov, Vasilevsky and Eremenko were
there, but the talking was done by Malenkov and not by the
generals. Malenkov wanted to know the names of the commanders
of air regiments or units which, 'according to the notes which he
held in his hand', had been insufficiently effective in the air fighting
over Stalingrad. The majority of those named were present.
Malenkov, the Politburo member, according to Lugansky, 'without raising his voice gave brief orders for their court-martial or
reduction in rank'; he abused and insulted Khriukin in front of his
junior officers.[33]

Nor did the Red Army in the Caucasus fare better at the hands
of Beria, the GKO representative. He told Tiulenev that 'he would
break his back' and he threatened Malinovsky with arrest. According to Tiulenev, Beria deliberately discredited the generals of the
Red Army.[34]

On 17 November, hardly more than twenty-four hours before the
counter-offensive was due to begin, Vasilevsky was recalled to a
GKO meeting in Moscow to discuss a private letter sent to Stalin
by Vol'sky, the commander of a mechanized corps of the Stalingrad Front, stating 'that the plan was unreal and doomed to failure'.

Vasilevsky re-affirmed that the counter-offensive should not be delayed or altered. Stalin instructed Vasilevsky to get Vol'sky on the telephone and, said Vasilevsky, 'to the amazement of everybody present' Stalin had a short comradely and 'not at all brusque' conversation with him. Stalin then told Vasilevsky to take no further notice of the incident, for 'the final decision regarding Vol'sky would be made in accordance with his performance during the next few days'.[35]

The Stalingrad Front offensive on 20 November was delayed by a few hours because of heavy fog, and the general staff in Moscow plagued Eremenko with messages demanding an immediate start. Stalin himself does not appear to have intervened. Later Eremenko reported the course of the battle direct to the Supreme Commander three times during that day, for, like other Soviet generals, he was quick to notify success.[36] On 23 November, Eremenko joined with Vatutin near Kalach-on-Don, so encircling 6 Army and part of 4 Panzer Army. Twenty German and two Rumanian divisions had been enveloped in an operation which had lasted only four days.

Vasilevsky proceeded with method and circumspection. On the evening of 23 November he telephoned Stalin from the South-West Front to suggest that a westward looking cordon, strong in mobile troops, should be established to prevent the enemy forcing a new corridor into Stalingrad. This was agreed by Stalin.[37] But since some of the intelligence communicated by Vasilevsky was not to the dictator's liking, Stalin sent a signal to Rokossovsky, saying that Galanin was slack, that Zhadov should attack and pin the enemy, and that Rokossovsky should give Batov 'a bit of a push' (*podtolknite*), since he could have re-acted more energetically. This was, presumably, an arbitrary exerting of pressure on the army commanders.

Stalin had instructed Vasilevsky that same evening to explore the possibility of launching *Saturn*, a second strategic blow which had already been discussed in Moscow, this being close to what Hitler had earlier termed the 'standard Stalin offensive of 1920'. *Saturn* was to take the form of a thrust by the left flank of Golikov's Voronezh Front, and the right wing of Vatutin's South-West Front, from the area of Pavlovsk and Kalach-in-Voronezh southwards to Rostov, along much of the same route travelled by Budenny's 1 Cavalry Army a quarter of a century before.

On 25 November Vasilevsky was at the Voronezh Front with Golikov, Voronov and Novikov, and the next day he was in the forward area with Vatutin on the right flank of the South-West Front. From there Vasilevsky had a direct line conversation with the Supreme Commander, telling him that both the Voronezh and South-West Fronts would need to be heavily reinforced before they could carry out *Saturn*. Vasilevsky's estimates were, however, acceptable to Stalin. The dictator directed that Vasilevsky should henceforth apply himself 'only to the business in hand', that is to say the liquidation of the Stalingrad pocket, leaving the co-ordination of *Saturn* to Voronov. Stalin intended, he said, to transfer the left-flanking formations of the South-West to the Don Front, so that Vatutin could concentrate on *Saturn*. Vatutin would remain responsible for the defence of the outer perimeter as far south as the Chir. The area beyond that would be covered by Eremenko.[38]

Vasilevsky, who had meanwhile based himself on the Don Front, asked for his orders in writing, and these were teleprinted to him by Stalin in five short paragraphs. Vasilevsky was to control the Don and Stalingrad Fronts, his mission being to destroy the encircled enemy, to the exclusion of any other activity; he was to receive a further tank corps which he could use at his discretion, and an air corps of Pe2 bombers. Stalin followed up this conversation by dictating new orders to Vatutin, and Rokossovsky and Eremenko were informed of the change of plan.[39]

The earlier attempts to destroy Paulus's 6 Army had been unsuccessful, so Vasilevsky believed, because both he and the Soviet High Command had estimated that there were only 90,000 troops in the pocket, whereas in fact the strength stood at a quarter of a million. The first hastily mounted offensive on the shrinking pocket had been undertaken by three fronts. Rokossovsky has said that he telephoned Stalin urging that all the besieging troops be put under a single command, and it is in fact possible that this conversation prompted Stalin to order Vasilevsky's return to the Volga. But when Vasilevsky did arrive from the South-West Front on 29 November, he brought with him what Rokossovsky called 'Stalin's insistent order' that the Don Front renew the offensive at the beginning of December. Thereupon Rokossovsky drove the enemy back another twenty miles, where, in the Rossoshka valley, in a temperature of minus 32 degrees centigrade, the offensive came once more to a standstill.[40] On 4 December Vasilevsky reported this check to Stalin, who agreed, with reluctance, to divert Malinovsky's 2 Guards Army from Vatutin to Rokossovsky, 'for Stalin had set great store on the use of that newly formed and well equipped formation for *Saturn*'. Stalin demanded that the Stalingrad offensive be resumed by 18 December. On 9 December Vasilevsky signalled to Moscow his new plan known as *Kol'tso*, to destroy 6 German Army, but in the event it came to nothing due to the intervention of von Manstein's relief thrust from the south-west.[41]

Meanwhile, Zhukov, who was still with the West and Kalinin Fronts, told Stalin on 29 November, in response to a request for his views, that he considered that the enemy relief attempt would be made either from the south-west along the Kotelnikovo railway, or by the more direct approach from the west from the enemy bridgehead near the junction of the Don and the Chir. Zhukov suggested that 'a reserve of about 100 tanks' should be concentrated in each of these areas.[42] In consequence, that same day, Rotmistrov, still commanding 7 Tank Corps, was ordered to the Stalingrad area, arriving at the Nizhne-Chirskaya *stanitsa* on 7 December. According to Rotmistrov, Vasilevsky told him, 'with a look at the telephone', that the Supreme Commander 'demanded the immediate destruction of the enemy strong point', that is to say the Chir bridgehead and the Rychkovsky *khutor*, preparatory to an offensive beyond the Chir against what was believed to be an enemy relief force near Tormosin. When Rotmistrov asked for two days in which to prepare his attack, Vasilevsky, so said Rotmistrov, 'still very much under the influence of his recent conversation with Stalin', declined to agree without first telephoning Moscow. When Rotmistrov presented his final plan on 11 December, his intention to make a surprise attack without artillery preparation was greeted by Vasilevsky with amazement; the Chief of General Staff insisted on quizzing Rotmistrov's tank brigade commanders to confirm that they were in agreement with their chief, and even then, said Rotmistrov, reported the details back to Stalin.[43] Rotmistrov, however, tends to overelaborate his criticism, for this degree of centralization was common everywhere. On the other flank of the South-West Front, Krasovsky had no fighter formations to cover the concentration of ground troops for *Saturn*, so he suggested using a division of *Shturmoviki* II-2 single-engined ground attack aircraft for that purpose. He put the proposal to Voronov, and did not consider it unusual that Voronov, in his turn, should obtain the necessary permission from Stalin.[44]

Eremenko's Stalingrad Front covered both of the likely approaches to Stalingrad. Eremenko was convinced, or so he has subsequently said, that the main German offensive would come from Kotelnikovo on his left flank; Stalin and Vasilevsky believed that the main danger lay on his right flank at Tormosin.[45] When the Stalingrad Front military council pleaded with Stalin for more armour for the Kotelnikovo sector, he promised them only 'an insignificant reinforcement of sixty tanks'. For Eremenko had no power to use his front resources as he thought fit.

Between 28 November and 3 December cavalry probes into Kotelnikovo revealed the presence there of a strong panzer division, off-loading from the rail flats. Eremenko, believing that the arrival of these enemy troops presaged von Manstein's main offensive, reported this intelligence to Stalin. The Supreme Commander, however, was not convinced by Eremenko's deductions and replied that he would reinforce Kotelnikovo 'as far as the situation would allow'. Nine days later, at dawn on 12 December, von Manstein's main offensive in the area of Kotelnikovo began in earnest; when the news was reported to Stalin, the dictator became agitated, telling Eremenko that the Stalingrad Front should not give ground for it would be sent reserves immediately.[46]

On the evening of 12 December Vasilevsky was unable for many hours to get a signal connection to Moscow; while waiting he spoke, presumably by telephone, to both Rokossovsky and Malinovsky warning them that he intended to ask the *Stavka* for permission to transfer 2 Guards Army from the Don to the Stalingrad Front.[47]

Later that night Vasilevsky explained the situation to Stalin. The suggestion, that 2 Guards Army should be moved south and that the destruction of the encircled 6 German Army should be delayed, met with an angry refusal from the dictator, 'coupled with some plain and unpleasant speaking'. He who had so often presented crude ultimata to Lenin accused Vasilevsky of trying to blackmail the *Stavka* into handing over reserves to the sectors for which he was responsible.[48] Vasilevsky was indeed unfortunate in that 2 Guards Army had already been re-routed twice, following in the wake of the Chief of General Staff, but he said that he felt Stalin's anger to be unjustified since he, Vasilevsky, had been charged with the destruction of the encircled pocket, and the removal of Malinovsky from the Don Front was against his (Vasilevsky's) interests since he had 'no responsibility for the out-ward defence against a relieving enemy force'. Stalin's directive of 27 November certainly said so; yet if Vasilevsky was not responsible for the outer perimeter, it is not clear why he had, only the day previously, presided over Rotmistrov's preparations for the west-ward attack towards Tormosin.[49]

Stalin declined to give Vasilevsky a decision, saying that he would first discuss the matter with the GKO. Vasilevsky waited the whole of that night in a state of anxiety and tension, and not until 0500 hours did he hear that Malinovsky would be released to the Stalingrad Front, 'the sole responsibility for the defeat of von Manstein being placed on the shoulders of the Chief of General Staff'. Voronov was to be responsible for Stalingrad.

Rokossovsky, in an account which is probably based on recollec-tion, has said that a *V Ch* telephone conversation took place at this time between Stalin and Vasilevsky. Vasilevsky handed him the instrument, saying that Stalin wanted to hear what Rokossovsky thought about the transfer of 2 Guards Army. The Commander of the Don Front was emphatically against it, preferring, he said, to finish off Paulus quickly and then turn on von Manstein. Stalin then took up his conversation again with Vasilevsky, at the end of which Stalin told Rokossovsky that 'his plan was a bold one and certainly merited attention, but in the circumstances was too risky'. Stalin agreed that the Stalingrad operation should be postponed.[50] But the *Stavka* directive, issued at 2230 hours on the night of 14 December, ordered Eremenko and Rokossovsky 'to continue the systematic destruction of the encircled enemy, allowing him no respite, by night or by day'.

On the night of 13 December the *Stavka* took the decision to alter Vatutin's axis from due south to Rostov, to another running south-eastwards on Tatsinskaya and Morozovsk, in the immediate rear of von Manstein's Army Group Don. The altered plan was known as *Malyi Saturn*. The reasons for the change were set out in a clear and concise five paragraph directive sent to Voronov, Vatutin and Golikov over Stalin's 'Vasil'ev' signature. Von

Manstein, Stalin said, posed a serious threat, and Tatsinskaya and Morozovsk were *Luftwaffe* air supply bases; secondly, the removal of 2 Guards Army from the South-West Front had weakened Vatutin's striking power; and, finally, Vatutin's outer cordon armies could not be counted on to assist the main thrust.[51]

On 18 December Vasilevsky sent to the *Stavka* a draft proposal for the counter-attack to be made on 22 December against von Manstein's relief thrust, Vasilevsky subsequently publishing his draft in full, in order to disprove Eremenko's claim that the plan was his own.[52] The draft proposal timed at 1520 hours on 18 December was approved by Stalin in a signal timed at 0050 hours on 19 December.

Von Manstein reached a point about twenty-five miles from Paulus's perimeter where he was brought to a halt by that part of Malinovsky's 2 Guards Army which had arrived in the forward area. Paulus, contrary to the Soviet expectation, made no attempt to break out to the south-west. The Stalingrad Front counter-offensive towards the south, beginning on 24 December, was immediately successful, but in any case the outcome of the Stalingrad Front's battle had already been decided by the success of *Malyi Saturn* being fought nearly 200 miles away to the north-west.[53]

The military and geographical conditions which made *Malyi Saturn* possible were the same as those which contributed to the success of *Uranus* – a long over-extended enemy salient, with the exposed northern flank held by German allies inferior in fighting quality to the Red Army. Vatutin repeated his south-eastward thrust deep in the Axis rear, and in five days his armour had advanced nearly 150 miles, scattering and largely destroying 8 Italian Army. Von Manstein was forced firstly to move his armour westwards, to meet the new threat, and then finally to give up the Stalingrad relief attempt. This led to the loss both of the encircled 6 German Army and of Caucasia.

Since Voronov had departed for the Stalingrad area on 20 December, the control of Vatutin's South-West Front was under-taken directly by Stalin and Zhukov.[54] Meanwhile, on 1 January, Vasilevsky had been instructed to quit the Stalingrad Front and join the Voronezh Front to organize and co-ordinate the last of the succession of offensives, this to be made by Golikov and Reiter against 2 Hungarian Army to the west of the defeated 8 Italian Army. The Hungarian force was speedily destroyed and 2 German Army, north-west of Voronezh, had to withdraw rapidly westwards to escape encirclement. Much of its heavier equipment was abandoned. Von Weichs's Army Group B had ceased to exist as a fighting force and Army Groups A and Don were already with-drawing rapidly westwards so that they should not be pinned against the Sea of Azov. The German Army in Russia had lost the strategic initiative.

Towards the end of December 1942, during a GKO meeting, Stalin proposed, probably at Voronov's or Rokossovsky's prompt-ing, to make the Don Front alone responsible for the destruction of 6 German Army. The committee agreed. Zhukov, when asked for his opinion, said that Eremenko would be offended; Stalin im-mediately silenced him. That night, when Zhukov informed Eremenko of the GKO decision, Eremenko 'gave way to his emotions'. Zhukov was sufficiently hardy to raise the matter once more with Stalin, and for this the dictator abused (*vyrugal*) him. Only the susceptibilities of the two generals might occasion some surprise.[55]

The *Stavka* directive was issued on 30 December, and, on 1 January 1943, Eremenko's Stalingrad Front became the new South Front responsible only for operations against von Manstein's withdrawing troops. Eremenko's three armies on the southern perimeter of Stalingrad were transferred to Rokossovsky's command.

At the beginning of January Zhukov was sent to Leningrad with Voroshilov as the *Stavka* representatives responsible for co-ordinating the offensive of Govorov's and Meretskov's fronts. Meretskov described an incident when Mekhlis, the political member of the Volkhov Front, addressed 'some curt and insulting remarks to Voroshilov'. Normally, if Mekhlis and Meretskov only had been present, Voroshilov would, thought Meretskov, have put Mekhlis in his place and no more would have been heard of the matter. 'But we were not alone', said Meretskov, 'and that meant that Stalin would hear of this unpleasant incident'. From whom, Meretskov does not say, but Zhukov was undoubtedly there. On Meretskov's advice Mekhlis sent an immediate written report to

Stalin before the dictator should hear of the incident from other sources.[56] Meretskov, like Rokossovsky and Kuznetsov, preferred to deal directly with Stalin.[57]

The *Stavka* directive of 30 December instructed that the offensive against Paulus should be mounted by 6 January and be completed in the course of five or six days. The chief of the front intelligence department still put the encircled enemy at 86,000 men, and it was only when a German transport plane was brought down carrying soldiers' mail destined for the Reich that it became apparent that he had much underestimated the German strength. On 3 January Rokossovsky called on Voronov to tell him that he must have a further six or seven days to prepare for the offensive. Voronov, who was certain that the *Stavka* would not allow so long a delay, sent an immediate report to Moscow, using the same tactic he later criticized in Eremenko, in that he compromised by making an arbitrary cut in the postponement suggested by Rokossovsky. Stalin telephoned 'some harsh reproaches' about both Voronov and Rokossovsky, but finally agreed the new date of 10 January.[58]

The first phase of the Don Front offensive began on 10 January, followed by the second twelve days later. All enemy resistance ceased by 2 February. With the surrender of Paulus the Red Army claimed to have counted 147,000 enemy dead and 94,000 prisoners. According to German documentary sources the loss at Stalingrad, not including the two Rumanian divisions, was 209,000 men. German losses outside the encirclement probably amounted to a further 100,000 men and two Rumanian armies, an Italian and a Hungarian army had been virtually destroyed.

Voronov and Rokossovsky were brought to Moscow on 4 February. At the Kremlin Stalin was 'obviously very pleased', coming forward to meet them, shaking them warmly by the hand and congratulating them. 'For', said Rokossovsky, 'when he felt it to be necessary, Stalin could literally charm a person by his warmth and attention'.[59]

On 28 July 1942 Budenny's North Caucasus Front had absorbed the remnants of Malinovsky's South Front after its retreat from the Ukraine. Malinovsky lost his command. Tiulenev, whose Transcaucasus Front had hitherto been responsible for the defence of the Turkish and Iranian frontiers, assumed the overall command of the theatre and Budenny returned to Moscow. From September onwards the Transcaucasus Front was reinforced by levies from the local peoples, and by formations sent from the Russian interior over the railway track hastily constructed along the west shore of the Caspian. Once more a proliferation of GKO commissions and representatives of the GKO and *Stavka* appeared in the area, some coming from the Politburo or NKVD and others from the general staff, their activities and rivalries, according to Shtemenko, causing duplication and confusion.[60]

Officers of the general staff sent back their findings to Moscow, and Tiulenev began to receive a volume of directives and critical reports, issued over Stalin's signature or in his name, with the shortcomings set out in detail, illustrating the lack of supervision by front and army commanders.[61] Control, including close tactical control, was not lacking from Moscow, however. A *Stavka* directive of 2 October 1942 outlined the general mission of the Black Sea Group as 'the defence of Tuapse and the Black Sea ports', and then detailed the tasks of each of its formations.[62] Yet this tight control from the centre did not appear to have lessened Tiulenev's responsibility in the event of failure.[63]

At the end of that month Stalin became interested in a proposal originating from Tiulenev, at one time a cavalry brigade commander under Budenny, that a new cavalry army should be formed in the North Caucasus, where horsemen were particularly plentiful. Stalin had asked the opinion of Kirichenko, a cavalry corps commander, but, in the end, he agreed with the general staff that cavalry was too vulnerable for modern war except in support of other mobile troops.[64]

On 29 December Zhukov, speaking on behalf of the Supreme Commander, instructed Tiulenev that Petrov's Black Sea Group should strike north to Rostov and the rail junction of Tikhoryetsk, joining up with Eremenko's Stalingrad Front. A successful double envelopment of this kind would have closed the two exits from Caucasia and trapped von Kleist's Army Group A. Tiulenev could see no means by which he could carry out his orders, for the lowlands were flooded and deep snow lay on the mountains, the few roads and tracks were unusable and he lacked engineer resources. On the other hand some road and track preparation had already been carried out in the Maikop direction. But when

Tiulenev spoke to Stalin on the telephone urging that a thrust on Maikop further to the east would be more practical than the Krasnodar axis, Stalin would hear none of it.[65] Tiulenev's and Petrov's plans, sent to Moscow on 31 December, were rejected that same day since the forces were, in the opinion of the *Stavka*, too widely dispersed. With the rejection Moscow sent back its own proposals for the offensive which was to start not later than 12 January.[66]

On the afternoon of 4 January Stalin telephoned the general staff and dictated to Shtemenko the outline of a directive formulating his strategy. The centre of gravity of the whole of the Transcaucasus Front rested with the Black Sea Group 'and neither Maslennikov nor Petrov as yet understood that fact'. It was not to the Soviet advantage to push the enemy out of the Caucasus and for this reason Maslennikov would henceforth have only a secondary role; so he could give up a rifle corps to Petrov immediately. Petrov was to start his offensive on time without awaiting the arrival of his reserves, and 'because he has had little experience of offensive action he must get himself into an offensive frame of mind'. In conclusion, said Stalin, Tiulenev should be in attendance all the time with the Black Sea Group.[67] On 7 January the general staff prepared a memorandum for the Supreme Commander complaining about Maslennikov and this resulted in an angry signal being sent by Stalin to Maslennikov and Tiulenev on 8 January, reminding them that he held them both personally responsible; henceforth he wanted, he said, reports twice a day.[68]

Stalin had told Petrov to submit two separate plans, one for the Novorossisk area which the dictator called *More* and another, *Gory*, covering the thrust over the Caucasus range. For Stalin alone selected nicknames and code names.[69] On 8 January these plans were received by the general staff; no exception was taken to *More*, but it was noted that the *Gory* plan took the Black Sea Group only as far as Tikhoryetsk, no provision being made for exploitation northwards to Bataisk-Rostov. Although Shtemenko conconsidered that Petrov would indeed be fortunate to get as far as Tikhoryetsk, he could, he said, foresee trouble with Stalin, for 'the Supreme Commander never forgot what he had ordered or suffered others to do so'. So it transpired, for, on 8 January, Stalin dictated another signal requiring the Transcaucasus Front to repair this omission.[70]

Stalin had hoped to entrap another 20 divisions, but Army Group A had already begun to withdraw and Eremenko and Petrov could make little headway. On 24 January Maslennikov's North Group became the new North Caucasus Front, independent of Tiulenev, and on 16 March Petrov's Black Sea Group was amalgamated with Maslennikov's command. Tiulenev's Transcaucasus Front then returned to its earlier responsibilities of guarding the southern frontiers.

The German 17 Army continued to hold a bridgehead in the Taman peninsula, covering the Crimea and the Sea of Azov and forming, as Hitler intended that it should, a springboard for a renewed campaign into the Caucasus in the following summer. Stalin wanted the bridgehead eliminated and in March Beria was sent to the area once more. Zhukov followed on 17 April, taking Novikov, N. G. Kuznetsov and Shtemenko with him. Zhukov's activity took its usual whirlwind pattern.[71] But throughout the next three weeks' fighting he was unable to drive in the bridgehead and the party were obliged to return to Moscow on 13 May, Shtemenko says 'in low spirits for they knew Stalin would be displeased and they prepared themselves for his rebukes'.[72] Maslennikov, however, was the only casualty, for he was replaced as front commander by Petrov.

Kuznetsov's descriptions, published in 1966 and 1968, have said that Stalin was completely immersed in the affairs of the fronts, that he knew their needs and talked regularly to the military leaders, with whom he had developed close ties. Several times Kuznetsov observed how front commanders were unable to agree with Stalin's opinion, 'and Stalin would then re-examine the question', Kuznetsov believing that the dictator even admired people who were not afraid to stand up for their own point of view.[73] Kuznetsov confirmed that the dictator's immediate reaction to failure was to remove or punish the commander.[74]

Samsonov, describing in 1968 Stalin's role during the Stalingrad battle, has said that Stalin had the particular ability to evaluate the recommendations of the military men about him, since his great experience of state and political matters enabled him quickly to

master the specialist knowledge necessary for the day to day conduct
of operations. Stalin 'had other competent advisers [*sic*] in addition
to Vasilevsky and Zhukov' and during the course of the Stalingrad
battle the level of generalship within the *Stavka* continued to
improve. The concentration of power in Stalin's hands and 'his
undisputed authority' endowed all his orders and demands with a
special arbitrariness (*kategorichnost'*), which, on the whole,
thought Samsonov, played a decisive role. However, the dictator's
confidence in the infallibility of his own judgements and opinions
and his intolerance of any objections, gave rise to occasions when
his interpretation of the situation was incorrect. 'While punishing
severely [this could mean shooting] those who were answerable
for failure at the front, Stalin did not always judge the causes of
lack of success with objectivity'. These facts, said Samsonov, 'are
known, but one should not evaluate the *Stavka* on the basis of the
characteristics of one personality or underestimate the contribution
of the military figures forming the *Stavka* or its executive'.
Although Stalin and the *Stavka* were far from the theatre of operations, continued Samsonov, they directed the day by day struggle
in the greatest of detail, and this applied to the direction of the
political and government bodies remaining in Stalingrad. Admittedly, the *Stavka* decisions of an operative-tactical nature were,
in some cases, a hindrance, restricting or stultifying initiative and
action on the spot. 'However, in analysing the events of the battle,
if one examines not any one part in isolation but the whole, then
the firm and positive aspect of the function of the High Command
during the Stalingrad battle is apparent for all to see.'[75]

Vasilevsky considered that political acumen and political
strategy endowed Stalin with a fine sense of military strategy;
moreover, Stalin soon became expert in the operative field,
especially after Kursk in 1943. Stalin's strategic and operative
ability was far superior to his knowledge of tactics, but, concluded
Vasilevsky, a detailed understanding of tactics was not necessary
anyway.[76] The dictator's attitude to the general staff gradually
changed during 1942, particularly after September when it showed
its worth in the planning of the Stalingrad counter-offensive, and
he began to take into account views, recommendations and plans,
not only of the general staff, but also of the commanders of fronts
and the deputy heads of the NKO. From this period onwards the

general staff was sufficiently hardy to present its prognoses of future war developments, and Stalin was content at least to read them, although, as Shtemenko said, mindful of his own November 1941 forecasts when the dictator had declared that Germany was already worn out by its endeavours – he had given the Reich six months or 'a little year' (*godik*) at the most – the dictator now regarded any forecasts with some scepticism.[77] Stalin the bureaucrat, with his love of order and method, began to insist that responsible or interested commanders or staffs be consulted before he would commit himself to a new proposal, and he would ask, 'What is the view of the general staff?' or, 'Has this matter been cleared with Voronov?'. Shtemenko linked this new trend with Stalin's wish to uphold the authority and prestige of his immediate subordinates, for he was very conscious of the dignity of office. Voronov, on the other hand, stressed Stalin's demand for the highest degree of centralization; for not only did he require that he himself should know everything, but he expected his subordinates to be fully informed of what went on in their commands or departments. Yet there were many occasions, described by Shtemenko, when Stalin the autocrat asked the general staff if it had any comment, but it did not reply because it knew that he had decided the question 'and was only asking us for form's sake'.

Politburo, GKO or *Stavka* meetings, which were never held in Stalin's absence, usually took place either in the Kremlin office or at Kuntsevo. It was sometimes not clear whether a Politburo or GKO meeting was in session except in the recording of the protocol or issue of decrees, and the *Stavka* was frequently attended by Politburo and GKO members. Vasilevsky has related, with amusement, how some of his colleagues have since asked him for a photograph of the *Stavka* in session. Stalin was the *Stavka* and he frequently gave orders, personally or by signal, no other members of the Politburo, GKO or High Command being present, usually as a result of telephone consultations with the fronts or the general staff.

Stalin's confidence in the military had been partially restored and, on 9 October 1942, one man command was revived, the military commissars losing their right of veto and reverting to the status of deputies for political matters (*zampolit*). In December 1942, 140 political workers, mainly political members of front and army military councils and senior commissars, for the first time in the history of the Red Army, received general rank. At Stalin's order, Khrulev produced for his inspection tsarist officer shoulder boards (*pogony*), and the tsarist patterns were introduced, with only minor variations, into the Red Army.[78] So it came about that, according to the painting reproduced in the *Ukrains'ka Radians'ka Entsiklopediia,* Khrushchev was pleased to wear the uniform of a lieutenant-general, with the gold braided *pogony* and the traditional grey tsarist greatcoat edged with crimson.

Stalin expected Vasilevsky, Zhukov and his other *Stavka* representatives to make routine reports to him by *V Ch* telephone or Baudôt twice a day, at noon and again at 2200 hours; unusual or important events had to be notified straightaway. The routine reports were given in the form of a diary time-table showing how they had filled in their day and what they had seen or heard. The dictator had to be kept informed of their whereabouts and they were not allowed, without Stalin's prior permission, to leave the fronts to which they had been allocated.[79]

Vasilevsky's burden was particularly onerous since, at Stalin's order, he was constantly at the fronts; yet he was still responsible for the general staff in Moscow. Vasilevsky tried to overcome the problem by selecting an officer of experience and outstanding ability to remain in the capital as his deputy. In May 1942 when he had asked Stalin that Vatutin, then chief of staff of the North-West Front, be transferred back to the general staff, Stalin, 'in all seriousness', said Vasilevsky, had asked, 'Why? Isn't he any good at the front?'. A few months later, after Vatutin had succeeded in having himself posted away from the general staff to command the Voronezh Front, Vasilevsky had to find a replacement to be his first deputy, and his choice fell on Antonov, the chief of staff of the North Caucasus Front. Stalin agreed, but apparently without enthusiasm. Antonov, the son of a tsarist artillery officer, had started his military service as a *praporshchik* and junior officer in a tsarist *eger* regiment of chasseurs, which regiment is not clear, for the only *eger* unit remaining in the 1914 Army List was the Egersky Regiment of Foot Guards. Stalin, however, did not want Antonov, and he ordered that Bokov, the political deputy to the general staff, should continue to make the daily reports to him when Vasilevsky was away. Antonov notified Vasilevsky of this arrangement and asked to be relieved of the post, whereupon Vasilevsky telephoned Stalin from the Voronezh Front and again warmly recommended Antonov. Stalin listened without comment and then told the Chief of General Staff that he, Vasilevsky, could have Antonov as the deputy *Stavka* representative with the Voronezh Front. For, said Vasilevsky, 'Stalin was a careful and mistrustful person, particularly of new faces'. Antonov stayed with the Voronezh Front for three months, where he was to earn much distinction, before resuming his duties as deputy chief of general staff and chief of the operations department.[80]

9
From Kursk to Kiev

The Voronezh Front offensive had caused the precipitate with-drawal of 2 German Army, so encouraging the *Stavka* to instruct Golikov to draw up hurried proposals for the occupation of Kharkov, nearly 200 miles away. Golikov's plan was confirmed by Stalin on the night of 23 January when he dictated to Bokov a directive for the new operation to be known as *Zvezda*.[1] Zhukov had been with the Voronezh Front, and when he returned to Moscow he was, according to Shtemenko, so optimistic that the general staff took the view that the Voronezh Front was strong enough to move west and south-west on divergent axes, taking Kursk as well as Kharkov. This variation to the original *Zvezda* directive was issued on 26 January. Contrary to established practice the offensive was not to be made in operative depth, that is to say with armies in echelon, but in line.

Meanwhile Vatutin had submitted to Moscow a plan, known as *Skachok,* for a southerly thrust aimed at cutting von Manstein's communications in the Ukraine. On 19 January Stalin agreed Vatutin's proposal in principle and ordered him to reach the Sea of Azov within seven days of starting the offensive; the launching was to be delayed, however, until after the taking of Kharkov. Meanwhile Stalin began to extend the scope of *Skachok* to include the cutting of the Crimean escape route from the Caucasus, and, on 8 February, he ordered Vatutin to widen his assault frontage to take in Dnepropetrovsk and Zaporozhe.[2] Golikov and Vatutin were sure that the enemy was in full retreat, and this confidence spread to the general staff.[3]

Stalin had formulated even more ambitious plans, for he had come to believe that, by turning Golikov's troops south-westwards towards Poltava, he could encompass a secondary envelopment of von Manstein, to the west of that to be mounted by Vatutin. In addition he intended to interpose another front between the Bryansk and the Voronezh Fronts, which, striking north-west-wards, would outflank von Kluge's Army Group Centre from the south. Rokossovsky was given this assignment on 4 February, Stalin telling him that part of his front was to move from Stalingrad to Elets, there to be joined by two more armies from the *Stavka* reserve; then, as the newly designated Central Front, it was to launch an offensive in the direction of Gomel and Smolensk, this being co-ordinated with other offensives to be made by Konev's West and Reiter's Bryansk Fronts; the operation was due to start on 15 February. Rokossovsky considered this early date to be unrealistic, but his views failed to influence Stalin and he was given his written directive on 5 February.[4]

According to Shtemenko, Stalin personally took charge of the preparations for this operation and gave Reiter a severe dressing down for suggesting that the Bryansk Front attack might be delayed by only one day.[5] When Rokossovsky complained that the railway capacity was inadequate to ferry forward the troops of the new Central Front, Stalin's remedy was to hand over the railway personnel to the NKVD, who so terrorized the officials that the result, according to Rokossovsky, was near chaos. Eventually Rokossovsky's request for a nine days' postponement was granted, but, by 25 February, when Rokossovsky was obliged to begin the offensive, only half of his troops had arrived in the battle area.[6]

On 17 February, when Hitler was actually visiting Zaporozhe, Kursk and Kharkov had already fallen to Golikov's Voronezh Front, and Vatutin's South-West Front was nearing Dnepropetrovsk. Hitler had intended to dismiss the Commander of Army Group Don, redesignated that February as Army Group South, and he was mollified only when von Manstein produced a plan for a counter-offensive to envelop Vatutin's and Golikov's rapidly advancing troops and to retake Kharkov.

On 17 February Stalin telephoned Vatutin to implement *Skachok* and told him to take Zaporozhe. The Red Army troops had, however, outrun their supplies and tactical air support, and the reversal of the air situation in the German favour was to prove the key to the subsequent battle. Von Manstein's counter-offensive, beginning on 19 February, destroyed the advanced elements of Vatutin's South-West Front and then began to move rapidly north-eastwards through a great gap in Golikov's Voronezh Front, reaching Kharkov by 12 March. Six days later the Germans were in Belgorod and appeared to be threatening the southern flank of Rokossovsky's newly arrived Central Front. Meanwhile Rokossovsky's own offensive had petered out, in spite of Stalin's agreement that its axis should be changed to the nearer and less ambitious objective of Orel; Reiter had advanced only a few miles. Stalin was subsequently blamed for the reverse.[7]

Stalin's reaction was characteristic; he considered that the Voronezh Front needed strengthening from a political as well as a military point of view and Khrushchev and Vasilevsky were ordered to report there; but not until he had heard Vasilevsky's report from near Belgorod did the dictator realize the danger to the Central and the Voronezh Fronts. After Vasilevsky spoke again to Stalin on 10 March the Supreme Commander decided to allot Golikov two more armies and a tank army.[8]

On or about 13 March Stalin telephoned Zhukov, who was with Timoshenko at the headquarters of the North-West Front. At Zhukov's recommendation Stalin agreed that Konev should take over the North-West Front after handing over the West Front to Sokolovsky, so that Timoshenko could be attached to the South and the South-West Fronts as the *Stavka* representative. Zhukov himself was to return to Moscow and then go on to the Voronezh Front. Zhukov used the formations allocated by Stalin, the two armies detached from Rokossovsky and the tank army from the *Stavka* reserve, as the nucleus of a force for counter-attacks in the area of Belgorod to restore Golikov's broken front.[9] By the end of March the situation was stabilized and the great Kursk bulge came into being, its northern face being held by the Central and its southern by the Voronezh Fronts. To the north and south of the Kursk bulge the cities of Orel and Kharkov remained in German hands. Golikov was removed from the command of the Voronezh Front which was taken over by Vatutin, the vacancy at the South-West Front being filled by Malinovsky who gave up the South Front to Tolbukhin. The Central Front did not escape investigation, for a commission headed by Malenkov and including Antonov, Khrulev and Ponomarenko, of the Belorussian Central Committee, was sent to Rokossovsky to look into the causes of his failure.[10]

Hitler was of the opinion that the best means of defence in Russia would be a limited offensive, to be made immediately after the thaw had dried out and before the Americans and British could mount their second front in Western Europe, and in this belief he had been encouraged by the success of von Manstein's recent Kharkov battle. He wanted to attack the Soviet enemy before the Germans were themselves attacked, in order to reduce, if only temporarily, the offensive capability of the Red Army. Hitler chose the Kursk bulge as the area for his new *Zitadelle* operation, for what was to have been a repetition of the destruction of the Izyum salient, the great Kharkov victory of May 1942; he did not intend, however, to continue the offensive into the Russian interior. The planning for *Zitadelle* began in early March in preparation for an attack in mid April, but the date was repeatedly postponed because of delays in the assembly of the troops.

Zhukov took the view that the enemy preparations were a preliminary to a thrust between Elets and Voronezh, striking northeast towards Ryazan and enveloping Moscow from the rear; such a suggestion was in harmony with Stalin's obsession that all German strategy had as its aim the taking of the Soviet capital. In his written report of 8 April to Stalin, the Deputy Supreme Commander said that he was against a pre-emptive Soviet attack; although he was 'unfamiliar with the disposition of the Red Army operational reserves', he believed that they should be used in depth to cover the southern and south-eastern approaches of the capital.[11] When Stalin read this report Vasilevsky was present. The dictator already knew that the general staff supported Zhukov's paper, but he said that he must first have the front commanders' opinions; he himself spoke on the telephone to Rokossovsky and Vatutin. Meanwhile Vasilevsky was to go to Zhukov to discuss the situation on the ground.[12]

The appreciation from the Central Front dated 10 April was in the form of a personal signal to Antonov from Malinin, the front chief of staff. Malinin thought the enemy aim to be the reoccupation of the Ukraine and he urged that a pre-emptive attack should be

made against the enemy's Orel grouping.[13] The appreciation of the
Voronezh Front, sent on 12 April under the signatures of Vatutin,
Khrushchev and Korzhenevich, considered that the enemy might
have abandoned his aim to occupy the south-east in favour of the
envelopment of Moscow; nothing was said about a pre-emptive
attack.[14] On the evening of 12 April, Zhukov, Vasilevsky and
Antonov attended a Kremlin meeting to consider these reports.
Stalin was agitated and worried in case mass German attacks
should result in a repetition of Izyum.[15] He showed anxiety about
Moscow. But since the enemy offensive was not believed to be
imminent, Zhukov, together with Shtemenko, was sent on 18
April to the North Caucasus Front, while Vasilevsky and Antonov
began to marshal the necessary reserves for the Kursk battle.

The newly concentrated reserves to the south of Moscow were
under a Reserve Front commanded by Reiter, who had given up
his Bryansk Front to Popov. But Stalin appears to have been
unwilling to entrust what was to become a key formation to this
Latvian former colonel of the tsarist army, and he was replaced by
Konev, Stalin personally impressing on Konev the importance of
his role in the coming Kursk battle.[16] But whereas the general
staff had proposed that the Reserve Front should be given no
defensive tasks, in order that it might be committed fresh and intact
to the counter-offensive, Stalin ruled, on 23 April, that Konev's
force should be used for secondary defence in strategic depth,
covering a great belt of rearward defences behind the Bryansk,
Central, Voronezh and South-West Fronts.[17] From 10 April the
Reserve Front was redesignated as the Steppe Military District.

Stalin was usually unwilling to hear out lengthy opinion as to
the enemy's intentions. On this occasion, however, the situation, as
Shtemenko said, forced him to give weighty consideration to the
courses open to the enemy. Zhukov affirms that Stalin's natural
inclination was to go over to the offensive before the German blow
should fall, but he lacked confidence in the ability of his own troops,
for hitherto the successful Red Army offensives had been in mid
winter.[18] Zhukov, Vasilevsky and the general staff were opposed
to mounting an offensive until after the enemy had dissipated his
strength against the formidable Kursk defences. In the Central
and Voronezh Fronts opinions were divided, but, on 21 April,
Vatutin reported to Moscow that a pre-emptive Red Army offen-

sive might be necessary if the enemy continued to delay his attack, this view, as Zhukov and Shtemenko have since stressed, being supported by Khrushchev. Rokossovsky had written a paper for forwarding to Stalin, favouring the defence.[19]

In May and June Vatutin began to press, firstly Vasilevsky and then Stalin, that the Red Army should begin the offensive, urging the dictator not to lose the benefit of the summer weather. Stalin told Vatutin to forward his proposals in writing. Vatutin's frequent urging began to have its effect, so that, Vasilevsky said, it took all his efforts and those of Zhukov and Antonov, to dissuade the dictator. From his daily conversations Vasilevsky noted, with concern, how nervous Stalin was becoming. On 22 June Stalin ordered that Vasilevsky should bring Malinovsky to the Kremlin as he wanted to hear the latter's views, and Vasilevsky afterwards learned, to his surprise, that Stalin had kept Zhukov in ignorance of his fact and opinion finding activities.[20]

Stalin would not commit himself as to which he believed to be the correct course and it became obvious to the general staff that he was unable to come to a decision. On 10 and 20 May, and again on 2 June, the German offensive appeared to be imminent and the fronts stood to, only to be stood down again some days later. Vacillation and the prolonged waiting affected Stalin's temper, and this, according to Shtemenko, was the underlying cause of the fearful Kremlin scene when the dictator was informed, in a personal letter written by fighter pilots, of the defective fabric paint on the wings of the Iak 9 interceptors, which was causing them to break up in flight.[21] Vasilevsky, Voronov and Iakovlev were sent for, and Iakovlev, who had had long and close dealings with the dictator, said he had never seen him in such a rage. He abused his silent staff, calling them 'Hitlerites'; Iakovlev, according to his own account, began to shiver with fear. They escaped further wrath only by promising that all planes would be repaired within two weeks, a promise impossible of fulfilment. Meanwhile Stalin ordered that the military prosecutor's office should begin its immediate investigations to seek out traitors.[22] So the long wait continued until the first week in July.

The Soviet counter-offensive, timed to begin after the enemy offensive had been contained, was to consist of two main thrusts, one in the south against von Manstein and the other westwards against von Kluge. The offensive to the south by the Voronezh, the South-West, and later the Steppe Fronts, had as its primary aim the destruction of von Manstein's grouping at Belgorod-Kharkov, this operation being known as *Rumiantsev*. Opinions were divided as to the strategy to be subsequently adopted. Vatutin and Khrushchev are said to have urged that the Voronezh, South-West and South Fronts, together with the left wing of the Central Front, should be deflected south-westwards and occupy the southern Ukraine as far as the 32nd meridian, securing not only the rich industrial and agricultural areas of the south but also a springboard for mounting a campaign into Rumania and Hungary. Stalin decided against this plan, since it bypassed Kiev to the south and left von Kluge's Army Group Centre intact and still within 200 miles of Moscow; he himself favoured a thrust from Poltava west-north-west on Kiev; and, added Shtemenko, it was believed that an extension of this Soviet axis from Kiev towards the Carpathians would drive a deep wedge between Army Groups Centre and South, threatening both with envelopment.[23] This is what happened and it proved to be the corner-stone of the 1943 and 1944 Soviet victories in Central and South-East Europe.

The Soviet counter-offensive to the north of the Kursk bulge, known as *Kutuzov*, was to be made by the West and the Bryansk Fronts against the flank and rear of the Army Group Centre's Orel grouping, as soon as this had become bogged down in its attack against Kursk. These two fronts, together with the Central Front, would then move westwards into Belorussia forming the north flank of the Kiev thrust.

The detail for *Kutuzov* had been worked out by Sokolovsky and Popov and forwarded to the general staff for approval. Stalin presided at the co-ordinating Moscow conference which was attended by the front and army commanders. Antonov's presentation was so exhaustive and clear, said Bagramian, that little remained to be said. Stalin asked a few questions and expressed himself in agreement with the general substance of the plan. Bagramian, then the Commander of 11 Guards Army, had some reservations as to his own role on the left wing, but judged that it was not the moment for him to express an opinion. So he kept silent. Those present began rolling up their maps, when suddenly Stalin asked whether anyone had any different views. Bagramian said that he had. Stalin looked up at him 'quite surprised', but told him to continue. Everyone unrolled their maps again. Determined not to panic, Bagramian outlined how he thought his army should be used. At the conclusion he waited to be crushed by what he called the great trinity, Stalin, the general staff and the front commanders. This did not happen, however; at first nothing was said while the maps were being studied; then Bagramian's proposals were accepted without serious amendment.[24]

However nervous and unreasonable Stalin might have been at this time, the military were not subordinated to purely factional party interests. He refused a party request that the civilian population should be evacuated from the Kursk bulge, not only because this might be construed as an indication of an intention to withdraw, but also because the construction of the military defences depended on civilian labour. Again, when Rokossovsky asked Stalin that Zaporozhets, a tried and trusted old Bolshevik of the Civil War, should be removed from his appointment as the political member of 60 Army since the youthful Cherniakhovsky found it impossible to work with him, the dictator immediately ordered Zaporozhets's recall.[25]

In mid-April Peresypkin had been sent by Stalin to the Reserve, Voronezh and Central Fronts to organize the signal communications. The existing radial state line network was developed into a grid system (USON), based on connecting up a chequer board of signal centres with duplicated and triplicated telephone and telegraph links, so that severed connections could be bypassed by alternative routes.[26] Although each army headquarters operated thirteen separate radio networks, wireless was sparingly used, even in the forward areas, except by the air and tank forces.

On 30 June Vasilevsky was attached to the Voronezh Front while Zhukov was ordered to remain with Rokossovsky; in the first week in July Konev's district was converted to a front and ordered forward, Stalin recommending that Konev should report personally to Vatutin in order to familiarize himself with conditions in the area.[27] On 1 July 1943 the Central and Voronezh Fronts are said to have included over 1,300,000 men and nearly 3,500 tanks, in all sixty-seven rifle divisions; the West, Bryansk and Steppe Fronts on 10 July numbered a further sixty-five divisions.[28]

The German probes against the Voronezh Front began in the

late afternoon of 4 July, developing into a full offensive that night. There was a hurried discussion between Zhukov and Rokossovsky as to whether they should order the firing of the front counter-bombardment and harassing fire programme or report to the *Stavka* for instructions; Zhukov telephoned for Stalin's approval. Stalin did not go to bed that night and, from time to time, he spoke on the telephone to Zhukov, Vasilevsky and Vatutin. The next evening Rokossovsky, whose troops were by then under great pressure, telephoned Stalin to ask for reinforcements, but his gratitude on being given another army was short-lived when Stalin re-routed it a few hours later to Vatutin who, according to the dictator, was 'in a grave situation'.[29]

Von Manstein had already begun to cut deeply into Vatutin's defences. Rokossovsky has professed to believe that the fault lay in the front's deployment; Zhukov doubts this view. Khrushchev, blaming both Stalin and Zhukov, has described, or allowed others to describe, his (Khrushchev's) own personal influence 'not merely with his own front but much further afield . . . as an inspiration and a guide'. Khrushchev said that, on 6 July, Stalin and Zhukov were against the digging in of tanks and that both the Voronezh Front military council and Vasilevsky had great difficulty in persuading Stalin to permit it.[30] Vasilevsky and Ivanov, Vatutin's chief of staff, say otherwise, however, and German air photo reconnaissance has disclosed the presence of over eighty Red Army tanks dug-in in that area before 4 July. At 1820 hours on 6 July, Vatutin telephoned Stalin to describe the growing German panzer threat. Vasilevsky, who was present with Vatutin, recommended to Stalin that two tank corps should be hastened to the threatened sector and that Rotmistrov's 5 Guards Tank Army should be moved south. Stalin then gave Vatutin his orders, confirming the allocation of the tank army and 'demanding that the enemy be stopped *on the prepared defensive positions*'. The members of the Voronezh military council should, he said, be with the forward troops; only Vatutin was to remain at the field headquarters; Khrushchev should join Chistiakov's army, Ivanov go to Kriuchenkin, and Apanasenko to Shumilov, while Vasilevsky was to meet the arriving strategic reserve force consisting of Rotmistrov's and Zhadov's armies.[31] Even Rotmistrov appears to believe the dictator acted correctly ordering a rigid defence on a given line.[32]

Since Vasilevsky had moved over to the South-West Front, Zhukov was ordered by Stalin, on 12 July, to fly to the area of Prokhorovka, where the 800 tanks of Rotmistrov's army were engaging about 500 tanks of the SS panzer corps, to co-ordinate operations between the Voronezh and the Steppe Fronts. The counter-offensive against the Orel grouping in the north began that day, but Hitler had already decided that *Zitadelle* offered no prospects of early victory, and, on 13 July, he ordered that the German offensive be broken off as he intended to move a number of divisions to Western Europe.

Stalin had earlier ruled that the front commanders should themselves decide when the time was opportune for the counter-offensive.[33] But when the defensive battle was actually at its height it was Stalin who took control; he liked his situation reports direct from the man on the spot and, not content with telephoning Zhukov, Vasilevsky and Voronov, he was in continuous touch with the front commanders. As early as 9 July he had been pressing Zhukov that the Bryansk Front might begin the counter-offensive, and, from 12 July onwards, so Zhukov has said, Stalin was co-ordinating all the offensives.[34] By 15 July, when the Voronezh and Steppe Fronts had gone over to the attack, Stalin was goading everyone forward, so that Zhukov and Vasilevsky had the greatest difficulty in persuading the 'heated and grudging' Supreme Commander that occasional pauses were necessary for preparation and resupply.[35] On 5 August an artillery salute was fired in Moscow in honour of the taking of Orel and Belgorod, the first of the many salutes to be fired during the war.

The Supreme Commander had reverted to his earlier strategy of attacking frontally from Velikiye Luki in the north to the Sea of Azov in the south. When, in early August, Zhukov had suggested that the withdrawing enemy should be enveloped, the dictator replied that 'the Germans are still too strong for that'; nor would he change his opinion when Zhukov returned to the theme later in the month.[36] Meanwhile the Supreme Commander tried to keep close control of operative detail, telling Popov on 17 July to keep his tank army well clear of the built-up area of Orel, and criticizing Vatutin on 6 August for failing to concentrate two of his armies on a narrow frontage of assault. Nor did Zhukov escape direction and censure, for, three days later, Stalin sent him a telegram detailing the action to be taken to envelop Kharkov. When the Voronezh Front failed to envelop the Kharkov grouping, suffering heavy casualties in the enemy counter-attack, Stalin, on 21 August, dictated to Shtemenko a strongly worded telegram to both Vatutin and Zhukov, blaming them for 'dissipating their forces by attacking everywhere to cover as much ground as possible', the faults which Zhukov later attributed to Stalin.[37]

On 17 August, when calling at a forward army headquarters, Vasilevsky found the following teleprint awaiting him:

> Marshal Vasilevsky. It is now already 0330 hours 17 August and you still have not seen fit to send to the *Stavka* a report on the outcome of operations on 16 August and your appreciation of the situation . . . Nearly every day you forget this duty . . . Again you have been pleased to ignore your responsibility to the *Stavka* by not reporting. It is the last time that I give you notice that in the event of your allowing yourself to forget your duty you will be removed from the post of the Chief of General Staff and recalled from the front. J. Stalin.[38]

Vasilevsky has said that he was much shaken, for he had never before failed to report or received a reprimand on this score, although the report on the night of 16 August had, admittedly, been delayed for several hours. Vasilevsky immediately telephoned Antonov in Moscow, to learn that Stalin had been agitated by the poor results of the offensives and had tried in vain to get in touch with the Chief of General Staff. Antonov confirmed that Stalin had actually dictated the telegram to Antonov after receiving Vasilevsky's report. Vasilevsky subsequently concluded that all *Stavka* representatives were subjected to Stalin's discipline and rigorous control, and added, somewhat philosophically, that 'the absence of any indulgence towards us was in the interest of the conduct of the armed struggle'. For, said Vasilevsky, 'the Supreme Commander followed the course of front operations very attentively and held the direction of the troops firmly in his own hands'. On 19 August Vasilevsky was in trouble again when he telephoned Stalin from Malinovsky's headquarters, asking for a six day delay in the offensive in order to regroup. Stalin was dissatisfied and once again 'the conversation was unpleasant', with 'not entirely justified reproaches' being levelled at both Vasilevsky and Malinovsky.[39]

On the morning of 23 August the Steppe Front occupied Kharkov. Konev immediately tried to telephone Stalin, only to be told by Poskrebyshev that the Supreme Commander always slept at that hour. Ignoring Poskrebyshev's instructions, Konev telephoned Stalin direct and, after long ringing, Stalin eventually picked up the receiver. Stalin was apparently not irritated at having been woken, and Konev's reward was a 'first category' 224 gun salute.[40] This desire by front commanders for recognition was to develop into a race to occupy cities; and Stalin, who took a personal interest in the framing of the *Sovinform communiqués* and the firing of the salutes, may have intended that it should. In September Rokossovsky felt himself robbed of a rich prize and complained in vain when his left front boundary was moved to the north, as a result of which Kiev fell within the zone of the Voronezh Front.[41]

There was no pause between the defensive and offensive phases for *Rumiantsev,* and, according to Shtemenko, there was no master plan for the operation, since this developed according to circumstances, recommendations by Zhukov and the front commanders being referred back to Moscow for confirmation or variation.[42] Thereafter Stalin would appear to have been in control, for Zhukov was only one of a number of *Stavka* representatives and front commanders who were formulating plans and proffering advice. Nor does Zhukov appear to have been in Stalin's confidence when grand strategy or the command and control of the Red Army and its reserves were decided, so that his designation as Deputy Supreme Commander was, in this respect, a misnomer. Zhukov appears to have relied on the occasional staff briefing by Antonov and on what he could extract from the general staff representatives when they visited him in the field, for any information outside of the Voronezh and Steppe Fronts.[43]

On 25 August at a joint GKO/*Stavka* meeting Stalin demanded immediate measures to prevent the enemy stabilizing his positions on a new East Wall line, and at the same time to halt the destruction by the enemy of the industrial and agricultural resources in the area through which he was withdrawing. An operation was to be mounted involving a rapid approach march and a breaching of the obstacle belt on a wide front. Zhukov was to stay with the Voronezh and Steppe Fronts while Vasilevsky acted as the *Stavka* representative with the South-West and South Fronts; Voronov remained with Sokolovsky's West Front and co-ordinated its operations with Eremenko's Kalinin Front, in what was to become the Smolensk operation. The Bryansk Front was shortly to be withdrawn. Later that same evening, Stalin examined Zhukov's requests for men and materials to reinforce the Voronezh and Steppe Fronts; and, said Zhukov, 'after comparing the list with his own figures of availabilities he took up a pencil and slashed the request by thirty to forty per cent'.[44]

On 3 and 5 August Stalin is said to have visited the headquarters of the West and the Kalinin Fronts, the only time during the course of the war that he entered a theatre of operations.[45] Stalin came no further forward than Yukhnov, Sokolovsky and Voronov being ordered to return to the rear area to meet him; they found him in an unsightly little *dacha* and concluded that the setting was being staged for a propaganda film.[46]

At the end of August when Voronov was told to check the readiness of the Kalinin Front for the Smolensk offensive, he thought that the preparation had been inadequate and was out of keeping with Eremenko's display of confidence; so he instructed the military council to ask Moscow for a postponement. Both Eremenko and Leonov, the political member, refused. Voronov has said that he himself was reluctant to telephone Stalin, as in the past he had often been a petitioner for others and had earned in return the dictator's unpleasant abuse. But in the end he was obliged to do so, and he was fortunate in that Stalin was preoccupied with some other matter and irritably agreed to put off the date. Eremenko's subsequent actions were to surprise Voronov and anger Stalin. For, if Voronov is to be believed, he had to veto Eremenko's decision not to inform his commanders and troops of the six day postponement, but to put off the attack day by day, 'so as not to unwind his subordinates'. When the offensive did start, Eremenko refused to let his staff inform Moscow – even when asked – of the extent of his success, because he wanted to do this personally at the end of the day.[47]

On 8 September a *Stavka* order promised the award of the Order of Suvorov to commanders who forced the Desna, and the title of Hero of the Soviet Union to those officers and men who were first across the Dnieper. The approach march of 120 miles began on 18 September. On the night of 24 September two parachute brigades were dropped beyond the river line, but since these were scattered over a wide area the operation was a failure. The ground troops did, however, seize numbers of small bridgeheads to the north and south of Kiev, the largest of which was near Bukrin, fifty miles below the Ukrainian capital. Both Zhukov and the general staff were convinced that the main offensive would have to be shifted from Bukrin, for surprise had been lost and the wooded and broken ground there was unsuitable for the use of tanks. Stalin, however, was unwilling to listen to argument. He was still angry at the failure of the parachute brigades and had drafted a special order censuring the incompetence of its organizers. He told Zhukov to continue the break-out 'for the front was giving up the Bukrin attacks before it had really tried'. Fighting continued into October, still without success. The Supreme Commander, said Shtemenko, was very dissatisfied, and he reproached both Zhukov and Vatutin for lack of decision and drive, comparing their failure with Konev's good progress on the lower Dnieper. Not until 24 October would he agree to call off the Bukrin attacks and shift the main weight of the offensive to the Lyutezh bridgehead to the north of Kiev.[48]

Moskalenko was with Vatutin on the Bukrin bridgehead on 23 October, when Stalin called on the *V Ch*. Stalin expressed displeasure that the Bukrin offensive was still being continued and he made a detailed verbal appreciation of the tactical and operative factors – the enemy build-up on the ground and in the air, the broken country, which, though favouring the German defence, was unsuitable for tank troops. He wanted Vatutin to consider moving part of his force by night northwards to Lyutezh. Moskalenko said that, at the time, he marvelled at the thoroughness with which the *Stavka* analyzed the local situation.[49] The reasoning thus attributed to Stalin forms the first paragraph of the directive of 24 October sent over Stalin's and Antonov's signatures, this being a sharp reprimand to Zhukov and Vatutin for their failure in reading ground and in appreciating troop characteristics. For, when it so suited him, Stalin adopted as his own the opinions of those who had disagreed with him, and attributed to his opponents the discredited arguments which had stemmed from himself.

On 6 November Zhukov and Vatutin sent a joint telegram to Stalin announcing the occupation of Kiev, but this did not save the front headquarters from the rigorous inquiry which led to the dismissal of Ivanov, its chief of staff. Shtemenko believed that Ivanov was removed because he failed to report the loss of a major town.[50] In fact, the front was also charged with lack of control, for Vatutin wrote a personal letter to Antonov, defending the front signal organization and detailing the whereabouts of the members of the military council and the deputy commanders during the battle. Vatutin defended Ivanov and asked Antonov to show the letter to Stalin. By 1972, however, Moskalenko had become Stalin's champion, for he concluded that Antonov, not Stalin, was responsible for Ivanov's removal.[51]

On 20 October 1943 the designation of all the fronts in the Ukraine was changed to Ukrainian Fronts numbered consecutively from north to south, so that the Voronezh, the Steppe, the South-West and South Fronts became 1, 2, 3 and 4 Ukrainian Fronts. The Central Front became the Belorussian Front.

The more forceful front commanders, particularly those who enjoyed a measure of Stalin's confidence, appear to have been uninhibited by the presence of *Stavka* representatives in maintaining their link with Stalin. Rokossovsky put his own plan for the taking of Kiev not to Zhukov but direct to Stalin.[52] At about this time, Konev telephoned Stalin, again not Zhukov, to report that it was essential that the right wing of Malinovsky's 3 Ukrainian Front mount an immediate offensive to prevent the enemy escaping from encirclement near Krivoi Rog.[53] Nor did Stalin always deal with the *Stavka* representatives. For when one of Zhukov's two fronts was in difficulties and Vatutin lost Zhitomir to a German counter stroke on 18 November, Stalin telephoned Rokossovsky, Vatutin's right hand neighbour, instructing him to go at once to 1 Ukrainian Front and, if necessary, assume command of that formation and halt the enemy advance.[54]

In mid-December Zhukov and Vasilevsky had been recalled to Moscow to prepare, together with the general staff, the detail of the new offensive by the four Ukrainian fronts, which was to destroy the enemy salient in the Dnieper bend and take the Red Army into Galicia and Rumania. This, according to Zhukov, took five days from the conclusion of the main *Stavka* conferences during which Stalin reversed his earlier order forbidding encirclement operations.

The offensive began on 24 December and quickly made ground to the west and south-west. On the extreme left, however, Tolbukhin's 4 Ukrainian Front became bogged down in front of the enemy Nikopol bridgehead, and it became obvious to Vasilevsky that to continue the attacks would lead to enormous casualties with no gain. He telephoned Stalin in Tolbukhin's presence suggesting that 3 Ukrainian Front should be reinforced, so that the bridgehead might be outflanked. Once more Stalin abused them, but Vasilevsky could do no more, he said, than maintain his opinion; Stalin's excited voice involuntarily aroused Vasilevsky's resentment. In the end Stalin 'threw down the phone'.[55]

A day later, however, Stalin had regained his composure. Vasilevsky had taken up temporary residence with Leliushenko's army in front of the bridgehead, when, on 16 January, he was called to the telephone by Stalin. Vasilevsky took Leliushenko with him. Leliushenko, overhearing part of the conversation, was able to gauge the situation by the unruffled and measured tones. Stalin then wanted Leliushenko on the line. When asked for his appreciation, Leliushenko told the dictator that the frontal attack by his army held little prospect of success unless made in conjunction with a second offensive by 3 Ukrainian Front to the north. Stalin listened in silence. Action on these views was not long delayed, however, for the next morning Leliushenko received orders to hand over a proportion of his armour to 3 Ukrainian Front and prepare new plans for his remaining forces.[56]

Further to the west the flanks of Vatutin's and Konev's fronts had, on 28 January, encircled two German corps at Korsun. Information about the progress of an enemy relief thrust quickly came to Stalin's ears, and, at midday on 12 February, he spoke to Konev on the telephone angrily asking for confirmation that the enemy was beginning to break out through the 27 Army sector, part of Vatutin's 1 Ukrainian Front. Konev replied that 'Comrade Stalin should not worry himself, as he [Konev] had taken all necessary measures to prevent the enemy's escape', moving Rotmistrov's tank army into the area to provide a pivot between 1 and 2 Ukrainian Fronts. Stalin was surprised and pleased at this unusual initiative and said that he would consult the *Stavka*. He telephoned Zhukov, rousing him from his sick bed, and berated him for not knowing the detail of the local situation. According to Zhukov's version, Stalin said that Konev wanted the responsibility for the destruction of the enemy corps to be given to 2 Ukrainian Front. Zhukov opposed this course. Stalin merely hung up. Fifteen minutes later Stalin spoke again to Konev telling him that all troops in action against the encircled enemy would be placed under his command. Konev said that he protested against having to accept 27 Army, for the army communications and rear services ran through the 1 Ukrainian Front organization at Belaya Tserkov and Kiev. Stalin, however, brushed these objections aside, saying that Vatutin could remain responsible for both communication and supply, but that [*manes* Kameneva] Konev could pass his signal traffic to 27 Army through 1 Ukrainian Front headquarters.[57] The telegraphed directive was issued a few hours later. Vatutin, in his turn, complained to Zhukov against being robbed of the opportunity of gaining a Moscow saluted victory.[58]

Konev subsequently contradicted Zhukov's version of events, and, presumably motivated by malice, has published a signalled reprimand from Stalin to Zhukov, dated at 1645 hours that day, saying that the enemy breakthrough had occurred since the command weaknesses of 27 Army had not been rectified on the spot, and because Zhukov had not taken decisive measures to destroy, in accordance with Stalin's orders, the enemy Stablev grouping. On 18 February 1944, 2 Ukrainian Front was saluted by the guns of Moscow, nothing being said of Zhukov's and Vatutin's part in the victory; Konev was promoted to marshal of the Soviet Union, the third since the beginning of the war, for Zhukov and Vasilevsky had already been granted that rank in January and February 1943. Rotmistrov became a marshal of tank troops.

Vatutin had, however, remained responsible for blocking the path of the relief thrust of the incoming German armour during the Korsun battle. In this connection Novikov, the Commander-in-Chief of the Red Air Forces, has told how he was unexpectedly summoned to the Kremlin on 13 February. As he entered the dictator's room, Stalin, sitting on a divan and smoking his pipe, raised his right hand to his head as a sign of welcome. Rising, he walked up and down the room in silence and, approaching Novikov, looked him in the face and asked whether it was possible for air-craft to halt the advance of tanks. The question was unexpected, but Novikov had worked two years with Stalin and, so he said, 'already had his measure'. A direct 'Yes' or 'No' was called for, for Stalin wanted rapid and clear decisions and could not endure verbosity, or flabbiness and vagueness in thought. In reality the answer to the question depended on the circumstances, but Stalin would never allow others to cross-examine him. Without a moment's hesitation Novikov replied that they could. Stalin did not disguise his satisfaction and told Novikov to fly to Vatutin immediately. Khudiakov, the Chief of Air Staff and the man on the spot, sent by Novikov to co-ordinate the two air armies there, had obviously, said Novikov, fallen foul of the Supreme Commander, for Stalin gave his customary order, 'that he did not need such a man and that he was to be removed'. Novikov said that he attempted to defend Khudiakov but was quickly silenced by the sharpness of Stalin's reply, 'You fly to Vatutin and see that you stop those tanks'. That, said Novikov, was the end of that. The next two days were the most tense of his life, but he was rewarded by promotion to the rank of chief marshal of air troops.[59]

On 18 February Stalin restored Zhukov to his post as the *Stavka* representative and co-ordinator of 1 and 2 Ukrainian Fronts, but, on 1 March, the day after the fatal wounding of Vatutin by Ukrainian nationalists, Zhukov was appointed to command 1 Ukrainian Front, and the control over 1 and 2 Ukrainian Fronts reverted directly to Stalin.

Djilas visited Konev's headquarters at about this time and was shocked at the drinking party arranged in the Yugo-Slavs' honour. Konev, callous and taciturn, gave Djilas a verbal picture of the more senior Soviet military leaders: Voroshilov, he said, was a man of inexhaustible courage but incapable of understanding modern warfare; Budenny never knew much and he never studied anything – he was, in Konev's view, completely incompetent; Shaposhnikov he dismissed as a technical staff officer; but Stalin was 'universally gifted, brilliantly able to see the war as a whole and this made it possible for him to direct it so successfully'.[60]

Tolbukhin's 4 Ukrainian Front had already reached the mouth of the Dnieper, isolating the enemy 17 Army in the Crimea. At first there had been a difference of opinion in Moscow as to whether priority should be given to the reoccupation of the Crimea, or whether the peninsula should merely be sealed off at the Perekop isthmus, so freeing the larger part of 4 Ukrainian and the North Caucasus Front for service elsewhere. The general staff, said Shtemenko, was very conscious of the precedents of 1920, when Wrangel had attacked from the Crimea into the Kuban and the Taurida plain in the rear of the Red forces engaged against the Poles.[61] So no doubt was Stalin, for he regarded an enemy held Crimea as a threat to the Soviet forces in the western Ukraine. Vasilevsky, on 22 September, had given as his opinion that the main offensive should be made by Tolbukhin's forces from the north, down the Perekop isthmus and across the shallow and brackish Sivash. In addition part of the North Caucasus Front was to be put across the Kerch narrows, and this, together with the left wing of 4 Ukrainian Front, would attack on converging axes. This course was approved by Stalin, who decided to send Voroshilov, together with Shtemenko, to Petrov 'to have a look round and see what could be done'.[62]

Shtemenko has portrayed Voroshilov as a man of education and culture, a description at variance with the impression which Voroshilov made on western observers. But Shtemenko is agreed with Meretskov that Voroshilov was something of a showman, exuding cordiality and *bonhomie,* making a parade of his courage and thinking that he would be better received by the Terek and Kuban Cossack infantry by riding out to inspect them on a horse. Petrov had complained about the naval support provided by Vladimirsky, and Voroshilov presided over the co-ordinating conference held on 25 December to settle their differences. When Shtemenko proposed to forward the minutes of the meeting to Stalin as part of the routine reports, Voroshilov, said Shtemenko, 'thought otherwise and had the proceedings drawn up as a protocol, insisting that the ten representatives should all sign it'. The ladder of signatures angered Stalin, who likened it to the minutes of a meeting of a collective farm; he was surprised, he said, that all the participants had not taken a vote before coming to a decision.

Petrov's troops made a second successful sea-borne assault on 10 January and widened the beach-head. Yet Stalin, presumably acting on complaints from the navy and without consulting or informing anyone on the spot, decided to replace Petrov. The first that Voroshilov and Shtemenko knew of Petrov's replacement was the arrival of Eremenko's train in the Kuban; Petrov, who had only been promoted to the rank of general of the army three months before, was downgraded to a colonel-general. Voroshilov was re-called to Moscow for briefing, prior to being appointed to join Vasilevsky as a *Stavka* representative to 4 Ukrainian Front with a special responsibility as a co-ordinator between Tolbukhin and Eremenko in the successful campaign which was to end in the complete destruction of 17 German Army and the reoccupation of the Crimea.[63]

Hull, Eden and Ismay had been attending the conference held in Spiridinovka Street from 19 October until 1 November, 1943, together with Molotov, Litvinov, Vyshinsky, Voroshilov and Gryz-lov, whose main interest was centred on whether the Anglo-American forces would invade northern France in the spring of 1944. Ismay and Deane made the presentation disclosing the invasion plans, the Russians, according to Ismay, listening atten-tively but giving no indication of their feelings one way or the other.[64] Voroshilov and Gryzlov did not, however, conceal their suspicions when the time came for questions.[65] In the political field, Hull and Eden had been instructed to arrange a meeting of the three heads of governments, but Stalin refused to leave Russia on the grounds that his presence was indispensable to the conduct of the fighting there. At the time, Eden was sceptical, but after-wards conceded that Stalin might have been speaking the truth, for on one occasion during the Kremlin talks Birse overheard the dictator on the telephone directing operations in the Crimea.[66] On 27 October Eden and Ismay had to return to the Kremlin on Churchill's telegraphed instructions, to explain that, due to unfore-seen difficulties in Italy, the invasion of France might have to be postponed from the spring to the summer. To Ismay's surprise Stalin appeared 'perfectly happy once he had received Eden's assurance that a short postponement and not a cancellation was involved'.[67]

In the early hours of 25 November Stalin, together with Molotov and Voroshilov and accompanied by his personal NKVD body-guard, boarded his train in the sidings near Kuntsevo *en route* for Stalingrad and Baku, from whence he was to fly to Teheran.

Shtemenko, carrying a set of marked-up maps covering the whole of the fighting fronts, was with the party as the general staff liaison officer responsible for briefing Stalin on the battle on the eastern front and passing Stalin's orders to Moscow for onward transmission to the front commanders. The special train stopped at scheduled halts from Michurinsk onwards, where there was access to the NKVD *V Ch* telephone circuit, Shtemenko's compartment being plugged in to the terminal at each of these stops so that he could speak to Gryzlov in Moscow and mark up his maps with the latest situation. At Teheran Shtemenko and his cipher officer were given a single room in Stalin's villa adjoining the signal centre, but that evening Stalin himself appeared in the office, ordering that it be changed since it was too small and dark. The effect, said Shtemenko, 'was immediate'. Shtemenko continued his morning and nightly briefings, and the drafts of all military orders requiring Stalin's signature, telegraphed or telephoned from Antonov, were presented to the dictator; the authorized version was then signalled back to Moscow, the original document bearing Stalin's signature being retained for safe keeping by the cipher officer. Stalin spoke to Antonov in Moscow during the Teheran conference and on one occasion had a direct signal conversation with Vatutin and Rokossovsky.[68]

At the first plenary meeting on 28 November Stalin appeared wearing the uniform of a marshal of the Soviet Union. Birse thought the dictator more care-worn than when he had last seen him in Moscow, but at the same time more affable.[69] His interventions were made in a quiet voice, without any gestures, but at the same time were direct and decided; sometimes they were so abrupt as to be rude. He left no doubt in anyone's mind, said Ismay, that he was master in his own house.[70] Deane noted that, in contrast to the British and American groups, each of which numbered twenty or thirty and had a strong military representation, Stalin had with him only Molotov, Voroshilov and Pavlov, his interpreter, and, as far as the Americans could tell, these three completed his entourage. Although, from time to time, Stalin had whispered consultations with Molotov and Voroshilov, Stalin was the sole spokesman; and, said Deane, there could be no doubt of his authority as there was never the slightest indication that he would have to consult his government.[71] Stalin said that he saw no point in separate chiefs of staff consultations, for that was his business and that was what he had come for; only reluctantly would he agree to be represented on the military committee, for he explained that he had brought no military experts with him; Voroshilov, however, 'would do his best'. His other comments were blunt, terse and to the point. On one occasion he capped Churchill's oratory by asking whether the British were only 'thinking' of *Overlord* in order to satisfy the Soviet Union; at another, after a particularly long speech from Churchill, he asked: 'How long is this conference going to last?'.[72]

Brooke, who was in agreement with Ismay on the poverty of Voroshilov's capabilities, was of the opinion that Stalin had a military brain of the highest calibre. Never once in any of his statements, said Brooke, did Stalin fail to appreciate all the implications of a situation with a quick and unerring eye, and 'in this respect he stood out compared with Roosevelt and Churchill'.[73]

Roosevelt surprised and disturbed his own chiefs of staff by bringing up the possibility of a Mediterranean operation across the Adriatic through Yugo-Slavia into Rumania, to effect a junction with the Red Army in the area of Odessa; Churchill associated himself with this suggestion. Stalin then gave his own opinion of the strategy which his allies should adopt. It was unwise, he thought, to scatter forces in various operations throughout the Eastern Mediterranean, since *Overlord* should be the basis of all operations in 1944; it would be better to abandon even the capture of Rome, so that the bulk of the allied troops in Italy might be used to invade southern France. Stalin said repeatedly that he was quite sure that Turkey would not come into the war, as if to emphasize that the Black Sea would remain closed to Anglo-American naval forces.[74] At the committee meeting the next day, attended by Voroshilov, Leahy, Marshall, Portal and Brooke, Voroshilov continued to press Stalin's views, while Brooke insisted, stubbornly according to Leahy, that all available Mediterranean forces should be used in Italy and the East Mediterranean. At the military meeting on 30 November a measure of agreement was reached in that the date of the cross-Channel operation was put off until 1 June 1944, since this would fit in with the proposed date of the Russian spring offensives. Stalin accepted the date with satisfaction.

Stalin had supported the United States' plan that all available allied forces should be landed in France, and Brooke and Deane subsequently ascribed motives of self-interest to the Soviet leader's proposals. Apart from securing an obvious diplomatic advantage in siding with the Americans against the British, Stalin wanted, suspected Brooke, to keep his American and British allies away from the Black Sea left flank, out of the Balkans and clear of the East Mediterranean.[75]

Stalin made a number of observations which, although not relevant to the proceedings, were of interest. His opinion of Hitler, much the same as that given to Eden the previous month, was that he did not share Roosevelt's view that Hitler was mentally unbalanced; indeed Stalin thought Hitler a very able man; his weaknesses were that he was greedy and thought too much of prestige and could not relate military aims to capabilities.[76] Stalin said he was in favour of shooting '50,000, perhaps 100,000 German officers', and the impression which he made on Churchill and Birse was that he was not joking. The dictator elaborated on the fighting qualities of the Red Army, saying that it had fought heroically because 'the Russian people' would not have tolerated otherwise; 'those who did not fight bravely were killed'. In 1939, he went on, the Soviet forces had done very badly against the Finns, and in 1941, in spite of the extensive re-organization, it could not be said that the Red Army was a first-class fighting force. But it had improved steadily, and now, he felt, it was genuinely a good army.[77] The Soviet margin of superiority over the enemy, said Stalin, was about sixty divisions, which could be moved rapidly from place to place over the extended front to provide the concentrations necessary to breakthrough in the selected directions. The Germans, so Stalin thought, had 260 divisions in the east against the 330 Red Army divisions opposing them.[78] And it was at Teheran that Stalin first hinted that when Germany was defeated the Soviet Union might be prepared to take a hand in the war against Japan.

10
Into Central Europe

Towards the end of 1943 the Red Army ground forces in the north and the centre of the Russo-German front were reorganized and redeployed. Popov's Bryansk Front handed over formations to Rokossovsky's Central Front at the beginning of October and moved to the area between Velikiye Luki and Lake Ilmen to form a new Baltic Front; on 20 October Rokossovsky's enlarged Central Front, consisting of ten armies, was redesignated as the Belorussian Front; Eremenko's Kalinin became 1 Baltic Front and Popov's Baltic was renumbered as 2 Baltic Front. On 24 February 1944 Rokossovsky's Belorussian Front was renamed as 1 Belorussian Front, and Kurochkin's North-West Front headquarters was sent south to take over the sector on Rokossovsky's left, where it was redesignated as 2 Belorussian Front. On 13 February the Volkhov Front was broken up and its formations shared between Govorov's Leningrad and Popov's 2 Baltic Fronts, Meretskov assuming the command of the Karelian Front from Frolov. On 21 April 1944 a new 3 Baltic Front, under Maslennikov, was formed in the Pskov area, taking over troops which had formerly belonged to the Leningrad and the Volkhov Fronts.[1]

Although Sandalov, Popov's chief of staff, subsequently said that he could see little sense in this reorganization and that Antonov would give him no information as to the reasons for it, the truth of the matter was that Stalin sent Popov north because he wanted the threat removed from Leningrad and an early reoccupation of the Baltic States.[2] But the rapid success of the Ukrainian fronts created a new situation in the centre with an ever-widening gap

between Rokossovsky and Vatutin along the southern edge of the
Pripet Marshes. This gap had to be filled by Kurochkin's headquarters taking over Rokossovsky's left flanking army and two
further armies allocated from the *Stavka* reserve. Sandalov's
criticism that the High.Command formed a new front headquarters under Maslennikov when the Volkhov Front headquarters
had been available in the area, would appear to be justified, however, for, according to Shtemenko, Stalin listened too readily to
Govorov's urging that the Leningrad Front alone should be
entrusted with the offensive operations to the south-west of the
city.[3] So Stalin decided to break up the Volkhov Front, softening
the blow to Meretskov by telling him that he was the most suitable
commander for operations against the Finns, and by allowing
him to take his headquarters with him and superimpose it on that
of the Karelian Front.[4] Later, when Govorov's Leningrad Front
stretched from the Finnish sector north of Leningrad down to
Ostrov, Stalin had second thoughts as to whether Govorov could
in fact handle such an extended sector which faced in two directions. In a telephone consultation with Vasilevsky, he said that he
was inclined, in spite of Govorov's objections, to cut the Leningrad Front in two once more, setting up a new 3 Baltic Front to be
interposed in the area of Pskov.[5]

On 16 November 1943, Stalin had Bagramian, still commanding
11 Guards Army, recalled to Moscow. When Bagramian reported
to Antonov and asked the reason for his summons, he was told that
'the boss (*khoziain*) is not in the habit of making his thoughts
public'. Bagramian accompanied Antonov and Shtemenko to the
Kremlin where he learned that his army was to be transferred from
2 Baltic to 1 Baltic Front and that he himself was to replace
Eremenko as the front commander. It only remained, said Stalin,
to post an experienced commander to 11 Guards Army; Chibisov,
he thought, would be suitable. Antonov began to praise Chibisov's
military virtues, but Stalin, quick to note Bagramian's silence,
asked whether the new front commander had anything against
Chibisov. Bagramian said that he thought Colonel-General
Chibisov a most experienced commander, but pointed out that
Chibisov had been a lieutenant-general when Bagramian was a
colonel. Would it not be possible instead to have Galitsky. Not
only did Stalin agree, but, summoning Poskrebyshev, he ordered

him to prepare a *Sovnarkom* order promoting Bagramian from colonel-general to general of the army.[6]

In February 1944 the general staff worked out a plan, which was approved by Stalin, involving a joint thrust on Riga by Bagramian's 1 and Popov's 2 Baltic Fronts, in order to envelop Army Group North. Timoshenko co-ordinated the operation and Shtemenko accompanied him as his chief of staff. Since no progress had been made following two days of heavy fighting, Timoshenko referred the plan back to Stalin, asking in vain for permission to vary it. The offensive was resumed a week later, with no greater success, and it was eventually broken off on 18 March. Shtemenko drafted the report to Stalin explaining the failure, a failure which in all probability led the next month to the replacement of Popov by Eremenko. Shtemenko's description of Timoshenko during this period shows the marshal to have been suspicious and testy, still living the glories of the Civil War, jealous and contemptuous of the younger commanders and staffs. He was at first openly hostile to Shtemenko and assumed that he had been sent as Stalin's spy.[7]

Following the loss of the Ukraine, the German held territory in the centre protruded far to the east in the form of a balcony, the right flank of the salient running from west to east for a distance of nearly 200 miles along the southern skirts of the Pripet Marshes. The front line showed a similarity to that of July 1941 when the Germans had used the salient as a springboard to attack southwards into the Ukraine and launch the offensive on Moscow. It was considered necessary, therefore, to evict the enemy from the Belorussian bulge to eliminate this threat and, at the same time, open the way for the Red Army into the Baltic States, East Prussia and Poland.

The findings of a GKO commission of enquiry held the cautious Sokolovsky responsible for the Soviet lack of success in the earlier offensives north of the Pripet, and the general staff used the report to support its own suggestion that the West Front, because it was over-extended, should be broken up into two new fronts, and that these should be reinforced preparatory to a main offensive into Belorussia.[8]

Although Stalin had said that he would make his offensives coincide with the launching of the second front in Western Europe, he had yet to make up his mind as to his strategic objectives, where he would strike his main and subsidiary blows and their timing. Zhukov, Vasilevsky, Rokossovsky and Shtemenko have confirmed that Stalin sought out opinions on these matters not only from the Deputy Supreme Commander, the Chief of General Staff and members of the *Stavka*, but also from the front commanders, continuously talking to them in turn on the telephone.

When Rokossovsky wanted to press his views he talked directly to Stalin and not through Antonov, for, said Rokossovsky, Antonov rarely insisted on a point in the face of Stalin's objections, and his usual reply to Rokossovsky's requests was that 'Comrade Stalin would decide for himself'. Rokossovsky was in favour of a major offensive into Belorussia, and he outlined to Stalin how, in his opinion, this could be done. A massive armoured blow from the area of Kovel would bypass the Pripet Marshes from the south and strike northwards on Brest; simultaneously a second tank thrust could be made to the north of the Pripet in the direction of Minsk and Bobruisk. Rokossovsky thought that both of these thrusts should be made by his own 1 Belorussian Front, and he urged that, as a preliminary, the armies of Kurochkin's 2 Belorussian Front should be transferred to him. As chance had it, Kurochkin got into difficulties soon afterwards when he lost Kovel, and his front was broken up on 4 April and its formations were transferred to Rokossovsky or withdrawn to the *Stavka* reserve.[9] Stalin liked Rokossovsky's plan and ordered the general staff to examine it, but its sequences and timing were not adopted because of the difficulty in marshalling a large tank force near Kovel. The general concept of a 1 Belorussian Front thrust south of the Pripet from Kovel on Brest, exploiting north-eastwards into Poland, was, however, included in the design of a second offensive. It thus became linked to a Zhukov plan, in which 1 Ukrainian Front was to wheel north on Lvov prior to advancing across southern Poland.[10]

On 12 April Stalin confirmed the general staff plan, based in part on Rokossovsky's and Zhukov's recommendations; the West Front was to be broken up into newly formed 2 and 3 Belorussian Fronts, which, together with 1 Belorussian Front, would provide the main striking force for the Belorussian operation north of the Pripet. The second offensive by 1 Ukrainian Front and the left wing of Rokossovsky's 1 Belorussian Front to the south of the Pripet, would follow immediately after the Belorussian operation.

Petrov had been temporarily restored to favour and given the command of the new 2 Belorussian Front. The Commander of 3 Belorussian Front was to be Cherniakhovsky, a former army commander only thirty-eight years old, promoted by Stalin in response to a recommendation by Zhukov, and appointed a front commander at the beginning of April following a Stalin telephone conversation with Vasilevsky in the Crimea.[11] Since Cherniakhovsky considered that he would need a tank army to smash the enemy reserves in the area of Minsk and Borisov, a conspiracy was entered into whereby Cherniakhovsky was to initiate a formal request to the *Stavka,* on the understanding that the general staff would support it when it was considered. In the event this came to nothing and Stalin was not apprised of Cherniakhovsky's views until the final presentation was made to the dictator.

The general staff was out of favour with Stalin through recommending the suspension of offensive operations over the whole of the Russo-German front, in order to rest the troops and prepare for the summer offensive. At first Stalin said that preparations for the summer operations should not be allowed to interfere with the attacks then in progress, although he was aware that the front commanders were against this course. Not until 15 April would he agree to calling off offensive operations in the north and west; and, since Red Army troops were still making some gains in the south, he instructed the general staff 'to be in no hurry to suspend the attacks, but to bring the Ukrainian fronts over to the defence gradually as they lost momentum'. The last of the orders calling off the offensives was issued on 7 May.[12]

Zhukov was summoned for consultation on 22 April, and, on arriving at the capital, Antonov briefed him on the supply and reinforcement position, at the same time warning him not to reveal to Stalin that he had done so, since the dictator had forbidden that such information be divulged. At the afternoon meeting attended by Zhukov, the general staff and the arms directors, Stalin surprised the meeting by proposing that the 1 Ukrainian Front thrust from the south should provide the opening to the Belorussian campaign, so drawing the enemy reserves southwards; but he quickly dropped the idea when Antonov brought his attention to the good lateral roads available to the enemy. Zhukov and Antonov were ordered to spend the next six days in drawing up outline plans, during which time Vasilevsky and the front commanders were to be asked for their further views.[13] At the beginning of May Zhukov gave up the command of 1 Ukrainian Front to Konev, in order to be free to concentrate his attention on Belorussia. Malinovsky replaced Konev, and Tolbukhin took Malinovsky's vacant command; 4 Ukrainian Front was to be taken into reserve.

Vasilevsky has said that when he was in the Ukraine and the Crimea he was continually consulted by both Stalin and Antonov. The general staff, he said, did not really get down to working out the operational plan of the Belorussian campaign until April, and it was envisaged that Army Group Centre could be destroyed by two mighty blows on the flanks of the salient, one from the north towards Borisov and Minsk, the other from the south to Bobruisk and Minsk. Both he and Zhukov were summoned to Moscow from time to time for talks with Stalin, Antonov being present, but often Stalin discussed the details of individual plans with them by telephone; during these conversations he would refer to talks which he had had with front commanders, 'particularly with Rokossovsky'. During the month of April Vasilevsky was repeatedly reminded by the Supreme Commander that the Ukraine operations must be completed that month, come what may, in order that the Chief of General Staff might devote his full attention to the Belorussian operation. On the night of 29 April, shortly before the successful storming of Sevastopol which ended the fighting in the south, Stalin had a long telephone conversation with Vasilevsky, in which he expressed himself entirely satisfied with future plans and with the progress to date. But then, when the subject passed to a new postponement of the Sevastopol operation by only a few days, Stalin, according to Vasilevsky, 'entirely lost his mental equilibrium'.[14]

If Vasilevsky is to be believed, the liaison between Stalin and himself was close even though he was at that time in the Crimea. Daily, sometimes hourly, consultations went on over the *V Ch* telephone, Stalin asking him for his views on operational planning, reorganization and senior appointments. Vasilevsky gives the credit for the closeness of the relationship between himself and Stalin, and for the efficiency with which business was conducted, to Antonov and the general staff in Moscow, for they briefed him regularly day by day on events in all the battle areas, so that the

Chief of General Staff usually understood the problem before the Supreme Commander consulted him. Vasilevsky shared Shtemenko's high opinion of Antonov's ability, and he praised the systematic efficiency and good order in the general staff, which, he said, still reflected the personality of Shaposhnikov, its founder.[15]

It was decided that the first major offensive would be that against Finland, at the same time as the opening of the second front in Western Europe. The great offensive into Belorussia would then begin at the end of the third week in June. As soon as the enemy Army Group Centre was fully engaged, its neighbour to the south, Army Group North Ukraine, was to be attacked south of the Pripet Marshes in the Lvov offensive. Then finally, towards the end of the summer, the Soviet left wing, on the Balkan flank, was to mount another massive campaign into Rumania, Bulgaria and Hungary. In May and June a number of deception measures were undertaken, indicating troop concentrations in the areas of Pskov and Kishinev. Meanwhile all the Soviet tank armies were left in the south.[16]

In mid-February when the unwilling Meretskov had been transferred to the Karelian Front, Stalin had told him that Frolov had done good work, but that he and his staff had been on the defensive so long that they no longer had the mentality needed to mount an offensive. In any event, the Karelian Front had become a perpetual mendicant (*vechnym prositelem*) always whining for more.[17]

Stalin had still not determined how the Finnish War was to be fought, for, at the end of March, Antonov told Shtemenko to go to the Kuntsevo *dacha*, 'so that the boss might look at the maps and operational plans for the northern flank'. Having studied the maps, Stalin asked questions about the strength and state of the troops there; he walked up and down the room, reasoning with himself while Shtemenko noted down the purport of his ideas. Stalin thought that if the Leningrad Front mounted simultaneous operations in the Karelian Isthmus, then the Karelian Front, in the huge open territories to the north, could strike two operational blows in sequence, the first against the Finns and the second against the Germans.[18]

In the weeks that followed, Stalin's attention was continually occupied with 20 German Army in Lapland, for he was repeatedly to warn Meretskov not to weaken the Red Army forces facing it.[19] Meretskov had the greatest respect for Stalin but little for his own military superiors and subordinates; he was demanding and tactless, and he took a pride in that his own staff found it difficult to work with him. Although closely acquainted with Stalin, he frequently misjudged him.

Meretskov had been at work for nearly three months organizing operations in the far north against the enemy in Lapland when the priorities were suddenly changed by Moscow and he was ordered to prepare an immediate offensive across the Svir against the Finns in Southern Karelia. Meretskov came to the capital on 30 May bringing with him panoramic aerial photographs and a model of the Finnish defences, and he insisted on taking these with him into Stalin's room, against the advice of the general staff who warned him 'that Stalin did not like to be presented with unnecessary material and could not bear predictions about the enemy'. Meretskov made matters worse by introducing his models before making his address, so that he was quickly cut short by Stalin who said that the front commander was hypnotized by the enemy's defences and was trying to frighten the *Stavka* with toys; the dictator was, he said, beginning to have doubts as to whether Meretskov was the man for the task. Meretskov then came out with his request for heavy tank regiments; he was silenced by accusations of blackmail. Yet, when the meeting was about to break up and Stalin's anger had cooled, he wished Meretskov luck and advised him in future not to be afraid of the enemy.[20] Meretskov had always been one of Stalin's favourites.

Meretskov went direct to 7 Army to prepare for the coming attacks, but was recalled to the Kremlin on 9 June for further planning talks. Stalin told him that he could have ten days to complete his preparations, and, as it would be impossible to redeploy the Karelian Front in time, he would be allocated additional outside forces for the operation. Stalin was ready to meet Meretskov's request for two infantry corps and additional tanks, but when Meretskov asked for yet another infantry corps he was subdued by the strong objections from Zhukov and Vasilevsky. After the two marshals had left and Meretskov had accompanied Stalin, at the dictator's invitation, to watch the firework display and gun salute in honour of the Leningrad Front, Stalin told

Meretskov, on parting, that he would in fact let him have the additional infantry corps.[21]

The Leningrad Front's success had been greater than expected for it was already preparing to storm the third and last line of defence near Viborg. On the night of 17 June Stalin spoke by telephone to Govorov, in Vasilevsky's and Antonov's presence, to hear the latest situation report, before discussing with Vasilevsky the objectives to be taken after Viborg. He then rang Meretskov and, after pointing out that Govorov's success must lighten the Karelian Front's task, he demanded that the offensive should start not later than 21 June.[22]

Matters were still not going smoothly for Meretskov. It had been agreed earlier that 7 Army would make its main river crossing below the fifty foot high dam of the Svir-3 hydroelectric station, but after looking at the ground Meretskov had come to the conclusion that he must first control the area of the dam to prevent the enemy opening the flood-gate. In consequence, he introduced certain minor changes to the original plan. Immediately afterwards, he and his front military council were hauled back yet again to the Kremlin, personally to explain their actions. In recounting this incident, Meretskov said that 'it was just like Stalin to call the front commander to Moscow to explain modifications . . . for summonses of this sort were not infrequent'. Stalin insisted on personal contact because, Meretskov suspected, he liked to size up people by talking to them; moreover, in this way he could find out more about the local situation than by reading reports. Stalin had, said Meretskov, a marked ability to acquire knowledge from others, 'so that he learned his military expertise from his generals'. Stalin was closely interested in all policy and general matters, but his weakness, thought Meretskov, was 'that he would, on occasions, go into the minutest details, when experience must have shown him that it was impossible to plan and make contingency arrangements for the entire course of an operation'.[23]

Novikov had been detached to the north to co-ordinate the 200 aircraft of the Baltic Fleet and the 1,000 aircraft of the Leningrad Front. Stalin had earlier asked Golovanov, the Commander of the Long Range Air Force (ADD) directly subordinate to the Supreme Commander, whether night bomber divisions of Il 4 and Tu 3 aircraft might not be used to augment the air support by day. Golovanov thought not, and Stalin had thereupon asked for Novikov's opinion. Novikov, whom even Zhukov characterized as always 'highly optimistic', disagreed with Golovanov and requested Stalin to allocate two long range air divisions to him for daylight use during the Karelian operation, since the Finnish interceptor force was already much weakened. During the battle, when Stalin telephoned asking to be briefed on the air situation, he did not forget to ask Novikov how the two air divisions had fared, and their success established a precedent for the daylight use of ADD formations in a tactical ground support role in Belorussia.[24]

The plan for the Soviet Belorussian campaign was based on a double envelopment made on Minsk, which lay over 100 miles in the German rear, the right pincer from the north-east being provided by Cherniakhovsky's 3 Belorussian Front supported on its right flank by Bagramian's 1 Baltic Front, and the left pincer from the south-east being formed by Rokossovsky's 1 Belorussian Front. Meanwhile Petrov's 2 Belorussian Front, which was sandwiched between 1 and 3 Belorussian Fronts, was to make a series of frontal attacks to pin Army Group Centre.

Rokossovsky's plan had been based on two powerful blows and a two-pronged advance, one to the east and one to the west of the Berezina, this unusual solution having been forced on him by the relatively few areas in the Pripet which afforded good going. An author with the odd name of Nepomniashchy, writing in 1964, has described how Stalin disagreed with this dispersion of forces into two tactical blows, and twice ordered the front commander to retire from the Kremlin study to reconsider the matter; Molotov tried to persuade Rokossovsky not to oppose Stalin. But in spite of this, said Nepomniashchy, Rokossovsky would not be moved and it was Stalin who finally gave way.[25] Batov, who was unlikely to have been present, repeated this story, and Rokossovsky himself said that the incident occurred on the night of 22 May.[26] Zhukov, however, says that the incident never happened, 'for the general staff accepted and Stalin authorized the plan without question'.[27] Zhukov is supported in part by Telegin, who was the political member of Rokossovsky's Belorussian Front.[28]

At the time the military opinions on the aims, methods and scope of the Belorussian operation were divided; even now the accounts of the participants still differ.[29] Since the enemy had little tactical and virtually no operational depth in Belorussia, there was little doubt that the breakthrough would be successful, but there was disagreement on what should happen thereafter. According to Shtemenko, the general staff wanted to strike deeply and swiftly into the enemy rear and was opposed even to the use of the word 'encirclement', for it reasoned that a series of envelopment battles would be costly in casualties and time, allowing the enemy sufficient respite to reform his front. This view, however, found little favour with Zhukov.[30] On 23 May Stalin sided with Zhukov when he ruled that the object of the campaign was to be the encirclement and destruction of Army Group Centre. Within the fronts the arguments on tactical detail continued.[31]

Stalin was apparently convinced that the largest armoured formation which could be employed in Belorussia was the tank corps, while in the wooded sectors nothing larger than a brigade or a regiment might be used. Cherniakhovsky, who was himself a tank officer, had urged that he must have a tank army, in addition to independent corps and brigades. The general staff did not care, however, to raise the subject with Stalin.

The first general staff plan for the Belorussian operation had been completed on 14 May and recorded in a short manuscript text, written by Gryzlov, together with a marked map. On 20 May at a preliminary meeting attended by Zhukov and Vasilevsky, who had just returned wounded from the Crimea, Antonov presented the outline of the operation to Stalin, who ordered that Rokossovsky, Cherniakhovsky and Bagramian, together with their military councils, should report to the Kremlin on 22 and 23 May for co-ordinating presentations. Petrov, the Commander of 2 Belorussian Front, was not invited. Stalin called the new operation *Bagration*, after yet another Russian prince and general, the descendant of the *Bagratidae* of the royal house of Georgia.

The *Stavka* meetings on those two days were attended by Zhukov, Vasilevsky, Antonov, Voronov, Novikov, Iakovlev, Vorob'ev, Peresypkin and Khrulev. On 22 May Rokossovsky's military council presented its plans and, since these had been worked out in parallel with the general staff, they were immediately approved by the Supreme Commander. On the following day, however, there were some changes, for Bagramian thought that the operation might have greater success if he attacked westwards towards Polotsk to drive a wedge between Army Groups North and Centre. The proposal was accepted by Stalin.

Cherniakhovsky arrived in Moscow on 24 May, and he and Makarov, the political member, went over their plans with Zhukov and Vasilevsky; these did not take into account the allocation of a tank army. On the following day when the plans were presented to the *Stavka*, the moment appeared propitious to raise the question and Stalin agreed that Rotmistrov's 5 Guards Tank Army should be transferred from Malinovsky to Cherniakhovsky. Cherniakhovsky was to produce a new plan that night. Before dawn, Cherniakhovsky, Makarov and Shtemenko drove out to Stalin's far house on the Dmitrov road, where the dictator listened to their revised plan and confirmed it without comment.[32]

Vasilevsky said that the plans were built up by discussion and amendment, the general staff being ordered to correct and re-correct, each of the corrections being taken back to be confirmed by the Supreme Commander. On 30 May Stalin confirmed what was believed to be the final plan, and the date of the start of the offensive was provisionally set as 19 June. That evening, Stalin, as he had done frequently on such occasions in the past, emphasized that since the central planning was complete, it was the task of the GKO, the *Stavka* and the general staff, to go out into the field and help the commanders to get the troops ready. The dictator thought that there were quite enough people in the general staff and Commissariat of Defence for day to day work and would prefer that Zhukov and Vasilevsky did not outstay (*zasizhivalis'*) their welcome in the capital.[33] Zhukov would be responsible, as the *Stavka* representative, for Rokossovsky's 1 Belorussian Front making the main thrust in the south, while Vasilevsky would co-ordinate Bagramian's and Cherniakhovsky's offensive in the north. Before leaving for the fronts, Zhukov and Vasilevsky visited the dictator again to receive his final instructions; he warned them both that they must keep him closely informed of all developments.[34]

Shtemenko had been appointed as the *Stavka* representative with 2 Belorussian Front, being responsible in the first instance to Zhukov, and it was his unpleasant duty to replace, on the Supreme Commander's orders, its commander Petrov by Zakharov.

According to Shtemenko, Stalin was prejudiced against Petrov, who was unfortunate in having Mekhlis as the political member of his military council. Gorbatov described Mekhlis at about this time as being 'subdued, but still indefatigable, severe, inflexible, and extreme, and so mistrustful that he would not allow anyone else to write his messages for him'. Mekhlis continued, however, to write private letters to Stalin, and in one of these, so Stalin told Antonov and Shtemenko, he had described Petrov as being flabby and incapable and always under the doctor's care.[35]

Extracts from both Zhukov's and Vasilevsky's time-tables and diaries during this preparatory phase have since been published. On 5 June Zhukov was with Rokossovsky discussing the plans with heads of arms, and visiting the army commanders; the next morning he made his telephone report to Stalin asking him to ensure that Kaganovich and Khrulev completed the transportation plan in good time. On 6 June he set out to see the forward corps in Gorbatov's sector and, for the second time that day, reported the situation to the dictator. On 7 June, accompanied by his entourage of the front military council and members of the staff, he motored from Rogachev, arriving unannounced in the forward area of Batov's army. If Batov's 1962 account is to be believed, the hectoring Zhukov was much out of temper and entirely unreasonable, for without good cause he summarily ordered the removal of a corps commander and the committal of the commander of an infantry division to a penal company.[36] On 8 June Zhukov, accompanied by the artilleryman Iakovlev, toured 2 Belorussian Front forward area, together with Zakharov and Shtemenko.

On 10 June Zhukov and Rokossovsky were again in the forward areas and, when the Deputy Supreme Commander spoke to Stalin that day, he suggested that the whole of the long range air force should be allotted for operational and tactical air support in Belorussia and, when Stalin agreed to this, asked that Novikov and Golovanov should report to him by 11 June. On 11 June Zhukov was still complaining about the supply deficiencies. So day followed day, telephone reports being made direct to Stalin twice daily. On 19 June the conversations took a more optimistic note, Zhukov considering that preparations should be complete by 21 June. On 19 June Novikov, Khudiakov and Golovanov, together with the commanders of the two tactical air armies, began to prepare a joint artillery air support programme with Iakovlev, covering Rokossovsky's and Zakharov's fronts.[37]

The arrangements were excellent, but, according to Shtemenko, the two marshals, Zhukov and Vasilevsky, had taken everything for themselves. Vasilevsky had been assigned 350 long range aircraft as 3 Belorussian Front's share and 2 Belorussian Front got nothing. Shtemenko complained repeatedly to Zhukov, who eventually made what Shtemenko called some paper allocations, but as no representative of the long range air force ever appeared at Zakharov's headquarters, no use could be made of them. In the event, Zhukov was granted permission to postpone Rokossovsky's offensive by one day, as a result of which a number of his air formations were switched to support Zakharov for a period of twenty-four hours.[38]

Vasilevsky, who was with the 3 Belorussian and 1 Baltic Fronts, had with him Iakovlev's and Novikov's deputies, Chistiakov and Falaleev. Like Zhukov, he spent his time in visiting fronts and armies, and had long telephone conferences with Stalin. On 8 and 9 June Vasilevsky expressed his disquiet at the slow rate of arrival of reinforcements; on 11 June he spoke to Kaganovich telling him that the reinforcement and supply build-up and the move of Rotmistrov's army from the south must be completed by 18 June, and on the same day he warned Stalin that it was possible that the fronts would not be ready on time. Rotmistrov himself had come on ahead and it was, presumably, because of his reconnaissance reports that Vasilevsky began to have doubts about the wisdom of using the Orsha axis, and he reported these to Moscow on 17 June, suggesting that the tank army should be used north of Orsha where the enemy's defences were weaker. In reply Stalin made Vasilevsky responsible for selecting the axis and the timing for Rotmistrov's force. But until these were satisfactorily resolved Stalin proposed to keep 5 Guards Tank Army under his own hand by retaining it in the *Stavka* reserve.[39]

On 17 June Vasilevsky was still complaining about the lack of schedule on the railways, but matters improved thereafter, Stalin, as Shtemenko worded it, 'apparently having managed to exert his influence over the transport people'. That day Vasilevsky was recalled to Moscow and he and Antonov went to the Kremlin that night. After a discussion on Finland, Stalin turned to Belorussia.

First he told Antonov to report on the latest information coming from Normandy; and, after what Vasilevsky called 'an exchange of opinions', Stalin decided on the evening of 18 June as the latest report time for the preparations of the Belorussian offensive.

On the night of 18 June Vasilevsky and Antonov returned to Stalin's office, to make the final general staff presentation. Zhukov was still in Belorussia. During Vasilevsky's briefing, 'Stalin, as always, interested himself in the detail concerning the disposition, preparedness and security of the troops, and even in the working of the front command'. Stalin decided to postpone the offensive until 23 June. But then, while Vasilevsky was still in Moscow, Zhukov asked the Supreme Commander that Rokossovsky should be allowed a further day's preparation. Stalin asked for Vasilevsky's opinion. The Chief of General Staff consulted Cherniakhovsky and Bagramian on the telephone, and the three of them came to the conclusion that the postponement in the south would benefit the main offensive in the north since they, like Shtemenko, hoped to get some of Zhukov's share of Golovanov's long range air force for the interdiction tasks of 23 June.[40]

Peresypkin had been sent by Stalin out to the fronts, and he has since given some detail of the signal facilities of Cherniakhovsky's 3 Belorussian Front headquarters, based on a fleet of nineteen vehicles carrying Baudôt and ST-35 teleprint telegraph, telephone and radio, together with short wave radio telephone.[41] It was at about this time that the high frequency (V Ch) telephone appears to have been used on a radio link, for Konev has said that he was given 'a mobile V Ch station with a direct channel', to the Moscow circuit.[42]

On 22 June Stalin called Konev and Krainiukov to Moscow to outline their plans for the offensive into south-east Poland, and Krainiukov has described how members of the Politburo, the *Stavka* and the general staff had been summoned to Stalin's office to hear the presentation. Neither Zhukov nor Vasilevsky appears to have been there. Konev explained how he proposed to strike Army Group North Ukraine two major blows, a double envelopment aimed at encircling and destroying the enemy grouping near Brody. This plan had already been accepted in principle by Stalin and the general staff. Stalin, however, suddenly harked back to Zhukov's original concept, wanting to know why two separate blows should be aimed at the enemy; perhaps it wouldn't come off; why not one mighty shattering blow at Lvov. Stalin walked up and down reasoning with himself before finally accepting Konev's plan. The discussion continued and, according to Krainiukov, Stalin did not press his views; he closed the meeting by telling the military council that he would want to hear the plan again in its final form after the detail had been worked out, and he reminded the front commander that he was personally responsible for the success of the operation, which must be conducted without a flaw (*bezuprechno*).[43]

The Belorussian operation is said to have been mounted by 120 divisions of the 166 divisions forming the four fronts, and numbered over 5,000 tanks and 6,000 aircraft, not including the 1,000 aircraft of Golovanov's long range air force.[44] Busch's Army Group Centre comprised 38 infantry and two panzer divisions.[45] The violence of the Red Air Force bombing and machine-gun attacks paralyzed Army Group Centre so that the Red Army success was immediate and, since Hitler forbade any withdrawal by German troops, the Soviet front commanders retained the initiative throughout. By 28 June Soviet tanks were already over the Berezina and to the west of Lepel, and about 100,000 enemy had been cut off to the east of Minsk. Between 5 and 11 July the Soviet command began the destruction of this great pocket, without halting the rapid westward movement of its tank forces, so that, of the whole of Army Group Centre, only the wings remained, leaving a gaping hole in the German front; about 28 German divisions had been lost and the total casualties were put as high as 300,000 men.[46] The defeat was as great as that of Stalingrad.

On 6 July Burrows and members of the British Military Mission were taken on a three day visit to 3 Belorussian Front, the only time that Burrows had been permitted to go into a war theatre. The Soviet intention, so Burrows told London, was to impress on their allies the magnitude of the victory. Burrows had been for long a severe critic of Soviet obstructionism and was contemptuous of Slavin, the general staff liaison officer; he was all the more surprised, therefore, by the friendliness of Vasilevsky, whom he had not met before. Vasilevsky said that the Soviet success had been mainly due to the Red Air Force and artillery, but he detected deterioration in the fighting value of the Germans, who had 'a blockhouse mentality' and were nervous of their rear because of the partisans. The captured senior German officers with whom Burrows talked, said they had been surprised at the skill of the Soviet High Command. Burrows, an experienced observer, was amazed at 'the considerable disorder' in which the Red Army advanced, but, so well had Slavin done his work and so reticent were his hospitable Russian hosts, that Burrows was unaware of the appointments held by many of the officers with whom he talked; he conjectured, rightly, that F. F. Kuznetsov might be the Director of Military Intelligence, but he was convinced that the military commissar Makarov was Cherniakhovsky's chief of staff, so much was he in the front commander's confidence.[47]

Further to the south, on 6 July, Zhukov was with Batov's army, abusing its military council, so Batov said, in case Vasilevsky should be in Vilna before Zhukov had taken Baranovichi. The next day Stalin telephoned, ordering the Deputy Supreme Commander to return to Moscow.

Shortly after midday on 8 July Zhukov and Antonov joined Stalin at his summer *dacha*. Stalin wanted Zhukov's and Antonov's opinion as to whether Konev and Rokossovsky were strong enough to reach the Vistula unaided. Zhukov thought that the task was well within their capabilities and he suggested that Konev's front, which numbered 1,200,000 men, 2,000 tanks and 3,000 aircraft, was unnecessarily large, and could afford to transfer formations to Vasilevsky so that he might cut off Army Group North against the Baltic and occupy East Prussia. Vasilevsky, according to Zhukov, had already made a similar request to the Supreme Commander. Stalin, however, took the view that the enemy would defend East Prussia to the last and that Vasilevsky might get bogged down there. It would be preferable, he thought, to make sure of over-running the area of Lvov, and what he called the eastern regions of Poland.[48] Presumably the obtaining of a foothold in south-east Poland was, for political reasons, of greater priority.

Zhukov had been made responsible for the offensive south of the Pripet, the co-ordination of Konev's Lvov operation with the thrust of Rokossovsky's left wing from the area of Kovel. On 9 July Stalin and Zhukov jointly considered Rokossovsky's plan to strike with his reinforced left to the south of the marshes, destroy the enemy Lublin grouping, and advance on a broad front securing bridgeheads across the Vistula, at the same time thrusting north-wards on Brest, round the western edge of the marshes. Then, on 10 July, Zhukov studied Konev's plan before leaving the next morning for 1 Ukrainian Front, where he sited his command group near the inter-front boundary between Konev and Rokossovsky. The customary higher commander and staff planning rehearsals were held in the area of Kovel immediately before the attack, these being attended by Zhukov, Rokossovsky, Novikov and Peresypkin.[49]

Konev's attacks began on 13 July and four days later, when Rokossovsky joined in the general offensive, Konev's three tank armies had already entrapped a German corps of over 40,000 men at Brody. By 21 July, however, Konev's tanks were unable to make any ground towards Lvov, and the next day Zhukov agreed with Konev that a tank army should outflank Lvov from the north. Meanwhile the troops on Konev's right flank continued to move north-westwards on Sandomir.

In the early morning of 23 July, Konev told Zhukov that he had just received a telephone call from Stalin, asking what he and Zhukov 'were up to (*zateiali*) going for Sandomir'. The priority task, said Stalin, was to take Lvov. Zhukov was to telephone Stalin. The opportunity presented itself almost immediately afterwards when Rokossovsky's armoured troops took Lublin, Zhukov hastening to report the good news. Stalin was still resting in his Kremlin flat, but had already heard about Lublin. Khrush-chev, said Stalin, had been opposed to Zhukov's and Konev's tank raid and had told him about it. The whole trouble, continued Stalin, was that the two marshals were in too much of a hurry to get to the Vistula – after all it would not run away from them. They had better take Lvov first.[50] The general staff, so Shtemenko subsequently said, shared Stalin's view that Zhukov's tendency to undertake broad but inadequately supported offensives had to be checked.[51]

On 27 July, when the enemy had evacuated Lvov, a *Stavka* directive ordered Konev to secure a bridgehead over the Vistula by nightfall the next day, prior to seizing Sandomir. On 30 July Konev was across the Vistula, having covered over 130 miles in nineteen days. Rokossovsky's advance immediately to the north,

NORTHERN EUROPE
(Frontiers as in 1923)

0   200
Miles

SWEDEN

Baltic Sea

Tallinn
Yamburg
ESTHONIA
Tartu
Pskov
Ostrov
KURLAND
Riga
Libau
LATVIA
Daugavpils
(Dvinsk)
Memel
Siavliai
LITHUANIA
Rostock
Tilsit
Kaunas
(Kovno)
Vilnius
(Vilna)
Gdynia
Königsberg
MECKLENBURG
Danzig
EAST PRUSSIA
Kolberg
Marienburg
Suwalki
POMERANIA
Neustettin
Allenstein
Stettin
GERMANY
BERLIN
Küstrin
Bialystok
Baranovichi
Potsdam
Frankfurt
BRANDENBURG
Poznan
Cottbus
WARSAW
Leipzig
Brest Litovsk
Pinsk
Dresden
POLAND
SAXONY
Breslau
Radom
SILESIA
Lublin
Oppeln
PRAGUE
Sandomir
Rovno
C Z E C H O
Ratibor
Cracow
Lvov
S L O V A K I A
VIENNA
AUSTRIA
BUDA-PEST
RUMANIA
H U N G A R Y

had been even more rapid. The Pripet Marshes had been left far behind and the forward troops were within twenty miles of Warsaw. The long advance from Galicia into southern Poland had, however, given rise to a long and exposed Carpathian flank to the south of 1 Ukrainian Front. At the end of July when Konev had asked for a separate command to take over responsibility for his two flanking armies in the south, Stalin had replied that, as Petrov and the 4 Ukrainian Front headquarters were held in the *Stavka* reserve, they could report on 4 August and become operational the next day.[52] Mekhlis was ordered to join the new headquarters.

On 27 July there had been a *Stavka* meeting to discuss future strategy, attended by Stalin, Zhukov, Vasilevsky, Antonov, Shtemenko and Gryzlov; the question of an advance into East Prussia was brought up yet again. Stalin ruled that operations in the north should be undertaken systematically and in sequence, the area of the Baltic States being encircled and chopped off from East Prussia, following which East Prussia would be enveloped and cut off from the rest of Germany. Stalin told the meeting that several generals had complained about those *Stavka* representatives 'who took the conduct of operations out of the hands of the front commanders'; Zhukov gave his opinion that *Stavka* representatives should have the right to do this, and, as Shtemenko commented, 'Zhukov, with his powerful personality, did so anyway'. A compromise was announced in a special decree of 29 July, whereby only Zhukov and Vasilevsky were permitted to take over control of field operations.[53]

Lvov, as the western allies were yet to learn, was regarded in Moscow as Ukrainian and not Polish; Lublin, however, was recognized as being inside Poland, and there, as Rokossovsky said, the Polish National Liberation Committee assumed control. On 1 August Bor-Komorowski, the Commander-in-Chief of the London supported Polish Home Army (AK), began the ill-fated insurrection against the Germans in Warsaw. The AK leaders in the areas held by the Red Army were being hunted down and arrested, but Stalin was apparently unwilling to involve the Red Army in openly fighting Polish patriots. At first Stalin pretended to his western allies that there was no rising in Warsaw, then that the AK was friendly to the Germans, and finally, claimed that its leaders were both criminal and irresponsible in needlessly sacrificing Polish lives. On 16 August Moscow informed the British Government that it proposed to have nothing to do with the affair, and, three days later, Moscow refused a British and United States request for air-landing facilities on Soviet soil so that the insurgents might be supplied by air with arms, ammunition and medical supplies. On 22 August in a message to Churchill Stalin referred to the AK as a group of criminals.[54]

After Soviet protestations of friendliness and gratitude, the local Vilna AK leaders had been invited on 17 July to a staff conference with Cherniakhovsky, only three days before Deane and the United States mission arrived there. The Poles were not seen again. Yet Rokossovsky complained that the AK leaders near Lublin were shy of his offers of help. Though the Kremlin protested afterwards that it had been informed of the rising only after it had begun, it is also true that it had dropped manifesto leaflets from the air, inciting the Poles to take up arms against the Germans and that, on 29 July, Moscow radio was calling on Warsaw to do the same.[55]

Rokossovsky, who knew of the uprising on 2 August, has absolved the Soviet leadership of responsibility simply by postulating in a single sentence that the problem was his own, saying that 'certain critics in the western press did at one time accuse the 1 Belorussian Front and its commander of deliberately not supporting the Warsaw insurgents'.[56] If Rokossovsky is to be believed 'Stalin wanted to give all possible help to the insurgents and ease their plight'. An earlier communist view of capitalist Poland was that expressed in Lenin's instructions to Skliansky.[57] Time was to show that Stalin had no intention of restoring the former Polish government, for, as he told Zhukov in March 1945, the Soviet Union 'could not permit Churchill to establish a *bourgeois* alien Poland on its borders'. Concern over the fate of the AK supporters was hardly likely to move a man who had already purged Poland in 1939, destroying or transporting its leaders, intellectuals, priests, landowners and much of its working class and peasantry, in their tens of thousands, and who intended to do it yet again as soon as Poland was overrun.

At the end of September Stalin ordered that Warsaw should be outflanked from the north, much in the same way as Tukhachevsky had attempted in 1920. But the enemy artillery was so strong in the area that Red Army casualties mounted rapidly, forcing Rokossovsky to cancel the offensive; he immediately informed Stalin by telephone and the dictator confirmed the decision. Zhukov has a different version in that he said that it was he who telephoned the Supreme Commander and asked for permission to halt the offensive. Zhukov's report, or the way he delivered it, angered Stalin, and he ordered Zhukov and Rokossovsky to report to him in Moscow the next day. Molotov and Antonov were present there, and, according to Zhukov, the dictator was restless and displeased. He sat silent, leaving it to Molotov to question the wisdom of going over to the defence when faced with a beaten enemy.

When Zhukov was asked for other proposals for an offensive against Warsaw, he suggested encircling the capital from the south-west. Stalin became heated and told them to go to the waiting room 'and think some more'. Twenty minutes later Stalin recalled them to say that 1 Belorussian Front might go over to the defensive; future plans would be discussed later. Zhukov said that he and Rokossovsky left in silence, 'going their separate ways, each preoccupied with his own thoughts'. The next day Zhukov learned that he was to cease being the *Stavka* representative and co-ordinator of fronts and was to take over the command of 1 Belorussian Front from Rokossovsky, a decision which he associated in part with Stalin's displeasure.[58] Rokossovsky mentions nothing about this meeting but says that Stalin did not inform him about his transfer until 12 November.[59]

It is not impossible that Zhukov's account may have been meant to emphasize to the present day Polish reader that Stalin did his utmost for the Warsaw insurgents. On the other hand Zhukov may have been removed from his post as a *Stavka* representative, as he said, due to a difference of opinion with Stalin, not necessarily that which he described, for it can be deduced from his memoirs that he remained sensitive about the incident which was a blow to his dignity and self-esteem. He has assured his readers that he remained the Deputy Supreme Commander, which was indeed the case, and that all other *Stavka* representative posts were abolished at this time, this latter statement being untrue. For it was not until the end of the year that Stalin asked his commanders and staffs whether they considered the use of *Stavka* representatives still necessary. Zhukov, by then a front commander, replied that they were not, as the shortening frontages meant that fronts could easily be co-ordinated from Moscow. When the same question was put to Antonov, he 'as usual', said Shtemenko, rang Vasilevsky for his views. Vasilevsky thought that *Stavka* representatives should be retained in certain circumstances where the local conditions were complicated, particularly to the flanks in the area of the Baltic and in the Balkans. Stalin agreed with Vasilevsky, and Vasilevsky, Govorov and Timoshenko remained as *Stavka* representatives throughout the early months of 1945.[60]

Vasilevsky had remained in the area of the Baltic from June 1944, responsible for the co-ordination and supervision of 1 and 2 Baltic Fronts and 3 Belorussian Front. At the beginning of July when it appeared that the Red Army formations which had thrust forward in a great salient to the Lithuanian frontier were about to envelop the enemy Army Group North, the Supreme Commander issued a series of directives. Govorov's Leningrad and Maslennikov's 3 Baltic Fronts were to attack on both sides of Lake Peipus into Estonia, while Eremenko's 2 Baltic Front was to advance due west, supporting Bagramian's wheeling movement in the direction of Riga. On 6 July Stalin signed the directive to 3 Baltic Front, but two days later, when the general staff were making the customary briefing report, Stalin decided that as no one had been out to see Maslennikov, whom he described as a young commander with an inexperienced staff, Shtemenko should go, taking Iakovlev and Vorozheikin with him.[61] Eremenko and Maslennikov began to make ground westwards, but the situation was changed yet again when, on 27 July, Bagramian took Siauliai, a main road and rail communication centre, midway between Riga and Tilsit. A *Stavka* telephone and written directive was then sent to Bagramian ordering him to turn his main forces northwards on Riga, but, at the same time, to continue westwards with a subsidiary thrust on Memel to sever the coastal railway between Tilsit and Riga. By 31 July the Red Army reached the Bay of Riga near Tukums, but was driven back again when an enemy counter-attack re-established a narrow coastal corridor reconnecting Army Group North with Kurland.

Many Soviet historians consider that in its strategic concept the Baltic operation was one of the largest and most important of the

1944 campaigns.[62] Stalin was of the opinion that the Baltic area should be cleared before the main thrust on the Warsaw-Berlin axis could begin, because he regarded Army Group North as a threat to his flank.[63] Bagramian's rapid success presented the first opportunity to encircle Army Group North and pin it against the sea east of the Bay of Riga, and in order that Vasilevsky might devote his attention to this task he was ordered temporarily to relinquish his responsibility for Cherniakhovsky's 3 Belorussian Front and concentrate on co-ordinating the three Baltic fronts in a renewal of the offensive on Riga. The offensive, which began on 14 September, made good progress and, so Moscow believed, had some influence on Finland's decision on 19 September finally to withdraw from the war. The Germans began to pull back from the Narva area, Tallinn was evacuated on 22 September, and four days later the whole of the Estonian coast had been cleared.

By 24 September it had become obvious that the enemy was withdrawing the bulk of his forces from Estonia to Kurland, and in consequence Stalin no longer showed interest in closing the Riga gap. Since the enemy was also trying to envelop Bagramian's right flank from the west, Stalin decided to shift the main thrust in a 90 degree arc due west on Memel, both to envelop the enveloper and to cut off the whole of Army Group North in Kurland. Bagramian's 1 Baltic and Cherniakhovsky's 3 Belorussian Fronts were to provide the main force. Vasilevsky reassumed control as the *Stavka* representative of 3 Belorussian Front on 1 October and gave up Eremenko's and Maslennikov's fronts to Govorov, who henceforth was responsible to Stalin as the *Stavka* representative for clearing the area of the Baltic States and islands, using 2 and 3 Baltic Fronts and his own Leningrad Front.[64]

According to Shtemenko, Stalin took a close interest in the preparation of the Memel operation, discussing with Vasilevsky all details concerning the grouping of the forces and the deception measures required to conceal the movement of nearly half a million men, 10,000 guns and 1,300 tanks from Bagramian's right to his left, over distances of up to 150 miles.[65] The operation began on 5 October and, after a six day engagement, Vol'sky's tank army reached the sea; Memel was invested and Army Group North was finally isolated in Kurland.

Further to the north Govorov had been ordered by a *Stavka*

directive of 6 October to reduce the Riga enclave, then about 30 miles in depth. Govorov, whom Shtemenko described as grim, reticent and sombre, was, apparently, held in high regard by the troops; his career had not been easy, for it had always been held against him that he was once a White Guard artillery officer with Kolchak; in 1936 he had not been allowed to complete the course at the General Staff Academy, and it was said that in 1940 he was again under a cloud and in danger of arrest. In 1942, however, he was accepted into the party without candidate status, presumably at Stalin's nomination, and between 1943 and October 1944 he had risen rapidly in rank from colonel-general to marshal of the Soviet Union. In the field, south of Riga, he made a strong and favourable impression on Kazakov, the Commander of 10 Guards Army, by his thoughtful and taciturn manner and by the firm way in which he handled Eremenko, the Commander of 2 Baltic Front, refusing to allow him to reinforce defeat and insisting that Kazakov's army be regrouped south of the West Dvina.[66] Riga was cleared of the enemy who withdrew westwards into Kurland. Immediately afterwards, on 16 October, Maslennikov's 3 Baltic Front was disbanded.

Further attempts by the two Baltic Fronts to reduce the enemy Kurland group, consisting of no fewer than 26 German divisions, failed, and the Soviet High Command was forced to turn its attention to more important theatres and accept the existence of this isolated enemy force far in its rear. The enemy Kurland group remained in being until after the end of the war.

A department had been formed within the general staff responsible for publishing regular training bulletins summarizing 'the lessons learned at the front during the course of the fighting', and Stalin studied each copy as soon as it appeared. Its editor was Vechny, who was conscious that he had to rehabilitate himself in Stalin's eyes for the spring 1942 *débâcle* in the Crimea, where he had been Kozlov's chief of staff.

It was by his careful reading of this military periodical that Stalin became aware in the autumn of 1944, that Voronov had issued two regulations (*ustavy*) concerning field and anti-aircraft artillery, both countersigned by Zhukov, without the dictator's knowledge – Stalin called it 'without the authority of the *Stavka*'. When Stalin queried the matter with the general staff, Antonov knew nothing and was given two days to investigate. When the general staff report was made to the Politburo, Stalin's irritation was increased when he realized that his two illustrious marshals did not understand the difference between an *ustav* and a *prikaz*.

According to Shtemenko, who was present at the time, Stalin thought the matter over as he walked up and down. Then, turning to the Politburo members, he said that an order must be given out, but, 'since it would be improper for the general staff to do this to two generals of such rank', the Politburo itself would perform the duty. He then dictated an order, extracts from which are shown below.

> One. Marshal Zhukov, without sufficient checking, without calling for or consulting the people at the front, and without notifying the *Stavka,* confirmed and enacted the *ustav.* [At this point Stalin included definitions explaining the difference between an *ustav* and a *prikaz.*]
> Two. I reprove Chief Marshal of Artillery Comrade Voronov for his light-hearted attitude to artillery regulations.
> Three. I make it incumbent upon Marshal Zhukov to display circumspection in deciding serious questions.

Stalin then appointed a commission under Bulganin to investigate the matter.[67]

Rumania had for long wanted to leave the war. In April and May 1944, secret peace talks were held with the Soviet Union's repretives in Cairo, and these contacts appear to have continued in Stockholm and in Bessarabia throughout the summer. Bucharest was not, however, a free agent, as there were 360,000 German field troops inside Rumania, forming, together with about 450,000 Rumanians, Friessner's Army Group South Ukraine. Since the Rumanian monarch and an influential part of the political and military leadership intended that Rumania should seek an armistice, there was little question of prosecuting the war with vigour. This political and military background, and the fact that Rumanian resistance was not to be reckoned with, are not, however, admitted in Soviet historical accounts, all of which depict the August 1944

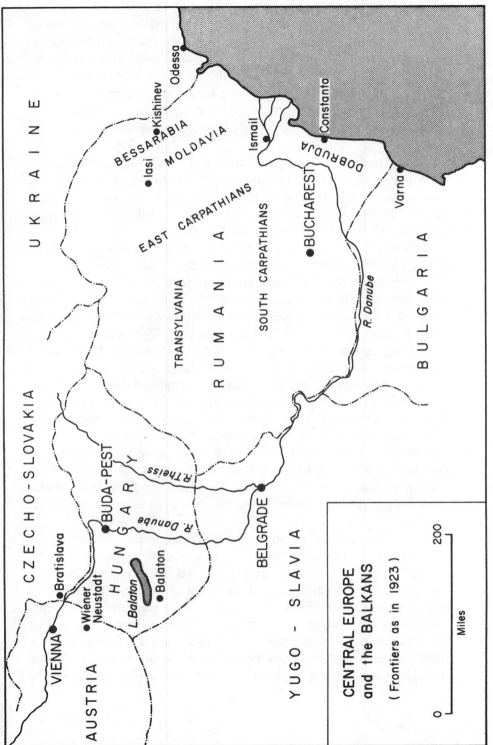

CENTRAL EUROPE
and the BALKANS

(Frontiers as in 1923)

Miles

0   200

campaign as a well planned and ably executed operation, a model of a victory of Soviet arms over the joint German and Rumanian forces. The Soviet invasion of Rumania was undertaken by Malinovsky's 2 Ukrainian and Tolbukhin's 3 Ukrainian Fronts under Timoshenko's co-ordination as the *Stavka* representative. Together the two fronts numbered over 90 divisions, six tank and mechanized corps, in all 939,000 men, 1,400 tanks and 1,700 aircraft.[68]

Stalin took a close interest in the planning of the campaign and personally went over Malinovsky's plans, even altering the sectors selected by the front commander for the main breakthrough. On 21 August Stalin is said to have dictated a directive to Timoshenko ordering the encirclement of 6 German Army, and, according to Shtemenko, only 24 hours later sent off his congratulations on the mission having been satisfactorily accomplished.[69]

When the offensive began on 20 August the Rumanian forces gave way without a fight and refused to obey German orders. On 23 August Antonescu, the Rumanian dictator, was arrested, and the king broadcast that the war was at an end. The Axis defence in Moldavia rapidly fell apart and Malinovsky's and Tolbukhin's spearheads joined in a double envelopment entrapping the main element of twenty German divisions. Only five days afterwards this great pocket on both sides of the Pruth, numbering nearly 200,000 men, had been completely destroyed, a remarkable achievement when compared with the protracted operations necessary to destroy the earlier 6 German Army at Stalingrad.[70] In Soviet military annals this Rumanian victory takes precedence only after that at the Volga and in Belorussia.[71] Both Malinovsky and Tolbukhin were promoted to the rank of marshal of the Soviet Union.

Soviet motorized columns were overrunning the whole of Rumania and, on 8 September, Zhukov was already with Tolbukhin when the 3 Ukrainian Front crossed the Bulgarian frontier unopposed.[72] The Bulgarian declaration of war on Germany and the approach of Tolbukhin's 3 Ukrainian Front to Yugo-Slavia threatened the communications of the German Army Group E in Greece, and, following the widespread partisan uprisings of 8 September, German troops began to withdraw from the Greek islands and mainland. Tolbukhin eventually wheeled northwards coming up on the left flank of Malinovsky's 2 Ukrainian Front which was moving north-westwards from Rumania into Hungarian occupied Transylvania. On 29 August Stalin signed a directive to Petrov's 4 Ukrainian Front, which was facing 1 Hungarian Army in the East Carpathian foothills, ordering it to go over to 'a firm defence, based on three entrenched systems echeloned to a depth of not less than twenty to twenty-five miles, with strong corps, army and front reserves in the main sectors'.[73] Since Petrov was by then flanking the withdrawing remnants of Friessner's forces and was well placed to put pressure on the enemy held Szekler salient from the north while Malinovsky attacked it from the south, 4 Ukrainian Front was, shortly afterwards, transferred to Timoshenko's control.

On 1 October a Hungarian delegation arrived secretly in Moscow to sign an armistice, but three days later the Germans became aware of the negotiations and seized all Hungarian communication centres. On 16 October, the day after Horthy had broadcast that the war was at an end, the Hungarian government was arrested and removed to Germany, for Hitler had decided to hold Hungary and the Transylvanian plateau for its oil, manganese and bauxite. In no other theatre was the German resistance so bitter in this final stage of the war.

Timoshenko's offensive, which had started on 6 October, moved across the Hungarian plain, reaching, on 28 October, a point about forty miles south of Budapest. On that day Mekhlis sent a personal telegram to Stalin from 4 Ukrainian Front telling him that the Hungarian forces were totally demoralized, from which Stalin concluded that the capital could be easily occupied. Together with the general staff he drew up a hasty plan whereby the German right, between the Theiss and the Danube, which was held by elements of 3 Hungarian Army still in the Axis service, was to be attacked. Stalin transmitted the plan to Malinovsky by telephone and demanded the immediate taking of Budapest; and, said Shtemenko, 'since Antonov was not aware of the local conditions, he was unable to represent to Stalin that Mekhlis's report was false'.[74] Malinovsky had asked if the offensive could be put off for five or six days, so that it might be properly prepared, but was told that he was to attack on the morrow. It was necessary, said Stalin, whatever the cost, to take the Hungarian capital immediately for political reasons.[75] Malinovsky then suggested a two day postponement until a mechanized corps could be brought up on 1 November; but Stalin would not allow even this, and he accused the front commander of stubbornness, and, after ordering him 'categorically to attack Budapest', abruptly hung up. A few minutes later Antonov rang Malinovsky, asking for the time of the attack, in order that he might report it to the Supreme Commander. Malinovsky named the date as 29 October and he subsequently blamed Stalin for the ill-judged haste which, although it brought Red Army troops to within a few miles of the city outskirts, failed to take the capital.[76]

The general staff soon came to the conclusion that Malinovsky's appreciation of the local situation was the correct one, but, said Shtemenko, 'as the decision to attack from the Theiss was made personally by Stalin, no one could alter it'. But Antonov suggested that Malinovsky should put his case to the Supreme Commander on 4 November and he promised to give it general staff support. This, however, availed Malinovsky nothing, for Stalin merely demanded that the offensive be renewed by not later than 7 November, and in a written directive he laid down the mechanized-cavalry group's tasks. Not until 24 November, following the receipt of a report from Timoshenko, would Stalin agree to call off the attacks in favour of an offensive which was to encircle Budapest from the north.[77] This new operation was to be made in conjunction with Tolbukhin's 3 Ukrainian Front which was by then entering South Hungary from Yugo-Slavia.

11
The Year 1945

Since Stalin had directed that Antonov should be the principal speaker when the Soviet military plans were presented to Churchill and Eden during their mid-October Moscow visit, Antonov's draft was sent down to Kuntsevo to be checked and corrected. The dictator disagreed with Antonov's description of the aims of Soviet strategy, and he began to rewrite the offending paragraphs. The Soviet Union, he told Shtemenko, had a primary interest in occupying and holding Hungary as the centre of Europe; let us convince the allies, he continued, that we are much stronger on this Balkan flank than we really are; and we will tell them that the basis of our strategy in this theatre is to get into Germany from the south as quickly as possible, by first smashing Hungary.[1]

Antonov was particularly reticent in the presence of foreigners, but, on 14 October, Brooke found him most friendly and communicative. Antonov explained how the Red Army forces had been attacking on the Baltic and Balkan flanks where the going was softer, and how the capitulation of Hungary might open up possibilities for attacks on Germany from the south.[2]

That same evening the British delegation, together with Harriman and Deane, attended a military presentation in Stalin's Kremlin conference room. Brooke described to the meeting the allied operations in Europe and Burma, and Deane gave an address covering the Pacific War. This was followed by a description of operations in the Russo-German theatres, given by Antonov, who, according to Eden, was lucid and fluent but always looking to Stalin for confirmation.[3] He was continually interrupted by

Stalin, who, in Deane's view, was determined to impress Churchill with the tremendous accomplishments of the Red Army. Eventually Antonov's caution in revealing Red Army plans seemed to irritate Stalin, who took the pointer from him and outlined the proposed Soviet operations.[4] It was Stalin, whom Ismay described as 'much on the ball', who answered most of the questions put by the allied delegations.[5]

At six o'clock the next evening, when the talks were resumed, Stalin told the meeting that the Soviet Union would deploy 60 divisions in the Far East, 30 more than were already there, and it would take three months to do this after the war with Germany was ended. In reply to a question from Harriman, Stalin said that the Soviet Union would go to war against Japan three months after Germany's defeat, provided that the United States would assist in building up the necessary reserve supplies and provided that 'the political aspects of the Soviet Union's participation had been clarified'. He agreed that the Petropavlovsk naval base and airfields in the maritime provinces should be put at the disposal of the United States forces, but made it clear that the Americans would have to use the Pacific and not the Trans-Siberian route.[6]

Brooke asked Antonov whether the 60 Red Army divisions could be maintained by the Trans-Siberian railway, and said subsequently that 'Antonov undoubtedly knew the answer but was not certain what Stalin would require him to say'. Antonov looked at Stalin for guidance, but got no help; at a loss, he said that the railway could supply the force, and he was at once brushed aside by Stalin who launched into what Brooke called 'an astounding presentation of technical railway detail': the railway capacity was limited to 36 pairs of trains a day of which five pairs were required for railway maintenance and five for the civilian population in the maritime provinces. In Stalin's view the balance of 26 trains available to the military, with a lift of 600–700 tons each, would not be adequate for 60 divisions and the air forces in the Far East, and he quoted the example of Kuropatkin who was brought to a standstill through lack of supplies during the Russo-Japanese War. It was essential, concluded Stalin, to stockpile two to three months' maintenance reserves in the Far East before the start of operations. Brooke said that he was more than ever impressed by the dictator's military ability.[7] However, a military logistic planner, using Stalin's own figures, can easily deduce that the force would require a daily supply of little over 5,000 tons and that three months' maintenance reserves could be stockpiled in 45 days. Antonov was therefore right and Stalin was wrong; but Stalin was determined to receive United States sea-landed supplies in the Far East, and, at the same time, deny the Americans the use of the Trans-Siberian railway.

The third military meeting on 17 October was attended only by Soviet and United States representatives. Stalin illustrated on a map the strategy he intended to use in his Far Eastern offensive, and then presented what Deane called his bill, a list for a two months' supply of food, fuel and transport based on a Far East force of one and a half million men, 3,000 tanks, 75,000 motor vehicles and 5,000 aircraft, in all the surprisingly high figure of over a million tons of goods. The deliveries were to be completed by 30 June 1945 and were additional to the supply programme already agreed under the current fourth protocol. At this meeting Stalin was agreeable to all the American counterproposals on the use of Soviet air and naval bases; joint planning could begin at once. But, said Deane, these promises were not met and the end result was that the Russians got their supplies and the United States got nothing. On 27 October Deane succeeded in obtaining a meeting with Antonov, but found that he was interested only in having confirmation that the supply programme was approved; and Antonov brushed aside the other points raised, saying that they were under consideration by the general staff. Deane's experience of dealing with Moscow led him to conclude that an American air force would never be based in Siberia.[8]

Shtemenko, more than 20 years after the event, described the strategic survey drawn up by himself, Antonov, Gryzlov and Lomov at the beginning of November 1944, recommending that the main offensives should be switched to Hungary and East Prussia so that the enemy would be obliged to reinforce his flanks at the expense of his centre. Then Zhukov's and Konev's fronts, side by side on the Vistula, would strike westwards in a swift offensive against Army Group A to a depth of up to 430 miles in 45 days, a distance which would take them to the west of Berlin and Dresden, 'the attack on Berlin being made quickly, and without a pause'.[9] Such a plan comes strangely from one who had censured Zhukov for so boldly outflanking Lvov.

In preparing the campaign plan for 1945 Stalin did not follow his usual practice of holding a general conference of all front commanders, but he summoned each front commander in turn to Moscow. The fronts' axes were decided at this time; Cherniakhovsky's 3 Belorussian Front was to strike for Königsberg; Rokossovsky's 2 Belorussian Front was to make two blows, one at Marienburg to envelop the East Prussian forces and the other at Allenstein, to assist Cherniakhovsky; Zhukov was to bypass Warsaw and advance on Poznan, while his left would co-operate with Konev's right. Konev and Petrov were to take Cracow in the initial offensive while Tolbukhin and Malinovsky were to clear Hungary and enter Austria. Stalin approved the plans in principle, said Shtemenko, and agreed that the offensive in the centre would probably begin about 20 January; no directives were issued however. Since the Supreme Commander had decided personally to control the four fronts which were advancing into Germany, Vasilevsky gave up his co-ordinating role for 3 Belorussian Front but took from Govorov the responsibility for 2 Baltic Front.

Zhukov was already at work with the general staff in late October and early November, primarily in connection with the central sector, and he was subsequently critical of Stalin for rejecting his earlier advice to give priority to the destruction of the enemy in East Prussia. From November onwards Zhukov concerned himself only with the projected operations for the 1 Belorussian Front. Contrary to what Shtemenko has said, Zhukov has made it clear that there was no question of striking directly for Berlin, for Stalin had agreed only to the first phase, that is to say the offensive into East Prussia by Cherniakhovsky and Rokossovsky, while Zhukov thrust towards Poznan and Konev reached the Oder between Glogau and Ratibor. It was even considered possible, said Zhukov, that 1 Belorussian Front might have to move a considerable part of its forces northwards to support Rokossovsky, for the entire 2 Belorussian Front was spearheaded against (*natselen protiv*) the East Prussia grouping.[10]

Rokossovsky's account of his mission reads yet differently. He had been aggrieved at losing the command of 1 Belorussian

Front, and Stalin's purpose in summoning him to Moscow, on or about 17 November, was, so Rokossovsky said, to assure him that 2 Belorussian Front was a main and not a secondary front. Stalin personally outlined Rokossovsky's task, saying that he was to advance on a north-westerly axis, ignoring the East Prussia grouping which was Cherniakhovsky's responsibility; indeed no mention was made of any co-ordination with this right hand neighbour, although, as Rokossovsky added, 'subsequent events forced the 2 Belorussian Front to turn a large number of troops to the north'. On the other hand, special emphasis was placed by Stalin on the necessity for co-ordination with Zhukov on the left, and Stalin drew a red arrow on the map to demonstrate how Rokossovsky was to attack the flank of the enemy in front of Zhukov 'if 1 Belorussian Front's advance should slow down'.[11]

Vasilevsky has attempted to put these differences into perspective. He had been recalled to the *Stavka* at the beginning of November and immediately started work, where Zhukov had left off, on the plans for the winter and spring offensive. Several members of the GKO and Politburo were involved in the planning, which, said Vasilevsky, took place under Stalin's direction. Opinions had been divided as to what action should be taken against the enemy in East Prussia, but, emphasized Vasilevsky, in the plan accepted by the Supreme Commander the aim was *to destroy* Army Group Centre. In the first stage, 2 and 3 Belorussian Fronts were to envelop the enemy, cutting him off against the sea, and in the second, while 1 Baltic and part of 3 Belorussian Fronts were rolling up the encircled enemy, 2 Belorussian and 1 Belorussian Fronts would overrun Pomerania. Vasilevsky has reiterated the established planning sequence. When the plans had been drafted by the general staff and the front military councils, they were presented to Stalin for approval. The front commanders were then summoned to Stalin and the plans were presented and examined yet again. Vasilevsky admitted that he was back in the Baltic area when Rokossovsky was interviewed, but he obviously doubts Rokossovsky's account of the talk with Stalin, for, said Vasilevsky, Stalin did not mince matters or words, always speaking with firmness and bluntness (*tverdost' i nepokolebimost'*) and there was never any doubt that all his verbal orders were confirmed in writing without the slightest material change.[12]

Vasilevsky's explanation does not, however, refute Rokossovsky's contention that the *Stavka* plan was a bad one. The *Stavka* directive of 28 November gave Rokossovsky the principal task of sealing East Prussia from the south-west by a thrust on Marienburg, and a secondary, in co-operation with Zhukov, to destroy the stronghold of Modlin on the inter-front boundary. Not until 20 January did Rokossovsky learn, so he has said, that he would have to turn four armies northwards to break up the enemy grouping in East Prussia.[13] He certainly remained responsible for supporting Zhukov's right flank, and, as events proved, Zhukov did not hesitate to complain to Stalin when Rokossovsky lagged behind.[14] This *affaire de rien* between the Soviet marshals cannot be resolved by their reproduction of incomplete, contradictory and possibly out of context directive extracts. The truth of the matter appears to have been that Rokossovsky came to be given two separate missions on widely divergent axes by Stalin, tasks which should have been entrusted either to two separate fronts or, more logically, have involved the transfer of Rokossovsky's right flank armies to Cherniakhovsky. In this particular instance Rokossovsky was not directed to hand over his armies to Cherniakhovsky until 10 February.

When Konev had been called to Moscow in November to discuss his final plan, members of the GKO were present. As usual the address and explanations were given by the front commander, although the details of the operation were already known to Stalin. Konev has said that he well remembered how Stalin discussed the plan in detail and emphasized the economic importance of the industrial region of Silesia by pointing it out on the map with his finger and repeating the word 'gold'.[15]

Although preparations for a Soviet offensive were ready in early December, the Red Army lay inactive, and in German quarters the erroneous view was expressed that the delay was deliberate, in that the Kremlin was trying to bring pressure on its western allies to recognize the Lublin Poles as the *de jure* government.[16] In truth, Moscow was unwilling to begin an offensive in the heavy mud and poor visibility, since these would make it impossible to exploit the Soviet fire, armoured and mechanized superiority. As early as 14 December Stalin had told Harriman that he was awaiting a spell of fine weather before starting any major action, and the fact that the Red Army had long been ready and was waiting for clear and frosty weather had been noted in German war diary entries at the time.[17] On 6 January Churchill had sent a personal communication to Stalin asking whether a renewal of the Vistula offensive could be counted on during January, the Ardennes battle being, in Churchill's words, very heavy; in reply Stalin explained that he was awaiting a change in the weather but promised an offensive not later than the second half of January.[18] On 8 January, however, there were definite indications that Poland was about to have cold and hard weather and this was confirmed by the meteorological reports the next day. On 9 January Antonov spoke in Stalin's name to Konev on the *V Ch*, ordering the offensive to begin three days later. The cold spell lasted for only nine days, but was sufficient to take the Red Army to the Oder.

On 15 January, Tedder, the Deputy Supreme Commander to Eisenhower, had a meeting with Stalin at which they discussed details of impending operations, including the targets of the western air operations, and Stalin assured his listener that he had begun his own offensive early, on 12 January, in response to Churchill's request, and that operations would continue for about two and a half months, their objective being the line of the Oder. A second offensive would then be mounted about the end of May.[19]

Vasilevsky was recalled to Moscow to remain in the capital while Stalin and Antonov went to the Crimea for the Yalta conference, his *Stavka* representative duties in the area of the Baltic having been assumed by Govorov.[20] When Stalin and Molotov called on Churchill at Yalta on the afternoon of 4 February, Churchill suggested, without the agreement of his own chiefs of staff, that a British force should be sent from Italy through northern Yugo-Slavia to operate on the Soviet left flank, a suggestion which, according to Shtemenko, was most unwelcome to Stalin.[21] Stalin gave his view that the war might go on until the summer and that it was desirable that there should be some co-ordination of the offensives between east and west. Co-ordinating discussions were accordingly held on 5 and 6 February between Antonov, Kuznetsov and Khudiakov and the United States and British chiefs of staff. On the Soviet side Antonov was the main speaker. Since the British and Americans were not in complete accord and Antonov was unwilling to commit himself without reference to Stalin, little was effected.[22]

Konev had begun his attacks on 12 January and the other fronts went over to the offensive in the course of the next three days. The German defence could not hold, because it was tied rigidly to ground, had no mobile reserves and lacked operative depth. On 17 January a *Stavka* directive laid down a time programme for the taking of the objectives, Zhukov to be on the Poznan line before 4 February, Konev to be on the Oder by 30 January, and to take Cracow, together with Petrov, by 22 February.

On 25 January Zhukov telephoned Stalin to say that the enemy was demoralized, and, since the enemy grouping to the north in East Pomerania was no immediate danger, there was nothing to prevent a westward advance and the seizing of a bridgehead across the Oder at Küstrin. Stalin was at first doubtful of the wisdom of Zhukov's suggestion since such a thrust would be unsupported by Rokossovsky or Konev, but after some days he agreed that Zhukov should advance to the Oder, on the firm understanding that 1 Belorussian Front should protect its own right flank.[23]

While Stalin was considering the Küstrin proposal, Zhukov had, on 26 January, put forward an even more ambitious plan. He suggested that 1 Belorussian Front should cross the Oder on 1 February from the line of march, with a view to striking to the north of Berlin. Two days later Konev, not to be outdone, sent his plan to the *Stavka*, asking that he should be permitted to advance into Brandenburg with the aim of reaching the Elbe before the end of February, taking Berlin by a double envelopment in conjunction with 1 Belorussian Front. According to Shtemenko these plans were approved in principle on 27 and 29 January. Yet subsequent events showed that Stalin attached no importance to them.[24] On 31 January, as 1 Belorussian Front was about to pass over the Oder near Küstrin only fifty miles from Berlin, Zhukov and Telegin sent a signal to Stalin complaining of the vulnerability of their troops. To this message they received, in Zhukov's words, neither prompt reply nor material help. This was not surprising in view of Stalin's warning given only a few days before.

On 4 February, Zhukov, Malinin and Telegin signed a directive to their armies and staffs warning them to be in readiness by 9 February to resume the offensive towards Berlin, which, according to their estimate, would be taken seven days later.[25] If Chuikov is to be believed, Zhukov had that day called a conference of his army commanders; Chuikov sat next to Zhukov, close to the telephones, so that he became an involuntary listener to a telephone conversation between Stalin and the front commander. Stalin wanted to know where Zhukov was and what he was doing, and when told that the conference was planning the strike for Berlin, the dictator told him that he was wasting his time; he must first consolidate on the Oder and then turn his force northwards to destroy, in conjunction with Rokossovsky, the enemy's flanking force in Pomerania. Thereupon Zhukov postponed indefinitely the offensive against Berlin. Chuikov subsequently said that he was at a loss to understand why Zhukov had agreed with Stalin 'without a murmur'. 'Everyone', said Chuikov, 'just waited for Stalin to say what should be done next'.[26]

Chuikov is a retrospective 'if only' man. The rapid advance of 300 miles across Poland was, he admitted, a remarkable achievement; but, he continued, if only the *Stavka* and fronts had got the necessary supplies to the Oder, if only the air force had the use of forward airfields and if only the bridging had been where it was wanted on the river bank, then the four Soviet armies would have reached Berlin. Telegin has marvelled that Chuikov first saw fit to raise this matter twenty years after the event.[27] There was nothing to have prevented Chuikov writing a private letter to Stalin at the time giving his views. Others did, and at least one illustrious general is known to have paid the extreme penalty. Zhukov has denied Chuikov's story, saying that 'there was no such conference on 4 February'. Shtemenko similarly dismisses Chuikov's account, telling his readers that, at the time, Chuikov was for ever complaining to the front about the lack of ammunition and transport.[28]

On or shortly after 4 February the projected axis of 1 Belorussian Front was turned from Berlin to Kolberg on the Baltic, and Zhukov subsequently defended the decision, although this must have been Stalin's and not his own. The general staff was apparently on the side of caution, for it was rightly believed that the new enemy Army Group Vistula was about to mount an offensive from Stargard into Zhukov's right flank; and although this danger was in fact much exaggerated, neither the general staff nor the front commander could have gauged this at the time.

Zhukov had obtained Stalin's permission to remain on the

defensive until his right hand neighbour Rokossovsky started to thrust northwards to cut the enemy East Pomeranian grouping in two.[29] Rokossovsky pressed Vasilevsky, who was in Moscow, that Zhukov's offensive should begin on 24 February, and the Chief of General Staff, according to Rokossovsky, 'promised he would attend to this'.[30] Co-ordination was presumably lacking, however, for Rokossovsky had to commit all his forces to the initial action, and his anxiety was increased when he found that his left was un-covered since Zhukov was not supporting him and that enemy forces were concentrating in Neustettin on the exposed flank. When Rokossovsky complained to Moscow on 26 February a puzzled and suspicious Stalin eventually came on the line. He asked whether Rokossovsky thought that Zhukov 'was playing some crafty game (*khitrit*)'. Rokossovsky did not think so, but said that the fact remained that 1 Belorussian Front was not advancing. Stalin in-quired whether Rokossovsky could not take Neustettin using his own troops, for if he did, a Moscow salute would be fired in his honour. Rokossovsky would try, and meanwhile Stalin, who 'sounded quite pleased', promised to hasten Zhukov's offensive. The co-ordination between the fronts appears to have been effected through Stalin or Vasilevsky in Moscow. Only personal and rela-tively unimportant messages and those which were so impolitic as to make their transmission through Moscow unwise, went directly between the fronts. On 8 March, for example, when the *Stavka* ordered Zhukov to loan a tank army, Zhukov telephoned Rokossov-sky, warning him that he wanted the army back 'in the same condition as when it was dispatched'.[31]

Stalin had 'expressed a wish' that the Chief of General Staff should go to East Prussia, for it was essential that the enemy there be destroyed quickly 'in order that troops might be transferred to the Berlin axis, while two or three of the better of the armies could be sent to the Far East'. Vasilevsky, said Stalin, should be ready to take over as Commander-in-Chief for the war against Japan. Vasilevsky 'in thanking Stalin for his continued confidence' had asked to be relieved of his post as Chief of General Staff, a post from which he had been a virtual absentee since the beginning of 1943. Vasilevsky recommended that Antonov should take the appointment, although he knew that Antonov did not want the post. Stalin, according to Vasilevsky, showed surprise and asked whether the loss of the appointment would not cause Vasilevsky offence; Stalin would, in any event, think about it.

On the night of 18 February Vasilevsky was at the Bolshoi Theatre when he was called to the telephone by Stalin, who told him of the death of Cherniakhovsky at Mehlsack. The *Stavka*, said Stalin, intended to appoint Vasilevsky to the vacant command. The next evening he was again with Stalin from whom he received, 'during an exceptionally warm talk, much valuable advice'. Vasilevsky particularly remembered being handed two sealed letters by Poskrebyshev. One was merely a letter appointing him to the command of 3 Belorussian Front from 21 February. The other envelope contained a GKO decree changing the 10 July 1941 composition of the *Stavka* to Stalin, Zhukov, Vasilevsky and Bulganin, the three latter being deputy commissars for defence, together with Kuznetsov and Antonov. Vasilevsky involuntarily commented to Poskrebyshev that, as the Chief of General Staff and deputy commissar of defence and the co-worker and co-signatory with Stalin for most of the war, it had not been necessary for him to be appointed as a member of the *Stavka*; why, asked Vasilevsky, had it been considered timely to appoint him now. Poskrebyshev could volunteer nothing by way of reply.[32]

Although the enemy-held territory in East Prussia had been compressed in ten days to half its former size, the failure to reduce Königsberg was taken hard by Stalin; Bagramian's 1 Baltic Front was held to be responsible and was downgraded to a group and incorporated into Vasilevsky's 3 Belorussian Front. The Soviet offensive was postponed until 13 March. Meanwhile Vasilevsky decided, with Stalin's agreement, to alter the earlier priorities and attack the southern grouping about Heiligenbeil before dealing with Königsberg and the enemy Samland force. When launched, the offensive began to make slow but steady progress. On 16 March Vasilevsky produced his plan for the final destruction of Army Group North, signed by himself, Makarov and Pokrovsky, a concise draft order of 800 words under the usual Red Army general staff numbered paragraph sequence, information about the enemy, own aim, grouping, air support, phases, timings, and reinforcements and equipment.[33] Within twenty-four hours the *Stavka* confirmed the order, except that it required that the operations in the south of the Frisches Haff should be concluded by not later than 22 March so that the offensive against Königsberg might start on 28 March.

Vasilevsky said that on the night of 18 March he told Stalin by telephone that the amended *Stavka* timings were unrealistic (*nerealen*) and he asked that the offensive against Königsberg should be delayed until April, the air and artillery assault beginning during the first four days of that month. This time he met with no difficulties for Stalin immediately agreed his proposal and, on reflection, said that 3 Belorussian Front should have the additional air support of a long range air army and the air armies of the Baltic Fleet and 2 Belorussian Front; he would dispatch Novikov and Golovanov to East Prussia immediately.[34] Königsberg fell on 9 April, amid scenes of fearful barbarity.

With the evacuation of the enemy Samland group on 16 April, East Prussia had been finally cleared of the enemy, after a bitter and bloody campaign lasting 105 days. Soviet historians give the credit for the German success in prolonging the struggle to the fact that the enemy was able to make good use of its sea communications uninterrupted by the Baltic Fleet or Red Air Force.

On the far southern wing a fierce struggle was being waged by Timoshenko's force in Hungary. By the end of the year Malinovsky and Tolbukhin had entrapped four German divisions and a Hungarian division in Budapest and had successfully beaten off enemy attacks to relieve the capital. On 11 February the Axis garrison was finally destroyed when trying to break out to the west.

At the end of the Budapest fighting, Timoshenko was ordered to give his recommendations on a projected advance to Vienna. Small planning staffs from 3 and 4 Ukrainian Fronts set to work on the problem, but a dispute immediately arose as to which of the fronts was to make the main thrust. Since each of the two front commanders considered this to be his duty, alternative plans were sent to Moscow. The *Stavka* decided in favour of Malinovsky and on 17 February put out a directive on the lines of his proposal. Meanwhile Tolbukhin, remaining convinced of the soundness of his own plan, pressed his views on Timoshenko, who demanded new facts and figures, which, when produced, eventually persuaded him that the offensive should be mounted by Tolbukhin. Timoshenko reported his opinion to Stalin, who ordered the plans to be re-examined. The *Stavka* then reversed its earlier decision and issued a revised directive on 9 March in favour of Tolbukhin.[35]

By the end of February, however, Tolbukhin had become aware that a German offensive was imminent against his front and, when this was reported to Moscow, the *Stavka* decided to delay the launching of the Vienna operation until after the enemy's effort was spent. Tolbukhin's troops were defending low lying ground interlaced by a network of rivers and canals. In the forward area the ground favoured the defence but to the rear it made movement and supply difficult; moreover, the Danube to the east formed a great obstacle across the front's lines of communications, since the ice floes threatened the pontoon bridges and ferry points.

The main German offensive began on 5 March when Wöhler's Army Group South, reinforced by Dietrich's 6 SS Panzer Army, recently arrived from the Ardennes, attacked to the north and south of Lake Balaton and advanced about sixteen miles in four days. When Tolbukhin informed Moscow of the presence of 6 SS Panzer Army, a disbelieving Antonov asked the front commander whether he really thought that Hitler would move such a formation to Lake Balaton at a time when Berlin was threatened with destruction. Ivanov, who was the front chief of staff, has said that the arrival of this panzer force apparently worried Stalin, for during a telephone discussion with Tolbukhin he wanted to know whether it would be feasible to withdraw 3 Ukrainian Front eastwards behind the Danube. The question surprised Tolbukhin but he and his council recommended that they remain where they were.[36]

Shtemenko has a very different version of the incident. On 6 March the Germans attacked with 'exceptional ferocity', and, on 9 March, Tolbukhin, who, according to Shtemenko, enjoyed indifferent health and lacked the resolution and ruthlessness of the other marshals, asked that 3 Ukrainian Front should be permitted, in case of necessity, to withdraw behind the Danube. The matter was referred to Stalin. Antonov and Shtemenko were present in Stalin's office when Tolbukhin telephoned the dictator. Stalin reflected for a moment and then, said Shtemenko, without anger or emotion, replied in an even and calm voice:

Comrade Tolbukhin! If you are thinking of extending the war by five or six months then please do withdraw your troops behind the Danube. It will of course be quieter there. But I doubt whether that is your intention. Therefore you must defend the right bank and stay there yourself with your headquarters. I am sure that the troops will do their duty and fulfil their difficult task. All that is necessary is that they should be commanded properly.[37]

By 16 March Tolbukhin knew that he had won the defensive battle without Malinovsky's forces or the *Stavka* reserve army coming to his assistance. When that evening Tolbukhin asked for a tank army to be transferred to him from 2 Ukrainian Front for use in accordance with the counter-offensive directive of 9 March, Stalin agreed and immediately telephoned Malinovsky, ordering him to concentrate the army the next day.[38] The reserve army, which had been previously refused to Tolbukhin, was ordered to move across the Danube to join the tank army in the thrust which was to outflank Army Group South and reach Vienna by the middle of April.

Meanwhile, to the north of Malinovsky's 2 Ukrainian Front, Petrov's 4 Ukrainian Front had left Cracow behind it and had begun the thrust on Moravska-Ostrava. Progress was slow. On or about 15 March, Moskalenko, one of Petrov's army commanders, had been called to the front headquarters where he was invited to sit at his ease and drink tea with Petrov and Mekhlis, 'unofficially' discussing the reasons for the lack of success. Moskalenko gave as his opinion that the main thrust was being made in the wrong sector; he would have preferred to have seen the axis further to the north where the going was better. Moskalenko said that, as he spoke, he noted that Mekhlis was scribbling on a pad, and he discovered afterwards that the political member was writing up the conversation on signal sheets for telegraphing to Moscow.

At 0300 hours the next morning Moskalenko was awakened by a telephone call from Antonov, who, said Moskalenko, first talked about trivialities in order to allow him sufficient time to shake off the effects of sleep and compose himself. The Supreme Commander, said Antonov, wanted to know more about Moskalenko's views on the lack of success of the operation, and, when Moskalenko answered that he could hardly talk behind the commander's back, Antonov told him that Stalin already knew of the conversation from Mekhlis's signalled report; Stalin just wanted a little more detail. Following this conversation, Petrov was ordered to explain himself, which he did by an answering signal on 17 March. That evening, at 1830 hours, Stalin and Antonov signed a personal signal to both Petrov and Mekhlis, saying that the Supreme Commander considered the explanation of General of the Army Petrov dated 17 March as unconvincing. If General Petrov had been of the opinion that his command was not yet ready for battle he should have told the *Stavka* so and have asked for more time; this would not have been refused. The member of the military council, Colonel-General Mekhlis, had informed the Central Committee of the shortcomings in the preparations only after the failure of the operation. The message ended 'The *Stavka* warns (*preduprezhdaet*) General of the Army Petrov for the last time'. Petrov and Korzhenevich were removed from their posts on that day but Mekhlis was allowed to remain.[39] Eremenko and Sandalov arrived from the old 2 Baltic Front to replace the outgoing commander and chief of staff.

By 4 April the enemy's main East Pomeranian grouping had been destroyed except that an isolated pocket of German troops remained near the mouth of the Vistula. The occupation of Pomerania finally removed, as Shtemenko said, any danger of the Soviet offensive against Berlin being wrecked by attacks from the flank or rear, and 'for this reason the postponement could not have been avoided'. On 23 March Montgomery's 21 Army Group had established a firm foothold over the lower Rhine and started to move eastwards, while further to the south Bradley's 12 Army Group extended its bridgeheads at Remagen and Mainz. Two United States armies then began the double envelopment which ended on 1 April with the encirclement of Model's 325,000 strong Army Group B in the Ruhr; Stalin was surprised by the scale and speed of the operation.

On 28 March, when the Anglo-American troops were already advancing into Germany, Eisenhower, without consulting the Combined Chiefs of Staff or his British deputy, sent a telegram directly to Deane in Moscow for handing to Stalin. Eisenhower explained that his primary mission, after he had destroyed the Ruhr pocket, would be to split the enemy forces by making a junction with the Soviet armies in the east, and that the main axis to be taken by the Anglo-American forces would be from west to southeast in the direction of Erfurt, Leipzig and Dresden.[40]

Although Germany and Europe had been politically dissected at Yalta there had been no agreement on the co-ordination of military strategy between the Red Army and the Anglo-American forces. In the previous September Eisenhower and Montgomery had been in accord that the main political and military objective was the capture of Berlin. Even as late as 27 March, the day before Eisenhower had sent his telegram to Moscow, Montgomery had informed Churchill that he was thrusting for the Elbe and Berlin, and Churchill intended that he should do so.[41] Eisenhower's military objectives were apparently unrelated to post-war political strategy since, in Pogue's view, the President and the United States Chiefs of Staff left the final stages of the war to their military commander.[42]

Stalin told Deane that Eisenhower's plan fitted with that of the Red Army; he agreed with Eisenhower 'that Berlin no longer had its former strategic significance' and said that henceforth the main effort of the Red Army would be in the direction of Dresden to form a junction with the United States forces.[43] The Soviet offensive, said Stalin, would begin in the second half of May, although this date might be subject to alteration.[44]

Immediately after the western delegation had gone Stalin sent for Zhukov, who arrived in the capital on 29 March from 1 Belorussian Front. Stalin told him that although the Red Army had serious fighting ahead of it, the enemy defence in western Germany had collapsed; Zhukov thought that he could be ready to start an offensive against Berlin in a fortnight and imagined that Konev could too; Rokossovsky, however, was likely to be delayed as the larger part of his troops were still in East Pomerania. Stalin concluded that the offensive would have to start without Rokossovsky.[45] Stalin told Zhukov that he had been informed by telegram that the enemy had made overtures to the western allies and in consequence the possibility could not be dismissed that the Germans would let the Anglo-Americans through to Berlin; 'as for Churchill', said Stalin, 'he might do anything'. Although Zhukov has misrepresented the content of Eisenhower's message and omitted Stalin's reply, it is not improbable that Stalin expressed himself in these terms.[46]

Zhukov and Antonov were ordered to continue planning the offensive until Konev should arrive from 2 Ukrainian Front, and Zhukov makes the point that, before 30 March, the strategic plan involving fronts other than his own was unknown to him.[47] On 31 March they were joined by Konev, 'who became very excited (*ochen' razvolnovalsia*)' over the inter-front boundary between himself and Zhukov; but since this was Stalin's work, no one in the general staff, Shtemenko drily commented, could do anything about it.[48] Konev has told how the concept of the 1 Ukrainian Front plan originated from his front staff and, when approved in Moscow, was incorporated in the *Stavka* directive. On this particular occasion Stalin had ordered that the front commanders were not to leave Moscow without having the directives, agreed and signed, in their hands.[49]

On 1 April Zhukov, Konev, Antonov and Shtemenko were summoned to a GKO meeting. Antonov first gave a strategic introduction presenting the situation on all the German fronts both in the west and in the east. The need, said Stalin, was to take Berlin before the western allies, and the offensive would have to start not later than 16 April and be completed within fifteen days. Zhukov and Konev in turn presented their plans based on a frontal offensive by 1 Belorussian Front on the Küstrin-Berlin axis, its two tank armies outflanking the city from the north, while 1 Ukrainian Front advanced on the axis Spremberg-Beelitz (immediately south of Potsdam) making only subsidiary thrusts in the direction of Dresden and Leipzig. Antonov again drew Stalin's attention to the inter-front boundary, which ran from Gross Gastrose on the Oder to Gross Michendorf twenty miles south of the capital and thence to Brandenburg, since this demarcation line prevented Konev from entering the Berlin suburbs. Konev, whose orders with regard to his right flank had up to this time been by no means clear, also spoke in favour of directing his tank armies into Berlin from the south-west.

Stalin would not abandon his original idea that Zhukov should take Berlin. Nor, on the other hand, would he accept the general staff's and Konev's view. So, taking a pencil, he silently crossed out the inter-front boundary leaving only that part which ran from Gross Gastrose to Lübben, a distance of about twenty-five miles from the start line. Stalin gave no explanation for his action and made no further comment, but Konev believed that the dictator deliberately introduced an element of competition between the two fronts; and this view is confirmed by Shtemenko, for Stalin later told the general staff that Berlin should be taken by whoever broke in first.[50]

The directives to the two fronts were signed by Stalin on 1 and 3 April. The mission paragraph of the directive to Zhukov instructed him 'to conduct an offensive and capture Berlin, and, not later than the twelfth–fifteenth day of the operation, reach the Elbe'. The mission given to Konev read 'to destroy the enemy grouping in the area of Cottbus and the south of Berlin and, not later than the twelfth–fifteenth day of the operation, reach the line Beelitz–Wittenberg exploiting towards Dresden'. The tank and reserve armies intended for the break-out battles were not to be committed until the enemy defences had been pierced. No mention was made in the confirmatory directive of the possibility that 1 Ukrainian Front would be called upon to turn its tank armies into Berlin. Although the directives were specific in covering the break-in battles, the break-out and exploitation phases were left open; Konev, in particular, has emphasized that there was no pre-determined or centralized plan covering the Berlin operation; as the battle developed orders were passed according to the changing situation, and the hour by hour control of the fronts was exercised from Moscow.[51]

Konev saw Stalin again on 3 April and asked for two more armies to form the reserve for the break-out operations. Stalin consulted his pad and allotted two armies from the Baltic area. The problem immediately arose as to whether these troops could arrive with Konev by 15 April, and Stalin wanted to know the answer from the general staff there and then. The rail movement authority could not guarantee their arrival until after the offensive had started, but this was apparently acceptable to Konev.

On 6 April, two days after Zhukov and Konev had returned to their fronts, Rokossovsky was called to Moscow for briefing on his part in the new offensive, the advance into Mecklenburg to cover Zhukov's right flank. The troops of 2 Belorussian Front were still 150 miles away, having, only a few days before, cleared the enemy in the areas of Gdynia and Danzig. Rokossovsky was to close up to the lower Oder and take over the sector held by a single army, the right hand formation of 1 Belorussian Front. But whereas Zhukov has said that Stalin had accepted that Rokossovsky's offensive could not begin until 20 April, Rokossovsky has maintained that the postponement of four days was given grudgingly by Stalin, and then only after he had heard an explanation of the difficulties to be overcome.

When Rokossovsky was given his written directive on 6 April, his men were already on the march and the army commanders and staffs had begun their reconnoitring of the banks of the Oder. But Rokossovsky's offensive differed from those of Zhukov and Konev in that no front plans were in existence to form the outline of the *Stavka* directive, and much of the planning had, of necessity, to be done from the military council's reading of the map. When the troops did arrive many of them were ordered piecemeal into the attack, with little or no time for preparation. However that may be, on 19 April Rokossovsky reported to Stalin by telephone that his front was ready to begin the offensive at the time appointed by the *Stavka*.[52]

The 1 Belorussian Front plan agreed in Moscow envisaged the committal of two tank armies north of Berlin as soon as the enemy defences had been overcome and there was sufficient room for manoeuvre. But Zhukov became apprehensive about the strength of the enemy Seelow defences facing the Küstrin bridgeheads and recommended, in the second week in April, that Katukov's tank army be moved further to the south in support of Chuikov's army in the break-out battle against Seelow. Stalin told Zhukov to act as he thought fit since he was best able to see the local situation.[53] In the event, Zhukov was, quite rightly, to bear the blame.

In the first week in April Stalin had decided to strengthen the command of 1 Belorussian Front by allotting Sokolovsky to Zhukov as a front deputy commander, and in this way, only seven days before the opening of the offensive, Konev lost his chief of staff, who had been with the front for nearly a year. Stalin had telephoned Konev to offer Petrov, by way of replacement, and, whether willingly or not, Konev had accepted him. Not surprisingly, he found that Petrov was more at his ease commanding troops than sorting paper: and Konev was later to send him as his representative to where the battle was in doubt, to put what Konev calls some heart into the troops.

By 15 April the western allies had become aware of the imminence of the Soviet offensive through monitoring the German radio and, in answer to a direct question from the United States Embassy in Moscow, the information was given that the offensive would begin on the morrow, Stalin still insisting, even at that late hour, that the main thrust was to be made on Leipzig.[54]

Zhukov's overall frontage had been reduced from 200 to 120 miles by the arrival of 2 Belorussian Front, but the actual assault frontage of the main offensive was only twenty-eight miles, so that each of the four first echelon armies in the area of the breakthrough had a sector of little more than 12,000 yards. The three Soviet fronts are said to have numbered two and a half million men, 41,000 guns and mortars, 6,200 tanks and 7,500 aircraft, with an artillery density of up to 400 gun and mortar barrels to the mile in the area of the main assault.[55] Figures by themselves, however, tend to be misleading due to the Soviet practice of counting all aircraft as warplanes and including even 82mm infantry mortars as artillery. The war diary entry of Busse's 9 Army, after the first day of Zhukov's offensive, estimated that it had been under the fire of only 2,500 guns and 450 tanks.[56]

Zhukov was beset with difficulties. His decision to blind the enemy defenders by the direct illumination of searchlights and to move Katukov's tank army forward on to the bridgehead had not been a happy one. The marshy and broken ground restricted deployment so that the roads and tracks became jammed with vehicles, and the lights confused the Red Army troops. The enemy resistance was bitter. At two-thirty on the afternoon of 16 April, when, after nine hours fighting the attacking troops had moved forward only four miles, Zhukov decided to commit both of his tank armies, although the infantry formations had not yet broken out and the Seelow defences were still intact in front of him. Half an hour later when he telephoned a description of the position to Stalin, the dictator listened quietly, merely ordering him to reinforce the strike of the tank armies with bomber aircraft. Konev, Stalin said, had found matters easier and was already across the Neisse. Zhukov was to call again that night and report the situation.

That evening, when Zhukov made his second call, Stalin spoke 'somewhat less calmly'. The dictator blamed Zhukov for having altered the axis of Katukov's tank army to a sector where the enemy defences were so strong, and he asked if he could have an assurance that the Seelow would be taken the next day. Zhukov believed that it would be taken by the next night and he justified the changing of the axis by claiming that he was drawing enemy troops out of Berlin 'where they could be more easily defeated in the open'. Stalin's reply, that he was 'thinking of taking the capital using Konev from the south and Rokossovsky from the north', made it clear that he had lost confidence in Zhukov's handling of his front. Nor was he prepared to listen to Zhukov's long-winded objections that Rokossovsky would have difficulty in advancing from the Oder before 23 April, for the dictator merely cut him off with, as Zhukov expressed it, 'a dry good-bye in lieu of reply', and hung up.[57]

On the evening of 17 April Konev was about to cross the Spree when he was telephoned by Stalin who explained that Zhukov was having difficulty in penetrating the enemy defences; then he fell silent, obviously weighing up the situation. Konev remained waiting for the dictator to take up the thread of the conversation. When Stalin began again he asked whether Konev thought it would be possible to pass Zhukov's motorized troops through the 1 Ukrainian Front gap in the area of Spremberg. Konev was against this solution, as it would take time and cause confusion; in any case, he said, it was unnecessary, as his own tank armies were already there and in a favourable position to take Berlin from the south. When Konev outlined how he could direct his armour on Zossen, fifteen miles south of Berlin, Stalin was obviously having difficulty in following place names, for he asked the scale of the map which Konev was using. After a short pause, he spoke again, agreeing that Konev should direct Rybalko and Leliushenko on Berlin.[58] That night the military council issued its directive requiring that Potsdam and south-west Berlin be taken by 21 April.[59] In the three days from 18 to 21 April, during which time 1 Ukrainian Front broke into Zossen, Konev spoke only once to Moscow, although detailed situation reports were sent regularly from his headquarters to the general staff. Virtually no queries were raised on these reports and, as Konev said, 'there was no interference from above on those days'.[60]

Whereas Konev's remarkable success could hardly have been improved, Zhukov was to come in for much criticism. Looking at the problem in retrospect, he thought that 1 Belorussian Front should have been concentrated on closer assault frontages. But, said Zhukov, such a proposal would have been out of the question at the time, since Stalin favoured only the offensive on the broad front.[61] As an alternative, said Zhukov, all the troops deployed in the taking of Berlin could have been entrusted to 1 Belorussian Front alone, since this would have avoided the friction between the fronts, particularly during the fighting in the capital.

Meanwhile, in the middle of April, Eisenhower had sent another message to Deane for delivery to the Red Army general staff, suggesting that all the allies, whether in the east or west, should be free to advance until contact was imminent. This proposal alarmed Antonov. Agreement was eventually reached, but when, on 4 May, Eisenhower said that he proposed to advance deeper into Czecho-Slovakia to the west banks of the Elbe and Vltava rivers, this brought such a violent protest from Antonov that the Supreme Allied Commander in the west acceded to Moscow's wishes.[62]

By 21 April Zhukov's right wing had at last gained operative depth and began to penetrate the northern outskirts of Berlin. Four days later Leliushenko's tank army joined with Perkhorovich's troops of 1 Belorussian Front to the west of the capital, so encircling the city, and that same day United States and Red Army patrols met at Torgau on the Elbe. Konev's and Zhukov's troops were fighting their way against bitter resistance towards the centre of Berlin, 1 Belorussian Front from the east and north and 1 Ukrainian Front from the south and west, and the difficulties of observation and control resulted in the supporting front air forces bombing their own troops and those of the adjoining fronts. On 25 April Konev and Zhukov appealed to Stalin to lay down a firm inter-front boundary.[63] Up to this time both Zhukov and Konev had been striving to occupy the city centre, the suspicious Zhukov (the description used by Chuikov) sending out reconnaissance patrols to seek information, not about the enemy but about Konev's troops, in case these should penetrate into the heart of Berlin before him.[64]

On 29 April Stalin telephoned Konev asking for his opinion as to who should clear and occupy Prague. American troops had already arrived in the western Czech territories, while Malinovsky's 2 Ukrainian Front had overrun Slovakia in the east and south; the northern Czecho-Slovakian border was, as Konev described it, overhung by the 1 Ukrainian Front. When Konev told Stalin that his front would be able to take Prague, Stalin altered his right front boundary in Berlin further to the west. This allowed Zhukov to complete the overrunning and occupation of the Berlin city centre.[65]

On the afternoon of 30 April Hitler had committed suicide and, early the next morning, Krebs, the last Chief of German General Staff, arrived at the command post of Chuikov's army with a written proposal from Goebbels for peace negotiations. The text of the letter was telephoned to Zhukov who, having sent Sokolovsky to represent him at Chuikov's headquarters, called up Moscow to report to Stalin. When Stalin, who was at Kuntsevo, was awakened, he ordered that there should be no negotiations or talks, only unconditional surrender. Fighting in the capital continued for a further two days, until the German surrender on 2 May. Elsewhere the war in Europe was virtually at an end, and, on 7 May, the emissaries sent by Doenitz, the new head of the German government, signed the surrender at Rheims, a document on which Susloparov, the representative to Eisenhower's headquarters, obligingly added his signature.

That day Stalin telephoned Voronov, asking angrily who was 'this celebrated general of artillery Susloparov' who, without even telling the Soviet government and certainly without its authority, had dared to sign a document of such tremendous international importance. Stalin vented his anger on Voronov, who as a marshal of artillery, 'had failed to educate his artillery officers'. Susloparov, said Stalin, would be recalled to Moscow immediately and harshly punished.[66] That same day Stalin telephoned Zhukov in Berlin to say that he disagreed with the signing of the document in Rheims, for it was the Soviet people who had borne the main brunt of the war, not the allies. Stalin demanded a second signing of a surrender document, this time before the Supreme Command of all the countries of the coalition, and not just before the Anglo-American Supreme Commander. Zhukov was to represent the *Stavka* at the ceremony. Thereafter Zhukov was to remain as the head of the Soviet zone of occupation and the commander of the Soviet troops in Germany, and Vyshinsky would join him as the deputy commander for political affairs.[67]

Werth has described the press conference which Zhukov and Vyshinsky gave a little later. Zhukov described how *he* (Werth's italics) had attacked along the whole front and at night, and 'very soon' had broken the German defences; the main point, emphasized Zhukov, was that the Germans were smashed on the Oder, for Berlin itself was just one immense mopping-up operation. It was, added Zhukov, very, *very* (Werth's repetition and italics) different from the battle of Moscow, for out of more than half a million German soldiers who had taken part in the Berlin operation, 300,000 were taken prisoner even before the capitulation, about 150,000 had been killed and the rest had fled. Werth was to note later that Zhukov had mentioned nothing of the part played by Rokossovsky's or Konev's forces, or of the 2,000 Soviet tanks destroyed and the 300,000 Red Army casualties. Werth commented that the tenor of Zhukov's account had little in common with the official Soviet history which described German resistance as fanatical, fighting continuing to the end, even in the corridors of the Reichstag in the heart of the city. Zhukov had added a tribute to Comrade Stalin 'and to his great understanding of military affairs', but this had come almost as an afterthought. None of the other Soviet marshals had been mentioned. Zhukov, said Werth, had a very high opinion of himself, and with a curious mixture of modesty and almost boyish boastfulness he had tended to take the credit for nearly all the decisive victories the Red Army had won. Vyshinsky outwardly treated Zhukov with admiration, almost obsequiousness, but in reality the political supervision was always in evidence, and Werth had the vague feeling that Zhukov resented it.[68]

Berzarin, the first military commandant in Berlin, perished on 16 June 'in the performance of his duties', either in a car accident or, according to the current Russian rumour in Berlin, at the hands of Nazi terrorists. He was replaced by Gorbatov.

When Prague had been taken, Konev was surprised to witness an altercation between Rybalko and Leliushenko as to who had arrived in the city first and who, by right, should be its first military governor; Konev solved the problem by selecting Gordov to be the chief of the Prague garrison. When he reported his decision to Stalin by telephone that evening, he at first met with an unexpected objection over the title of the post, and a long hair-splitting discussion followed as to the designation and duties of district commanders, governors, city commandants and town majors. The dictator finally ruled that Gordov should be styled 'commandant', since, said Konev, the sound of the name pleased Stalin better.[69]

Throughout the duration of the war in Europe there were five armies in the Far East, but whereas the order of battle had been increased in terms of front and army headquarters, the real fighting strength sank to about thirty divisions.[70] In the spring of 1942 Zhigarev, who had previously commanded the air forces of 2 Independent Red Banner Army, was returned from Moscow to command the Far East air forces, and, in April 1943, Purkaev replaced Apanasenko as the commander of the Far East Front. The most important staff change was that of Shevchenko, formerly head of the Far East section of the general staff operations department in Moscow, who was exchanged for Lomov, the deputy chief of staff of the Far East Front. Shevchenko was later promoted and became the front chief of staff.

On 4 October 1944, when Harriman raised the question of allied military staff talks covering the war against Japan, Stalin said that he had sent for Shevchenko and Zhigarev to come from the Far East to brief him on the constantly changing situation there. The primary reason for the summons to Moscow was connected with the instructions Stalin had given to the general staff a few days earlier, when, at the conclusion of a routine *Stavka* briefing, he told Shtemenko, 'almost casually', to begin work on drawing up plans and estimates for the new war, since, as Stalin worded it, 'it looked as if they would soon be needed'. These figures, produced within a fortnight, were those used by Antonov and Shevchenko when Stalin briefed Churchill and Eden in the second half of the month.[71] In February 1945 Stalin's political conditions for entering the war, three months after the end of the war in Europe, had been agreed with his allies, and on 5 April the Soviet government renounced its non-aggression pact with Japan.

On 26 March Vasilevsky was withdrawn from 3 Belorussian Front to begin his task of co-ordinating the fronts which were to destroy the Japanese Kwantung Group of Armies in Manchuria.[72] Stalin had ruled that the existing Far East field organization should not be altered and that full use should be made of the local knowledge of the commanders and staffs already there. On the other hand he wanted battle-experienced headquarters and troops brought from Europe as complete formations, these to be fitted into the Far East order of battle with a minimum of dislocation, so that the newly arrived 'westerners' were in command, with the 'easterners' as their deputies.[73] The strategic and operative plan put forward for Stalin's approval appears to have been drafted by Lomov and Shevchenko, working under Antonov's and Shtemenko's supervision.

The Transbaikal Front, on the right, had the main role, since this was to involve the rapid movement of large armoured forces over a great distance, from Transbaikal and Outer Mongolia south-eastwards towards Tsitsihar, Changchun, Mukden and Chinwangtao. At Vasilevsky's suggestion the command of this front was given to Malinovsky, an officer who had much experience in handling mobile troops, and whose calm, thoroughness and judgement were highly regarded. Kovalev was to remain as Malinovsky's deputy, with Zakharov as the new chief of staff. In the centre, the battle-experienced Purkaev was left in command of the Far East Front, later to be redesignated as 2 Far East Front, his task being to cross the Amur and advance on Tsitsihar. On the extreme left, the maritime group in the area of Vladivostok, recently under Purkaev, but now subordinated directly to Stalin, was to be redesignated as 1 Far East Front, this command being given to Meretskov, who was waiting at Yaroslavl with the former Karelian Front headquarters in *Stavka* reserve; the former maritime group commander, Parusinov, was to remain with the group as Meretskov's deputy. Stalin rated Meretskov's ability to overcome fortified areas highly, for, in making this appointment he gave as his opinion that 'the wily man from Yaroslavl' would soon smash the Japanese. Meretskov's task was to provide the left wing of the double envelopment which would move from the maritime provinces north of Vladivostok to Harbin, Changchun and into North Korea, joining with Malinovsky's armoured columns coming from the Transbaikal. Three armies were on their way from Europe to the Transbaikal Front, while a further army joined the maritime group. In addition a number of experienced army commanders were transferred from the west to take over the armies already in the theatre.

The Japanese were poorly prepared to withstand an offensive from the Transbaikal area and Outer Mongolia; this, and geography, dictated the Soviet strategy, since the open country, without fortified areas, water obstacles or taiga, favoured the use of motorized forces by the Transbaikal Front, although the Hingan mountain range would eventually have to be overcome. Meretskov's 1 Far East Front on the other hand would have to penetrate the wire and concrete static defences built up long before the war on the old Russo-Japanese frontier; Purkaev had yet a different problem in that he had to cross the broad Amur. The area of operations extended over 1,000 miles, and since the three widely separated fronts were to converge from the outer circumference on to a central point, co-ordination and timing of the initial offensives were to present a difficult problem. Stalin ruled that plans should be prepared in detail covering a number of variations, since it would be easier to know which to choose nearer the time.[74]

Meretskov, having arrived at Vladivostok, took over from Parusinov and set to work on his plans, reconnoitring selected points of the frontier dressed in the uniform of a private soldier of NKVD border troops. He and Parusinov were well acquainted from the time of the Finnish Winter War, but, as they were unable to work together, Stalin withdrew Parusinov to the *Stavka* reserve.[75]

All front and army commanders were to attend the Moscow victory parade celebrations in the last week in June, and Stalin had ordered that Malinovsky and Zakharov should come earlier in order to work on an outline plan. They were given the mission to destroy the enemy Kwantung force within a space of eight weeks from the beginning of the offensive on 20–25 August. At the end of five days' work in the general staff, they produced a plan which Malinovsky presented to Stalin on 18 June. But the general staff was unable to agree that Malinovsky should keep his tank army in reserve as part of his second echelon of armies, for it believed that such a course would tie the rate of advance of the tank formations to that of infantry. Moreover, the tanks would be unable to seize the mountain passes by a *coup de main*, or indeed be in the forward area to support the forward infantry. Stalin told Malinovsky to reconsider his own plan when he had arrived in the Transbaikal area, and then make the final decision. Malinovsky's decision, when eventually made, conformed to the plan of the general staff. In reality Malinovsky appears to have had little choice, nor did

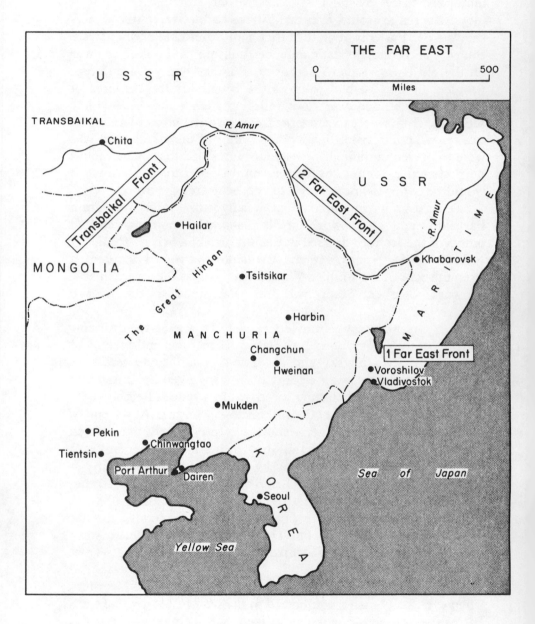

THE FAR EAST

0   500

Miles

Stalin intend that there should be any doubt on the matter, for when he came to sign the directive to the Transbaikal Front he had the following paragraph inserted:

6 Guards Tank Army, operating in the main sector in the general direction of Changchun, shall by the tenth day of the operation force the Great Hingan, seize the passes and seal the area off from the enemy reserves from Central and Southern Manchuria until the arrival of the main infantry forces.[76]

The war in the Far East raised a new problem, however, since it was likely to be a fast moving campaign in a remote theatre involving a million and a half men in three converging and possibly simultaneous offensives from widely separated start lines. It would be impossible to control operations from Moscow, and for this reason, so Stalin is said to have told Vasilevsky in Antonov's and Shtemenko's presence, a Commander-in-Chief was essential to the theatre, to command the three fronts and the supporting air and naval forces. Vasilevsky was to set up his headquarters at Khabarovsk, with arms advisers and staff, fifty-two officers in all, detached to him from the Commissariat of Defence. Novikov was to control the air forces, Shikin was to be the political member of the military council, and Stalin recommended that Zakharov should be Vasilevsky's chief of staff. In the event, however, Zakharov asked to be allowed to remain with Malinovsky; the post was offered to Kurasov, but he, too, asked to be excused; finally Ivanov was selected.

At the time, Deane was certain that Stalin would retain operational control in Moscow, notwithstanding the distances involved. Deane wanted to establish a link between Vasilevsky and MacArthur and Nimits, and he proposed to Antonov that there should be an exchange of liaison staffs and the provision of radio teleprint equipment from United States resources. Deane suggested that the Soviet answer should be given at the time of the Potsdam conference.

At the Potsdam conference Stalin's military attendants included Zhukov, Kuznetsov, Antonov, Gryzlov and Slavin. Leahy gave Antonov an *aide-mémoire*, listing five requests from the United States chiefs of staff concerning the forthcoming operations in the

Far East. The answers came by hand of Stalin to Truman. The request for weather stations at Khabarovsk and Petropavlovsk was agreed, after some quibbling, and modifications were required to the United States' suggestions concerning naval and air operational boundaries. In answer to the fourth American point, a request for information, Deane was surprised to hear that Vasilevsky 'would have complete control of all Soviet operations in the Far East, without supervision from Moscow'.[77] Stalin had already informed Truman, and Antonov afterwards told the assembled chiefs of staff, that Soviet operations against the Japanese in the Far East would begin in the latter half of August.

Stalin had rejected a Japanese approach asking that the Soviet Union mediate between Tokyo and the western allies, and had informed Hopkins earlier, on 28 May, that the Soviet Union preferred to go through with the war until unconditional surrender and the occupation of the Japanese mainland were achieved. An undefeated Japan would, Stalin thought, start to plan a war of revenge. Stalin admitted that insistence on unconditional surrender would mean that the Japanese would go on fighting until the end, and he hinted that milder terms could be offered provided that these involved the occupation of the Japanese homeland by the victorious allies. Then, once the allies were in occupation, Stalin saw no reason why, in Hopkins's words, the Japanese should not 'be given the works' and the same results thus obtained as under unconditional surrender.[78] In the event, the Potsdam declaration, promulgated with Stalin's concurrence although the Soviet Union was not a party, demanded unconditional surrender.

On 22 July, after a consultation with Churchill and Eden, Truman and Byrnes had decided that an atom bomb would be dropped on Japan if it did not accept immediate surrender. Stalin was to be told of the intention without giving him the details of the new weapon or how it was to be used, and he was in fact informed in these terms by Truman at the conclusion of a meeting on 24 July. His response, according to Eden, was a nod of the head and a brief 'Thank you'. He made no other comment.[79] Stalin told Antonov of this conversation, but according to Shtemenko he had little idea of the potential of the bomb.[80] Vasilevsky has recounted how Stalin telephoned him at Chita from Potsdam, and asked whether the Japanese War could not be brought forward by about ten days.

But Vasilevsky has given the date of this conversation as 16 July, roughly the date, he said, of the successful atomic explosion at Los Alamos; Vasilevsky added that he did not know 'to what extent Truman had informed Stalin of this trial but later it became obvious that Stalin's 16 July telephone conversation had a direct bearing on that event'.[81]

The first atom bomb was dropped on Hiroshima on 6 August and the second on Nagasaki three days afterwards. On the afternoon of 8 August the heads of the American and British military missions in Moscow were sent for by Antonov and given a copy of a note sent to the Japanese Government declaring war as from midnight that same day. When the Soviet Ambassador in Tokyo handed the Japanese Foreign Minister this declaration of war, the minister had replied that Japan was prepared to accept the Potsdam declaration subject only to certain reservations about retaining the Emperor as the sovereign ruler. According to Deane's view of the situation, although the Hiroshima atomic bomb received scant notice in the Soviet press, it must have been given the greatest attention in the inner councils, for 'Russia had to buy her ticket to the Pacific peace conference, but she had to hurry or the show would have started and the seats would all be taken'.[82]

Soviet historians portray what they call the rout of the Kwantung Army as a mighty campaign involving a Red Army force of one and a half million men, 5,500 tanks and 4,000 combat aircraft. The atom bomb, they say, did not influence Japan's ability to continue the fight; even after 14 August, when the Japanese government finally capitulated, the Kwantung Army continued to resist 'for a further three days'.

Stalin had told Truman at Potsdam that the new Japanese war would begin in the latter half of August and Malinovsky had been given from six to eight weeks to accomplish his mission. According to the present Soviet account, when Vasilevsky made his report to the Supreme Commander in Moscow on 3 August, he pressed that the war might be brought forward, basing his argument on the intelligence that the number of Japanese divisions in Manchuria and Korea had been increased in June (*sic*) from nineteen to twenty-three.[83] This factor seems scarcely pertinent. If the bringing forward of the war by two to three weeks was, as Soviet writers affirm, entirely unconnected with the use of the atomic bomb or the readiness of the Japanese to surrender, the real reason for the haste to rush into a campaign before the end of the rains, remains obscure.

In spite of what had been said at Potsdam, it was somewhat doubtful whether it was really intended that Vasilevsky should command the Far East forces without supervision from Moscow. On 3 August he had proposed to Stalin that the main body of Meretskov's 1 Far East Front should go over to the offensive five to seven days after Malinovsky's Transbaikal Front. Stalin had the timings 'checked mathematically' by the general staff before rejecting the idea, and decided that the offensive should start simultaneously on all fronts. The *Stavka* decision was immediately transmitted to Vasilevsky, but the final directive confirming the tasks already given to the fronts, and including dates and timings, was not signed by Stalin until 1630 hours on 7 August. Operations began at 0010 hours in the early morning of 9 August, and the war took on the character of an exercise in movement.

On 11 August, Molotov called Harriman and Clark Kerr to his office to discuss the appointment of a Supreme Commander to whom the Japanese Emperor and Government were to be subordinated 'in case the Japanese decided to surrender'. To Harriman's suggestion that this might be MacArthur, Molotov replied that there might have to be two Supreme Commanders, MacArthur and Vasilevsky. Harriman did not think so; the United States had carried the main burden of the war in the Pacific for four years 'and kept the Japanese off Russia's back'; the Soviet Union had been in the war only two days. Molotov, too, became heated, and said that he did not wish to reply as he would have to refer to the war in Europe. He would consult with Stalin. Antonov's Potsdam statement that Marshal Vasilevsky would have complete control, without supervision from Moscow, of all Soviet operations in the Far East, should probably be viewed against this political background.

The Soviet military representative Lieutenant-General Derevianko, who was a co-signatory to the final surrender document signed on the *Missouri* at Manila, was nominated for this duty by Stalin in a personal communication to Truman. The lesson of Susloparov had not been forgotten.

12
Epilogue

Trotsky said of Stalin that his ambition had acquired an untutored Asiatic cast of mind, intensified by European techniques, so that he had to have the press extol him extravagantly every day, publish his portraits, refer to him on the slightest pretext, and print his name in large type. Everything had to revolve around Stalin.[1] At a later period Khrushchev said much the same.

With the partial rehabilitation of Stalin, however, the military men have been constrained to voice a qualified view. Zhukov in his 1968 memoirs has glossed over the pre-war purges in a passing reference of a few lines; in Vasilevsky's 1974 autobiography they are not even mentioned. Zhukov and Shtemenko maintain that Stalin 'did not decide and, in the main, did not want to decide important military questions personally, for he well understood the necessity for collective work in these complicated spheres', notwithstanding that their own memoirs are brimming with descriptions of Stalin taking capricious and wrongful decisions of great moment, without consulting anyone.[2] It is clear that the dictator continued to do so until the time of his death. In 1946, for example, following a chance conversation with Voronov immediately after the May Day parade, he decided, on the spur of the moment, to create a special academy of artillery sciences, for he had always had an admiration for that arm which he called 'the God of War'. The general staff and Commissariat of Defence were against the decision, but, as Shtemenko said, 'no one could point out to Stalin that the project was illogical and in truth no one tried to do so'. The academy was formed in the following September, only to be disbanded shortly afterwards.[3]

Numbers of present day Soviet writers have attempted to explain Stalin's character against the background of the infallibility of the Communist Party. Shtemenko wrote, in 1973, that Stalin had enormous power and that it was fitting to regard this as the recognition of his services to the Communist Party, at the head of which he stood. Stalin's authority and the respect in which he was held by the people were, continued Shtemenko, created by the party, although they were strengthened by the man's own personal qualities; indeed 'in the latter years of his life' the ugly pattern of the cult of the individual emerged, and although Stalin made some efforts to protest against the glorification of his person, these were not convincing.[4] Yet at a 1946 meeting of the Supreme Military Council (VVS) which was presided over by Stalin, all present had to listen to a long harangue by the chairman, directed against 'one of our most important soldiers [presumably Zhukov]', on the subject of immodesty, unjustified conceit and megalomania.[5] Vasilevsky has included a number of paragraphs in his memoirs which appear to have been written by a hand other than his own, since they contradict the conclusions to be drawn from the body of his book. These paragraphs emphasize that the credit for the successful leadership of the armed forces and the people lay with the Communist Party, 'for all principal questions concerning the war were decided by the Central Committee – the Politburo, Orgburo and Secretariat'. This point is accepted and re-emphasized by his literary reviewers.[6]

Soviet historians writing in the period of Khrushchev's ascendancy have blamed the Stalin personality cult for the slowness of the Soviet armed forces between 1946 and 1953 to adapt to the likely conditions of rocket and nuclear warfare.[7] At the time, Stalin said that 'the artificially sustained hullabaloo about the danger of a third world war' was meant for people with weak nerves, and he refused to be frightened 'by their atomic blackmail'.[8] Yet he wasted neither opportunity nor effort in launching a massive atomic and rocket research programme and, in the event, although probably by good fortune rather than by sound judgement, he lost nothing by leaving his ground forces equipped and trained in the fashion of the great armoured battles of 1945.

In 1942 Stalin had produced his own principles of war, based on permanently operating and transitory and fortuitous factors.[9]

Three of the constantly operating factors, quantity and quality of divisions, equipment, and the organizing ability of the commanders, being based on substance rather than theory, certainly reflected Stalin's cast of mind and were in contradistinction to the military principles accepted by the other great powers. In Soviet terminology 'morale' became 'morale of the army' and the fifth factor, stability of the rear, was adopted directly from Lenin.[10] By 1949 Stalin had become 'the greatest man on our planet' and Soviet military science, which embraced not only the purely military elements of the military art, strategy, operations, tactics and the organization and training of troops, but also social-political, economic and home-morale factors, was known as 'Stalin military science'. The dictator's infallible pronouncements assumed the style of oracles so that, according to the 1964 military textbooks, the principles enunciated by Stalin blocked further research and development in the military field. Yet the principles of war promulgated in 1964 differed little, except in their manner of presentation, from those originally formulated by Stalin.[11]

In the summer of 1949 Stalin was lecturing the Politburo that 'Hitler's generals, raised on the dogma of Clausewitz and Moltke, could not understand that war is won in the factories'. Out of a population of eighty million, continued Stalin, the German adventurists maintained armed forces totalling thirteen million, whereas 'history tells us that no single state could maintain such an effort'. Stalin contrasted this with the 194 million population of the Soviet Union at the beginning of the war and the maximum size of the Red Army – which he put at eleven and a half million men.[12] Stalin's statement was not entirely correct, for Hitler's generals had as little effect on the outcome of the Russo-German War as Stalin's generals, and Stalin does not take into account many other pertinent factors which contributed to the Soviet victory. But what does emerge from these pronouncements is Stalin's insistence on a firm home economic base, together with the stability of the Soviet military rear. Lenin once said that 'the unstable rear of Denikin, Kolchak, Wrangel and the imperialist agents, predetermined their defeat'. In the Second World War the Soviet rear was safeguarded by the party and by NKVD troops; and Stalin, as the chairman of the *Tsentral'nyi Shtab*, which was outside the *Stavka*, controlled partisan activities aimed at destroying the authority of the occupying power and the security of the enemy lines of communication.

Stalin was unresolved as to the relative position of the Soviet Navy within the High Command and, in February 1946, he joined the Commissariats for Defence and for the Navy into a single Ministry of the Armed Forces. Four years later this was split again into separate Ministries of Defence and of the Navy. There was, in addition, other re-organization, for within the Ministry of Defence Stalin had created a Headquarters Ground Forces responsible for doctrine and training, which was later redesignated as the Headquarters of the Soviet Army. In 1947 Stalin formally relinquished the post of Commissar for Defence to Bulganin.

Most of Stalin's senior generals continued to hold high appointments, some for a decade or more after his death. There were, however, some changes. Vasilevsky was one of the ablest and best educated of the marshals belonging, like Shaposhnikov, to a bygone age; his writings show that he stood intellectually head and shoulders above Zhukov. Vasilevsky replaced Antonov as Chief of General Staff in November 1948 and then, four months later, became Minister of Defence in place of Bulganin. Zhukov's education was largely self-acquired, but he was a decisive and hard character of genius who willingly accepted, or took, responsibility for the conduct of operations. According to Vasilevsky, Zhukov had marked originality and creative ability, particularly in the operative field, and Stalin frequently called on him for advice; Zhukov was, concluded Vasilevsky, 'one of the most brilliant of the military leaders of the Second World War'.[13] Zhukov was removed from his post as Deputy Supreme Commander in March 1946 and sent to relatively subordinate appointments, the command of the Odessa and then the Ural Military Districts, and disappeared, at least from public notice, for several years. At about this time Gordov was arrested when in command of the Volga Military District and became, according to Konev, 'a victim of the repression'. Novikov and Kuznetsov were soon under a cloud and Stalin took a dislike to Antonov, who was sent off to the Caucasus. When Montgomery visited Moscow in 1948, he noted that all the ministers and marshals stood in the greatest awe of Stalin 'and shut up like an oyster in his presence'.[14]

Konev held a special position among the marshals because he was favoured by Stalin as a counter-weight to Zhukov. He was a strong, somewhat brutal character, a man of limited education but great energy, unable to express himself well on paper; but he realized his own limitations and sorted out operative and tactical problems on the spot with the forward troops, leaving all other matters to his staff. Konev became the Commander-in-Chief of the Ground Forces from June 1946 until March 1950 when he was appointed as Inspector-General. Rokossovsky was particularly talented militarily, for he had the ability, rarely met in the Red Army, of using, and relying on, his subordinates, and he had an excellent relationship with Malinin, his chief of staff. Rokossovsky became Soviet Commander-in-Chief in Poland and then the Polish Minister for Defence. No one could use his staff better than the gloomy and taciturn Govorov, whose powers of organization were the envy of all; he was persistent and demanding, and, according to Vasilevsky, no officer in his headquarters found that time hung heavily on his hands. Govorov knew staff work well, though he took good care never to do it. From 1947 Govorov became the first Inspector-General of the Armed Forces. Meretskov, Malinovsky, Tolbukhin and Bagramian went to internal military districts. Vasilevsky has agreed with Stalin's evaluation of Meretskov, who was distinguished for cunning, circumspection and thoroughness; when working out solutions, Meretskov tried to agree his decisions with the general staff by 'first finding out the opinion of the highest power in the land'. Malinovsky and Tolbukhin had worked on the staff and they took a prominent part in their own staff planning, often doing the work of the chiefs of staff, a failing which Vatutin had shared. But whereas Malinovsky was a hard character, Tolbukhin was of a particularly mild disposition. Tolbukhin's control did not suffer on this account as he was most ably supported by his chief of staff Biriuzov, a practical man of strong views. Bagramian was a man of education, of clear sight and lucid expression, and in Vasilevsky's view, a hard and single-minded commander.[15] Stalin used his marshals in accordance with their capabilities, but owed no great debt to any one of them. The higher their rank and the more popular their fame, the less they enjoyed his trust, so that the command of by far the largest and most experienced front in the Soviet Army held on a war footing, the Group of Soviet Forces in Germany, was to be given to Chuikov, a general of no great importance who had commanded only an army throughout most of the war and who was not on close terms with his more illustrious fellows.

Later in life Stalin became a glutton, but his mind was never confused by strong drink although he encouraged that failing in others; for his own drinking was a pretence, and the special carafe of colourless vodka, from which he drank his many toasts, was in fact water.[16] Stalin was always sober. Yet once during a Kuntsevo supper in 1944, the dictator got up, hitched up his trousers as though he was about to wrestle or to box, and cried out: 'The war will soon be over. We shall recover in fifteen or twenty years and then we will have another go at it!'.[17] In this was revealed the mentality of the man. By 1948 his intellect was already declining but his control over the affairs of state was as tight as ever. He became even more suspicious and quicker to take offence. A foreigner, Djilas, could discern tension between the dictator and Molotov, and, according to Khrushchev, Stalin had formed the notion 'to finish off' both Molotov and Mikoian. Voroshilov, too, was in some danger, for Stalin, toying with the suspicion that Voroshilov was an English agent, had for several years past forbidden Voroshilov to attend Politburo sessions or receive documents.[18] Voznesensky, another Politburo member, had been shot and, as a result of the Leningrad affair, Stalin had purged Zhdanov's associates and protégés. At home a new terror began to gather momentum, while abroad the former western allies were deliberately provoked by the Berlin blockade. The Soviet armed forces were rapidly increased by a partial mobilization so that the 1948 strength of 2,874,000 rose to near the six million mark.[19]

A woman doctor, one Timashuk, wrote a private letter to Stalin criticizing the treatment prescribed by eminent Soviet medical specialists, and this was enough to cause Stalin to believe, so he said, that the doctors were conspiring to murder prominent leaders loyal to himself. Vasilevsky, Konev, Govorov and Shtemenko were the military names among the so-called plot victims. The doctors' plot, according to Khrushchev, was a fabrication from beginning to end, the whole case having been set up by Stalin, 'who did not, however, have the time to bring the matter to the end which he had mapped out'.[20] Stalin's sudden death was a temporary reprieve for his courtiers and henchmen, and perhaps for the populations of the Soviet Union and the rest of the world. For so died one whom Djilas, a fellow communist, called 'the greatest criminal in history'.

Stalin's military qualities were not conspicuous during his stay at Tsaritsyn and Petrograd in 1918 and 1919, for, like Trotsky, he was without training or experience, a political figure who wanted to shine militarily. His judgement was clouded not by political prejudice but by personal ambition, envy and rancour. Yet the Perm and Polish War correspondence shows that he had organizational ability which was, in due course, to stand him well in the military field. There is little doubt that, at the time, Stalin was highly regarded, both by Lenin and by Trotsky, as a political and military worker of outstanding force of character; and Voroshilov was correct when he said that from 1919 onwards Stalin was moved from theatre to theatre, being sent by the Politburo to those fronts where the threat was most dangerous. Although his personal achievements may be questioned, his experience during the Civil and Polish Wars was later put to good use. Stalin learned much from Lenin.

The subversion and demoralization of the Imperial Russian Army led directly to the destruction of the last of the Romanovs; this was a lesson which Stalin was not likely to forget. During the period between the two world wars he quickly gained control of the police and of the Red Army and, from 1926 onwards, he interested himself closely in military affairs. The political controls over the armed forces, introduced by Trotsky in what was probably intended as a temporary expedient, were never to be loosened, notwithstanding the occasional experiments with unified command; the NKVD para-military organization was created to form a counterweight to the Red Army. Although the collegiate and commissar system and the secret police organization within the armed forces detracted from military efficiency, they effectively served their purpose in safeguarding Stalin against further revolution. The purges and terror were two of the measures used to destroy or deter possible opposition.

During Stalin's dictatorship it had been obligatory for the Soviet press to denigrate all capitalist states, the tsars, the Russian Empire and the old army. Whether Stalin believed his own propaganda organs is perhaps doubtful, for he was a strange revolutionary with complexes of inferiority unexpected in such a man; he admired the Great Russian and the old tsarist army, with its centuries of tradition and its imposing imperial names. Like the Russian, he had a healthy respect for German efficiency and for French military *élan*.

During the late twenties and the thirties Stalin, in the final outcome, controlled senior Soviet military appointments, and approved or directed military theory, training, organization, equipment and deployment. Stalin alone was responsible for the purges which destroyed the larger part of the senior command of the Red Army. Stalin's principal positive contribution at this time was the creation of a well-developed home industrial base, responsible for the production of a great quantity of military equipment, much of it of modern design and good quality at the time it was taken into service. But by 1941 the Red Army was already paying the penalty for over-production and was using a large variety of weapons, diverse in model and pattern, many of them obsolete or obsolescent. Although Soviet small-arms and artillery were generally of high quality, tanks and aircraft were much inferior to those of German design, an inferiority which was only partially redressed when some of the post-1940 production became available. The fighting efficiency of aircraft, tanks and guns and of air and ground formations, depends largely, however, on the associated fire-control, communication and auxiliary equipment, and this was woefully lacking in the Soviet Union in 1941. All in all, however, Russia went to war immeasurably better prepared and equipped than it had ever done in tsarist times and, in quantitative terms, took the field with the greatest army in the world. Qualitatively, however, it was, at the time, hardly to be compared with the German Army.

Stalin's failure in the opening days of the war was political rather than military, for it was the direct consequence of his own political misjudgement. It is doubtful whether a military commander of genius could have saved the Soviet Union from a series of defeats and an enormous loss of territory in the first few months of the war, so great were the effects of surprise and the superiority of the *Wehrmacht*. According to the account said to have originated from the Soviet Chief of General Staff, Stalin was aware of this truth, even before the outbreak of war. If this was in fact the case, Stalin's fault becomes even more grievous, for he would have been wiser to have adopted a mobile defence, following the example of Barclay de Tolly, withdrawing his armies eastwards to the outskirts of Moscow and Rostov in preparation for a winter campaign. For the winter, not Kutuzov, destroyed Bonaparte. Stalin's insistence on the holding of ground was responsible for the loss in the first nine months of the war of three and a half million Red Army men as prisoners, in addition to the heavy casualties in killed and wounded. Stalin repeated his error in May 1942, when, buoyed by his successes during the winter fighting, he tried to enter the western Ukraine.

The Stalingrad battle on the other hand was fought deep in the interior of Russia, near what was once Sarai, the Tatar capital of the Golden Horde, at the gateway to Asia. The Axis troops, badly clothed and poorly supplied, were extended to their limit and the hard weather was approaching. In the previous winter the enemy Army Groups Centre and South had retreated up to distances of 200 miles, often in defiance of the Führer's standstill orders, and so saved themselves from destruction. In Stalingrad, however, 6 German Army had a commander who implicitly obeyed his orders to remain on the Volga.

Stalin alone was responsible for the heavy losses of 1941 and 1942. But if he is to bear the blame for the defeats of the first two years of war, he must be allowed the credit for the amazing successes of 1944, the *annus mirabilis*, when whole German army groups were virtually obliterated with lightning blows in Belorussia, Galicia, Rumania and the Baltic, in battles fought not on the wintry steppes, but in midsummer in Central Europe. Some of these victories must be reckoned as among the most outstanding in the world's military history.

The reasons for the improvement in the Soviet leadership and High Command during the course of the war will be obvious to the reader. Yet a comprehensive analysis of the factors which brought victory to the Soviet Union can only be undertaken with a concomitant study of the reasons for the German military defeats, a subject outside the scope of this work. Hitler's failure in the winter of 1942 was due to an over-ambitious strategy based on inadequate resources and a wilful underestimate of enemy potential; as he himself told Goebbels, he had been unable to overcome the problem of movement and supply in Russia, and he had done what once he had said he would never do, entrusted the security of German troops to his allies. Moreover the Stalingrad victory has to be seen against the world background of war as the first major landmark along the road to victory; not as a cause of German defeat in the Second World War but as an effect of the heavy preponderance of allied resources over those of the Axis powers. By the end of 1942 the balance was already weighted against Germany, and from then onwards this was to show itself in a series of disasters for the Axis, not only in Russia but in the Far East, the Atlantic, the Mediterranean and in Europe. During 1943 it was apparent to the world that Germany's fortunes were on the wane. Air superiority had been lost even in daylight over the Reich, and the Axis allies were ready to capitulate. Not only had the German Army lost its old offensive power, but it no longer disposed sufficient troops to defend and garrison occupied Europe for German manpower was to prove inadequate to maintain the number of field formations in existence. German industry was still not on a war footing and, through failing to recognize the seriousness of the position until it was too late, Hitler lost three years which might have been better used to equip the German forces.

As military commanders Stalin and Hitler had much in common. By 1944, however, the situation had been reversed, so that Axis troops were fighting under conditions of air inferiority, lacking fire support and mobility. Hitler's military strategy became rapidly bankrupt in that he was determined to hold territory by a rigid defence, and he assumed the role acted out by Stalin in 1941. No withdrawal, however limited, could be undertaken without his express permission. Those generals who disagreed with him were dismissed, for the halcyon days of the brilliant panzer envelopments were long passed. So the German formations fell into the Red Army maw, an easy prey to the fast moving Soviet tank armies. The wheel of fortune had turned full circle.

Appendix
The Russian and
Red Armies

Before 1870 the French were regarded as the prominent military thinkers and the most competent soldiers in the world, so that Napoleon Bonaparte's army organization continued to serve as a model for all the great powers, including Prussia and Russia. After the Franco-Prussian War military interest became focussed on Prussia and the new army of the German Empire, and from then on followed the German lead. So it came about that the methods, organization and tactics of the armies of France, Germany and Russia were all in accordance with a common European continental pattern. The basic field formation devised by the French and still in use over a century and a half later was the infantry division, an all arms grouping, principally of infantry, with artillery and engineer supporting troops. Infantry was the main fighting element and all other arms existed merely to assist it. Other than infantry, only cavalry could, in certain phases of war, operate as a main arm, but then solely for very limited periods on ground suitable for mounted action.

The infantry division was said to be basic because it was designed to be capable of operation in isolation on any terrain, and was self-contained and self-supporting; the military might of a nation came to be reckoned in the number of infantry divisions which it could muster. The strength of a division varied from ten to 17 thousand men, of whom about three-quarters were infantry, but its effectiveness depended not so much on its numbers as on its fire power, mobility, training and tactical handling. There was no hard and fast rule for the grouping of infantry divisions into higher

273

formations. Several divisions, usually three, made up a corps, several corps made up an army, and several armies were formed into an army group, known in Russian as a front. Army groups were controlled directly by a General Headquarters or High Command, known in tsarist days as the *Stavka*.

According to French military thought *strategy* is regarded as the art of preparing, mobilizing, deploying, concentrating and moving forces between theatres of war or within a theatre, with a view to success in battle. *Tactics* is the art of actually fighting the resultant battles. German thought extended this doctrine by interposing *operations* (sometimes known as the *operative art*) at an inter-mediate stage between strategy and tactics, since the experience of the Franco-Prussian, Russo-Turkish and Russo-Japanese Wars showed that separate tactical engagements, instead of being restric-ted in time and space as they were in Napoleonic times, developed by degrees into prolonged battles covering vast areas and involving large numbers of troops. The preparation and conduct of these major battles within a theatre were held, according to the Berlin school, to be within the sphere of operations. This German concept was assumed by the Soviet High Command in 1924. At the risk of over-simplification it may be said that the Russians tend to regard the warlike activities of divisions and corps as tactical, while armies and fronts are usually employed on operative tasks; the co-ordina-tion and control of two or more fronts comes within the definition of strategy. The distinction between strategy, operations and tactics is admitted to be very fine on occasions since this depends not only on the size of the forces engaged but on frontages, depth, the time element and the nature of the task; for example, tactical formations can perform roles which have an operative significance, particularly when they receive independent missions at critical moments of an action.

The 1914 Russian Army was a short term conscript force or-ganized on the Prussian pattern. The Russian infantry division had two infantry brigades each of two infantry regiments, making four regiments in all, together with a divisional artillery brigade and attached Cossack squadrons. The division was usually commanded by a lieutenant-general, a brigade by a major-general, and a regi-ment by a colonel; at full strength it totalled 16,000 men, 36 guns, 27 machine-guns and about 200 sabres. An infantry

regiment normally had three battalions, commanded by lieu-
tenant-colonels or majors, each battalion having three or four
rifle companies. A cavalry or Cossack division usually comprised
two brigades each of two cavalry regiments, together with horse
artillery batteries; it rarely mustered more than 4,000 sabres. These
tsarist organizations were used, with some variations, both by the
White forces and by the Red Army; equipment, words of command, uniform (except for the identifying scrap of white or red
cloth) were common to both sides.

During the Civil and Polish Wars the Bolsheviks dispensed with
the corps headquarters so that infantry divisions were grouped
directly under armies, and, in 1918, they experimented by increasing the size of certain Red Army infantry divisions, so that
each had three rifle brigades firstly of two and then of three rifle
regiments each, together with nine artillery battalions. This raised
the strength of the division to 60,000 men, 24,000 horses and 116
guns and was found to be impracticable since the division was too
unwieldy. The old tsarist divisional organization was then re-
adopted at a reduced strength of about 10,000 men.

During the 1920s the infantry brigade headquarters were
abolished and infantry divisions henceforth comprised three
infantry and one artillery regiment with an engineer and signals
battalion. During the late 1930s a tank component was added to
the majority of the infantry and cavalry divisions.

Originally tanks had a role something between that of artillery
and engineers in that they were intended to assist infantry to fight
and to move by providing fire power and by overcoming obstacles,
but the military theorists between the two world wars began to
envisage the use of a large number of tanks, supported by infantry
and other arms, exploiting the flexibility of tactical air power and
outflanking and encircling the slow moving infantry armies of the
enemy. In such a role tanks became co-equal with infantry, a main
rather than a supporting arm. Except in Germany, these theorists
were without position or influence. In the Soviet Union there were
repeated changes of policy regarding the employment and organization of its tank forces, as it followed firstly the French and then
the German lead.

Russian built tanks had become available from 1927 onwards,
the first tank brigades of 90 fighting vehicles being formed in 1931.

By 1932 mechanized corps had been raised, each consisting of three tank brigades and a supporting motorized rifle brigade, totalling in all 490 BT and T 26 tanks. These mechanized corps were redesignated in 1938 as tank corps. In November of the following year, however, it was decided that the primary function of the tank was to support infantry, and the large tank formations were disbanded and reformed as 35 light and four heavy tank brigades, each of three or four tank battalions, the light tank brigade totalling 258 tanks while the heavy tank brigade had 156 (T 28 and T 35) tanks. Each of the fifteen motorized divisions retained its complement of 257 tanks and a further 98 independent tank battalions were allocated to the infantry divisions; in addition there were 20 independent tank regiments forming part of the cavalry divisions. From midsummer 1940 Soviet armour was re-organized once more to a close copy of the new German panzer arm, mechanized corps being formed, each consisting of two tank divisions – each of 410 tanks – and one motorized division. The 1940 Soviet mechanized corps at full strength totalled 1,030 tanks, of which 126 were of KV and 420 of T 34 type.

The Red Air Force had always been an integral part of the Red Army, the aviator being a soldier whose main task, together with the artillery, was to provide fire support for the ground forces. He wore army uniform and could only be distinguished by a different headdress and the light blue colour of his arm of service gorget patch. In 1930 the largest air formation within the Red Army was the air brigade of three squadrons, in all 100 aircraft. Three years later the brigades had been grouped into air corps and by 1936 the first air army had been formed. In 1940 this air organization was abolished in favour of the air regiment, usually consisting of 60 aircraft, and the air division of two or three air regiments.

The heavy Soviet losses in men and equipment at the outbreak of the Russo-German War made it necessary to abolish the corps headquarters as a temporary staff economy measure until 1943 when they were restored to the chain of command. Because of the lack of tanks, the large armoured formations were broken up in July 1941 and reformed as independent tank brigades each of 93 tanks, later reduced to a holding of 67 tanks. By 1942, however, new tanks corps were being formed, although on a much reduced establishment of 168 tanks, together with mechanized corps formed in three variants with a tank strength of 175, 204 or 224 fighting vehicles. Tank and mechanized corps had a brigade but not a divisional organization. In addition independent tank brigades continued their separate existence, by 1943 having been reduced to 53 tanks; the independent tank regiment had 39 and the heavy tank regiment only 21 tanks. From 1943 onwards tank and mechanized corps were grouped into tank armies, the fighting strength of which might vary from 400-1,000 tanks, together with a strong motorized infantry component.

The Soviet Union ended the war with its armies organized in a traditional pattern, the line or 'combined arms' armies having the usual corps and divisional organization while the shock armies had an additional artillery element to assist them in their break-through role. Air armies were usually concentrated directly under front command. Towards the end of Stalin's life, however, it became apparent that the corps organization was going to be dropped once more, while the tank armies were to be re-organized on a divisional pattern, without the corps headquarters, very much in the style of the 1941 German panzer corps.

Notes

Chapter 1

1. Cit., Souvarine, pp. 112–4.
2. *Pravda*, 7 Feb 28 and 20 Dec 29; Yaroslavsky, p. 72.
3. *Stalin Kratk. Biogr.*, p. 56.
4. *Prot. Ts. Kom. RSDRP (29)*, p. 124.
5. Trotsky, *Stalin*, p. 232.
6. Ibid., p. 234.
7. Stalin, *Soch.*, Vol. 3, p. 423; *Hist. Civ. War in USSR*, Vol. 2, pp. 174, 195, 201, 221.
8. Trotsky, *Stalin*, p. 243.
9. Cf., *50 Let*, p. 33.
10. *V. Ist. Zh.*, 6/67, p. 79.
11. Littauer, pp. 246–7.
12. Cf., Rotmistrov, Vol. 1, p. 212; Zaionchovsky, *V. Ist. Zh.*, 3/73, pp. 42, 45–7.
13. Shaposhnikov, *V. Ist. Zh.*, 1/67, pp. 77–8.
14. Knox, Vol. 1, p. xxix.
15. Trotsky, *Hist. Russ. Rev.*, Vol. 1, p. 274.
16. Denikin, p. 159.
17. Trotsky, *Stalin*, p. 278; Lenin, *Poln. Sobr. Soch.*, Vol. 39, p. 313.
18. Trotsky, *Kak Voor. Rev.*, Vol. 1, pp. 17, 151; *Trotsky Papers*, Vol. 1, pp. 148, 544.
19. Cf., *Arm. Sov.*, p. 31.
20. *Iz Ist. Grazhd. Voin.*, Vol. 1, p. 473.
21. *Dir. Kom. Front.*, Vol. 1, p. 250.
22. Stalin, *Soch.*, Vol. 4, pp. 419–20 note 21.
23. Ibid., pp. 116–7; *Trotsky Papers*, Vol. 1, p. 46.
24. *Leninsk. Sborn.*, XXXVII pp. 88–90.
25. *Dir. Kom. Front.*, Vol. 1, p. 265.
26. Ibid., p. 269.
27. *Iz Ist. Grazhd. Voin.*, Vol. 1, p. 470.
28. *Hist. Civ. War in USSR*, Vol. 2, p. 41.
29. *Ist. Grazhd. Voin.*, Vol. 1, p. 231.
30. Denikin, p. 165.
31. Stalin, *Soch.*, Vol. 4, pp. 118–9.
32. Ibid., pp. 120–1.
33. Voroshilov, *Stalin i Kr. Arm.*, p. 10.
34. *Iz Ist. Grazhd. Voin.*, Vol. 1, p. 478.
35. Trotsky, *Stalin*, p. 270.
36. Cf., Souvarine, p. 245.

37. *Dir. Glav. Kom.*, p. 74.
38. Budenny, Vol. 1, pp. 80–3.
39. *Dir. Kom. Front.*, Vol. 1, pp. 289–302.
40. Voroshilov, op. cit., p. 13.
41. Ibid., p. 14.
42. *Grazhd. Voin.*, Vol. 1, p. 20.
43. Stalin, *Soch.*, Vol. 4, pp. 122–4.
44. *Stalin Kratk. Biog.*, pp. 72–3.
45. *Trotsky Papers*, Vol. 1, p. 164.
46. *Grazhd. Voin.*, Vol. 3, p. 252.
47. Stalin, *Soch.*, Vol. 4, pp. 122–6.
48. Denikin, p. 45.
49. Cf., Budenny, Vol. 1, pp. 135–6.
50. Denikin, p. 152.
51. *Dir. Kom. Front.*, Vol. 1, pp. 304, 306–7.
52. Ibid., pp. 309, 314, 722 note 77.
53. Stalin, *Soch.*, Vol. 4, pp. 127–8.
54. Ibid., p. 129; *Iz Ist. Grazhd. Voin.*, Vol. 1, p. 491.
55. Lenin, *Voen. Perep.*, p. 78.
56. *Leninsk. Sborn.*, XXXVII, p. 101; *Trotsky Papers*, Vol. 1, pp. 92–6, 106, 116.
57. *Iz Ist. Grazhd. Voin.*, Vol. 1, p. 494.
58. Stalin, *Soch.*, Vol. 4, p. 453.
59. *Dir. Kom. Front.*, Vol. 1, pp. 322–9.
60. Ibid., p. 336.
61. Ibid., p. 343.
62. Ibid., p. 345.
63. Rotmistrov, Vol. 1, p. 386.
64. Genkina, *Prol. Rev.*, 2/39, p. 101.
65. *Trotsky Papers*, Vol. 1, p. 116.
66. *Dir. Kom. Front.*, Vol. 1, p. 348.
67. *Iz Ist. Grazhd. Voin.*, Vol. 1, p. 496.
68. Sverdlov, Vol. 3, p. 28.
69. *Dir. Glav. Kom.*, pp. 82–3.
70. *Trotsky Papers*, Vol. 1, p. 140.
71. Stalin, *Soch.*, Vol. 4, p. 453.
72. *Trotsky Papers*, Vol. 1, p. 135.
73. *Dir. Glav. Kom.*, p. 118.
74. Ibid., pp. 84–5.
75. *Dir. Kom. Front.*, Vol. 1, pp. 353–4, 358.
76. Cf., Efimov, *V. Ist. Zh.*, 1/67, pp. 108–10.
77. *Trotsky Papers*, Vol. 1, pp. 158–60; *Leninsk. Sborn.*, XXXVII, pp. 106–7.
78. *Grazhd. Voin. na Ukr.*, Vol. 1, Bk 1, pp. 386, 449.
79. *Stalin Kratk. Biog.*, p. 73.
80. Stalin, *Soch.*, Vol. 4, pp. 174–6, 422.
81. *Grazhd. Voin. na Ukr.*, Vol. 1, Bk 2, p. 23.

Chapter 2

1. Lenin, *Voen. Perep.*, p. 88; *Trotsky Papers*, Vol. 1, pp. 194–6.

2. Ibid., pp. 228, 230; Trotsky, *Stalin*, p. 293.

3. Stalin, *Soch.*, Vol. 4, pp. 186–8.

4. *Leninsk. Sborn.*, XXXVII, p. 120.

5. Voroshilov, *Stalin i Kr. Arm.*, pp. 20–3.

6. Stalin, *Soch.*, Vol. 4, p. 425 note 50; Lenin, *Poln. Sobr. Soch.*, Vol. 50, p. 243.

7. Stalin, *Soch.*, Vol. 4, p. 211.

8. Ibid., pp. 197–224.

9. Voroshilov, op. cit., pp. 22–3.

10. Cf., Ironside, p. 167 *et seq.*; *50 Let*, p. 72.

11. *KPSS v Rez. i Resh.*, Pt I, p. 446.

12. *Leninsk. Sborn.*, XXVII, pp. 135–40.

13. Trotsky, *Stalin*, p. 307.

14. *50 Let*, p. 88; Stewart, p. 217.

15. *50 Let*, p. 89.

16. Kamenev, *Vosp. o Lenine*, Vol. 2, pp. 261–2.

17. *Bol'shevik*, 3/47, p. 6.

18. Trotsky, *Stalin*, p. 277.

19. Lenin, *Poln. Sobr. Soch.*, Vol. 50, p. 317.

20. Ibid., pp. 325, 331.

21. Ibid., pp. 334–5.

22. *Trotsky Papers*, Vol. 1, pp. 542–4, 546, 552; Lenin, *Voen. Perep.*, pp. 146–7.

23. Stalin, *Soch.*, Vol. 4, p. 431 note 73; cf., *Arm. Sov.*, p. 74.

24. *Iz Ist. Grazhd. Voin*, Vol. 2, p. 328.

25. Stalin, *Soch.*, p. 431 note 74.

26. *Leninsk. Sborn.*, XXXVI, p. 77.

27. *Dir. Kom. Front.*, Vol. 2, p. 99.

28. Voroshilov, op. cit., p. 25.

29. *Dir. Kom. Front.*, Vol. 2, pp. 100–3.

30. *Iz Ist. Grazhd. Voin.*, Vol. 2, p. 341.

31. *Trotsky Papers*, Vol. 1, p. 520.

32. Lenin, *Poln. Sobr. Soch.*, Vol. 50, pp. 334–5.

33. *Trotsky Papers*, Vol. 1, p. 520.

34. Trotsky, *Stalin*, p. 308.

35. *Ist. Grazhd. Voin.*, Vol. 4, p. 335.

36. *Dir. Glav. Kom.*, p. 384.

37. *Leninsk. Sborn.*, XXXVII, p. 161.

38. Stalin, *Soch.*, Vol. 4, pp. 272–4.

39. Kameneva, *Nov. Mir*, 3/69, p. 169.

40. Ibid., pp. 173–7; Kamenev, op. cit., p. 255.

41. *Trotsky Papers*, Vol. 1, pp. 442–4.

42. Ibid., p. 482.

43. Ibid., pp. 578–80; Trotsky, *Stalin*, pp. 313–4.

44. *Trotsky Papers*, Vol. 1, p. 594.

45. Denikin, pp. 279–80.

46. *Dir. Kom. Front.*, Vol. 2, p. 284.

47. Trotsky, *My Life*, p. 387

and *Stalin*, pp. 314, 322–3;
Voroshilov, op. cit., p. 31.

48. Souvarine, p. 242;
Deutscher, p. 211.
49. *Trotsky Papers*, Vol. 1,
p. 604.
50. *Dir. Kom. Front.*, Vol. 2,
p. 284.
51. *Dir. Glav. Kom.*, p. 439.
52. *Trotsky Papers*, Vol. 1,
pp. 610, 664–6.
53. *Iz Ist. Grazhd. Voin.*,
Vol. 2, p. 491.
54. Ibid., p. 499.
55. Ibid., p. 869 note 197.
56. Denikin, p. 283.
57. *Iz Ist. Grazhd. Voin.*,
Vol. 2, p. 521.
58. Ibid., p. 523 note 206.
59. Denikin, p. 159.
60. Lenin, *Poln. Sobr. Soch.*,
Vol. 51, pp. 54–6; cf.,
Rotmistrov, Vol. 1, p. 413.
61. *Trotsky Papers*, Vol. 1,
pp. 686–8.
62. *Stalin Kratk. Biog.*, p. 77.
63. Stalin, *Soch.*, Vol 4,
pp. 275–7.
64. *Dir. Kom. Front.*, Vol. 2,
pp. 353–6.
65. Kuz'min, *V. Ist. Zh.*, 5/69,
p. 8.
66. *Dir. Kom. Front.*, Vol. 2,
pp. 370, 375.
67. *Trotsky Papers*, Vol. 1,
p. 758.
68. Rotmistrov, Vol. 1, p. 414.
69. *Iz Ist. Grazhd. Voin.*,
Vol. 2, p. 547.
70. *Leninsk. Sborn.*, XXXIV,
p. 239.
71. Voroshilov, op. cit.,

pp. 33–4.
72. Trotsky, *Stalin*, pp. 274–5.
73. Budenny, Vol. 1, pp. 321,
335.
74. Rotmistrov, Vol. 1, p. 422.
75. Budenny, Vol. 1, p. 345.
76. Trotsky, *Stalin*, p. 270.
77. Budenny, Vol. 1, pp.
243–5.
78. Littauer, p. 234.
79. Budenny, op. cit., p. 404.
80. *Trotsky Papers*, Vol. 2,
pp. 24–8.
81. *Iz Ist. Grazhd. Voin.*,
Vol. 2, p. 594.
82. *Trotsky Papers*, Vol. 2,
pp. 61, 66–7.
83. *Iz Ist. Grazhd. Voin.*,
Vol. 2, p. 594.

Chapter 3
1. *Trotsky Papers*, Vol. 1,
p. 764.
2. Lenin, *Poln. Sobr. Soch.*,
Vol. 51, p. 158; *Voen.
Perep.*, p. 257.
3. *Trotsky Papers*, Vol. 2,
p. 197.
4. Lenin, *Poln. Sobr. Soch.*,
Vol. 51, p. 205; *Voen.
Perep.*, p. 240.
5. *Trotsky Papers*, Vol. 2,
p. 199.
6. Ibid., p. 206; Lenin, *Poln.
Sobr. Soch.*, Vol. 51, pp.
206–7, 428–9, note 228.
7. *Trotsky Papers*, Vol. 2,
p. 215.
8. *Grazhd. Voin. na Ukr.*,
Vol. 3, p. 166; *Dir. Glav.
Kom.*, p. 687.
9. Ibid., pp. 689–93.

10. Ibid., p. 693.
11. *Grazhd. Voin. na Ukr.*, Vol. 3, p. 306.
12. Budenny, Vol. 2, p. 226.
13. *Leninsk. Sborn.*, XXIV, pp. 333–4.
14. *Iz Ist. Grazhd. Voin.*, Vol. 3, p. 329; *Trotsky Papers*, Vol. 2, p. 240.
15. Lenin, *Poln. Sobr. Soch.*, Vol. 51, pp. 247–8, 441 note 280.
16. *Iz Ist. Grazhd. Voin.*, Vol. 3, p. 336.
17. Ibid., p. 338.
18. Ibid., pp. 339, 341.
19. Ibid., pp. 341, 343.
20. Ibid., p. 342.
21. Budenny, Vol. 2, p. 306.
22. *Iz Ist. Grazhd. Voin.*, Vol. 3, p. 346.
23. Budenny, Vol. 2, pp. 288–9.
24. Lenin, *Poln. Sobr. Soch.*, Vol. 51, pp. 254–5.
25. *Iz Ist. Grazhd. Voin.*, Vol. 3, pp. 348–9; *Dir. Glav. Kom.*, p. 709.
26. Budenny, Vol. 2, p. 308.
27. Golubev, *V. Ist. Zh.*, 8/66, pp. 90–1.
28. *Iz Ist. Grazhd. Voin.*, Vol. 3, p. 350.
29. Ibid., p. 351; *Dir. Glav. Kom.*, p. 711.
30. *Iz Ist. Grazhd. Voin.*, Vol. 3, p. 352.
31. No. 0361/SEK of 15 August; Budenny, Vol. 2, pp. 309–11.
32. *Iz Ist. Grazhd. Voin.*, Vol. 3, p. 355.
33. Ibid., pp. 361–2.
34. *Trotsky Papers*, Vol. 2, p. 260.
35. Lenin, *Poln. Sobr. Soch.*, Vol. 32, p. 149 and Vol. 51, p. 258.
36. Trotsky, *Stalin*, pp. 296, 329.
37. Tukhachevsky, *Izb. Proizved.*, p. 162.
38. Shaposhnikov, *Na Visle*, p. 200.
39. Todorsky, p. 66; Rotmistrov, Vol. 1, p. 426; *V. Ist. Zh.*, 9/62, p. 62.
40. *Trotsky Papers*, Vol. 2, pp. 21, 279.

Chapter 4

1. Bazhanov, pp. 29–30.
2. Ibid., pp. 17–22.
3. Ibid., pp. 22–5.
4. Svetlana, p. 27.
5. Bazhanov, pp. 27, 32–4, 94–5.
6. Ibid., pp. 48, 55, 61.
7. Ibid., pp. 40, 45, 91–2, 133–4.
8. Trotsky, *Stalin*, p. 374; Rigby, p. 27.
9. *Ross. Komm. Part. IX S'ezd*, pp. 351 et seq.
10. *KPSS v Rez. i Resh.*, p. 569.
11. Trotsky, *Mil. Writ.*, pp. 28, 54, 59, 63–9, 70–93.
12. Voroshilov, *Stat. i Rech.*, pp. 281, 563.
13. *Arm. Sov.*, p. 105.
14. Ibid., p. 106.
15. Bazhanov, p. 72; Voroshilov, op. cit., p. 8.

16. *Docs Germ. For. Policy*, C, Vol. 2, p. 333.
17. Stalin, *Soch.*, Vol. 7, p. 11.
18. Barmine, p. 219.
19. Voroshilov, op. cit., p. 601.
20. Cit., White, p. 277.
21. Von Manstein, pp. 140–3.
22. Cf., *O Sov. Voen. Nauk.*, pp. 170–8; Kolganov, p. 9.
23. Sokolovsky, *Voen. Strat.*, p. 147.
24. Shaposhnikov, *V. Ist. Zh.*, 8/66, p. 75; 9/66, p. 73.
25. Hilger, p. 207.
26. *Nazi-Sov. Rels*, p. 74.
27. Stalin, *Leninism*, p. 541.
28. *50 Let*, pp. 195–200.
29. *Sobr. Zakon. R. K.*, 27/5, No. 34.
30. Kuznetsov, *Oktiabr'*, 9/63, p. 174.
31. Hilger, pp. 290, 301–3.
32. Meretskov, pp. 168–9.
33. Grabin, *Oktiabr'*, 11/73, p. 151; 12/73, p. 123.
34. Voronov, p. 45.
35. Ibid., pp. 115–6; Samsonov, *V. Ist. Zh.*, 5/69, pp. 52–4.
36. Zhukov, pp. 214, 217, 307.
37. Vannikov, *V. Ist. Zh.*, 2/62, pp. 78–86.
38. *V. Ist. Zh.*, 6/73, p. 79; Kolganov, p. 320.
39. Sherwood, Vol. 1, p. 329.
40. Emelianov, *Nov. Mir*, 2/67, p. 85.
41. *Pravda*, 18 Jul 48.
42. Iakovlev, p. 192.
43. Rotmistrov, Vol. 1, pp. 377, 479–81.
44. Zakharov, *V. Ist. Zh.*, 2/71,

45. *Izvestiia*, 28 Feb 38.
46. Meretskov, p. 179; Vasilevsky, p. 100.
47. Rotmistrov, Vol. 1, p. 499.
48. Shtemenko, Vol. 1, p. 18.
49. *Ist. Vel. Ot. Voin.*, Vol. 1, p. 277.
50. *KPSS o Voor. Sil.*, p. 298; *Sots. Vest.*, 25 Feb 41, p. 47.
51. Zhukov, pp. 181–3.
52. Krupchenko, *V. Ist. Zh.*, 5/68, p. 42.
53. Rotmistrov, Vol. 1, p. 479.
54. Vasilevsky, p. 106.
55. Ibid., p. 107.
56. Meretskov, p. 195.
57. Vasilevsky, p. 110.
58. Golikov, *V. Ist. Zh.*, 5/66, p. 65.
59. Knox, Vol. 1, pp. 107, 137.
60. Vasilevsky, p. 110.
61. Meretskov, p. 196.
62. Ibid., pp. 198–200; Zhukov, p. 197; Kazakov, p. 56; Eremenko, *V Nach. Voin.*, p. 45.
63. *Nazi-Sov. Rels*, p. 252.
64. Kuznetsov, *V. Ist. Zh.*, 9/65, p. 73.
65. Zhukov, pp. 233, 244, 245.
66. Ibid., p. 249.
67. Rigby, p. 55; Tiulenev, p. 42; Voronov, p. 171.
68. Kuznetsov, *V. Ist. Zh.*, 9/65, p. 73; *Oktiabr'*, 11/65, pp. 146–7, 162–71.
69. Zhukov, p. 247; Voronov, p. 175; Rigby, p. 53.
70. *50 Let*, p. 235; Zhukov, p. 250.

p. 40.

71. Ibid., p. 212.
72. Ibid., p. 228.
73. Ibid., p. 272.
74. Ibid., p. 232; Vasilevsky, p. 112.
75. Rigby, p. 55.
76. Bagramian, *So Begann der Krieg*, p. 50.
77. *Nazi-Sov. Rels*, p. 326; *Docs Germ. For. Policy*, D. Vol. 12, p. 873.
78. Bagramian, *V. Ist. Zh.*, 1/67, p. 56.
79. Maisky, p. 148.
80. Teske, pp. 304–19.
81. Voronov, p. 171.
82. Bagramian, *So Begann der Krieg*, pp. 61, 82.
83. Maisky, p. 156; Tiulenev, p. 137.
84. Zhukov, pp. 251–3.
85. *Fremde Heere Ost (OKH)* apprec. 20 May 41; Halder, Vol. 2, pp. 351–3.

Chapter 5

1. Kuznetsov, *V. Ist. Zh.*, 9/65, p. 73.
2. Zhukov, p. 255.
3. *Ist. Vel. Ot. Voin.*, Vol. 2, p. 17; Halder, Vol. 3, p. 4.
4. Tiulenev, p. 137.
5. Zhukov, p. 257.
6. Vasilevsky, p. 122.
7. Zhukov, p. 259.
8. Peresypkin, *V. Ist. Zh.*, 4/71, p. 19.
9. Vasilevsky, *V. Ist. Zh.*, 6/74, p. 124.
10. Zhukov, p. 283.
11. Rigby, p. 57.
12. Voronov, p. 178.

13. Bagramian, *V. Ist. Zh.*, 3/66, p. 64.
14. Boldin, *V. Ist. Zh.*, 4/61, p. 67; Zhukov, p. 273.
15. Bagramian, *So Begann der Krieg*, p. 140.
16. Zhukov, p. 277.
17. Eremenko, *V Nach. Voin.*, p. 78.
18. Starinov, p. 210.
19. Biriuzov, *Kogda Grem. Pushk.*, p. 10.
20. Zhukov, p. 201.
21. Shtemenko, Vol. 1, p. 31.
22. *KPSS o Voor. Sil.*, p. 305.
23. Von Bock, *Tagebuch*, 8 Jul 41.
24. *Pravda*, 1 Jul 41.
25. Cf., Stalin, *On Great Patriotic War*, p. 50; Kuznetsov, *V. Ist. Zh.*, 9/55, p. 65.
26. *Ist. Vel. Ot. Voin.*, Vol. 2, p. 70.
27. Ibid., p. 62.
28. Von Bock, *Tagebuch*, 5 Aug 41.
29. Zhukov, p. 299.
30. Hubatsch, pp. 145, 148–9.
31. Zhukov, p. 310.
32. *KTB des OKW*, Vol. 1, p. 1062; Halder, Vol. 3, p. 192.
33. Khrulev, *V. Ist. Zh.*, 6/61, p. 64.
34. Sherwood, Vol. 1, pp. 328–47.
35. Vasilevsky, p. 140.
36. Guderian, p. 202; Halder, Vol. 3, pp. 194–5.
37. Zhukov, p. 318; Vasilevsky, p. 141;

Platonov, p. 318.

38. Bagramian, *So Begann der Krieg*, p. 274.
39. *Ist. Vel. Ot. Voin.*, Vol. 2, p. 104.
40. Vasilevsky, p. 139.
41. Ibid., p. 145.
42. Ibid., p. 147.
43. Bagramian, *Gorod-voin na Dnepre*, p. 120.
44. Bagramian, *So Begann der Krieg*, p. 317.
45. *Ist. Vel. Ot. Voin.*, Vol. 2, p. 107.
46. Zhukov, pp. 320–1.
47. Fediuninsky, p. 41.
48. Kuznetsov, *Vopros. Ist.*, 8/65, p. 114.
49. Zhukov, pp. 321–3; Vasilevsky, p. 148; Bagramian, *So Begann der Krieg*, pp. 319–22.
50. Ibid., p. 326; *Ist. Vel. Ot. Voin.*, Vol. 2, p. 108.
51. Vasilevsky, p. 150.
52. Gwyer, Vol. 3, Pt 1, p. 200.
53. Bagramian, *So Begann der Krieg*, pp. 326–34.
54. *Ist. Vel. Ot. Voin.*, Vol. 2, p. 108.
55. *KTB des OKW*, Vol. 1, p. 661.
56. Bychevsky, pp. 92–100.
57. Kuznetsov, *V. Ist. Zh.*, 9/66, pp. 65–6.
58. Hubatsch, p. 150.
59. Konev, *V. Ist. Zh.*, 10/66, p. 56.
60. Rokossovsky, *Sold. Dolg*, pp. 49–50.
61. Sokolovsky, *Raz. Nemets. Voisk pod Moskv.*, p. 30;

V. Ist. Zh., 3/67, p. 70.
62. Gwyer, pp. 155–61.
63. Ismay, p. 233.
64. Leliushenko, *Zar. Pobed.*, p. 43.
65. Livshits, p. 34.
66. Telegin, *Vopros. Ist.*, 9/66, p. 101.
67. Rokossovsky, op. cit., pp. 52–61.
68. *KTB des OKW*, Vol. 1, p. 702.
69. Ibid., p. 531.
70. Sbytov, *Bit. za Moskv.*, pp. 402–4.
71. Zhukov, p. 344.

Chapter 6
1. Halder, Vol. 3, p. 295.
2. Zhukov, pp. 345–52.
3. Konev, *V. Ist. Zh.*, 10/66, p. 65.
4. Leliushenko, *Moskv.-Prag.*, pp. 48–9.
5. Werth, p. 234; Birse, p. 79.
6. Pronin, *Bit. za Moskv.*, p. 465; Telegin, *Vopros. Ist.*, 9/66, p. 104.
7. Zhukov, pp. 362–6.
8. Vasilevsky, *Bit. za Moskv.*, p. 23.
9. Vasilevsky, p. 163.
10. *Ist. Vel. Ot. Voin.*, Vol. 2, pp. 271–4.
11. Shelakhov, *V. Ist. Zh.*, 3/69, pp. 56–9.
12. Shtemenko, Vol. 1, pp. 30–2.
13. Shtemenko, Vol. 2, p. 7; Vasilevsky, p. 125.
14. Ibid., p. 124.
15. Ibid., p. 126.

16. Shtemenko, Vol. 2, p. 39; Zhukov, pp. 305–8.
17. Ibid., p. 289.
18. Rotmistrov, Vol. 2, pp. 52, 57, 104.
19. Gorbatov, pp. 104–7, 169.
20. Shtemenko, Vol. 1, pp. 47–8.
21. Voronov, p. 180.
22. Shtemenko, Vol. 1, p. 44.
23. Ibid., pp. 138–9.
24. Ibid., pp. 34–5.
25. Peresypkin, *V. Ist. Zh.*, 6/70, p. 12; 4/71, p. 21.
26. Shtemenko, Vol. 1, pp. 113–8.
27. Voronov, p. 178; *Ist. SSSR*, 4/65, p. 3.
28. Iakovlev, p. 317.
29. Vasilevsky, p. 160.
30. Werth, pp. 897–901; Sherwood, Vol. 2, p. 904; Tedder, p. 685.
31. Voronov, p. 202.
32. Vasilevsky, p. 165.
33. Zhukov, p. 364; Rokossovsky, *Sold. Dolg.*, p. 75.
34. Leliushenko, *Zar. Pobed.*, pp. 82, 88–9.
35. Zhukov, pp. 369–70.
36. Rokossovsky, op. cit., p. 91.
37. Rokossovsky, *V. Ist. Zh.*, 11/66. p. 52.
38. Cf., Iakovlev, p. 202.
39. Rokossovsky, op. cit., p. 93.
40. Zhukov, p. 375.
41. Vasilevsky, p. 167.
42. Ibid., p. 168.
43. Ibid., p. 172.
44. Rotmistrov, Vol. 2, p. 130.
45. Sokolovsky, *Raz. Nemets. Voisk pod Moskv.*, p. 318.
46. Anders, p. 83.
47. Eden, pp. 289–99.
48. Ibid., p. 320.
49. *Ist. Vel. Ot. Voin.*, Vol. 2, p. 213, note 2.
50. Meretskov, pp. 251–75.
51. P. Egorov, *V. Ist. Zh.*, 6/69, p. 96.
52. Zhukov, pp. 379–81; *Bit. za Moskv.*, p. 77.
53. Vasilevsky, pp. 173–9.
54. Zhukov, *Bit. za Moskv.*, p. 89.
55. *Ist. Vel. Ot. Voin.*, Vol. 2, p. 359.
56. Khozin, *V. Ist. Zh.*, 2/66, pp. 35–45.
57. Meretskov, p. 290.

Chapter 7
1. Hubatsch, p. 186.
2. Vasilevsky, pp. 184–5; *Stalingrad. Ep.*, pp. 74–5.
3. Vasilevsky, p. 190.
4. Zhukov, p. 396.
5. Vasilevsky, *Stalingrad. Ep.*, p. 75.
6. Vasilevsky, pp. 190–1.
7. Vasilevsky, *V. Ist. Zh.*, 8/65, p. 3.
8. Timoshenko, *Bit. za Moskv.*, p. 97.
9. Vasilevsky, p. 191.
10. Ibid., p. 192.
11. Rigby, p. 58; cf. Eremenko, *Stalingrad*, p. 46 footnote.
12. Djilas, p. 113.
13. Vasilevsky, p. 234.

14. Shtemenko, Vol. 1, p. 49.
15. Ibid., p. 50; Vasilevsky, p. 187.
16. Samsonov, *Stalingrad. Bit.*, pp. 63–4.
17. Ibid., pp. 72–3.
18. Halder, Vol. 3, pp. 470–6; Hubatsch, pp. 183–8.
19. Vasilevsky, *Stalingrad. Ep.*, p. 76.
20. Samsonov, op. cit., p. 74.
21. Rotmistrov, Vol. 2, p. 160; Vasilevsky, *V. Ist. Zh.*, 8/65, p. 7.
22. Kazakov, *V. Ist. Zh.*, 10/64, p. 39; Vasilevsky, *Stalingrad. Ep.*, pp. 76–7.
23. Rotmistrov, Vol. 2, pp. 160–1; *Stalingrad. Ep.*, pp. 605–7.
24. *Ist. Vel. Ot. Voin.*, Vol. 2, pp. 420–1.
25. Kazakov, p. 130.
26. Rokossovsky, *Sold. Dolg.*, pp. 128–30.
27. Vasilevsky, p. 200.
28. *Ist. Vel. Ot. Voin.*, Vol. 2, p. 422.
29. Vasilevsky, *Stalingrad. Ep.*, p. 79; *V. Ist. Zh.*, 10/65, p. 14.
30. Eremenko, *Stalingrad*, pp. 36–9.
31. Zhukov, p. 418.
32. Vasilevsky, *V. Ist. Zh.*, 10/65, p. 17; Moskalenko, *Stalingrad. Ep.*, p. 219.
33. Eremenko, *Stalingrad*, pp. 89–91.

Chapter 8
1. Churchill, Vol. 4, p. 429.
2. Sherwood, Vol. 2, pp. 616–8.
3. Cit. Bryant, *Turn of the Tide*, p. 380.
4. Birse, p. 95; Deane, pp. 31–5.
5. Bryant, op. cit., p. 388.
6. Svetlana, p. 183.
7. Vasilevsky, *V. Ist. Zh.*, 10/65, p. 18.
8. Eremenko, *Stalingrad*, pp. 133–6.
9. Ibid., pp. 138–40.
10. Samsonov, *Stalingrad. Bit.*, p. 140.
11. Eremenko, op. cit., p. 325.
12. Zhukov, p. 410; Moskalenko, *Stalingrad. Ep.*, pp. 222–3.
13. Zhukov, p. 407.
14. *Ist. Vel. Ot. Voin.*, Vol. 3, p. 17; Rokossovsky, *Sold. Dolg.*, pp. 139–42.
15. Zhukov, pp. 413–4.
16. Vasilevsky, *Stalingrad. Ep.*, p. 83.
17. Zhukov, pp. 416–7.
18. *Stalin – Kratk. Biog.*, p. 197.
19. Rotmistrov, Vol. 2, p. 197.
20. *Ist. Vel. Ot. Voin.*, Vol. 3, p. 18.
21. Eremenko, op. cit., pp. 326, 329.
22. Vasilevsky, *Stalingrad. Ep.*, p. 85.
23. Zhukov, pp. 433–4.
24. Greiner, pp. 401–2.
25. *KTB des OKW*, Vol. 2, pp. 1305–7.
26. Samsonov, op. cit., pp. 526, 528 and footnotes;

Rokossovsky, *Velik. Pobed. na Volge,* pp. 254–6.

27. Leliushenko, *Stalingrad. Ep.,* p. 685.
28. Zhukov, pp. 438–9.
29. Kolganov, p. 364.
30. Kozhevnikov, *V. Ist. Zh.,* 2/74, pp. 31–5.
31. Nikitin, *V. Ist. Zh.,* 5/74, pp. 55–9.
32. Zhukov, p. 441.
33. Lugansky, p. 83.
34. Tiulenev, pp. 196–7.
35. Vasilevsky, *V. Ist. Zh.,* 10/65, p. 25.
36. Eremenko, op. cit., pp. 347, 354.
37. Vasilevsky, *Stalingrad. Ep.,* p. 92.
38. Ibid., pp. 94–5.
39. Samsonov, op. cit., pp. 436–7.
40. Rokossovsky, *Sold. Dolg,* p. 162.
41. Vasilevsky, *Stalingrad. Ep.,* p. 101.
42. Zhukov, pp. 446–7.
43. Rotmistrov, *Stalingrad. Ep.,* pp. 611–3.
44. Krasovsky, *Stalingrad. Ep.,* pp. 577–8.
45. Eremenko, op. cit., pp. 393–4.
46. Ibid., p. 400.
47. Vasilevsky, *Stalingrad. Ep.,* pp. 103–5.
48. Vasilevsky, *V. Ist. Zh.,* 3/66, pp. 26–7.
49. Vasilevsky, *Stalingrad. Ep.,* p. 102.
50. Rokossovsky, *Stalingrad. Ep.,* p. 173; *Sold. Dolg.,* p. 167.
51. Vasilevsky, *Stalingrad. Ep.,* pp. 107–8.
52. Ibid., pp. 112–3; *V. Ist. Zh.,* 3/66, p. 35; Eremenko, op. cit., p. 411, maps 20, 21.
53. Vasilevsky, *Stalingrad. Ep.,* p. 116.
54. Zhukov, pp. 453–4; Samsonov, op. cit., p. 484.
55. Zhukov, pp. 456–7; Eremenko, *Stalingrad,* p. 426.
56. Meretskov, pp. 319–20.
57. Rokossovsky, *Sold. Dolg,* pp. 175–6.
58. Ibid., p. 179; Voronov, *Stalingrad. Ep.,* pp. 200–1.
59. Rokossovsky, *Sold. Dolg,* p. 192.
60. Shtemenko, Vol. 1, p. 60.
61. Grechko, *Bit. za Kavk.,* pp. 154–5.
62. Ibid., pp. 158–9.
63. Ibid., pp. 161–2; Shtemenko, Vol. 1, p. 64.
64. Ibid., p. 65.
65. Tiulenev, pp. 247–9.
66. Grechko, op. cit., pp. 243–4.
67. Shtemenko, Vol. 1, pp. 68–9.
68. Ibid., p. 72; Grechko, op. cit., p. 232.
69. Vasilevsky, p. 236 footnote.
70. Shtemenko, Vol. 1, p. 75.
71. Zhukov, p. 477.
72. Shtemenko, Vol. 1, p. 91.
73. Kuznetsov, *V. Ist. Zh.,* 9/66, pp. 65–7.
74. Kuznetsov, *Stalingrad. Ep.,* pp. 414–5.
75. Samsonov, op. cit., pp.

164–7.
76. Vasilevsky, p. 127.
77. Shtemenko, Vol. 2, pp. 293–4.
78. Vasilevsky, p. 273.
79. Ibid., pp. 247, 280.
80. Ibid., pp. 281–2.

Chapter 9
1. Golikov, *V. Ist. Zh.*, 1/73, pp. 62–7; Shtemenko, Vol. 1, p. 97.
2. Ibid., p. 104.
3. Stalin, *On Great Patriotic War*, p. 49.
4. Rokossovsky, *Sold. Dolg*, pp. 193–4.
5. Shtemenko, Vol. 1, p. 107.
6. Rokossovsky, op. cit., pp. 196–7.
7. *Geschichte des Grossen Vaterländischen Krieges*, Vol. 3, p. 142. (not in the Russian original).
8. Vasilevsky, p. 300.
9. Zhukov, pp. 465–6.
10. Rokossovsky, op. cit., p. 202.
11. Zhukov, pp. 469–70.
12. Vasilevsky, p. 309.
13. Zhukov, pp. 471–3.
14. Shtemenko, Vol. 1, pp. 151–2.
15. Vasilevsky, pp. 309–10.
16. Konev, p. 9.
17. Shtemenko, Vol. 1, p. 156.
18. Zhukov, p. 483.
19. Rokossovsky, op. cit., p. 203; *Ist. Vel. Ot. Voin.*, Vol. 3, pp. 246–7.
20. Vasilevsky, pp. 316–8.
21. Shtemenko, Vol. 1, p. 167.
22. Iakovlev, pp. 330–2.
23. Shtemenko, Vol. 1, pp. 161–2.
24. Bagramian, *V. Ist. Zh.*, 11/67, p. 42.
25. Rokossovsky, op. cit., p. 212.
26. Peresypkin, *V. Ist. Zh.*, 7/73, pp. 51–9.
27. Konev, pp. 11–3.
28. *V. Ist. Zh.*, 6/68, p. 61; 7/68, p. 79.
29. Rokossovsky, op. cit., p. 219.
30. *Ist. Vel. Ot. Voin.*, Vol. 3, pp. 268–9.
31. Ivanov, *V. Ist. Zh.*, 8/73, pp. 11–20.
32. Rotmistrov, Vol. 2, p. 246.
33. Shtemenko, Vol. 1, p. 155.
34. Zhukov, pp. 198–9.
35. Ibid., p. 505.
36. Ibid., pp. 518, 523.
37. Shtemenko, Vol. 1, pp. 172, 182–4; Vasilevsky, p. 336.
38. Ibid., p. 335.
39. Ibid., p. 338.
40. Konev, p. 37.
41. Rokossovsky, op. cit., p. 235.
42. Shtemenko, Vol. 1, pp. 178–9.
43. Zhukov, p. 523.
44. Ibid., pp. 524–5.
45. Shtemenko, Vol. 2, p. 314.
46. Rigby, p. 57; Voronov, p. 384.
47. Ibid., pp. 391–7.
48. Shtemenko, Vol. 1, pp. 187–8.
49. Moskalenko, pp. 150–3.
50. Shtemenko, Vol. 1, p. 116.

51. Moskalenko, pp. 180–2.
52. Rokossovsky, op. cit., p. 240.
53. Konev, pp. 77–8.
54. Rokossovsky, op. cit., pp. 251–3; Batov, *V. Ist. Zh.*, 10/74, p. 65.
55. Vasilevsky, p. 371.
56. Leliushenko, *Moskva-Praga*, pp. 196–8.
57. Konev, p. 120; *V. Ist. Zh.*, 2/69, pp. 57–64.
58. Zhukov, pp. 553–5.
59. Novikov, *Nov. Mir*, 3/70, pp. 169–85.
60. Djilas, pp. 51–4.
61. Shtemenko, Vol. 1, p. 203.
62. Ibid., p. 206.
63. Ibid., pp. 206–21; Vasilevsky, *V. Ist. Zh.*, 5/71, p. 70.
64. Ismay, p. 325.
65. Eden, p. 411.
66. Ibid., p. 415.
67. Ismay, p. 327.
68. Shtemenko, Vol. 1, pp. 190–4.
69. Birse, p. 156.
70. Ismay, p. 338.
71. Deane, p. 43.
72. Ibid., p. 44.
73. Bryant, *Triumph in the West*, p. 90.
74. Sherwood, Vol. 2, p. 775.
75. Bryant, op. cit., pp. 91–4.
76. Eden, p. 413; Sherwood, Vol. 2, p. 777.
77. Ibid., pp. 784, 787.
78. Deane, pp. 145–7.

Chapter 10

1. *Ist. Vel. Ot. Voin.*, Vol. 3, pp. 372, 374 note 3; Vol. 4, pp. 46, 123.
2. Sandalov, pp. 3–10.
3. Shtemenko, Vol. 1, p. 269.
4. Meretskov, pp. 365–7.
5. Vasilevsky, *V. Ist. Zh.*, 9/69, p. 50.
6. Shtemenko, Vol. 2, pp. 152–3.
7. Shtemenko, Vol. 1, pp. 271–7.
8. Ibid., pp. 224–7.
9. Rokossovsky, *Sold. Dolg*, pp. 257–8.
10. Shtemenko, Vol. 1, pp. 231–2.
11. Kiseev, *V. Ist. Zh.*, 6/66, p. 36.
12. Shtemenko, Vol. 1, pp. 227–30.
13. Zhukov, pp. 564–5.
14. Vasilevsky, p. 408.
15. Vasilevsky, *V. Ist. Zh.*, 9/69, pp. 47–51.
16. Shtemenko, Vol. 1, pp. 232–5.
17. Shtemenko, Vol. 2, p. 373.
18. Shtemenko, *V. Ist. Zh.*, 6/72, pp. 64–5.
19. Shtemenko, *V. Ist. Zh.*, 7/72, p. 64.
20. Shtemenko, Vol. 1, pp. 280–1; Meretskov, p. 377.
21. Ibid., p. 379.
22. Vasilevsky, *V. Ist. Zh.*, 9/69, p. 55.
23. Meretskov, pp. 380–1.
24. Novikov, *Nov. Mir*, 3/70, pp. 168–9; *V. Ist. Zh.*, 7/69, p. 62.
25. Nepomniashchy, pp. 238–40.
26. Batov, *V. Ist. Zh.*, 12/66, p. 41; Rokossovsky, op. cit., pp. 260–1.

27. Zhukov, p. 570.
28. Telegin, *V. Ist. Zh.*, 9/69, p. 84.
29. Zhukov, pp. 570–1; Shtemenko, Vol. 1, p. 257.
30. Ibid., p. 239.
31. Ibid., p. 250.
32. Ibid., pp. 239–42.
33. Vasilevsky, p. 362.
34. Vasilevsky, *V. Ist. Zh.*, 9/69, pp. 47–52.
35. Simonov, *V. Ist. Zh.*, 9/66, p. 49; Shtemenko, Vol. 1, pp. 245–6.
36. Batov, p. 274.
37. Zhukov, pp. 574–6; *V. Ist. Zh.*, 2/69, p. 72.
38. Shtemenko, Vol. 1, p. 254.
39. Ibid., pp. 243, 252.
40. Vasilevsky, *V. Ist. Zh.*, 9/69, pp. 55–7.
41. Peresypkin, *V. Ist. Zh.*, 6/69, p. 70.
42. Konev, p. 274.
43. Ibid., pp. 233–4; Krainiukov, *V. Ist. Zh.*, 7/69, p. 77.
44. *Ist. Vel. Ot. Voin.*, Vol. 4, pp. 158–67.
45. *OKH Schem. Kriegsgliederung*, 15 June 44.
46. *KTB des OKW*, Vol. 4, p. 858.
47. Burrows, *PRO file WO/106/3273*.
48. Zhukov, pp. 583–6.
49. Rokossovsky, op. cit., p. 265.
50. Zhukov, pp. 591–2.
51. Shtemenko, Vol. 2, pp. 69–70.
52. Konev, p. 268.
53. Shtemenko, Vol. 2, pp. 75–6.
54. Churchill, Vol. 6, pp. 118–20.
55. Ibid., p. 114; Bor-Komorowski, pp. 212, 342–6; Feis, p. 380.
56. Rokossovsky, op. cit., pp. 284–91.
57. *Trotsky Papers*, Vol. 2, 279.
58. Zhukov, pp. 601–3.
59. Rokossovsky, op. cit., pp. 297–8; *V. Ist. Zh.*, 2/65, p. 25.
60. Shtemenko, Vol. 2, pp. 34–5.
61. Shtemenko, Vol. 1, p. 282.
62. Cf., *Ist. Vel. Ot. Voin.*, Vol. 4, p. 347.
63. Ibid., p. 345.
64. Ibid., p. 356.
65. Shtemenko, Vol. 1, p. 297.
66. Kazakov, *V. Ist. Zh.*, 2/67, pp. 37, 71.
67. Shtemenko, Vol. 2, pp. 19–20.
68. *Ist. Vel. Ot. Voin.*, Vol. 4, pp. 260–6.
69. Shtemenko, Vol. 2, pp. 125–33.
70. Cf., Matsulenko, p. 103; Biriuzov, *Surov. God.*, p. 423.
71. *Ist. Vel. Ot. Voin.*, Vol. 4, pp. 293–4.
72. Zhukov, pp. 596–8.
73. Grechko, *Cher. Karp.*, p. 15.
74. Shtemenko, Vol. 2, p. 253.
75. *Ist. Vel. Ot. Voin.*, Vol. 4, p. 390.
76. Malinovsky, *Budapesht-Vena-Praga*, pp. 81–3.

77. Shtemenko, Vol. 2, pp. 255–6.

Chapter 11

1. Shtemenko, Vol. 2, pp. 250–1.
2. Bryant, *Triumph in the West*, p. 304.
3. Eden, p. 488.
4. Deane, p. 155.
5. Ismay, p. 378.
6. Deane, pp. 245–7.
7. Bryant, op. cit., pp. 307–8.
8. Deane, pp. 248–51.
9. Shtemenko, Vol. 1, pp. 306–14.
10. Zhukov, pp. 608–12.
11. Rokossovsky, *Sold. Dolg*, p. 299.
12. Vasilevsky, *V. Ist. Zh.*, 3/69, pp. 35–9.
13. Rokossovsky, op. cit., p. 313.
14. *Dir. Glav. Kom.* 1455 of 8 Feb 45 signed by Stalin and Vasilevsky (when Stalin was still in the Crimea).
15. Konev, *Nov. Mir*, 5/65, p. 3.
16. *KTB des OKW*, Vol. 4, p. 993.
17. Ibid., p. 1002.
18. Churchill, Vol. 6, p. 243.
19. Deane, pp. 156–7; Birse, pp. 176–7.
20. Vasilevsky, p. 481.
21. Shtemenko, Vol. 2, p. 251.
22. Sherwood, Vol. 2, pp. 843–4; Bryant, op. cit., pp. 402–6.
23. Zhukov, p. 618.
24. Shtemenko, Vol. 1, p. 317.

25. Zhukov, p. 622.
26. Chuikov, *Oktiabr'*, 4/64, pp. 128–31; *Nov. i Noveish. Ist.*, 2/65, p. 6.
27. Telegin, *V. Ist. Zh.*, 4/65, pp. 62–4.
28. Shtemenko, Vol. 1, pp. 317–23.
29. Ibid., pp. 325–7.
30. Rokossovsky, op. cit., p. 326.
31. Ibid., pp. 334, 339.
32. Vasilevsky, *V. Ist. Zh.*, 3/69, pp. 41–3.
33. No 215/K of 16 March.
34. Vasilevsky, *V. Ist. Zh.*, 3/69, pp. 46–50.
35. Ivanov, *V. Ist. Zh.*, 6/69, p. 25.
36. Ibid., 3/69, pp. 14–18.
37. Shtemenko, Vol. 2, p. 275.
38. Ivanov, *V. Ist. Zh.*, 6/69, p. 28.
39. Moskalenko, pp. 569–70.
40. FWD – 18264 (SCAF 252).
41. *Command Decisions*, pp. 377–8; Churchill, Vol. 6, pp. 399–409; Eisenhower, pp. 433–40.
42. Pogue, p. 440.
43. Deane, p. 158.
44. *Ist. Vel. Ot. Voin.*, Vol. 5, p. 257.
45. Zhukov, pp. 640–2.
46. Cf., Djilas, pp. 70, 106.
47. Zhukov, p. 642.
48. Shtemenko, Vol. 1, p. 329.
49. Konev, *Nov. Mir*, 5/65, pp. 38–40.
50. Shtemenko, Vol. 1, pp. 329–31; Zhukov, p. 643.
51. Konev, *Nov. Mir*, 5/65,

pp. 44–7.

52. Rokossovsky, op. cit., pp. 351–2.
53. Zhukov, p. 648.
54. *KTB des OKW*, Vol. 4, pp. 1240–2.
55. Zhukov, p. 660.
56. *KTB des OKW*, Vol. 4, p. 1249.
57. Zhukov, p. 660.
58. Konev, *Nov. Mir*, 5/65, pp. 58–60.
59. 00215 of 17 April issued at 0247 hrs on 18 April.
60. Konev, *Nov. Mir*, 6/65, pp. 14–5.
61. Zhukov, p. 663.
62. Deane, p. 159.
63. Konev, *Nov. Mir*, 6/65, p. 47.
64. Chuikov, *Oktiabr'*, 4/54, p. 156.
65. Konev, *Nov. Mir*, 6/65, p. 59; 7/65, pp. 100–1.
66. Voronov, *Ist. SSSR*, 4/65, p. 24; Shtemenko subsequently denied that Susloparov was brought to account; Vol. 2, pp. 432–4.
67. Zhukov, p. 682.
68. Werth, p. 901; cf. also Sherwood, Vol. 2, p. 904.
69. Konev, *Nov. Mir*, 7/55, p. 134.
70. Shelakhov, *V. Ist. Zh.*, 3/69, pp. 56–9.
71. Shtemenko, Vol. 1, p. 334.
72. Vasilevsky, *V. Ist. Zh.*, 6/67, pp. 82–3.
73. Shtemenko, Vol. 1, pp. 336–7.
74. Ibid., p. 347.

75. Meretskov, pp. 411–2.
76. Shtemenko, Vol. 1, p. 354.
77. Deane, pp. 272–4.
78. Sherwood, Vol. 2, pp. 892–3.
79. Eden, pp. 547–8.
80. Shtemenko, Vol. 1, p. 359.
81. Vasilevsky, *V. Ist. Zh.*, 6/67, p. 86.
82. Deane, pp. 275–6.
83. Shtemenko, Vol. 1, pp. 359–61.

Chapter 12
1. Trotsky, *Stalin*, pp. 393–4.
2. Shtemenko, Vol. 2, p. 279.
3. Ibid., p. 300.
4. Ibid., p. 499.
5. Ibid., p. 500.
6. Cf., Matsulenko, *V. Ist. Zh.*, 5/74, p. 110.
7. *O Sov. Voen. Nauk.*, pp. 200–2.
8. Voroshilov, *Stalin and Armed Forces*, p. 144.
9. Ibid., pp. 105–114.
10. Lenin, *Poln. Sobr. Soch.*, Vol. 24, p. 544.
11. *O Sov. Voen. Nauk.*, pp. 292, 296.
12. Shtemenko, Vol. 2, p. 505.
13. Vasilevsky, p. 529.
14. Montgomery, p. 415.
15. Vasilevsky, pp. 530–1.
16. Shtemenko, Vol. 2, p. 77.
17. Djilas, p. 106.
18. Rigby, p. 81.
19. *O Sov. Voen. Nauk.*, pp. 201–2. In 1955 its strength was 5,763,000.
20. Rigby, p. 67.

Select Bibliography

This list is not a comprehensive bibliography but indicates the principal works to which reference has been made in the writing of this study.

I Books

Alliluyeva, S. *Twenty Letters to a Friend*. Hutchinson, London 1967.

Anders, W. *An Army in Exile*. Macmillan, London 1949.

Bagramian, I. Kh. *Gorod-Voin na Dnepre*. Moscow 1965.
So Begann der Krieg. Militärverlag, Berlin 1972.

Barmine, A. *Memoirs of a Soviet Diplomat*. Lovat Dickson, London 1938.

Batov, P. I. *V Pokhodakh i Boiakh*. Moscow 1962.

Bazhanov, B. *Stalin – Der Rote Diktator*. Aretz, Berlin 1931.

Biriuzov, S. S. *Surovye Gody*. Moscow 1966.
Kogda Gremeli Pushki. Moscow 1961

Birse, A. H. *Memoirs of an Interpreter*. Michael Joseph, London 1967.

Blumenthal, F. *Politicheskaia Rabota v Voennoe Vremia*. Moscow 1929.

Bor-Komorowski, T. *The Secret Army*. Gollancz, London 1950.

Bryant, A. *The Turn of the Tide*. Collins, London 1957.
Triumph in the West. Collins, London 1959.

Budenny, S. M. *Proidennyi Put'*. (Two Vols). Moscow 1958–65.

Butler, J. R. M. *Grand Strategy*. (Vol. 3, Pt II). HMSO 1964.

Bychevsky, B. V. *Gorod-Front*. Moscow 1963.

Chamberlin, W. H. *The Russian Revolution 1917–21*. (Two Vols). Macmillan, London 1935.

Churchill, W. S. *The Second World War*. (Six Vols). Cassell, London.

Danilevsky, A. F. *V. I. Lenin i Voprosy Voennogo Stroitel'stva na VIII S'ezde RKP(b)*. Moscow 1964.

Deane, J. R. *The Strange Alliance*. Murray, London 1947.

Denikin, A. I. *The White Army*. Cape, London 1930.

Deutscher, I. *Stalin – A Political Biography*. OUP, London 1967.

Djilas, M. *Conversations with Stalin*. Rupert Hart-Davis, London 1962.

Eden, A. *Memoirs – The Reckoning*. Cassell, London 1965.

Egorov, A. I. *Razgrom Denikina*. Moscow 1936.

Eisenhower, D. D. *Crusade in Europe*. Heinemann, London 1948.

Eremenko, A. I. *Stalingrad*. Moscow 1961.
  V Nachale Voiny. Moscow 1964.
  Pomni Voinu. Donbass 1971.

Fediuninsky, I. I. *Podniatye po Trevoge*. Moscow 1964.

Feis, H. *Churchill, Roosevelt, Stalin*. Princeton UP, 1966.

Frunze, M. V. *Sobranie Sochinenii*. (Three Vols). Moscow 1929.
  Izbrannye Proizvedeniia. (Two Vols). Moscow 1957.

Golikov, F. I. *V Moskovskoi Bitve*. Moscow 1967.

Golikov, S. *Vydaiushchiesia Pobedy Sovetskoi Armii v Velikoi Otechestvennoi Voine*. Moscow 1954.

Golovin, N. N. *The Russian Army in the World War*. OUP, London 1931.

Gorbatov, A. V. *Years off my Life*. Constable, London 1964.

Grechko, A. A. *Bitva za Kavkaz*. Moscow 1967.
  Cherez Karpaty. Moscow 1970.
  Osvodobitel'naia Missiia Sovetskikh Vooruzhennykh Sil vo Vtoroi Mirovoi Voine. Moscow 1971.

Greiner, H. *Die Oberste Wehrmachtführung*. Limes Verlag, Wiesbaden 1951.

Guderian, H. *Panzer Leader*. Michael Joseph, London 1952.

Gwyer, J. M. A. *Grand Strategy*. (Vol. 3, Pt I). HMSO 1964.

Halder, F. *Kriegstagebuch*. (Three Vols). Kohlhammer, Stuttgart 1962.

Hilger, G. *The Incompatible Allies*. Macmillan, New York 1953.

Hodgson, J. E. *With Denikin's Armies*. Lincoln Williams, London 1932.

Hubatsch, W. *Hitlers Weisungen für die Kriegführung 1939–1945*. Bernard u. Graefe, Frankfurt a.M. 1962.

Iakovlev, A. S. *Tsel' Zhizni*. Moscow 1966.

Ironside, E. *Archangel 1918–19*. Constable, London 1953.

Ismay, H. L. *The Memoirs of General the Lord Ismay*. Heinemann, London 1960.

Kamenev, S. S. *Vospominaniia o V. I. Lenine*. Moscow 1957.
  Zapiski o Grazhdanskoi Voine i Voennom Stroitel'stve. Moscow 1963.

Kazakov, M. I. *Nad Kartoi Bylykh Srazhenii*. Moscow 1965.

Knox, A. *With the Russian Army 1914–17*. (Two Vols).
Hutchinson, London 1921.

Kolganov, K. S. *Razvitie Taktiki Sovetskoi Armii v Gody
Velikoi Otechestvennoi Voiny (1941–5)*. Moscow 1958.

Konev, I. S. *Zapiski Komanduiushchego Frontom 1943–4*.
Moscow 1972.

Korolivsky, S. M. *Grazhdanskaia Voina na Ukraine 1918–20*.
Moscow 1968.

Kravchenko, G. S. *Voennaia Ekonomika SSSR 1941–45*.
Moscow 1963.

Krivitsky, W. G. *I was Stalin's Agent*. Hamish Hamilton,
London 1939.

Kurochkin, P. M. *Pozyvnye Fronta*. Moscow 1969.

Kuznetsov, N. G. *Nakanune*. Moscow 1966.

Leliushenko, D. D. *Zaria Pobedy*. Moscow 1966.
Moskva-Stalingrad-Berlin-Praga. Moscow 1970.

Lenin, V. I. *Leninskii Sbornik*. Moscow XXXIV (1942), XXXV
(1945), XXXVI (1959), XXXVII (1970).
Voennaia Perepiska (1917–20). Moscow 1956.
Polnoe Sobranie Sochinenii. (5th Ed.) Vols 8, 24, 29, 30, 32,
35–7, 39, 40, 50–1, 54–5.

Littauer, V. S. *Russian Hussar*. Allen, London 1965.

Livshits, Ia. L. *Pervaia Gvardeiskaia Tankovaia Brigada v
Boiakh za Moskvu*. Moscow 1948.

Löbell. *Jahresberichte 1908–14*.

Lugansky, S. D. *Na Glubokikh Virazhakh*. Alma-Ata 1966.

Lunacharsky, A. V. *Revoliutsionnye Siluety*. Moscow 1923.

Maisky, I. *Memoirs of a Soviet Ambassador*. Hutchinson,
London 1967.

Malinovsky, R. Ia. *Final*. Moscow 1966.
Budapesht-Vena-Praga. Moscow 1969.

Manstein, E. von. *Aus einem Soldatenleben*. Athenäum, Bonn
1958.

Martel, G. *The Russian Outlook*. Michael Joseph, London 1947.

Mazulenko, W. A. *Die Zerschlagung der Heeresgruppe
Südukraine*. Berlin 1959.

McNeal, R. H. *Stalin's Works (Bibliography)*. Stanford UP
1967.

Melikov, V. A. *Geroicheskaia Oborona Tsaritsyna 1918*. Moscow
1938.

Meretskov, K. A. *Na Sluzhbe Narodu*. Moscow 1970.

Miliukov, P. *Rossiia na Perelome*. Paris 1927.

Molotov, V. *Stalin and Stalin's Leadership*. Moscow 1950.

Montgomery, B. L. *Memoirs*. Collins, London 1958.

Moskalenko, K. S. *Na Iugo-Zapadnom Napravlenii 1943–45*. Moscow 1972.

Nepomniashchy, K. *Polki Idyt na Zapad*. Moscow 1964.

Novikov, A. A. *V Nebe Leningrada*. Moscow 1970.

Peresypkin, I. T. *Radio-Moguchee Sredstvo Oborony Strany*. Moscow 1948.

Sviaz' v Velikoi Otechestvennoi Voine. Moscow 1973.

Petrov, Iu. P. *Partiinoe Stroitel'stvo v Sovetskoi Armii i Flote*. Moscow 1964.

Stroitel'stvo Politorganov, Partiinykh i Komsomol'skikh Organizatsii Armii i Flota (1918–1968). Moscow 1968.

Petrovsky, D. A. *Voennaia Shkola v Gody Revoliutsii*. Moscow 1924.

Pilsudski, J. *Year 1920*. Pilsudski Institute 1972.

Platonov, S. P. *Vtoraia Mirovaia Voina*. Moscow 1958.

Pokrovsky, M. *Ocherki po Istorii Oktiabr'skoi Revoliutsii*. (Two Vols). Moscow 1927.

Reznichenko, V. G. *Taktika*. Moscow 1966.

Rigby, T. H. (ed.) *The Stalin Dictatorship*. Sydney UP, Sydney 1968.

Rokossovsky, K. K. *Velikaia Pobeda na Volge*. Moscow 1965.

Soldatskii Dolg. Moscow 1968.

Rotmistrov, P. A. *Istoriia Voennogo Iskusstva*. (Two Vols). Moscow 1963.

Samsonov, A. M. *Die Grosse Schlacht vor Moskau*. Militärverlag, Berlin 1959.

Stalingradskaia Bitva. Moscow 1968.

Sandalov, L. M. *Perezhitoe*. Moscow 1961.

Seaton, A. *The Russo-German War 1941–45*. Arthur Barker, London 1971.

Shaposhnikov, B. M. *Na Visle*. Moscow 1924.

Mozg Armii. Moscow 1927.

Sherwood, R. E. *The White House Papers of Harry Hopkins*. (Two Vols). Eyre and Spottiswoode, London 1948–9.

Shtemenko, S. M. *General'nyi Shtab v Gody Voiny*. (Two Vols). Moscow 1968–73.

Sokolovsky, V. D. *Voennaia Strategiia*. Moscow 1963.

Razgrom Nemetsko-Fashistkikh Voisk pod Moskvoi. Moscow 1964.

Souvarine, B. *Stalin*. Secker & Warburg, London 1939.

Stalin, J. V. *Na Putiakh k Oktiabru*. Leningrad 1925.
  Leninism. Lawrence & Wishart, London 1940.
  On the Great Patriotic War. Hutchinson, London 1947.
  Sochineniia. (13 Vols). Moscow 1946–51.
  Stanford Sochineniia. (3 Vols). Ed. R. H. McNeal. Stanford UP, 1967.
  Economic Problems of Socialism in the USSR. Moscow 1952.
  Stalin – Kratkaia Biografiia. Moscow 1950.

Starinov, I. T. *Miny Zhdut Svoego Chasa*. Moscow 1964.

Stewart, G. *The White Armies of Russia*. Macmillan, New York 1933.

Sukhanov, N. N. *Zapiski o Revoliutsii*. Moscow 1922.
  The Russian Revolution 1917. OUP 1955.

Svechin, A. A. *Strategiia*. Moscow 1927.

Sverdlov, Ia. M. *Izbrannye Proizvedeniia*. Moscow 1960.

Tedder, A. *With Prejudice*. Cassell, London 1966.

Teske, H. *General Ernst Köstring*. Mittler, Frankfurt a.M. 1966.

Tiulenev, I. V. *Cherez Tri Voiny*. Moscow 1960.

Todorsky, A. I. *Marshal Tukhachevskii*. Moscow 1963.

Trotsky, L. D. *Kak Vooruzhalas' Revoliutsiia*. Moscow 1924.
  My Life. Butterworth, London 1930.
  The History of the Russian Revolution. (Three Vols). Gollancz, London 1932–3.
  Stalin. Harper, London 1946.
  Military Writings. (Ed. Breitman). Merit, New York 1969.

Tukhachevsky, M. N. *Voina Klassov*. Moscow 1921.
  Manevr i Artilleriia. Moscow 1924.
  Izbrannye Proizvedeniia. (Two Vols). Moscow 1964.

Vasilevsky, A. M. *Delo Vsei Zhizni*. Moscow 1974.

Vorob'ev, F. D. and Kravtsov, V. M. *Pobedy Sovetskikh Vooruzhennykh Sil v Velikoi Otechestvennoi Voine*. Moscow 1953.

Voronov, N. N. *Na Sluzhbe Voennoi*. Moscow 1963.

Voroshilov, K. E. *Stat'i i Rechi*. Moscow 1937.
  Stalin i Krasnaia Armiia. Moscow 1938.
  Stalin and the Armed Forces of the USSR. Moscow 1951.

Werth, A. *Russia at War*. Barrie and Rockcliff, London 1964.

White, D. *The Growth of the Red Army*. Princeton UP 1944.

Yaroslavsky, E. *Landmarks in the Life of Stalin.* Lawrence &
  Wishart, London 1942.
Zakharov, M. V. *Osvobozhdenie Iugo-Vostochnoi i Tsentral'noi
  Evropy Voiskami 2go i 3go Ukrainskikh Frontov.* Moscow 1970.
Zhukov, G. K. *Vospominaniia i Razmyshleniia.* Macdonald,
  London 1969.

**II Anthologies, Edited Works, Printed Documents,
Official Publications and Reference Books**
Armiia Sovetskaia. Moscow 1969.
Bitva za Moskvu. Moscow 1968.
Bitva za Stalingrad. Volgograd 1973.
Bol'shaia Sovetskaia Entsiklopediia. (Three Eds). Moscow
  1926–70.
Command Decisions. Harcourt Brace, New York 1959.
Dekrety Sovetskoi Vlasti. (Five Vols). Moscow 1957–71.
Direktivy Glavnogo Komandovaniia Krasnoi Armii (1917–1920).
  Moscow 1969.
Direktivy Komandovaniia Frontov Krasnoi Armii (1917–1920).
  (Two Vols). Moscow 1971–2.
Documents of German Foreign Policy. HMSO, London.
Dokumenty o Geroicheskoi Oborone Petrograda v 1919 g. Moscow
  1941.
Dokumenty o Geroicheskoi Oborone Tsaritsyna v 1918 g. Moscow
  1942.
Geschichte des Grossen Vaterländischen Krieges der Sowjet Union.
  (Five Vols). Militärverlag, Berlin.
Grazhdanskaia Voina. (Vols 2 and 3). Moscow 1928–30.
Grazhdanskaia Voina. (2nd Ed. Four Vols). Moscow 1953–9.
Grazhdanskaia Voina na Ukraine. (Four Vols). Kiev 1967.
Istoriia Kommunisticheskoi Partii Sovetskogo Soiuza. (Vol. 3).
  Moscow 1968.
Istoriia Velikoi Otechestvennoi Voiny Sovetskogo Soiuza. (Six
  Vols). Moscow 1961–5.
Iz Istorii Grazhdanskoi Voiny v SSSR. (Three Vols). Moscow
  1960–1.
*KPSS o Vooruzhennykh Silakh Sovetskogo Soiuza
  (Dokumenty 1917–68).* Moscow 1969.
KPSS v Rezoliutsiiakh i Resheniiakh. (Vol. 2). Moscow 1970.
Kriegstagebuch des Oberkommandos der Wehrmacht. (Four Vols).
  Bernard u. Graefe, Frankfurt a.M.
Malaia Sovetskaia Entsiklopediia. (3rd Ed). Moscow 1958.

Nastavlenie po Postoiannym Liniiam Sviazi 1943 g. Moscow 1945.
Nazi-Soviet Relations 1939–41. Department of State
   Publication 3023.
O Sovetskoi Voennoi Nauke. Moscow 1964.
Osnovy Sovetskogo Voennogo Zakonodatel'stva. Moscow 1966.
Pogranichnye Voiska v Gody Velikoi Otechestvennoi Voiny.
   Moscow 1968.
Protokoly Tsentral'nogo Komiteta RSDRP (1929).
Sluzbba Sviazi. (uchebnik dlia shkol RKKA). Moscow 1935.
Sobranie Zakonov i Rasporiazhenii R.K. Pravitel'stva SSSR,
   27/5 1937, No. 31.
Spisok General'nago Shtaba. St Petersburg 1913.
*SSSR v Velikoi Otechestvennoi Voine (1941–1945) (Kratkaia
   Khronika).* Moscow 1964.
Stalingradskaia Epopeia. Moscow 1968.
Supreme Command. The United States in WW II. (Pogue).
   Department of the Army 1954.
The History of the Civil War in the USSR. (Vol. 2). Lawrence &
   Wishart, London 1947.
The Red Army Today. Moscow 1939.
The Trotsky Papers (1917–21). (Ed. Meijer – Two Vols).
   Mouton, The Hague 1964–71.
Ukrains'ka Radians'ka Entsiklopediia. Kiev 1959.
*Velikaia Otechestvennaia Voina Sovetskogo Soiuza 1941–1945
   (Kratkaia Istoriia).* Moscow 1965.
*Voprosy Strategii i Operativnogo Iskusstva v Sovetskikh Voennykh
   Trudakh (1917–1940).* Moscow 1965.
50 Let Vooruzhennykh Sil SSSR. Moscow 1968.

III Periodicals
Bol'shevik.
Istoriia SSSR.
Kommunist.
Kommunist Vooruzhennykh Sil.
Novaia i Noveishaia Istoriia.
Novyi Mir.
Oktiabr'.
Proletarskaia Revoliutsiia.
Sotsialisticheskii Vestnik.
Soviet Military Review.
Voenno-Istoricheskii Zhurnal.
Voprosy Istorii.

Index

Note: Tsarist and White Russian general ranks are shown thus: (Gen.). Where officers held in turn tsarist and Soviet ranks, only the Soviet ranks are shown. Soviet ranks are given without parenthesis and are the highest held during the Second World War, it being remembered that some officers e.g. Kulik, Mekhlis, Popov, Petrov and Kozlov were at times demoted during the war years.

IN MENDEL'S FOOTNOTES

IN MENDEL'S FOOTNOTES

An Introduction to the Science and Technologies of Genes and Genetics from the Nineteenth Century to the Twenty-Second

COLIN TUDGE

JONATHAN CAPE
LONDON

Published by Jonathan Cape 2000

2 4 6 8 10 9 7 5 3 1

Copyright © Colin Tudge 2000

Colin Tudge has asserted his right under the
Copyright, Designs and Patents Act 1988 to be identified
as the author of this work

First published in Great Britain in 2000 by Jonathan Cape
Random House, 20 Vauxhall Bridge Road, London SW1V 2SA

Random House Australia (Pty) Limited
20 Alfred Street, Milsons Point, Sydney,
New South Wales 2061, Australia

Random House New Zealand Limited
18 Poland Road, Glenfield,
Auckland 10, New Zealand

Random House South Africa (Pty) Limited
Endulini, 5A Jubilee Road, Parktown 2193, South Africa

The Random House Group Limited Reg. No. 954009
www.randomhouse.co.uk

A CIP catalogue record for this book
is available from the British Library

ISBN 0-224-05077-7

Papers used by The Random House Group Limited are natural,
recyclable products made from wood grown in sustainable forests;
the manufacturing processes conform to the environmental
regulations of the country of origin

Typeset by Deltatype Ltd, Birkenhead, Merseyside

Printed and bound in Great Britain by
Mackays of Chatham PLC

Contents

By Way of Introduction: The Future of Humankind and the Legacy of Mendel

Heredity matters. There would be no arranged marriages, no patricians and plebs, no feudalism or apartheid, fewer random beatings-up in lonely car parks and a great deal less genocide if we did not feel so keenly that this is the case.

Nowadays, it seems, we understand heredity. Of course, as I will argue throughout this book, understanding can never be complete: that is a logical, as well as a practical, impossibility. Any feeling of omniscience that may creep over us from time to time is an illusion, and a dangerous one at that. Our understanding, nonetheless, already gives us enormous control over the shape, size, colour and even the behaviour of our fellow creatures. Soon we might have crops like metaphorical Christmas trees – a basic plant whose species hardly matters (it might be a wheat, it might be a carrot) genetically adorned with whatever extra capabilities and quirks our fancy might care to impose. In a hundred years or so (technology takes longer to come on-line than its proponents are wont to suggest!) we might produce livestock like balls of flesh, churning out milk and eggs like a termite queen; at least we *could* do this if we allowed expediency to override sensibility. Most shockingly of all we could, in the fullness of time, redesign ourselves. We might refashion the human species to a prescription: eight feet tall for better basketball; an IQ of 400 to talk more freely with computers and win lost and unjust causes in courts of law. Plastic surgery will seem childish when we can restyle ourselves from the genes upwards.

1

Clearly, such technical power, which is not present-day, but pending in principle, has implications that stretch as far as our imagination can reach. No aspect of our economics, politics, philosophy, or religion is untouched by it. What prospect could be more momentous than the redesign of humankind? It is hardly surprising if the notions that have to do with heredity – both its theory and the technologies that spring from it – account for half the content of every modern newspaper. Most obviously, in Europe these past few years and now in the United States too, consumers, farmers, politicians, merchant bankers, environmental activists, everyone, has been talking about 'GMOs': 'genetically modified organisms' which, in effect, are the first generation of crops *qua* metaphorical Christmas trees. The birth of Dolly the cloned sheep at Roslin Institute near Edinburgh in 1996 (and the year before, though fewer people noticed them, of Megan and Morag) raised the possibility of human cloning. Far more importantly, though most commentators missed this point, human cloning technology paves the way for the 'designer baby': the human being genetically 'engineered' to a specification. More broadly, the emotions that spring from matters of heredity continue to ferment and to fester: racism and genocide dominate the world's international news.

Yet at the same time, on a more positive note, scientists known as 'evolutionary psychologists' are using what are essentially genetic insights to re-explore the principal theme of the Enlightenment: the true nature of human nature. Already there are encouraging signs that evolutionary psychology can improve on the forays of the eighteenth century, noble as they often were. The point is *not* to be 'genetically determinist' and to suggest that human beings are run by their genes, as the critics continue to proclaim. The point is that if we can understand ourselves more fully, then we have a greater chance of devising social structures which on the one hand are humane and just, and on the other are robust. The criteria of humanity and justice must of course remain the products of human intellect and emotion, as has always been the case: they will not derive directly from greater knowledge of our own biology. But social robustness does depend on such knowledge. There is no point in devising Utopias which

2

require people to behave in non-human ways. People have tried to do this throughout the twentieth century and millions died as a result, with no obvious gain at all. I still believe in the possibility of Utopia, or something very like it. It seems a proper ambition. But it will not be achieved unless we first understand how we really *are*. The vociferous critics of evolutionary psychology should do some homework to find out what it is in fact about. If they did, they would surely be ashamed of their own obduracy.

Then, of course, there's the matter of our fellow species: wildlife conservation. I believe this ranks in importance with the fate of humankind itself. The nature of the task for the twenty-first century and beyond is to create a world in which we can thrive *alongside* our fellow creatures. If we succeed at their expense, then this will be a partial failure; but it is absurd to suggest (as some unfortunately do) that other creatures should survive instead of us, as if human beings should or would commit mass *hara kiri*. Humankind and the rest of Creation must be catered for together as harmoniously as possible. Wildlife conservation has a huge and necessary emotional content – and indeed is driven by emotion, for if people do not care about other creatures, then they are doomed. It's unfortunate, though, that some of those who profess to care most deeply also feel that emotion is incompatible with what they see as the cool rationality of science. Yet poetry alone will not save our fellow creatures. Wildlife cannot survive without good science. Genetics, the science of heredity, is not the only discipline that's needed, but it is essential. To focus our efforts effectively we need to know which species are most endangered and in greatest need of immediate help. We cannot begin to make that judgement without knowledge of genes. Sometimes, too, we need to supplement all our efforts in the field with specific breeding plans, which are bound to fail unless guided by genetic theory.

Overall, the present worldwide discussion of all these issues, sensible and otherwise, must be welcomed. Nothing can be more important to life on Earth. No human concern is left untouched and what concerns us all we should all talk about, for that is part of what democracy means. The idea that we should leave everything to 'the experts' is an invitation to revert to the Middle

Ages at its worst. In the bad old days the peasantry were expected to take the word of the priest as gospel, while we are now invited to take our lead from scientists and politicians. At least, this is sometimes the case, although some scientists, more sensibly and humbly, are content to take guidance from the societies of which they are a part and to contribute as citizens, like the rest of us. We might argue that it's our *duty* to discuss these issues. The effort is the price we pay for democracy.

But this is where we seem to hit a snag. The issues that now need to be discussed are hugely various: breeding of crops and livestock, cloning, genetic counselling, designer babies, conservation, animal welfare, the nature of human nature. Worse: they are all highly technical, or can be. There are entire institutions devoted to each of them. Specialists in one field may disclaim worthwhile knowledge of any other. How can the rest of us, who aren't experts at all, hope to keep up? Worst of all: much of the discussion (perhaps most of it) is heavily overlaid with politics of one kind or another. Most perniciously (because they really should know better) some biologists seek openly to misrepresent some of the current endeavours, or at least display a sublime lack of understanding; and yet they are believed because they are perceived to have authority. Thus confusion is loaded on to something which is already complicated. So what hope is there? Perhaps we should be content to mount discussions in the manner of a party game, chatter away in the pub for the fun of it, but let 'the experts' run the show after all. We could do this except for various nagging suspicions: the experts aren't as expert as they sometimes make out; they don't agree with each other so they can't all be right; and they often seem to say things that leave us feeling uncomfortable. Besides we don't live in the Middle Ages any more, and although we may feel that priests are important (I certainly do) we should not be content to let them, or scientists masquerading as latter-day priests, tell us what to do. That way of running society is no longer acceptable. But how can we improve on this model if the issues are so disparate and difficult?

Well, I have been looking at aspects of genetics and related issues for about four decades now (I am alarmed to discover) and have concluded, after so many summers, that the problems are not as disparate and difficult as all that. It's important only to grasp the underlying principles. Once you see how genes really work – or seem to work, in the light of present knowledge – then the biology seems to fall into place. The ethical issues require further input, but at least we need not be waylaid by the technicalities. I am not a professional geneticist: I have never plucked the anthers from an antirrhinum, calculated 'gene drops' on a computer, or even tracked some inherited blight through the royal houses of Europe. But I did study genetics and evolutionary theory thoroughly during my formal education in the 1950s and 1960s when the world was celebrating some significant centenaries, and the new science of molecular biology was undergoing its spectacular birth (and genetic engineering had yet to be undertaken). Over thirty-five years of work I have had prolonged and significant dealings with medicine, agriculture and wildlife conservation and, particularly of late, at the London School of Economics Centre for Philosophy, involvement with many aspects of genetic and evolutionary theory, as well as the philosophy of science. So I haven't worn a white coat since undergraduate days and I'm not knee-deep in snails and fruit-flies, but I have had the opportunity to take a long hard look at these developments. It's a matter of swings and roundabouts: what you lose from daily contact with roundworms and oscilloscopes you gain (I hope) in intellectual mobility. In short, I want in this book to provide an overview and I hope to show that this is a valid approach.

More specifically, I want to demonstrate how much the modern world owes to the nineteenth-century Moravian friar called Gregor Mendel. As all the world knows, in the 1850s and 1860s Mendel carried out some irreducibly simple experiments with rows of peas in the monastery garden at Brno. Most people know less about his subsequent experiments with runner beans, antirrhinums, the hawkweed *Hieracium* and many others, and his final, brilliant flourish with bees, but never mind: peas carry the day. It's often suggested, however, that, because Mendel's experiments were simple, he was a simple man driven by simplistic thoughts. Because his results were so neat it has been suggested that he cheated and, more often, that he was lucky. If he had looked at other plants, or studied the hereditary pattern of different characters even within garden peas, he would not have achieved such tidiness.

Of course he didn't cheat (I can't prove this; but it wasn't his style and various alternative explanations seem far more likely). Neither did he rely on luck. He achieved such clarity because he was in principle a very modern scientist and knew, as the great British zoologist Sir Peter Medawar observed a hundred years later, that 'Science is the art of the soluble'. While others, including Darwin, pondered the huge complexities and confusions of heredity, Mendel perceived that no one would make any progress until they first identified and worked out the simplest possible cases. He did not stumble upon peas by accident. He chose them from the mass of candidates because he knew they would give simple results. He did not study particular characters, the shapes of the seeds and the colours of the pods, by chance. He knew before he began that in these particular characters the pattern of inheritance was relatively straightforward. Failure to 'breed true' is the bane of all commercial breeders and experimental geneticists: the fact that all creatures often give rise to offspring strikingly and apparently randomly different from themselves. But Mendel *knew* that his peas would breed true. He selected the species for this very quality, and he carried out at least two years' preliminary work to produce especially true-breeding lines.

In short, never in all of science have experiments been more beautifully conceived and executed. This is the simplicity not of a simple man, but of a genius, who sees the simplicity that lies beneath the surface incoherence: the deftness of touch that we associate with Newton, say, or Mozart or Picasso. Experiments that reveal so much with so little fuss are said to be 'elegant'. Such elegance, so much derived from so little, has been matched only by Galileo.

Nor did Mendel move on to beans, hawkweeds and bees out of stupidity. With peas, the simplest possible case, he worked out the ground rules. But he knew (as well as Darwin did) that most cases are more complicated. He wanted (as Darwin also did in another context) to find rules that were universal. I am sure he felt in his bones that the rules he derived from his peas *were* universal, and that with a little tweaking they could explain the odd patterns of inheritance in beans and bees and indeed in human beings, but he was one man working more or less on his own and he ran out of time. In the twentieth century it took hundreds of scientists several decades to work through the problems which Mendel set for himself after his work with peas was finished. He also, I think, lost heart, for few people recognised the greatness of his achievement and many fail to do so even now.

For the complex patterns of heredity seen in beans and bees and human beings follow straightforwardly from Mendel's unimprovably simple case. Skin colour in human beings is a far more complex character than the shape of the seeds in garden peas, but the theory that explains the latter also fits the former perfectly easily once we add in a few conditional clauses. We see in this some of the essence of the mathematical concept of chaos: the notion that very simple rules, once given a small twist, can lead to endlessly various outcomes. Most breeders and biologists became bogged down in the outcomes: Mendel saw the rules beneath. That is genius.

More than that: once we combine Mendel's ideas of heredity with Darwin's concept of evolution 'by means of natural selection' then we have two-thirds of the basic theory of all modern biology. Mendel's and Darwin's ideas together form 'the modern synthesis', otherwise known as 'neodarwinism'. Add in one more set of ideas from the twentieth century, the science of molecular biology, which is the study of what genes are and how they behave, and we have the core of modern biology. That is not quite true, of course. Ecologists and some psychologists will argue that their disciplines also belong to biology, and that they contain much that cannot simply be thrust into the canon of neodarwinism *cum* molecular biology. But the canon is the hard core nonetheless: the spring from which all may drink.

Hence the title of this book: *In Mendel's Footnotes*. The English philosopher A. N. Whitehead famously argued that 'all moral philosophy is footnotes to Plato': and I want to argue in the same spirit that all genetics is footnotes to Mendel. Of all the experiments that he began only the ones with peas were fully completed. But they will do. Only understand what he did and why he did what he did, his background thought and the details of his irreducibly simple method, and all the modern debates that seem so confusing start to fall into place. That at least is my thesis. If at the end you feel I have failed to make the case, well, I hope the journey will be worthwhile.

In Chapters 2 and 3 I make the general case: describing Mendel's own background, the society in which he worked and the people he knew, the science of his day and why heredity is so difficult, and how he cut through the knots with his rows of peas. In Chapter 4 I discuss the twentieth century's contribution: how Mendel's proposed 'hereditary factors' were given the soubriquet of 'genes' and how the chemistry and *modus operandi* of the genes were revealed. Chapter 5 describes how scientists worked out what genes actually are, and how they work, leading to the science of 'molecular biology'.

Then the thesis bifurcates: first into theory and then into practicalities – the modern biotechnologies. So Chapter 6 describes the synthesis, the fusion of Mendel's genetics with Darwin's evolutionary theory, and Chapter 7 describes how the notions of neodarwinism are now being applied to the Enlightenment issue of human nature through the discipline of evolutionary psychology. Chapter 8 then considers the practical issue: how modern genetic theory is applied to the 'improvement' of crops and livestock for economic purposes; and, in sharp contrast, how it can be pressed into the service of conservation.

Then in Chapter 9 I show how the two arms of the discussion, the deep theory and the practice, are being or soon could be brought together again to make the most fundamental changes to human life that are conceivable. It is rapidly becoming possible to redesign human beings: to create the 'designer baby'.

We have already reached the point, indeed, where we might reasonably argue that all the conceivable ambitions of biotechnology should be considered possible – provided only that they do not break what Medawar called 'the bedrock laws of physics'. There is nowhere for biotechnology to hide, in short. Scientists can no longer dismiss public misgivings with the peremptory comment that this bogey man or that need not be considered because they are 'not possible' or are mere 'fantasy'. Such dismissals just will not do. *Anything* that a physicist would allow, the biologists of the future might do. When anything is possible we have to ask as a matter of urgency, 'So what is *right*?' That is the subject of the last chapter.

Mendel has much to teach us here, too. Much less is known of his life than we should like. Most of his personal notes were destroyed. The literature about Mendel ought to be as rich as the writing on Darwin and it simply is not. So we do not know in detail much of what he thought or did, day to day. The little that is known, though, suggests that he was courteous, humble, generous and certainly conscientious. These are qualities our descendants will need in abundance if they are to come to terms with their own extraordinary power.

2

The Peasant and the Scientist

Modern biology began in the nineteenth century with two great, contrasting traditions. One was English, emphatically rational and in some ways more obviously modern, yet out of it came the great metaphysical overview of Charles Darwin: the notion of evolution 'by means of natural selection'. The other was German. This tradition was more 'Romantic' in the literal sense, pervaded as it was by the quasi-mystical insights of *Naturphilosophie* (which greatly influenced the Romantic movement, as manifest most obviously in Coleridge), and yet it gave us the more down-to-earth arm of modern biology. The German scientists showed how living systems work. Notably, in the early nineteenth century, they revealed that all large creatures, such as animals and plants, are compounded of many tiny cells; and how those cells divide and develop into embryos and hence into new, free-living individuals. Later in the century they invented biochemistry.

At the pinnacle of the Germanic tradition stands Gregor Mendel. By no means without help, but on his own nonetheless, he effectively created genetics, the science of heredity. The only experiments that he took to completion were with garden peas, which he grew in the monastery garden at Brno in Moravia, now in the Czech Republic not far from Prague. A child can understand those experiments (and many children do), yet you can build a universe of ideas upon them. Once you understand what Mendel *really* did, and why he carried out those particular experiments with those homely garden plants, and perceive as he did the problems that had to be overcome, then all that has

10

happened in the name of genetics in the twentieth century and everything that is happening now falls easily into place.

The textbooks generally assert that Mendel was Austrian, presumably because Moravia, where he was born and lived most of his life, then formed part of the Austro-Hungarian Empire. Ethnically, however, he was German. He and most of his family were German-speaking; he learnt Czech, the local language, fairly late in life, and not particularly well. European specialists at the BBC World Service tell me logically enough that he should be called 'a German-speaking Moravian'. Genetics is, of course, a branch of biology, but his first love was physics and his scientific friends and mentors included such great men as the physicist Christian Johann Doppler, who if he had lived a century later would certainly have won a Nobel Prize. 'The Doppler Effect' explains why the pitch of a police car siren drops as it races past, which might not seem particularly exciting in itself; but the same insight applied to light rather than to sound has become one of the key devices of modern cosmology, enabling astronomers to calculate the speed at which distant stars are retreating from us and hence to judge their distance. Such were the social and bureaucratic arrangements of mid-nineteenth-century Europe that Doppler at one point found himself interviewing Mendel for a job as a schoolmaster.

Mendel did teach science (though he never actually managed to pass the teaching exams), but he lived all his adult life in the monastery at Brno. Since his order was Augustinian he was technically a friar, although he is usually described simply as a 'monk'. It does not seem that he was particularly devout: the sparse personal notes left to us suggest that he entered the monastery largely for economic reasons and took holy orders because that is what monks did. But he was certainly conscientious and for the last seventeen years of his life he was abbot of Brno, fighting the monastery's corner against Catholic bureaucracy.

His life, however, and to some extent its aftermath, remain largely mysterious. After he died in 1884 (just sixty-one years old), a meddlesome monk burned nearly all his notes, including those on most of his experiments. Why? Probably the gesture was well meant, but in retrospect it seems the most extraordinary act of vandalism. He twice presented the results of his seminal experiments with peas in 1865 to audiences which must have included some of Europe's leading biologists, and published his findings in a paper in 1866 that is a model of thoroughness and clarity.

Yet his work was apparently ignored. He entered a long, fruitless and entirely dispiriting correspondence with a Swiss botanist called Carl Nägeli (famous in his time, but now more or less forgotten) and carried out many more experiments with different plants, and finally, brilliantly, with bees. But still no one took any serious notice. His research disappeared from view for several decades until his one published paper of 1866 was rediscovered in around 1900 by three biologists working independently: the German Carl Correns, the Austrian Erich Tschermak and the Dutchman Hugo De Vries. Then the science of heredity, which Mendel had so ably founded, soon to be named 'genetics', could properly begin. But when the English biologist William Bateson visited Brno in 1904 to find out more about the strange young monk who had done so much and then been lost to view, no one could throw much light on his work. They remembered the donation he had made to the fire station at Hynčice (the village of his birth), and that he had been amiable, courteous, hard-working and well loved, if a little tetchy at times (particularly with the Catholic bureaucracy). But peas? Hmm. Yes – maybe you'd better ask somebody else. Bateson returned to England, nonplussed.

Bit by painful bit, however, the bones of Mendel's life, work and education have been unearthed. His nephews, Alois and Ferdinand Schindler, provided much of the background. Their mother, Mendel's younger sister, had once given Mendel part of her dowry to help with his education; he in turn supported her sons through theirs. H. Iltis (1882–1952), a natural scientist from Brno, did most to fill in the remaining gaps and published a biography in 1924. This present account leans heavily on the excellent biography by Vítězslav Orel of 1996, *Gregor Mendel: The First Geneticist*. Thanks to these scholars and others, much though by no means all of the mystery has been resolved. At least it's clear now who Mendel was and what he was doing working in a monastery, for monasteries in today's world are not usually associated with seminal science. It's clear too, although many, perversely, still seem to prefer to believe otherwise, that his experiments with peas were beautifully designed, wonderfully modern in concept, and rooted in a huge understanding of the problems; problems that now seem difficult to envisage largely because Mendel solved them. Indeed we can hardly doubt that Mendel should be ranked among the elite which includes Galileo and Newton among physicists and Darwin (it is hard to think of another quite so significant) among biologists.

It is still not obvious (at least to me) why Mendel's many excellent friends and acquaintances did not appreciate him more than they did and why they allowed his work to disappear, to be rescued only by the skin of its teeth. Neither do I understand why Mendel's ideas apparently caused so much *angst* after they were rediscovered: why some scientists, including Bateson, found it hard to reconcile Mendel's genetics with the newly emerging knowledge of chromosomes, the structures which physically contain the genes; or with the 'biometric' tradition that had grown up in the late nineteenth century with Darwin's cousin, Francis Galton; or why, until the 1920s and beyond, it seemed so hard to reconcile Mendel's ideas with Darwin's. By the 1940s Darwin's and Mendel's ideas had finally been brought together to produce 'the modern synthesis' otherwise known as 'neodarwinism' – and this was one of the great intellectual triumphs of the twentieth century. But it seemed very hard work to get to that point.

That is the outline of the tale. We should look in more detail at Mendel's life and circumstances, for without some insight into them we cannot properly understand why he did the experiments he did.

Who Was Mendel?

Mendel's life-story is often related in the traditional manner of mythology: born in obscurity; self-taught; playing with plants in a monastery garden for no apparent reason, except to while away

13

the long quiet summers; hitting on experiments that changed the world by lucky accident. In almost every respect the myth is wrong, as most myths are. In fact he was born to intelligent and able people in a society that was obsessed with the problems of agriculture and particularly of crop improvement – it had to be because its livelihood depended on them. He was well educated and extremely appropriately, primarily as a physicist and mathematician, and he brought the precision of those austere disciplines to the problems of heredity, as others had recommended before, but rarely attempted. Indeed, it's almost as if he was destined to do the work he did: he was exactly the right kind of thinker in the right place at the right time, surrounded by fine scientists but far ahead of them all. Note, too, in the following account, how many good and talented people took an interest in his welfare. His family made sacrifices on his behalf and a succession of fine teachers, clerics and scientists helped him on his way: J. Schreiber, F. Franz, F. C. Napp, A. Keller, F. Diebl, Matous Klacel, Tomas Bratranek, Baumgartner, Christian Johann Doppler, A. Ettinghausen and Franz Unger. He was also acquainted, at least at one step removed, with the greats of nineteenth-century European biology, including Matthias Schleiden, Johannes Purkinje, Rudolf Carl Virchow and even R. W. Bunsen and Baron von Liebig. It is strange that his career as a scientist seemed to peter out so limply in the correspondence with Nägeli. Why, when he knew so many fine people, did he spend so much time on one who clearly did not appreciate his work? Mendel's life and work need no mythologising; but there is mystery in their *dénouement* nonetheless.

He was born in 1822 on 22 July, though the baptismal register says 20 July, in Heinzendorf (now Hynčice), a little village of seventy-two households. He was christened Johann and took the name Gregor later, when he became a monk. The Mendels, evidently from Germany, had lived in the area since the mid-1500s. In the Austro-Hungarian Empire of the early nineteenth century the prevailing politics were feudal – feudalism officially came to an end only in the revolutionary year of 1848. Mendel's family was of the kind sometimes classified as 'rich peasant'.

There is no precise English equivalent, although the Tulliver family in George Eliot's *The Mill on the Floss*, albeit millers rather than farmers, were of the same general class: people with no obvious political influence, but essential to the economy and not to be ignored. Mendel's father Anton was a farmer who owned their house and improved it, replacing the original wood with brick. Inevitably, as a good Moravian, he grew fruit trees in the garden and kept bees. But he also owed allegiance to the feudal lord, in whose fields and forests he was obliged to work for three days a week, with his two horses working alongside him. Johann's mother, Rosine (née Schwirtlich), was the daughter of market gardeners. Religion was also a powerful force. Moravia, like most of northern Europe, endured alternate bouts of Catholicism and Protestantism. Through Mendel's own life, the Catholics prevailed.

The feudal regime was oppressive but not generally brutal. At its best the ruling class acknowledged the ancient principle of *noblesse oblige* and, at least much of the time, sought to look after the peasantry through benign patronage. The Catholic Church the world over often seems to be a prime opponent of all intellectual adventure: the defender of dogma, the natural enemy of science. So it was in nineteenth-century Moravia, just as it had been in seventeenth-century Italy when it put a stop to Galileo. But (I am inclined to think) with a little bit of luck here and there, if only the coin had flipped the other way the Catholic Church *might* have emerged as the champion and bastion of science (and the course of Western philosophy and science would then have run quite differently). Galileo, after all, was a devout Catholic. The Jesuit intellectuals were entranced by his cosmology; it was the perceived threat to papal authority which they could not endure. The monasteries in general, in the centuries before Galileo, gave birth to modern science. In central Europe in the nineteenth century, although they had suffered mightily at the end of the eighteenth, the monasteries were still perceived as centres of intellectual activity, and science (embracing agriculture) was high among their pursuits. The monasteries might indeed be seen as the precursors of modern research stations, though all their research was carried out within the context of Catholic devotion. To a large extent, a particular monastery's intellectual pursuit was determined by the predilections of its abbot. Even so, in nineteenth-century Moravia, as in seventeenth-century Italy, any true spark of intellectual adventurousness was liable to be stamped out. There were plenty of *avant-garde* thinkers and teachers at St Thomas's monastery at Brno, where Mendel spent his professional life, and a striking proportion of them lost their jobs.

On the other hand, Moravia as a whole was emerging as a modern economy, rooted, as was usual in the early nineteenth century, in agriculture. There were two prevailing obsessions, and this is hardly too strong a word, for the whole economy depended on them. One was sheep (mainly for wool) and the other was fruit, including vines for wine but also apples and other fruits as a significant source of nutrition. Agriculture was already competitive internationally – the rise of Britain's Empire threatened Moravia's ascendancy in wool – and everyone knew that success would lie with those who could produce the *best* sheep and the *best* crops. In short, the national obsession with agriculture was underpinned by a national obsession with the breeding of livestock and crops. Brno was the capital of Moravia and not a backwater, as commentators often imply. At that time it was a rising industrial town, the centre of the Hapsburg's textile industry in a region where wool was at the core of the economy. In the early nineteenth century it established its own Agricultural Society and two more specialist groups: the Sheep Breeders' Association, and the Pomological (apple-growing) and Oenological (wine) Association. These associations were serious centres of intellectual activity. In 1849 the Agricultural Society created a Natural Science Section, which in turn (in 1860) achieved independence as the Natural Science Society. Mendel and most of his scientific friends were members, and the twenty-four honorary members of the section included many of the great scientists of the time, such as Bunsen, Unger, Virchow and Purkinje.

Thus alongside feudalism and religious bureaucracy, and to some extent as the product of them, Moravia had a significant intellectual and educational tradition with a practical and scientific edge, as befitted an agricultural and industrial society. Throughout its history we see a similar kind of fervour for self-improvement, and the enthusiasm of a few outstanding reformers to fulfil it, to that which ran through Britain and was typified by the workers' educational schemes of the nineteenth century. Mendel, both the young Johann and the mature Gregor, benefited enormously from the zeal of earlier Moravian reformers.

In the seventeenth century the great protestant liberal John Amos Comenius had insisted that education should be general and should include natural history: he was, after all, a follower of Francis Bacon. Inevitably, it seems, Comenius was forced into exile in 1620 when the Catholics returned, but he made his mark nonetheless and Mendel, two centuries later, was a beneficiary. In the era just before Mendel, at the end of the eighteenth century, the Countess Walpurga Truchsess-Zeil, supporter of the free-masons and of the Enlightenment, founded a private institution of learning at Kunin, where she paid bed and board for the local children of talent, both boys and girls. Science featured conspicuously in the education. One of the teachers was the outstanding reformer Christian Carl André, who also had a great influence on the region as a whole; and another was J. Schreiber, who went on to shape the life of the young Mendel in particular.

For Schreiber (1769–1850) was an innovator, a gardener, teacher, social reformer and priest as well. At Kunin he established a nursery for fruit trees – what else would a Moravian do? – with varieties imported from France. He and the countess sought to distribute the best strains among the villagers, but they knew that if they simply gave them away the villagers would not value them. So Schreiber and the countess put the word about that anyone caught stealing the new, world-beating, imported seedlings would be severely punished. They posted guards with strict instructions to make the loudest possible noise but never actually to arrest anybody. Within three days all the seedlings had been stolen. In our own times comparable strategies have been used to distribute contraceptives in the Third World. Official channels are simply not trusted. The black market is the vernacular route. We may note in passing the benign face of feudalism, the positive desire to help the people at large. Modern freedom is of course to be preferred, but with it has come the hard-faced market, where everything with an edge is patented and nothing can ever be given away.

Of course, the good times could not be allowed to last. The dank fog of bureaucracy soon closed in. The Austro-Hungarian authorities liked the school at Kunin well enough at first, but then became frightened by the Revolution in France. They invest-igated the teaching at Kunin, found it too 'liberal', took particular objection to the 'alien notions' of science and held Schreiber responsible for what they called the 'scandal'. Schreiber was forced to leave in 1802 and Kunin closed in 1814. The political scene, with each lurch towards liberality and modernity brutally and predictably checked after just a few years by a conservative and nervous regime, is all too reminiscent of modern times. We have seen it in the old USSR; and, lest we are tempted to be chauvinistic, in modern Kansas, where the teaching of evolution-ary theory has lately been suppressed. Kunin's misfortune, however, was to benefit Mendel. The sacked Schreiber became the priest of the parish which included Mendel's native village of Hyncice.

Anton Mendel, Johann's father, was born in the first year of the French Revolution, 1789, and took part in the last stages of the Napoleonic wars. He married Rosine Schwirtlich, the gardeners' daughter, in 1818. She was five years his junior. The Mendels' first child, Veronica, was born in 1820; then came Johann, their only son, in 1822; then Theresa in 1829. Two other children died soon after birth.

Anton clearly prospered for a time. Like all the people of Hynčice, the Mendels wanted their children to 'get on', and to 'get on' meant to be educated. Again we see the comparison with Eliot's Tullivers. There were pedagogues already in the family: Rosine's uncle had taught at the village school.

And Schreiber was already on the scene. As he had done at Kunin, he established a nursery of fruit trees in the presbytery garden at Vrazne. In 1816 he helped to found Brno's new Pomological Association; by then, too, he was a corresponding member of the Brno Agricultural Society. Schreiber taught young Johann the basics of fruit-tree improvement. Among other things, the key technique of artificial pollination had been in wide use in Europe since about 1820. When Mendel was eleven in 1833, Schreiber and the schoolmaster Thomas Makitta commended him to the school in Lipnik (Leipnik) where gifted pupils were primed for the Gymnasium, the secondary school, in Opava (Troppau). One year later, in 1834, twelve-year-old Johann duly graduated to the Gymnasium.

Schooldays

Johann's success was hard for his parents. Opava was thirty-six kilometres away and he had to live in (though his parents could only afford to pay half-board). Furthermore, they had lost the natural heir to their farm. Then came an unkind twist. In 1838, when Johann was in his fourth year at Opava, Anton was seriously injured in the forest while working for the landowner. Johann was then only sixteen, but already, as he later recorded in his *curriculum vitae*, he was 'in the sad position of having to cope for himself entirely'. The stress evidently wore him down, for he became seriously ill and had to spend much of the following year, 1839, at home. He was bright, though, and he still moved up to the next class. He also took his first formal steps to becoming a schoolteacher, his ambition, and attended a course at the teachers' seminary in Opava. Again he did well and was able to earn what he later called 'a scant living' teaching his less able schoolfellows. But life was hard. As he also recorded later, writing about himself in the third person, 'His sorrowful youth taught him early the serious aspects of life, and it also taught him to work.'

Johann remained at Opava for six years and apart from periods of illness returned home only in the holidays. Taken all in all, Opava was not a bad place for a young biologist to be. It had a museum of natural history (established in 1814 at the suggestion of Christian André) and a library that included books on meteorology (which became one of Mendel's lifelong passions).

Still, though, Johann was not ready for university. To qualify, students had to complete two more years at what the British would now call a 'sixth-form college': either at a Lycaeum (which was attached to a university) or at an independent Philosophical Institute. The nearest such institution was at Olomouc (Olmütz), and so, in 1840, he offered his services as a private tutor in Olomouc so that he could continue his studies. But he failed to find work, and again became sick. So yet another year at home with his parents followed. Again, though, life was not entirely bleak. At Olomouc he met P. Krížkovský, who achieved fame, at least locally, as a composer. At that time Krížkovský had just left the Augustinian monastery and was trying to find work as a teacher. Throughout his life Mendel made good friends outside science, as well as within. (Much later, as abbot at Brno, he employed the great Leoš Janáček as organist and choirmaster.)

Olomouc

Johann, now aged nineteen, finally joined the Philosophy Institute at Olomouc in 1841. He was being pulled in two directions, however, for his injured father was no longer able to work and asked Johann, one last time, to return home and take over the farm. Johann stayed where he was, although he must have been tempted to leave: he was in a strange city with no established friends, had little money and spoke the Czech language very poorly. He suffered yet another mental crisis in his first term and again went home to recover, but by then he had already passed Latin and Maths with top grades. So he returned to Olomouc to complete the course. At this point, however, he acquired a safety net. His elder sister Veronica got married and her new husband bought the Mendel family farm. The sale of contract, dated 7 August 1841, includes a clause that was to supply Johann with a small annual allowance if he entered the priesthood, while rooms were to be reserved for him at the farm if he failed. His younger sister, Theresa, then offered Johann part of her dowry to help him out – Mendel later paid her back by supporting her three sons in their studies (as good an example as you will find of kin altruism, as discussed in Chapter 7).

At Olomouc, Mendel was examined in religious studies, philosophy, ethics, maths, physics and pedagogics. Note that he did not take natural history and agriculture. He specialised instead in maths and physics: seven hours a week of maths in his first year, from a total of twenty hours; and eight hours per week of physics in his second year. He finished the course in 1843 and could then have gone to Olomouc's sixteenth-century university. But, presumably through lack of funds, he did not. Instead, we again see guiding hands at work. For his physics teacher at the Olomouc Institution was F. Franz and he it was who in July 1843 recommended Mendel to Abbot F. C. Napp at the monastery of Brno. Thirteen candidates applied for the novitiate and Mendel was one of four to be shortlisted. Franz was warm in his praise: 'During the two-year course in philosophy [he] almost invariably had the most exceptional reports.' Mendel was, said Franz, 'A young man of very solid character – in my own branch almost the best.' By 'my own branch', of course, he meant physics, which at that time seemed Mendel's destiny.

Life with the Monks

Napp accepted Mendel without interview on 7 September 1843, and his parents gave their written permission later in the month. He began his novitiate on 9 October 1843, now aged nearly twenty-one and a quarter. It was at this point that he took the name Gregor. It is pleasing to think of him in the great tradition of biologist-clerics, like England's Gilbert White, whose *Natural History and Antiquities of Selborne* of 1788 was such an inspiration to later biologists, including Darwin. In truth, though, Mendel leaves no evidence of serious religious commitment. He recorded in his *curriculum vitae* of 1850 that he entered the monastery because he was tired of overwork. He writes:

> It was impossible for him to endure such exertion any further. Therefore, having finished his philosophical studies, he felt himself compelled to enter a station in life that would free him from the bitter struggle for existence. His circumstances decided his vocational choice. He requested and received in the year 1843 admission to the Augustinian monastery of St Thomas in Brno.

21

Yet life at Brno was in many ways ideal. Mendel was a natural scholar and, as he tells us in his *curriculum vitae*, 'so long as he fulfilled his clerical duties, he was free to devote himself to private study'; while he had, he said, the security which was 'so beneficial to any kind of study'. Many a modern scientist would love to claim as much. As at Opava, he had specimens on hand and in his spare time 'he occupied himself with the small botanical and mineralogical collection which was placed at his disposal in the monastery'. As he gave more and more attention to natural science, he developed 'a special liking, which deepened, the more he had the opportunity to become familiar with it'.

As for Napp, he had become abbot in 1821 when he was only thirty-two; and he remained in the post until his death in 1867 when Mendel succeeded him. As Vítězslav Orel records, Napp was a passionate student of philosophy and theology who had wanted to be a university professor. He was also, inevitably, it seems, in nineteenth-century Moravia, a plant-breeder. Before he came to Brno he had organised a nursery garden in the monastery's farm at Sardice, eighty kilometres away, where he produced new strains of apples. In the 1830s he created a new experimental garden at the Brno monastery which was described as 'a jewel among nurseries'. Indeed, Napp's job description required him to 'promote pomology and wine-growing through experiments, observation, and instruction, enrich science, and propagate useful findings'. Note again the altruism implicit in this. Mendel himself, as a novice, was placed in the care of A. Keller (1783–1853), yet another member of Brno's Agricultural Society and an active member of the Pomological Association. Keller sought primarily to improve vines and fruit trees and had also published on melons.

The monastery at Brno had been founded in 1350 next to the church of St Thomas and for a time it flourished. It was rebuilt in the seventeenth century with a large library and accommodation for forty-two monks. But then in 1782 more than half the monasteries of Europe were abolished and those that remained had to serve the State as well as the Church. The monks were now obliged to work in parishes and hospitals and to teach religion in schools. Brno survived, but in 1783 the monks had to move from their fine building in the centre of town to a former convent on the outskirts, which had recently been vacated by Cistercian nuns. The formerly affluent monastery was now in debt. The monks' new home had been rebuilt in the fourteenth century and was in poor condition. It was still rundown in 1807, when orders came from Emperor Franz I (1792–1835) for the monks to teach maths and biblical studies in the newly established Philosophical Institute and at Brno's theological college.

So the monasteries had actively to recruit young men to teach: men like Mendel. P. F. Nedele (1778–1827) was the first teacher of biblical studies at Brno, but the bishop considered him too liberal (he was involved in the Czech national revival movement) and he was sacked in 1821, whereupon he became the prior and librarian. This is when Napp took over.

Napp too was constantly at odds with the Catholic authorities, who wanted him to cut down on teaching and focus on monastic discipline, but he had influence as a member both of the Lords Diet and of the Brno Agricultural Society and was able to resist. He welcomed the imperial order for monks to teach – and insisted that they should teach science. He also had plans to rationalise agriculture and to this end enlisted the advice of F. Diebl, whom he helped to become professor of agricultural science at Brno University. Diebl advised Napp on crop rotation, the cultivation of fodder crops and the breeding of sheep. The monastery, after all, obtained much of its income from the farm at Sardice, with most of the cash coming from wool. Napp carried out field trials and in 1826 he and Diebl analysed the reasons for a particularly bad invasion of pests (which they showed resulted from the warm autumn). In 1827 Napp was elected president of the Pomological Association and he was also involved with the Sheep Breeders' Society and its discussions on sheep breeding. One point with specific relevance to Mendel: Napp pointed out in 1836 that the problems of heredity could be solved *only* through experiments. All in all, Abbot Napp was a deep thinker and a fine scientist. Mendel may have entered the monastery at Brno primarily to escape privation; but the place and the people in charge of it could hardly have been better suited to him.

Mendel acquired the plot in which he grew his peas, perhaps

the most significant allotment in the history of humankind, by a route that also reflects the essential importance of and special concern for science and agriculture in nineteenth-century Moravia. The tradition was largely established by Christian André, but Moravia's first notable plant scientist was A. Thaler (1796–1843), yet another Augustinian, who taught maths at the Philosophy Institute. In 1830 Napp gave Thaler permission to establish an experimental garden in the monastery: a substantial 35m MUL 5m plot under the refectory windows. There Thaler grew rare Moravian plants and founded a herbarium.

Matous Klacel (1808–82) took over the experimental garden from Thaler in 1843, the year that Mendel joined the monastery. Klacel was primarily a philosopher who studied natural science. He was a follower of Hegel and embraced the German system of *Naturphilosophie*, which demanded that the natural philosopher should become emotionally involved in his subject. Indeed, said Klacel, 'deliberate university is the aim of all love and science'. Such a view these days might be subsumed in the general notion of 'holistic', though the currents of *Naturphilosophie* ran very deep and were essentially mystical. Klacel too was a member of the Agricultural Society and between 1841 and 1843 he published articles on the need for progress in the natural and social sciences. He also espoused the cause of Czech nationalism, which aroused the anger of the authorities; and in 1842 and 1843 he was accused of spreading pantheistic notions and the ideas of the philosopher Hegel in opposition to the Catholic faith. Napp defended him as best he could, but in 1847 Klacel, in the eyes of the Catholic authorities, finally went too far. He wrote a three-part essay on *The Philosophy of Rational Good*, which the official censors in Vienna declared contained 'harmful sentences' in the third part and (how drearily repetitive this becomes!) he was sacked from his post as philosophy teacher.

The following year, 1848, brought revolution throughout Europe. Klacel helped to organise the pan-Slavonic congress in Prague, and it was then that he asked Mendel, who had long been a firm friend, to take over the experimental garden. The congress was broken up by force and Klacel returned to the monastery to become the librarian (there is a thesis to be written about mavericks of all kinds who take refuge in librarianship). Nonetheless, on 13 March 1848 the absolutist government of Prince von Metternich was forced to resign and a new capitalist order was established. The Emperor, Ferdinand I, promised to abolish feudal labour, to lift censorship and to summon a legislative assembly. On 17 March there was a mass meeting in Brno, at which a revolutionary poem set to music by Křížkovský was sung by the newly formed revolutionary guard as they marched. Diebl marched among the students at the head of the procession. Napp added his support and also entertained revolutionary students from Vienna. Klacel gave a sermon, demanding the end of feudal labour, although the city's captains of industry objected and in turn demonstrated against the monastery. But the government in Vienna did finally abolish formal labour on 7 September. Thus feudalism officially came to an end. All in all, 1848 was a momentous year. It changed the face of Europe, and Mendel acquired the monastery garden in which he changed the world.

Eighteen forty-eight was also the year in which, on 6 August, Mendel was received into holy orders. He had already been given an ecclesiastical post as curate to a parish attached to the monastery. Nonetheless, he and five of his fellow monks signed a petition for the reform of the monasteries, which pointed out that monks were effectively deprived of civil rights, like patients in a mental hospital. The petition, inevitably, was written by the fiery Klacel, then aged forty. Klacel described the monasteries of the Empire as 'almshouses for poor and short-sighted youths' (did he have Mendel in mind?) who came to know 'enforced isolation' and lived in 'the nadir of degradation'. The petitioners demanded 'free, united, and indivisible citizenship'. The petition found its way to Vienna and there, apparently, was lost, for about a hundred years. It did not turn up again until 1955.

Mendel's curacy in the monastery parish began on 20 July, a fortnight or so before his ordination. His parishioners included the sick at a nearby hospital. He was, as all who knew him agree, a kindly man and well organised, but the priesthood did not suit him. He wanted freedom to teach and to study science. Once more, as so often in times of stress, he fell ill; and in January and February 1849 he was confined to his bed for thirty-four days.

The ever-accommodating Napp rescued him from his misery. In the summer of 1849 he recommended Mendel for a post as supply teacher in maths and classics for the seventh-grade pupils at Znojmo (Znaim) in southern Moravia.

So Mendel became a teacher on 7 October 1849. He had to borrow money to survive at first; but he had a salary nonetheless, of 360 guilders. However, he did not have a professional teaching qualification and a new law demanded that he take an exam at a university to prove his competence. On 16 April 1850 the headmaster at Znojmo applied for Mendel to take the exam to teach natural history at all grades and physics to the lower grades. The head thought highly of him for he had, he said, a 'vivid and lucid method of teaching'.

The exam was difficult; Orel tells us that it would have needed several years of full-time preparation and although Mendel worked hard for it, he was already teaching twenty hours a week. One of his essays, on meteorology, was well received. It was on the properties of air and the origin of wind and discusses the possibility of forecasting weather. (On this, he was at one with Robert Fitzroy, Darwin's captain and companion on the voyage of the *Beagle*, who devoted his last years to weather-forecasting). The examiner, Professor Baumgartner, who was then Minister of Trade, liked what Mendel wrote.

But his second essay, on geology, fell foul of the examiner, one R. Kner; yet the essay survives and seems very fine. Later scholars suggest that Kner was biased against him because he was a monk, but perhaps he was simply too revolutionary. Following Charles Lyell (1797–1875), the geologist who so inspired Charles Darwin, Mendel writes that 'the history of creation is not yet finished': evolutionary change continues to unfold. No modern scientist would deny this, but it offended the mid-nineteenth-century conservative notion that God's work was completed with His creation of man. In the event, Kner concluded that Mendel, one of the great scientists of all time, was not of a standard to teach natural history to sixteen-year-old pupils in the upper grades of a Gymnasium.

So with one success behind him and one failure, Mendel proceeded to further examination in Vienna in August 1850. His examiners in physics again included Baumgartner as well as the great Christian Doppler. Mendel's essay on how to make a permanent magnet impressed them both. Again, though, he came up against the recalcitrant Kner, who took exception to the way he described the classification of mammals. Kner had written a book on this, unbeknown to Mendel, who offered quotes from a different book. So he failed again. This time one of the world's greatest biologists was declared unfit to teach natural history even to the lower grades in the Gymnasium. This failure, Mendel later wrote, was a 'stunning disappointment'.

So he went back to Brno to become a supply teacher at the brand-new Technical School (it had been established in 1850). He did not need specialist qualifications for this, although without the formal certificates he had to make do on half-pay. At the school he was commended by the head and well liked by the pupils and his fellow teachers. He was also admitted as an extraordinary member to the newly established Natural Science Section of Brno's Agricultural Society. The Technical School went on to become an Institute of Technology (in 1867) and then, in 1873, the Technical University. With feudalism now officially buried, there was a bullish demand for more professionalism in agriculture and industry.

Now Mendel found yet another helping hand. Professor Baumgartner, whom he had so impressed in Vienna (and who was presumably irritated by Kner), wrote to Napp to say that Mendel should be allowed to study full-time at the University of Vienna. Napp agreed – perhaps he had already thought of this himself – and on 3 October 1852 he wrote to Baumgartner to say that he had decided to send Mendel for 'higher scientific training' and to this end would 'regret no expense'. In addition, no doubt covering his tracks but perhaps in some exasperation, Napp wrote to the bishop of Brno to say that Mendel would in any case have made a very bad parish priest. The mayor of Znojmo asked Mendel to return, but Napp replied that he had 'other plans'. So we should be grateful to Kner: but for him (and, as we will see, a later examiner called Fenzl) Mendel would surely have whiled away his days as a full-time small-town schoolmaster and never been heard of again. Kner himself seems to have passed into obscurity. His cussedness, however (and Fenzl's), liberated Mendel to become one of the world's most significant experimental scientists. God moves in mysterious ways.

Vienna

So in 1852, aged twenty-nine, Mendel enrolled for full-time study at the University of Vienna; there he came under the sway of physicists and biologists who, by any standards, must be considered outstanding. To a peasant's 'feel' for the importance of gardening and breeding he now added the techniques and insights of modern science. For although the uprising of 1848 did not bring all the changes the reformers wanted, it did transform university education. Thus Vienna had acquired a new faculty of philosophy, which embraced science, and Napp sent Mendel to study physics under Christian Doppler, who became head of the new Physics Institute in January 1850. The physics building was finished in 1851 and was designed to accommodate twelve students, although Mendel was in fact the thirteenth. The course was to last three and a half terms, but Mendel signed up for another, possibly because Doppler died in 1853 (aged only fifty) just as Mendel was beginning his second academic year. A. Ettinghausen (1796–1878) took Doppler's place. Mendel still considered himself to be, above all, a physics teacher; and physics was widely considered to provide a very good grounding both for teachers and for industry. Later, however, he also signed up for maths, chemistry, zoology, botany, the physiology of plants and palaeontology. He dropped zoology, however, because the lessons clashed with physics. The students worked very hard. Maths lectures took place on Saturdays, with physiology practicals on Sundays! For light relief Mendel bought lottery tickets. He was a down-to-earth fellow who had an eye for statistics, the fancy word for 'odds'.

Physics and maths, you may still feel, have little to do with plant breeding and the science of genetics. Yet I suggest that they were crucial: Mendel succeeded in making sense of heredity because he brought the precision and purity of physics to the subject. Naturalists like Darwin, who seem more obviously suited to the task, are too keen to pursue the myriad variations of nature, but the task is to find the underlying order. Both Doppler and Ettinghausen were wonderfully appropriate teachers. Doppler, above all, emphasised economy of experiment; that researchers should seek the most apt (we would say 'elegant') experimental approaches to their problems. Doppler had also published a book of maths, which included a discussion of probability. Ettinghausen had taught at Vienna since 1821 and he too had published books on maths, including a textbook on *Combinatorial Analysis* in 1826. Thus Mendel learnt (as Darwin, for example, never did) the absolute importance of statistics when seeking the patterns that lie within variety.

At the same time, though, and crucially, in Vienna Mendel was introduced to serious botany. It acquired the status of a specialty during his time at the university. Experimental plant anatomy and botany were taught by yet another renowned scientist, Franz Unger, who lived from 1800 to 1870 and taught at Vienna from 1848 to 1866 and who was also an honorary member of the Brno Natural Science Society. Unger was a fine botanist and, like Doppler, emphasised the need for sharp experiments. He was keen on the general approach of *Naturphilosophie*, but also on cytology, the study of cells. He was influenced in this by J. M. Schleiden (1804–81), who introduced the idea of the plant cell in the first place, and wrote *Principles of Scientific Botany* in 1848–50. Schleiden in turn was a pupil of Professor F. Fries (1773–1843), who had emphasised the mathematical philosophy of nature. Schleiden wrote in *Botany*: 'a complete theoretical explanation [of natural phenomena] is possible only on the basis of mathematics, and only in so far as mathematical treatment is feasible'. So even the botany that Mendel learnt had a mathematical pedigree: from Fries, through Schleiden and then Unger. Schleiden also had views on plant hybrids (crossing plants of different kinds) and Mendel's pea experiments were essentially an exercise in hybridisation. As Schleiden wrote in 1848: '– embryo formation [is] determined from both sides [parents] and in a way represents the mean'. All along the line Mendel was being prepared for the task.

Nature is much more confusing than we might choose to think

and it is far harder than it seems to find out anything for certain. Thus it is obvious that plants of any given kind vary, but is the variation due to innate differences or simply to the environment? Is this nature or nurture? The only way you can tell is by growing plants that are genetically identical (to put the matter in modern parlance) in different soils. The matter is easily resolved now that we understand the mechanisms of inheritance and can adjust soil chemistry and other conditions minutely. It was much harder in the mid-nineteenth century. It was certainly known then that plants of a given type vary according to how they are grown, but Unger was able to show that they also vary for reasons *other* than soil type. As we would say today: he was able to reveal the variation that is due to genes. Mendel himself transplanted plants to pin down the source of variation. It is, of course, impossible to make sense of the rules of inheritance if you don't take account of the variations brought about by environment.

Unger was also among the coterie of biologists who were considering evolution well before Charles Darwin wrote *Origin of Species*. In 1851 Unger wrote a book in which he describes extinct plants and talks of life developing from 'lower' forms to 'higher' – until man appeared. He rejected the idea, as did Darwin, that species are constant. 'Who can deny', he said, 'that new combinations arise out of this permutation of vegetation ... which emancipate themselves from the preceding characteristics of the species and appear as a new species?' Unger studied hybridisation, the theme closest to Mendel's own studies, and pointed out that artificial pollination was useful in creating new varieties. He wrote about all this in 1860 and mentioned species which Mendel himself made use of, including various fruit trees and fuchsias. Hugo de Vries (1848–1935), one of the 'discoverers' of Mendel's work, quoted Unger in his own thesis on Mendel: 'It is the task of physiology to reduce the phenomenon of life to known physical and chemical laws.'

However, in the mid-nineteenth-century Germanic tradition (and in the tradition of *Naturphilosophie*) Unger tended to conflate the changes seen from generation to generation in lineages of creatures, what we now call evolution, with the kind of changes seen in an embryo as it develops. Traditional German biology applies the same term to both forms of development: *Entwicklungsgeschichte* (which literally means 'development history'). Unger envisaged that one species might change into another by a kind of 'metamorphosis', comparable with the metamorphosis of a caterpillar into a butterfly. The notion that living creatures unfold the way they do because of their innate properties, like a bud unfolding to become a flower, is also reminiscent of Hegel's view of human history. But Darwin was keen to emphasise that his own vision of 'descent with modification' was quite distinct from the processes of embryonic development. In particular, an embryo is 'programmed' (as we would say today) to develop along a particular path, while, according to Darwin's idea, natural selection could prompt each and every lineage to change in any number of ways. A bear, said Darwin, might become a whale. Because he wanted to avoid confusion, Darwin more or less avoided using the word 'evolution' at all (let alone *Entwicklungsgeschichte*). So Unger's pre-Darwinian view of evolution was quite different from Darwin's. Nevertheless, Unger maintained that creatures change through time. Evolution *in general* was in the air, at least in some places, before Darwin wrote *Origin*; although only Darwin (and a few other visionaries) hit on a plausible mechanism (that of natural selection).

Finally, Unger was a populist, another widespread tradition among mid-nineteenth-century scientists seen in Britain in Michael Faraday, John Tyndall and Thomas Henry Huxley. Unger wrote weekly 'Botanical Letters' in the local newspaper, *Wiener Zeitung* (the 'Vienna Times'); in 1852 he wrote, 'botany . . . will come to be considered the physics of the plant organism', while the plant itself was a 'chemical laboratory, the most ingenious arrangement for the play of physical forces'. Unger knew in his bones that there is order in inheritance and that one day that order would be illuminated by applying the orderly thought processes of the physicist.

But, as always, anyone who thought clearly and radically in the Austro-Hungarian Empire was liable to be slapped down. The editor of the *Wiener Kirchenzeitung* (the 'Vienna Church Times') proclaimed that Unger's evolutionary views were 'scandalous'.

31

The University of Vienna was Catholic and moves were made to sack Unger. He was saved by the Minister of Education, Graf Leo Thun.

Still, Mendel's passion at Vienna was physics. He wanted to show how the workings of the universe can all be traced to 'a small number of laws', laws which should, he felt, be expressed in the language of maths. Of course in his later studies of heredity, though not of the universe at large, he did just this. He did indeed reveal 'a small number of laws' (although these were formally stated not by Mendel but by later writers, based on his results) and his approach was unremittingly mathematical. Many biologists today believe that biology can make robust progress only by applying maths, though the naturalists remain essential because only they can point out the problems in the first place. Maths plays a crucial part in modern evolutionary theory, not least in the guise of game theory; and modern methods of classification, based on the techniques of cladistics, cannot be carried out at a serious level without the statistical analyses of computers. Mendel might be acknowledged not simply as the father of genetics, but as one of the first biologists to show how maths can be used (and must at times be used) to solve the problems of life, just as it does of the physical universe.

Monk, Teacher, Scientist

Mendel finished his studies at Vienna and returned to the monastery at Brno in 1853. He could have resat the teacher's exams at that time, but he did not do so for another two years. No one knows why. Neither did he take a doctorate.

He did, however, probably in the following year, begin his experiments with peas. There is no direct reference to this – a gap exists in the records – but there is a reference to work in progress in 1854; another key year in Mendel's life and in the history of science and of humankind.

How he found time for his experiments is another mystery. For in 1853 he also went to work at the Realschule, which had opened two years earlier, where he taught 18–27 lessons of physics and natural sciences each week to classes of between 62 and 109 pupils. He was (so his pupils recalled when biographers enquired of them after 1900) a fine teacher, with 'blue eyes twinkling in the friendliest fashion through his gold-rimmed glasses'. He used to invite his pupils into the monastery garden; and one visitor from 1856 remembered that Mendel showed him 'the plants with which he was doing crossing experiments, and his beehives', although it is not clear that there were any beehives at that point. Mendel himself did not get any bees until 1870. Mendel is also said to have explained artificial fertilisation to his classes and he led botanical excursions into the countryside around Brno, where he dug up hawkweeds (the *Hieracium*, which were to plague him) to bring back to the garden.

The Realschule had a distinguished teaching staff, who formed the core of the Natural Science Section, which was established in 1849 within the Agricultural Society. Among them was the outstanding physicist A. Zawadski (1798–1868), who again stressed the need for organised research. Zawadksi also had a particular interest in botany, zoology, palaeontology and meteorology, and wrote in 1854 that we must 'learn to see sagaciously, think correctly, and feel warmly and deeply'. Again, this deliberate engagement of thinking and feeling was very much part of the tradition of *Naturphilosophie*. In the same year Zawadski was elected secretary to the committee of the Natural Science Section of the Agricultural Society. That year, too, he lectured on 'The Developmental History of Lower Animals, namely on the copulation of blending of two animals to a single one for the purposes of fertilisation'. This too, as we will see, was a crucial theme for Mendel. At that meeting (in 1854) Mendel was accepted as a full member of the Section, on Zawadski's recommendation. For Mendel, Zawadski was yet another excellent contact.

Meanwhile, the political life of the monastery, and indeed of that of Europe as a whole, remained precarious. After 1848 the forces of conservatism again raised their heads, including the more obdurate wing of the Catholic Church, which in 1855 reached a concordat with the State. The ecclesiastical authorities began a campaign to restore the spiritual life of the monasteries.

Orders came from the Vatican via the archbishop of Prague and so to the bishop of Brno, A. E. Schaffgotsche, to visit the Augustinian monasteries of Bohemia and Moravia. He arrived in Brno in June 1854 to interview the members of the community. In September he reported to the archbishop that Abbot Napp had committed many public offences and was unable to devote sufficient attention to his main responsibility, which was, of course, to run the monastery. In fact, said Schaffgotsche, 'the last ray of spiritual life' had faded away.

The monastery suited Napp and Mendel as it was, but the bishop saw their interest in science and teaching as being in contradiction to their spiritual calling. The list of aberrations by the members of this turbulent monastery was impressive. Nedele had been prevented from teaching because of his 'rationalist' approach to the Bible. Klacel had been sacked as a teacher for his 'pantheist fantasies'. One Friar Rambousek had been seen bathing in a public place 'almost naked'. Mendel had studied science in a secular institution so as to teach it at a Realschule. Yet, said the outraged Schaffgotsche, none of the monks would admit the errors of their ways. Instead, they stood behind their abbot, and even had the gall to ask for a change of rules so that they could spend more time in teaching and science! The pope, said the bishop, should dissolve the monastery. Napp should be pensioned off and the rest of the monks dealt with individually.

Napp, however, was not disposed of so easily. He sent a memorandum to the archbishop proposing that the monastery could be linked to the *Chorherren* Augustinians, which would allow them to continue studying science and teaching it. Like any good lawyer, he appealed to precedent: Pope Sixtus IV had granted comparable exceptions to the Augustinians in 1484. The archbishop acted reasonably swiftly. In 1855 he wrote to all the monasteries, listing their shortcomings. But he said nothing about dissolving Brno. Napp, for his part, agreed to repair the faults and so he, and the monastery, survived (though clearly by the skin of their teeth).

In 1855, too, Mendel went back to Vienna to sit the teachers' exams which he could, presumably, have taken in 1853. Evidently he was nervous and perhaps ill. In any case, he fell foul yet again of an examiner, Professor E. Fenzl (who, incidentally, was the grandfather of Erich von Tschermak, one of the biologists who rediscovered Mendel's genetics research).

To understand Fenzl's objections we must anticipate a thought from Chapter 3. For in the mid-nineteenth century it was not clear to everybody that both parents in a sexual union contributed to the offspring; and it still was not accepted universally that plants were sexual beings. Some, known as 'spermatists', maintained that only the male contributed hereditary material to the offspring. Fenzl was, in effect, a spermatist. At least, he maintained that the plant embryo arose from the pollen tube and that the female cells merely provided nourishment. Mendel, of course, maintained that both parents contributed equally and he made much of this in his published paper of 1866, which contains a definite note of triumph. For the moment, however, Mendel failed his teacher's exams yet again, apparently on this technicality. So he experienced yet another of his mental and physical crises. He returned to the Realschule as well respected as ever, but without the teacher's cerificate he was ranked as a supply teacher, and for the rest of his career he had to survive on half-pay. He also returned to his precious rows of peas as soon as he got back from Vienna; as Orel says, 'he was helping to unravel the very problem which may have led to his examination failure'.

Mendel's unfortunate father, now aged sixty-eight, died on 7 June 1857. Mendel was unable to attend the funeral and the letter that he wrote to his mother to apologise still survives.

Mendel was also active in Brno's Natural Science Society, which achieved independence from the Agricultural Society in 1860, albeit in the face of considerable protest from the latter. He was present at the meeting in December 1859 when Zawadski proposed the breakaway. Napp welcomed the new society, but said he hoped they would continue work on agriculture. Count von Mittrowsky was elected chairman, Zawadski became deputy chairman, while Dr Schwippel, who taught natural history at the Brno Gymnasium, was elected secretary. Johann Nave was treasurer: he was a pupil of Unger's who showed the process of fertilisation in algae, a key discovery. There were 142 founding members, including Mendel, and the number rose to 171 in the following year. The twenty-four honorary members included R. W. Bunsen, Franz Unger, Rudolf Virchow, Friedrich Wöhler and Johannes Purkinje, a distinguished line-up. Mendel, in short, was very well connected. The new Natural Science Society finally achieved autonomy at the end of 1861 and held its first working meeting in January 1862. Plant hybridisation was on the agenda. In February 1865 and again in March Mendel delivered a lecture on plant hybridisation to its monthly meeting. He published his one significant paper, based on those lectures, in 1866.

One last intriguing detail from this middle and main stage of his life. On top of all the teaching (and the work on peas at the monastery) Mendel looked after the natural science collection at the Realschule. So it was that he helped to prepare wall displays on crystallography which were sent to the Great Exhibition in London of 1851. He visited London a year later on a whirlwind tour in which, between 24 July and mid-August, he and his companions also went to Vienna, Salzburg, Munich, Stuttgart, Karlsruhe, Strasbourg and Paris. Many have wondered whether Mendel visited Darwin during his London visit, but there is no evidence that he did, and since Mendel did not speak English, nor Darwin German, it is not clear what such a meeting would have produced. Surely, too, the modest Mendel would have been far too diffident to visit the great man (even if he had had time for the journey out to Kent).

Overall, however, Mendel was extremely well connected and he delivered lectures on his work to what must have been one of the most distinguished societies of scientists in Europe. He also published. Yet no one seems to have registered what he was up to. Abbot Napp was his great champion and patron – he had a greenhouse built especially for Mendel – but even he does not seem to have appreciated his own protégé. Thus he commented in 1862 that hybridisation was still 'a problem for science', yet by this time Mendel's work was well in train. Why did he not realise that Mendel had already solved most of the problems, at least as they appeared at the time?

The Last Years and After

We will leave Mendel's biography here. The background science – the problems he set out to solve in his experiments with peas and the conceptual difficulties that lay in the way – is discussed in Chapter 3. The experiments themselves are discussed in Chapter 4. After 1866, however, Mendel did nothing of lasting significance. Abbot Napp died in 1867 and Mendel took over as head of the monastery. He was not the first choice, but the man who was, the brilliant Tomas Bratranek (1815–84) had become professor of literature at the University of Cracow. As abbot, Mendel spent much of his time locked in dispute with the Catholic bureaucracy.

He retained his interest in science, however, and attempted to take his work on peas through to the next logical stage. As we will discuss again in Chapter 4, Mendel's method, and his strength, was to identify problems that he knew were probably soluble and then move step by step into more difficult areas. He selected peas for study because he knew that of all the plants he might have looked at, peas were likely to give the clearest and most informative results. But he was also aware of the weakness of this approach: that nature cannot be second-guessed and that you cannot simply assume that rules discovered in very simple cases can necessarily be applied to more complex ones. He sought to pin down the universal laws of heredity (if they existed) and he knew that to do this he had at some stage to look at a wide variety of creatures. So, after the work on peas, he looked at patterns of heredity in at least seventeen other species. But apart from what he called 'some minor experiments' with *Phaseolus* beans (which he reported in his paper of 1866), all his later research remained unfinished. The climax was his superb researches into bees, which were technically and conceptually quite brilliant, and which took him up to the time of his death.

He did, however, spend an inordinate amount of time trying to make sense of the hereditary patterns in the hawkweed *Hieracium*. He got nowhere. Now, the reason why is known. *Hieracium*, like some other members of the daisy family Compositae (including the dandelion), is parthenogenic. That is, the next generation arises from an *un*fertilised egg, although to add further confusion

37

in *Hieracium* contact with pollen is required to trigger development. In the end, though, only the female genes are passed on to the offspring. In peas, as with most other plants and animals, both parents contribute to the offspring. Thus the patterns of inheritance Mendel saw in peas simply do not occur in hawkweeds.

In his paper of 1866 Mendel shows that he had a knack of identifying such intractable problems and steering around them. His instinct surely told him that there was something peculiar and for the time being incomprehensible about *Hieracium*, and he must have realised that persistence was a waste of time. Good scientists know when to retreat and fight another day. So why did he waste so much effort on this obvious anomaly?

The answer is that he was encouraged to do so by the Swiss botanist Carl Nägeli, with whom he corresponded for several years after 1867. This correspondence was made known to the world in 1905 by Carl Correns, one of the scientists who unearthed Mendel's 1866 paper. It reveals Mendel's rising frustration (and tells us a great deal more about his ideas). It is abundantly obvious, however, that Nägeli missed the point. Quite simply, he was not paying attention.

Mendel was not a fool: far from it. Neither was he a coward, as he showed in his many political forays. So why did he continue this correspondence with the astonishingly perverse Nägeli? Many have suggested that Mendel simply did not know anyone else of comparable stature, but we have seen that this explanation will not do. Napp was an outstanding figure and virtually Mendel's patron. He lived until the pea research was finished, although he does not seem to have realised its full significance. Through his membership of the Brno Natural Science Society, Mendel knew just about everybody. In the next chapter we will meet the great Rudolf Virchow and the incomparable Johannes Purkinje; both were honorary members at Brno. We will also meet J. M. Schleiden, a key figure. He was Unger's teacher and Unger was Mendel's teacher. Schleiden lived until 1881, and so was around for almost all of Mendel's life. Unger himself seems to have been a much more adventurous thinker than Nägeli, so why not talk to him? Johann Nave (more of him later, too) was a friend of Mendel's, as was A. Makowsky, who taught at the Realschule from 1858 to 1859, published on zoology and botany and visited Mendel in 1865 to discuss ideas when the work on peas was already more or less complete. Then there was J. Kalmus, who was a student of Purkinje's; and C. Theimer, who studied hybrids and presided at meetings of the Natural Science Society in 1865 and 1868 when Mendel talked about crossing peas and hawk-weeds. All these were obvious confidants, people to bounce ideas off, just as Darwin did with Joseph Hooker and T. H. Huxley. In short, Mendel knew many excellent scientists and was only a step away from the greatest. Why, apparently, did none of them see the significance of his work? Why did he waste so much time on Nägeli?

Well, in his time Nägeli was highly regarded, and among his most fervent admirers was Unger himself. Nägeli had also studied with Schleiden in 1842, at Jena. He had done excellent work in plant physiology. He had shown how plants grow, how the cells of a plant divide at the apex of the shoot and roots. This might not seem relevant to studies of heredity, but as we will see plant science was much more all of a piece in the mid-nineteenth century than it is now. Nägeli's was exciting work; showing how the common, everyday phenomena of plant growth are under-pinned by the manoeuvrings of cells. Unger predicted that Nägeli would penetrate 'deep into that labyrinth which no eye has yet seen' (although, as Orel comments, it was Mendel who truly did this). To Unger, the future seemed to belong to Nägeli. Perhaps – probably – Unger directed Mendel towards Nägeli. Perhaps Mendel felt that he could not abandon Nägeli without offending Unger.

So perhaps, in the end, it was Mendel's natural politeness, his peasant diffidence, and the fiercely hierarchical structure of German science that did for him. Some men were perceived to be great – Virchow, Schleiden, even Nägeli – and some were not. Mendel, for whatever reason, was not. He hadn't got a doctorate; he had failed his teacher's exams. Nowadays, at least in Britain and the United States, young scientists are expected to stand up for themselves. They have to fight their corner. The young James Watson, who together with Francis Crick worked out the three-dimensional structure of DNA, is the modern archetype (as he describes himself in his autobiographical *Double Helix*). But in nineteenth-century Germany young scientists without formal professional status were expected to defer; and that, apparently, is what Mendel did. Perhaps in the end nobody took any notice simply because, nice fellow that he was, he had no professional or social standing. He in turn seems to have sacrificed his career for a social nicety. Stranger things have happened.

But although Mendel's extraordinary work was forgotten for a time, personally he was not. As abbot he was a member of the Moravian Diet and attended many a meeting on local social matters. He was a popular teacher who stayed in touch with his pupils. So those who tried to reconstruct his life and work – in the early days, including Carl Correns, Erich von Tschermak and William Bateson – did find people who remembered him. But they remembered, mainly, his institutional work and personal character. Those who helped with the recovery process included Mendel's nephews, Alois and Ferdinand Schindler, whom Mendel had helped through their education.

Alois Schindler gave a lecture on Mendel in 1902 when the first memorial plaque was unveiled. This was at the fire station at Hynčice and mostly commemorates Mendel's initiative in raising money for the equipment. Nonetheless, because there was so little to go on, Bateson drew on this speech when writing a brief life on Mendel in a 1902 paper in which he gives an account of heredity in animals. Bateson also visited Brno in 1904 to find out more, but could find no record of the experiments. His visit aroused the procurator of the Augustinian monastery, one A. Matousek, to collect what documents there were referring to Mendel and to build a small Mendel museum. Orel does not record whether Matousek was aware of Mendel's true significance before Bateson's visit, although Mendel had died only twenty years earlier.

The man who did most to restore the world's knowledge of Mendel was his biographer H. Iltis (1882–1952), who found documents relating to his time at Vienna university. In 1943 another Brno scientist, O. Richter, criticised Iltis for presenting Mendel as a free-thinking scientist and an admirer of Darwin. Richter, in contrast, underlined Mendel's qualities as a cleric. His paper was published during the Nazi occupation of what was then Czechoslovakia.

By 1948 Stalin's communists were firmly installed in Czechoslovakia and Stalinist biology was dominated by Trofim Lysenko, who rejected Mendel's ideas on political grounds. Mendel had shown, after all, that the way an organism turns out is strongly influenced by its parentage: the begotten resemble their begetters. But the communist State, with its simplified and coarsened version of Marx's ideas, needed to argue that people can be shaped by their environment, which to their minds meant by the will of the government. The Mendelian notion that organisms, including people, were restrained by their biological inheritance was anathema. In a series of crude experiments Lysenko contrived to show that wheat is just as amenable to environmental manipulation as people are. Effectively he contrived to show that wheat could survive Russian winters if given a sharp talking to. It couldn't, of course, and under his guidance the harvests failed.

The 'conflict' between the long-dead Mendel and the all-too extant Lysenko was a grotesque example of the 'nature versus nurture' debate, which has rumbled through biology and philosophy for centuries and (grotesquely) still does. We will look at it in later chapters. Meanwhile Lysenko and Stalin between them demonstrate that 'environmental determinism' can be at least as horrible as any kind of 'biological determinism'. In truth (as Mendel well knew) organisms are a dialogue between their 'nature' (underpinned by their genes) and their 'nurture' (their environment). Lysenko's insistence that environment is all cost the lives of many thousands of Russians as their crops perished in the snows. It also showed how badly science and politics mix and that, in the end, politicians are obliged to work within the confines of the real universe. They cannot simply decree nature to be different, in the way that King Canute once tried to rule the tides (although Canute, unlike Lysenko, was expressly trying to show that nature could *not* be overruled). Lysenko's nonsense also encouraged Stalin to ban the otherwise burgeoning science of genetics. As a consequence, the Mendel museum was closed down in 1950; most of the Czech monasteries were closed at the same time, so the museum was caught in two ways. Fortunately, most of the documents and instruments from Mendel's time were rescued.

Iltis himself went to the United States before the Second World War, taking copies of documents relating to Mendel which are now at the Museum of Natural History at the University of Illinois at Urbana–Champaign, which may not be particularly well known to the world at large but has produced some fine biology. He died in 1952. In 1965 the Mendelianum in the Moravian Museum in Brno published 120 documents and photographs relating to Mendel – a hundred years after he published his paper.

So that, in outline, is Mendel's biography: a bizarre tale, which somehow manages to encapsulate much of Europe's history: the end of feudalism, the rise of modern agriculture and industry, science as philosophy, science as the generator and handmaiden of technologies, science versus religion, science versus the State, ideology versus ideology, the rise and fall of dictatorships. Mendel came of 'peasant stock' right enough, but he was not a country bumpkin, nor was he a primitive. His family was supportive, he was highly educated and he moved among the greatest scientists of Europe. Science was developing apace on deep (if sometimes confusing to modern eyes) philosophical foundations. The philosophy of science included the powerful notion that the universe is guided by laws and that these laws can be expressed mathematically; and at least some biologists were beginning to realise that the rigour of physics and maths should be applied to the problems of living creatures as well as to the physical world. Many scientists, too, including Mendel's own teachers – Doppler, Ettinghausen, Unger – were stressing the supreme importance of elegant experiment. Mendel took all this in. At the same time, he was steeped in agriculture willy-nilly: through his own family, through society at large, and through the particular inclinations of his monastery at Brno. In short, he seems made for the task. How that task appeared in the mid-nineteenth century, we will explore in Chapter 3.

3

Breeders, Scientists and Philosophers

Isaac Newton said in the seventeenth century that if he had seen further into the laws of nature than others, then it was because he had 'stood on the shoulders of giants'. Mendel could have said the same when he began his work with peas in the mid-1850s. As we have seen, there had been key advances in the philosophy of science – stress was laid increasingly on the need to quantify and to carry out experiments with a chance of producing a solution. In this chapter I will look more closely at the new ideas in science and, equally important, in the crafts of breeding. But in the mid-nineteenth century ideas that are now known to be good and accurate were mixed in more or less equal measure with notions that were wrong or hopelessly confused and yet were argued with equal vigour. We should look at the confusions, too, to show the emerging truths in proper perspective.

But what was the problem? At first sight heredity seems perfectly straightforward. Like begets like. Cats have kittens, women have babies, oak trees spatter the woods with acorns that become, miraculously, a new generation of oak trees. It is, though, as Niels Bohr said about particle physics: if you think it's easy, you haven't understood the problem. To begin with, the whole business of heredity has several threads to it. How, first of all, does any creature actually produce offspring at all? What are the mechanics of reproduction? This, in turn, has at least two discrete components: how the parents make an embryo, and how the embryo grows and develops to become the finished creature. Then there is the more abstract matter: how does the parent

43

ensure that the offspring does resemble itself? As we would say in modern parlance, what is the nature of the 'information' that passes from generation to generation?

Now that we understand each of these threads, up to a point, we can tease them apart. They are studied in separate university departments. How eggs and sperm are made, and come together, and how the resulting embryo is succoured, are the substance of reproductive physiology. How the embryo grows and develops is embryology, or 'developmental biology'. How hereditary information is passed from generation to generation is genetics. But before the details were understood these three areas of study were commonly conflated. This was far from stupid. Nature *might*, for example, make copies of creatures by taking a fragment from each part of the parent's body and cobbling them all together to form a new individual. In such a case the business of reproduction and the business of heredity would effectively be the same. There would be no genes providing instruction on how to make flesh: the flesh itself might be passed on. That is not how things happen, as it turns out, at least not in sexual reproduction as practised by human beings (although it is similar in some ways to the asexual reproductive strategy of corals or strawberries). But that *might* have been the mechanism. In the absence of better information, it seemed perfectly reasonable to study reproductive physiology, embryology and heredity all together. Such conflation, however, did not make life any less confusing.

Anyway, let us ask how 'like begets like' as the problem still appeared in the mid-nineteenth century and thus as Mendel confronted it. Not until we perceive the problems can we appreciate the answer, and be dazzled, not disappointed, by its simplicity.

Who Contributes What

Consider first of all what we now take for granted. All creatures are divided into two sexes: male and female. Both contribute to the offspring, and indeed, barring a few details that need not delay us for the moment, they contribute equally. Typically, the female provides a (relatively) big, yolky egg, and the male provides a spermatozoon, or some variation thereof: always tiny, usually motile. Both carry hereditary information. The two 'gametes' (female egg and male sperm) combine to form a one-celled embryo (technically known as a 'zygote'), which divides and divides again in careful choreography to form an embryo which grows and unfolds to become a facsimile, or near facsimile, of its parents: combining features of both. In these enlightened days of sex education every seven–year–old could tell you all this. Plants do the same kinds of thing in principle, although in seed plants the male gamete is cocooned within the protective pollen.

But if we didn't have the benefit of four hundred years of science, how much of this *should* be taken for granted? Almost none. At least, we could be sure that most of the creatures we are most familiar with, including us, are divided into male and female; that both are required for reproduction; and (in the creatures we are most familiar with) that the males must impregnate the females with semen, which is conspicuous enough. But then the difficulties begin.

Is it really obvious, for example, that both parents contribute to the offspring? Even if they do, *what* do they contribute? Some scientists, in not so ancient times, proposed that the sperm alone provides the hereditary information for the next generation and that the egg with its yolk merely provides nourishment; a hamper for life's journey. Others stated with equal vehemence that the egg provided all that was really necessary and that the sperm merely triggered development. The former were 'spermatists' and the latter 'ovists'. Of course, before microscopes were developed in the seventeenth century nobody had seen a sperm: they had seen the seminal fluid, right enough, but not the all-important whirling cells within, nor had they seen a mammalian egg; so before that, this debate was conducted in more abstract terms.

The microscope would surely resolve this issue. Well, in seventeenth-century Holland Anton van Leeuwenhoek (1632–1723), who made hundreds of microscopes in his long life and is generally acknowledged as the first great microscopist, did see sperm within his own semen and duly became a spermatist. Meanwhile in Italy Marcello Malpighi (1628–94) observed an entity in an unfertilised bird's egg, which he took to be the germ of the next generation, and became an ovist. The spermatists and ovists may sound, from this twenty-first-century vantage-point, like Jonathan Swift's Little Enders and Big Enders, who attacked their boiled eggs from different ends and sought to resolve the matter by going to war. But Leeuwenhoek and Malpighi were both great biologists. The question they were asking – who donates what? – just wasn't easy. Anyway, even if both parents did contribute hereditary material to the offspring, should we assume that they contribute equally? If so, why do children sometimes resemble one parent more than the other? Why is a son, sometimes, the 'spitting image' of his mother, or the daughter that of her father? Might it be that on different occasions each parent might contribute a different amount?

In the end, as is so often the case, the reality has proved more complex than anyone might have supposed. The sperm does indeed provide hereditary material (what we now call genes), but it also triggers development, in the way the ovists suggested, in the process known as 'activation'. In some plants the pollen may activate the egg without contributing genes. This is true of dandelions and hawkweeds, which is why Mendel could make no sense of hawkweeds when Nägeli persuaded him to study them. In all known cases the egg does of course provide hereditary information in the form of genes, but it also provides nourishment in the form of yolk. This is true even in mammals, before the embryo implants in the wall of the uterus.

Whether we are spermatists or ovists or concede that both contribute, we must ask what form the hereditary material takes. Here again there were two clear schools. The 'preformationists' believed that the sperm (or the egg) contained a complete little replica of the offspring. There are seventeenth-century pictures of spermatozoa with little foetuses coiled up in the head. Laurence Sterne lampoons this notion in *Tristram Shandy*, as he muses in his freewheeling way whether onanists commit mass murder as they scatter their seed upon the ground, each one a primordial human being. Perhaps some microscopist saw such a creature: the power of wishful thinking is wonderful. Leeuwenhoek described spermatozoa as *Samentierchen*, 'little animals' (or 'animalcules' as the expression is often quaintly rendered). Others maintained that the egg, or the sperm, or both, merely contributed something like modelling clay, to be fashioned into an embryo. This was the notion of 'epigenesis'. Aristotle, writing in the fifth and fourth centuries BC, was the first known author to suggest that both parents contribute to the hereditary make-up of the offspring, and he perforce was an epigenicist. He envisaged that the male contribution of 'modelling clay' took the form of semen, while the female's contribution was contained in the menstrual blood. Semen was also derived from blood, he thought, from 'sanguineous nutriment'. This seems a quaint idea, yet in the absence of better information it was perfectly reasonable.

In the early nineteenth century new ideas arose, which made it possible to think in modern terms. In particular, the further development of the microscope gave rise to 'cell theory' – the idea that big creatures like animals and plants are compounded from many tiny cells. The rise of cell theory is an example of what, in the 1960s, the American philosopher of science Thomas Kuhn called 'a paradigm shift': a sea-change in the way that scientists look at the world. (In reality, said Kuhn, all significant progress in science is made in jerks, in such 'paradigm shifts'.)

Malpighi set biology on the road to cell theory. At least, he showed the existence of the capillaries, the fine blood vessels in the body tissues which run between the arteries and the veins – the discovery that rounded off William Harvey's vision of blood circulation. But the final insight had to wait until the 1830s. In 1837 the great Czech (as he would now be called) Johannes Evangelista Purkinje (1787–1869) observed a general parallel between the structure of animal and plant tissue, both of which seemed to be compartmentalised. Then in 1838 the German botanist Matthias Schleiden (1804–81) proposed that all plant tissue is composed of nucleated cells, and in the following year his compatriot Theodor Schwann (1810–82) suggested that plant *and* animal tissue were compounded of cells. Indeed Schwann proposed in *Mikroskopische Untersuchungen* ('Microscopical Researches') that 'cellular formation' might be 'a universal principle for the formation of organic substances'. You may recall that Purkinje was an honorary member of the Natural Science

47

Society at Brno, of which Mendel was a founder member. He visited the monastery at Brno in 1850 and Mendel's close friend, Klacel, took him on a conducted tour. Schleiden, you will of course remember, taught Unger, who was Mendel's teacher in Vienna. Mendel was very well connected.

Schwann proposed that the individual cells simply condensed out of 'nutrient liquid', like crystals of salt precipitating out of a rock pool, but this misconception was soon put to rights. In 1841 the Polish–German anatomist Robert Remak (1815–65) described how cells divide and in 1855 the German pathologist Rudolf Carl Virchow (1821–1902) coined the dogma *omnis cellula e cellula* – 'all cells come from cells'. In other words, the vast battalions of cells of which a mouse or a sheep or a human being is composed (or an oak tree or a moss or a mushroom) each derive from a single, initial cell, dividing and redividing. The German role in this thread of life science is obvious: Schleiden, Schwann, Remak, Virchow; and German-speaking Mendel was close to the action. Virchow, too, was an honorary member of the Natural Science Society of Brno.

How, though, does the single, initial cell – the fertilised egg – multiply to form an entire, multicellular organism, like a sheep or a human being? What happens? What are the underlying mechanisms? Alongside German-based cytology grew German-based embryology. At first this new discipline was perceived as a branch of anatomy, but it was established as a specialty in its own right by the German-Estonian Karl Ernst von Baer (1792–1876). In 1827 in *De ovi mammalium et hominis genesi* ('On the Origin of the Mammalian and Human Ovum') von Baer described how all mammals, including human beings, develop from eggs. He showed, too, how the different organs form as the embryo develops, in which order they arise, and from which tissues. He also established comparative embryology, revealing the similarities and differences in the development of different creatures.

How, though, is the zygote formed in the first place? This is the key issue. This is the point at which presumably the parents pass on their inheritance to the offspring. The answer came straight out of cell theory and again was revealed in the 1830s. Thus in 1839 one M. Barry described how he had observed a spermatozoan penetrating a mammalian egg. This was a truly remarkable finding, although perhaps too remarkable because many people disputed it. Purkinje accepted the observation, however, and drew it to the attention of his friend, the physiologist R. Wagner, of whom more later.

Then in 1855 the German botanist Nathanael Pringsheim (1823–94) showed the same phenomenon in *Oedogonium*, a freshwater alga. Algae are primitive plants which produce motile gametes – sperm – rather than pollen, as in flowering plants. Mendel had already begun his own experiments at this point; and in 1858 his friend Johann Nave lectured on Pringsheim's work at the Brno Natural Science Society. Again, Mendel was in touch.

So the most important elements of cell theory were established before Mendel began his great breeding work in the 1850s, or soon after. Surely, then, most of the earlier confusions must already have been cleared up? Sperm and egg were known to be cells. They had been seen to fuse, both in animals and plants. The one-cell embryos to which they gave rise had been shown to divide, and divide again, to form the finished, multi-celled creature. There could be no more confusion.

Could there not? Nowadays we've all seen eggs and sperms combining on many a TV documentary. Students observe this under the microscope. In vitro fertilisation (IVF) is almost commonplace. But was Barry's report of fertilisation in mammals, the observation of one biologist with a shiny brass nineteenth-century microscope, really enough to carry the day? Closed-mindedness is the bane of science, as of every other human pursuit; but it is certainly proper to be sceptical. Besides, even if a new life did begin with the fusion of egg and sperm, what does this really demonstrate? Eggs are much bigger than spermatozoa, after all, so they might in reality contribute more to the offspring. On the other hand, they might simply provide nourishment, just as the spermatists maintained. Or the sperms might simply be triggering development, as the ovists thought. The general lesson is that in science one observation does not shift a paradigm all by itself, nor should it.

Indeed, as we have seen, Mendel failed his final attempt to qualify as a teacher in 1855, when he came up against an essentially spermatist examiner, E. Fenzl. Mendel's dissertation included a passage on the fertilisation of flowers. By then the cellular process was known: after the pollen lands on the stigma it sends out a 'pollen tube' that runs down the style into the ovary and fuses with the ovum. But Fenzl, who was clearly a die-hard, maintained that the new embryo grew entirely from the pollen tube; that the female cells in the ovary merely provided succour. His obduracy shows that the ancient arguments were by no means resolved.

These, then, are some of the uncertainties that surrounded even the most basic mechanism: the fusion of a male sperm with a female egg to create a zygote that contains elements of both. If the mechanics were different, then the rules and the patterns of heredity would also be different. Presumably the patterns of inheritance would be less consistent than they are if the two parents contributed differing amounts to the offspring on different occasions. But then, as all breeders of crops and livestock knew full well – and indeed, as all human beings know who have ever looked at their fellows and at other living creatures – the patterns of inheritance seem extremely inconsistent even as things are.

Like Begets Like – But Only Up to a Point

To be sure, women produce baby humans and cats produce baby cats. But although the offspring resemble their parents and each other, the resemblance is never exact, although it may be almost exact in the case of 'identical twins'. Variation is an obvious fact and one that requires explanation.

When two animals or plants that are slightly different are crossbred, or 'crossed', or 'hybridised', then we expect the resulting 'hybrids' to vary, both from each other and from the parent. But sometimes two parents which look the same, at least with respect to particular characters, also produce offspring that differ from themselves and each other. For example, a man and woman who both have brown eyes might produce a child with blue eyes. Worse: the quality of blue-eyedness might disappear from a family of brown-eyed people for generations at a stretch and then suddenly pop up. The overall distribution of blue-eyedness is, as biologists tend to say, 'spotty': Your grandparents might all have brown eyes, but your great-grandmother, and your Auntie Gertie, and your cousin George, have blue eyes. We need not assume double-dealing, or evict the blue-eyed lodger. That's just the way that heredity works.

Similarly, two blue-flowered garden lupins when crossed are liable to produce offspring with flowers of many different colours. Unexpected variation in colour is one of the attractions of traditional lupins, resplendent in their cottage gardens. On the other hand, the offspring of two blue-eyed human beings will *always* have blue eyes; and the offspring of two white-flowered garden peas will *always* have white flowers. Yellow-flowered garden peas, however, may produce at least some white-flowered offspring, just as brown-eyed humans may have some blue-eyed offspring. But it is possible at least in theory to identify some 'strains' or 'lineages' of yellow-flowered garden peas that *only* produce yellow-flowered offspring, and some brown-eyed people who *only* have brown-eyed children. The lineages that consistently produce offspring with a particular character are said to be 'true-breeding'. As will be revealed in Chapter 4, the rules that enable some lines to 'breed true', while others who may also look the same may have varied offspring, are actually very simple. You probably know those rules already. My point here, however, is that until you know the rules the facts of the case are extremely confusing.

Such variation, however, is only half of the matter. For sometimes, as all breeders know (and any large family of human beings is unfortunately likely to know), offspring are produced who look nothing like their parents or their siblings. Animals are sometimes born with strange deformities, and then were tradition-ally known as 'sports'. Children may be similarly afflicted, and are sometimes born with peculiar diseases. Such pathologies may result in various ways, which again are obvious when the rules are known. When such anomalies seem simply to drop from the sky, however, they muddy already difficult waters even further.

Then again, *some* anomalies that are present at birth are indeed

51

caused by the hereditary factors which we now call 'genes'; but some are not. Some may be caused by accidents in the womb, and some by pathogens that are passed from generation to generation ('vertical transmission') like congenital syphilis, which features powerfully in nineteenth-century literature. Not all such heritable pathogens are unremittingly evil, however. In the seventeenth century the Dutch developed a craze for tulips that at least matched England's South Sea Bubble and the present zeal for dot-com companies. Striped tulips were especially highly favoured. Stripiness is brought about not by particular genes, but by viruses, transmitted from bulb to bulb. It is a temporary feature: as the generations pass the infection takes hold, the plant is weakened, and the breeder must begin again. The seventeenth-century breeders did not know about viruses, but they knew that stripes were a strange character that followed its own rules, and they produced new lines of striped tulips not by the normal sexual methods but by exposing bulbs to infected lines. To the observer, however, stripiness is merely another 'inherited' character. All of this – peculiar characters arising out of the blue, other characters apparently passed on by peculiar rules – muddied the waters still further.

Then, as every breeder knows, and as all human tribes reflect in their folklore, some matings and marriages have a good outcome, while others are much less satisfactory. Again the underlying rules are simple; but again, before the rules were known, the picture was eminently confusing. Thus, in general, a fine, lusty male animal mated with a good robust female seem likely to produce exemplary offspring. Often, indeed, this is the case. But if the lusty male is related to the robust female, if indeed they are brother and sister, then their offspring could be a disaster. This would be an example of 'inbreeding' and (almost) everyone knows that 'inbreeding' is bad. It leads to what modern geneticists and traditional breeders alike call 'inbreeding depression'. Most human tribes have powerful taboos against the incestuous matings that lead to inbreeding. Oedipus tore out his own eyes when he realised he had inadvertently bedded his own mother. Aristocratic families who practise inbreeding to avoid contamination with commoners' 'blood', or, more to the point, to keep the wealth and power in the family, are commonly plagued with diseases of an inherited nature like the haemophilia and porphyria that ran among the many relatives of Queen Victoria. Many a family of inbred aristocrats has simply died out. In past times, before modern breeding protocols were developed, inbreeding scuppered most attempts to breed animals in zoos. Breeders, in short, are in a constant state of tension. They want to cross the best with the best. But the best individuals in any one population are quite likely to be closely related, one to another. But if relatives are mated, then this is liable to lead, sooner or later, to inbreeding depression; offspring with many kinds of enfeeblement.

So what's the answer? Obviously, to mate creatures who both have desirable qualities but are not closely related. Any kind of mating between non-relatives can be called 'outbreeding'. If the two potential parents belong to distinct 'varieties' or 'breeds' then such outbreeding is called 'hybridisation'. Sometimes the 'hybrids' produced by such matings are extremely fine, stronger and more intelligent than either parent. Then they are said to partake of 'hybrid vigour'.

Again, all this has been well known to breeders of crops and livestock for hundreds of years, probably for thousands. Hybrid vigour is widely recognised in human societies, too. The offspring of inter-racial marriages tend to have disparaging names, like 'mulatto', 'half-breed', 'half-caste', or 'Cape-coloured', implying 'neither one thing nor the other'. On the other hand, such 'mulattos' have often been disturbingly athletic and quick-witted. Similarly, the stable lad who bears an intriguing resemblance to the lord of the manor and is significantly more alert than any of the legitimate heirs is a stock character in many a pulp novel.

Again, though, all is not so simple: some hybridisations work very well and some do not. Thus matings between greyhounds and other breeds of hound produce wonderfully vigorous offspring known as 'lurchers'. Many a working dog – gun-dog, sheep-dog, what you will – was traditionally produced by judicious crossing of 'pure-bred' or 'pedigree' parents of different breeds. But some inter-breed hybridisations produce most unfortunate results. St Bernards and Great Danes are a sad mismatch. Nowadays the reason is clear. St Bernards are big because they produce a great deal of growth hormone, which makes them generally heavy and floppy. Great Danes are big simply because they have genes that produce long limb bones. St Bernards are *adapted* to a high output of growth hormone and are not distressed by it. They merely become large (if a bit lethargic). But the hybrid offspring of St Bernards and Great Danes produce excess growth hormone, yet lack the means to cope with it, and their general physiology is awry. In short, some exercises in outbreeding work very well, and lead to 'hybrid vigour'; but some have a poor outcome, leading to 'outbreeding depression'.

This brings us to an issue which taxed breeders and philosophers – and theologians – alike for many centuries, and still causes confusion among non-biologists (while even biologists continue to argue): the difference between 'varieties' (or 'breeds' or 'races') and 'species'.

Again, at first sight, the issue seems simple enough. Few of us have any problem with the idea that St Bernards, cocker spaniels and chihuahuas are all variations on a theme of domestic dog, different breeds of the same species, known to scientists as *Canis familiaris*; while wolves, though related, are of a different species, *Canis lupus*. Similarly (though somewhat more complicatedly), we can accept that cabbage, kale, cauliflowers and Brussels sprouts are all variations on a theme of the wild cabbage *Brassica oleracea* (although, of course, each of those main categories – cabbage, kale, cauliflower and sprouts – is further subdivided into the various seedsman's 'varieties'); while the turnip, though related, belongs to a different species, *Brassica rapa*. The principle, at least, is easy enough to grasp.

On what, though, is this principle based? In Mendel's day, species were still defined largely by what they looked like. As he said in his paper of 1866, by 'the strictest definition . . . only those individuals belong to a species which under precisely the same circumstances display similar characteristics'. But he must have known that definitions based on appearance do not get us very far. For St Bernards and spaniels, though casually classed within the same species, look as different as, say, a moose and a roe-deer (which are clearly placed in different species). On the other hand, some dogs, like Alsatians and huskies, look very like wolves; at least, their resemblance to wolves is much more striking than to, say, bulldogs. But again, huskies and bulldogs (like spaniels and St Bernards) are placed in the same species. Yet some wild creatures which are placed in different species are almost impossible to tell apart. Chiffchaffs and willow warblers seem almost the same, apart from their song. This example would have been well known to mid-nineteenth-century European naturalists. Many more such pairings have come to light in the twentieth century. North American ornithologists now recognise whole series of different owls that are almost identical and were formerly placed within one species. The owls recognise each other by their calls. Professor Simon Bearder, of Brook University in Oxford, studies bushbabies in West Africa and seems to find new species on every visit. Again, the different types look much the same but recognise each other by their calls (and DNA studies typically show huge differences between them). Owls and bushbabies are both nocturnal: to them appearance doesn't matter, but voice does. Why, then, do modern biologists insist that two creatures that look very different may be of the same species, while others that look almost identical are in different species?

The important point has to do with reproductive barriers. The standard twentieth-century notion, generally ascribed to the great German-American zoologist Ernst Mayr, is that two creatures will generally be ascribed to the same species if they can mate together sexually to produce 'fully viable' offspring. They are placed in separate species if their offspring are not fully viable. Arab horses and English Thoroughbreds, two breeds within the domestic species *Equus caballus*, produce excellent and much-prized offspring, both lithe and tough. But when *Equus caballus* stallions tup the mares of *Equus africanus*, the ass, then the result is a mule: a tough animal, right enough, but sexually sterile. A sexually sterile creature is clearly not 'fully viable'. If the two extant species of camel are crossed – *Camelus ferus* (or *bactrianus*), the two-humped Bactrian camel, with the one-humped *Camelus dromedarius*, the Arabian camel or dromedary – then the female offspring are fertile, but the male offspring are sterile. If camels are mated with horses (perish the thought) then there can be no offspring at all. The boundaries are too great.

Again, all this seems clear enough. Matings between different varieties (or breeds or races) of the same species, known as '*intra*specific' matings, produce 'fully viable' offspring. Matings between different species, '*inter*specific' matings, generally produce no offspring at all, but at best produce offspring that are not fully viable and indeed may be sexually sterile.

Yet there are complications, many of which, again, would have been well known to mid-nineteenth-century breeders and biologists. For one thing, intraspecific matings (between varieties of the same species) do not always produce 'fully viable' offspring. We have seen one example. The offspring of St Bernards and Great Danes are a sorry sight. Horticulturalists, however, would have been much more concerned with a phenomenon that occurs within many plants, including apples and plums. Such species go to great lengths to avoid matings between individuals which are too closely related to each other; in other words (to put the matter anthropomorphically) they seek to avoid inbreeding. To this end, they have developed 'specific mating barriers', which prevent mating between two individuals of the same variety or closely related varieties. To produce a crop, apple-growers have to plant individuals from different, but compatible, varieties side by side. So here we have mating barriers *within* species.

On the other hand, various pairs of discrete species will mate perfectly well together if given the chance. Domestic dogs and wild wolves will mate, given the opportunity, and the offspring are often formidable (and perfectly fertile). The wild cat of Europe, *Felis silvestris*, is tending to disappear as a distinct species because of excessive interbreeding with feral domestic cats, *Felis catus*. In zoos tigers and lions have often mated and the offspring are perfectly fertile. In the wild we often find 'hybrid zones' at the boundaries where the ranges of different species overlap. Thus carrion crows in general live south of a line that passes through Edinburgh, while hooded crows live north of that line. Where the two ranges meet, in Edinburgh itself, we find *inter*specific hybrids. Similarly, in a line running north–south through central Europe, we find a hybrid zone between the fire-bellied toads that live to the west and the yellow-bellied toads that live to the east.

In short, the standard twentieth-century view of a species

works well enough for most purposes, much better than any definition based on appearance, but there are still conditional clauses. In practice, wolves do not mate with domestic dogs if other wolves are available. Wolves *prefer* wolves. Similarly, tigers do not mate with lions in the wild. Their ranges *do* overlap in the wild; or at least they sometimes did until recent centuries, for although tigers do not live in Africa, there were plenty of lions in Asia and Europe well into historical times (and they still live wild in the Gir Forest of India). But in the wild each sticks to its own kind. As the South African biologist Hugh Patterson put it: animals of the same species recognise each others' mating signals, and certainly prefer them to the signals of other species.

Admittedly, hooded crows and carrion crows do interbreed in the wild. But the hybrid offspring have not spread into the home ranges of either parent species, suggesting that the hybrids do not compete well either with the pure-bred hooded crows to the north or with the pure-bred carrion crows to the south. So by the standards of crows, the hybrids are not 'fully viable'. In human prehistory, it's clear that our own Cro-Magnon ancestors lived side by side with the Neanderthals in Europe for at least 10,000 years. We need not doubt that they *could* have interbred and possibly did so from time to time. Yet their fossil remains suggest that the two kinds of human mostly kept themselves to themselves. They recognised mating barriers even if we cannot easily see what they were. So although modern humans and Neanderthals could have mated perfectly well together, in practice it seems they did not. Since in practice they did not then they should be treated as separate species. The same applies to the difference between, say, huskies, which are *Canis familiaris*, and wolves, which are *Canis lupus*.

The biological complications are not quite exhausted, however. For sometimes individuals which clearly belong to different species do mate together to produce offspring that are not only fully viable, but are in fact a new species: able to mate perfectly well with each other, but not able to mate successfully with either parent. We will look at the underlying mechanism in Chapter 4. (To anticipate, this results when chromosomes simply double, without ensuing cell division, to produce a 'polyploid'.) This

57

phenomenon is quite common in plants, though rare in animals. Mid-nineteenth-century breeders would not have known how this occurs, but they might well have known that the swede, placed in the species *Brassica napa*, is probably a hybrid between the cabbage, *Brassica oleracea*, and the turnip, *Brassica rapa*. Swedes seem to have appeared, apparently spontaneously, in seventeenth-century Bohemia.

All of this discussion brings us to an issue that was of key significance in the mid-nineteenth century, with connotations that ran from the practical crafts of breeding on the one hand through to the deepest reaches of theology on the other. Are the distinctions between species absolute, or is a species merely a variety writ large? Is it possible to turn one species into another? Can any one species divide to produce more than one daughter species?

To understand the full significance of this, we must explore the history of Christian orthodoxy – and appreciate that Christian orthodoxy underpinned the general world-view of the mid-nineteenth century. This was true even though many intellectuals at that time had been turned away from religion by the rationalism of the Enlightenment. In the Middle Ages first the Arab world and then the West rediscovered the art and philosophy of the Greeks. Through the offices of medieval scholars, notably but not exclusively Thomas Aquinas in the thirteenth century, the ideas of Plato and Aristotle were essentially fused with those of Christianity to produce a new, intricate, and satisfying theology; one that was to last for centuries (and indeed is still with us).

Locked up in this theological synthesis was the idea of species. For Plato argued that everything that exists on this Earth is but a model, a poor reflection, of some ideal that exists in Heaven. He seems to have believed that, somewhere on high, the ideal table or chair, or dog or cat, have a literal existence. Each ideal represents an idea of God. This became the Christian orthodoxy. The idea implied that species are not merely biological constructs. The notion of the species becomes, essentially, sacred. Each one represents an idea of God.

Some biologists before Darwin entertained some idea that

creatures had evolved through time: they had not simply been created in their present forms, as the story of Genesis suggests. Many, however, were able to reconcile the idea of evolution with the narrative of Genesis. They suggested that God, in the beginning, had created a series of primordial creatures which did indeed change through time: essentially, each original primordial form unfolded, generation by generation, as a rosebud unfolds into a flower. But the different lineages remained separate. The French pre–Darwinian evolutionist Jean-Baptiste Lamarck argued in this way. Lamarck did not envisage, however, that any one lineage of creatures could branch, such that any one primordial creature could give rise to several different lineages. That would have implied that at some stage God had changed His mind.

But Charles Darwin, in his seminal *On the Origin of Species by Means of Natural Selection* in 1859, does argue that species may divide to form several different species. In short, he does not envisage that many different, separate lines of creatures simply change through time. He explicitly proposes instead that all creatures now on Earth, and all that are known to have lived in the past, arose from one single ancestor, so that we are all part of one great family tree. Thus he argues emphatically that species barriers are not inviolable. Note, too, that the title of Darwin's book, *On the Origin of Species*, was more provocative than it seems today. Ernst Mayr records in *Toward a New Philosophy of Biology* that many of his critics objected more strongly to this particular idea of Darwin's than to his broad proposal that creatures evolve. Evolution in general could be made acceptable: but the splitting of species, the fragmentation of God's original ideas, was widely perceived as blasphemy. In short, the distinction between 'species' and 'variety' or 'breed' was not just a technicality in the mid-nineteenth century. The implications ran very deep indeed.

Despite all this deep thought, however, and alongside it, ran the simple, mild confusions that we find in any age. Many people still felt in a vague way that species do drift cryptically, one into another. Some claimed, for example, that many forms of wayside vetch were somewhat degenerate derivatives of peas and lentils.

These, then, are the broad problems of heredity as they still loomed in the mid-nineteenth century. But let us look more closely at the mechanisms of heredity. Whether we conclude that both parents pass on information to the offspring, or that only one does so; whether or not we concede that this information is packaged within the gametes; we still must ask, what *form* does the information take?

What Kind of Information Passes From Parents to Offspring?

In 1837 Mendel's mentor at Brno, Abbot Napp, asked in the context of breeding sheep: 'What is inherited, and how?' In particular, he and his contemporaries wanted to know: is the hereditary information poured from the parent into the gametes like a fluid? Or do the instructions come in discrete units, like particles?

Essentially, the fluid versus particle view of heredity reflects a dichotomy that has run through all philosophy and science from earliest times. Nowadays it manifests as the contrast between what computer and high-fi aficionados call 'analogue' and 'digital' technologies: the first envisaging things (substances, information) as continuous entities, like plasticine, and the latter envisaging the components of the universe as being compounded from tiny particles. Philosophers in the digital-particle school include the fifth-century BC Greek philosopher Democritus, who argued that the universe was built from a few kinds of particle; Francis Bacon, who in the early seventeenth century conceived that the complexities of visible phenomena reflect the orderly manoeuvrings of sub-visible particles (an idea that seems to presage modern chaos theory); Descartes, who felt that creatures inherited particles of information from their parents (in which, of course, he was right); Leibniz, who envisaged a universe compounded of 'monads', which, so the modern physicist Julian Barbour argues, are remarkably prescient of modern particle physics; Newton, who argued that light is compounded of particles (which are now called 'photons'); and John Dalton, who in 1804 first proposed the atomic theory which is the basis of modern chemistry. Nowadays we have modern particle physics and computer science, in which the codes are digital. Schleiden and Schwann's notion that all bodies are compounded of small cells is essentially digital in nature.

'Analogue' suggests not particles, but a continuum. Thus traditional clocks are analogue technology, showing the time by moving their hands continuously. And while Newton argued that light is particulate, Christiaan Huygens showed that it must be a wave (and modern physicists acknowledge that both points of view are correct). A common analogue view of inheritance is that instructions are passed from parent(s) to offspring by fluids. As we have seen, Aristotle envisaged a coalescence of seminal fluid and menstrual blood. Darwin did not follow Aristotle in this, but for a time he entertained the idea (certainly when he wrote the first edition of *Origin*) that heredity might operate as if by the mixing of inks. An artist mixes blue with yellow to make green; so might male 'ink' be mixed with female within their shared offspring. Many characters in the offspring do seem to be a straightforward averaging of the parents, though the mixing cannot be too thorough, or brown-eyed parents could not give rise to blue-eyed children. However, a polemical Scottish engineer called Fleeming Jenkin delivered the *coup de grâce* to this particular conceit of Darwin's. If heredity simply worked by averaging, he said, then natural selection could not possibly work. Any new and advantageous character that happened to crop up would soon be diluted away as the lucky individual mated with others who were less well endowed. Of course, Mendel's digital view of heredity was correct; while Darwin's analogue view was mistaken. Darwin was not mistaken very often, however.

Whatever form the hereditary material took, particle or ink, how did it get into the egg or sperm? How did the egg or sperm 'know' what the parent looked like? How could it encapsulate the parent's features? Darwin made this issue more complicated than he needed to since he believed, at least for a time, that offspring could inherit features of their parents which their parents had acquired during their own lifetime. This notion, 'inheritance of acquired characteristics', had most famously been espoused in the early nineteenth century by Lamarck. 'Inheritance of acquired characteristics' is now known to be profoundly untrue (at least for most purposes, although it still has a few champions). It now seems clear that the gametes develop entirely separately from the rest of the body and are not directly influenced by the body's strivings. Your father may have trained to be a brilliant flautist, but if you want to play the flute like him you must do your own practise. Darwin thought you could inherit your parents' acquired characteristics, however, and invented a mechanism that might make it work, which he called 'pangenesis'. He suggested that every region of the body donated some fraction of itself, a kind of bulletin, to the developing gametes. This idea is actually close to what Hippocrates of Cos, he of the Hippocratic oath, had suggested at the turn of the fifth and fourth centuries BC. Darwin's friends T. H. Huxley and John Lubbock warned him against this nonsense, but he seems to have persisted with it anyway. None of us is infallible.

Finally, the waters of the mid-nineteenth century were stirred by various forms of metaphysics. *Naturphilosophie* had several kinds of influence. Vitalism was powerful – the notion that the mechanisms of life required extra and special forces over and above mere chemistry and physics. The most powerful metaphysical pressures came, however, from the Church.

Some of the clashes between the Church and the emerging science of the eighteenth and nineteenth centuries were momentous: the general conflict between the concept of unwavering physical law and the biblical reports of miracles; the specific contradiction between the new geology and the creation story of Genesis. But there were other irritations too that now may seem rather comical, although they didn't at the time. In the eighteenth century the Swedish biologist Carolus Linnaeus, who established the 'binomial' system for naming different creatures (as in *Homo sapiens*, the human being, and *Bellis perennis*, the daisy) and laid the foundations of modern classification, also demonstrated that flowering plants are sexual beings. The male element is the pollen and the female lies within the ovary. No one doubts this now and breeders and farmers of the time (and obviously for many centuries before) clearly knew this was the case and acted accordingly.

But some clerics did object to the idea. Jesus surely would not have singled out the lilies of the field for such praise if they had been practising such covert naughtiness. Many biologists were clerics, too: you could not be a don unless you were ordained and, of course, the cleric-naturalist has been a key figure in biology since the Middle Ages. Even by the middle of the nineteenth century the sexuality of flowering plants was not universally acknowledged. But for a breeder, and anyone seeking to understand heredity, such basics are a *sine qua non*.

So much for the unfolding science of heredity in the decades and centuries before Mendel. The third thread in our story is that of the practical, craftsmen-breeders. They contributed a great deal, and their practical knowledge, the ideas that they seemed to take for granted, often seemed to run far ahead of the scientists and philosophers. 'Twas ever thus. Science and technology work extraordinarily well when they work together, but they do not always march in unison.

The Breeders

Scholars traditionally suggest that agriculture began around 10,000 years ago with the 'Neolithic revolution'. That at least is when the first clear signs of cultivation appear in the archaeological record: permanent settlements like Jericho and Catal Huyuk in Turkey, caches of grain that are obviously different from the wild types. I have argued, however, in *Neanderthals, Bandits and Farmers*, that people must have been controlling their environment to a significant degree long before they were full-time farmers. The artefacts of the Neolithic do not reflect the true beginnings of farming; they merely show farming practised on a scale that is large enough to show up in the records. The real beginnings almost certainly date back at least 30,000 years. As people controlled their environment, so they influenced the kinds of plants that grew around them; for example, they might protect particular trees with particularly juicy fruits from other predators. By this kind of selection, then, people have undoubtedly been 'breeding' plants informally for many thousands of years. I suppose we could say that the first farmers truly became 'breeders' when they first began consciously to encourage the particular plants and animals that they favoured. When that was is anybody's guess, and always will be. I would not be at all surprised, however, if the first true breeders in this sense lived at least 30,000 years ago (and possibly a lot earlier).

Be that as it may, we know that by the time we get to Classical times, farmers were conscientiously breeding. Although we traditionally refer to 'Ancient' Romans they were modern people, living a mere 2,000 or so years ago, and of course they were astute breeders (and were by no means the first). They distinguished between breeds of animals and varieties of plants, and carried out 'progeny testing': that is, waiting to see whether a particular bull or stallion was worth keeping for stud by assessing the quality of his first offspring. If his offspring was good, then they kept him. If not, then he was destined for the pot. Not every fine quality of an animal proves to be 'heritable'. Sometimes great-looking sires produce inferior offspring.

The crafts of breeding – selecting, progeny testing and judicious crossing – were practised on all fronts for many centuries: in serious agriculture in both crops and livestock; horticulture; and in all kinds of hobbies in many countries – pigeons, fancy carp, what you will. For centuries breeding remained a craft. But by the eighteenth century true science was beginning to creep in and a key player in this was the naturalist J. G. Kolreuter (1733–1806).

Kolreuter was the first to carry out experiments in hybridisation purely as an exercise in biology. His prime aim was to find out how organisms work rather than to make better crops and livestock – in particular, he wanted to pin down the differences between 'varieties' and 'species'. So he undertook a prodigious programme of hybridisation involving fifty-four species in thirteen genera, which he published in a three-part report between 1761 and 1766 – almost exactly a century before Mendel undertook his superficially less ambitious, but in the end more penetrating, studies. Kolreuter believed more or less as Aristotle had that both parents produced a uniform, fluid semen which blended in the progeny, so that the offspring were intermediate between the two. These semens had been 'designed by the Creator for joining'. When flowers formed, he suggested, the male and female semens separated out again. His studies supported the eighteenth-century suggestion that plants are sexual beings.

Much more intriguingly, though, Kolreuter also showed that different characters *segregated* in the hybrid progeny. That is, a parent plant with white flowers and green pods, if crossed with a parent with yellow flowers and grey pods, could give rise to offspring with white flowers and grey pods or with yellow flowers and green pods. In other words, the different characters were inherited independently of each other. Mendel showed this too a century later: it is recorded in the textbooks as one of his principal findings. Kolreuter also found, however, as all hybridists do, that the offspring often seemed to resemble one parent far more than the other and this he put down to irregular mixing of semens. It is one thing to suppose that both parents contribute to the offspring (which is what sex implies) and another entirely to infer that they both contribute equally on all occasions. Mendel cites Kolreuter in his paper of 1866.

Among the craftsman-breeders of the eighteenth and early nineteenth centuries, three names are outstanding. In America Joseph Cooper (1757–1840) was a remarkable breeder of crops, while in England Robert Bakewell (1725–95) bred livestock, including the famous Dishley sheep for meat. But of most direct significance for Mendel was the Englishman Thomas Andrew Knight (1759–1838). Knight also, following Bakewell, bred cattle and sheep. Most important, though, were his experiments with cultivated plants.

From 1787 Knight sought to increase the productivity of crops by systematic hybridisation – cross-breeding, or 'crossing', of different types. Among other things, he emphasised the technique of artificial pollination. Furthermore, Knight recorded that of all the plants he hybridised, 'none appeared so well calculated to answer my purpose as the common pea'. The reason, he said, was that peas come in many forms, sizes and colours and are ideal for hybridising, for hybridising means that you begin with parents with different qualities. But also peas were ideal 'because the structure of its blossom, by preventing the ingress of adventitious farina, has rendered its varieties remarkably permanent'. ('Farina', of course, literally means 'flour' and was an early term for 'pollen', which was used well before the true significance of pollen was appreciated.) Again, Mendel makes exactly this point in his paper of 1866. In modern parlance, we can say that garden peas are 'inbreeders' (meaning they fertilise themselves) and so they are also 'true breeding' (which means that unless they are officiously hybridised (cross-bred), the offspring closely resemble the parents). In Knight's work, then, we see the essential framework of Mendel's researches: hybridisation of different types by artificial pollination; and, specifically, the use of peas, whose breeding can be so tightly controlled since the structure of their flowers prevents pollination from outsiders.

There is much more. Knight perceived that the traits of the parents were passed individually to the offspring. Mendel showed this too. Knight also observed, as, again, Mendel was to do, that when two uniform parents were cross-bred, then the first generation (F1) were uniform; but when the first generation was bred again (the different F1s crossed with each other), then the traits that were present in the initial parent generation re-appeared. He did not quantify his results in the way that Mendel did later, but he observed the basic fact nonetheless.

Knight published his most influential paper on plant hybridisation in 1799 and in it he also states that hybrids between different species are generally infertile. Knight's paper was translated into German in 1800 and was well known on the Continent. There was certainly a copy in the university library at Brno, which bears the stamp of the Brno Agricultural Society. Did Mendel read it? It would be very surprising indeed if he had not.

But Mendel was not the first to pick up on Knight's work. Others who did included the Englishmen J. Goss and A. Seton, who also hybridised peas. In their publications of 1824 they showed the phenomenon of dominance: how some traits in one parent completely obliterate other traits in the other parent, so that (for example) *all* the progeny of a pure-bred yellow-flowered parent and a white-flowered parent could have yellow flowers. Again, Mendel showed precisely this effect in his studies in the 1850s and 1860s. Goss and Seton then worked on other species, as did Knight, who learnt from them in this and followed their example. Mendel again followed the same pattern: first peas, then other plants.

In Moravia itself, Mendel's own country, breeders focused both on crops (such as apples) and sheep; and again they explored and developed the basic techniques and discovered the difficulties and limitations. Bakewell's work was obviously highly relevant to them, although his great creation, the Dishley, had been bred for meat, while the farmers of mainland Europe were more interested in wool. Since the seventeenth century the wool farmers had focused on Spanish sheep, the merino. Books were published in the early eighteenth century on how to breed imported sheep. Crossing was recommended, as was consanguineous mating, although the Church, all-pervasive, objected to this on ethical grounds. Ferdinand Geisslern from Moravia (1751–1824) was known as 'the Moravian Bakewell'.

In the tradition of Kolreuter, the breeders became more and more aware that they needed to supplement their empirical studies with science. Christian André, who was introduced in Chapter 2 as a social reformer, was also an intellectual who had studied at the University of Jena; indeed he wrote a zoology textbook in 1795 (in which he rejected preformation, and asserted that both parents were involved in shaping the offspring). More grandly, in 1815, he drew up a general programme of scientific development. He argued that we need to understand the basic mechanisms of the world if we are to exercise some control over our own affairs, citing Copernicus and Newton, who had brought science to the ancient craft of astronomy. If Moravians applied the same principles to their own concerns, said André, then all civilisation would be indebted to them. His programme echoes the sentiments of Francis Bacon, who had said the same kind of thing two hundred years earlier.

As a good Moravian, André became involved in breeding sheep, which prompted him to think about heredity in general. In 1814, the year before he published his grand plan, with H. F. Salm he founded Moravia's Sheep Breeders' Society, which held meetings for breeders from throughout central Europe and included contributions on artificial selection and on the transmission of traits from parents to offspring.

André became involved in fruit, too, and in 1816 he drew attention to the work of Knight in breeding new varieties of vines and fruit trees. Out of these deliberations came Brno's Pomological and Oenological Association. Soon, the association established a nursery to create new varieties, while André made contact with the Horticultural Society of London, of which Knight was president, and with the Pomological Association at Altenberg (near Leipzig), where G. C. L. Hempel was secretary.

Hempel was also a forward thinker. In 1820 he wrote that 'higher scientific pomology' was moving to the point where breeders might create new varieties at will, according to specifications for size of fruit, shape, colour and flavour. This dream is now becoming true in precisely the way that Hempel envisaged. First, though, he said, it would be necessary to understand the rules of heredity, what he called 'the laws of hybridisation'. For this, 'A new type of natural scientist' would need to emerge: 'a researcher with a profound knowledge of botany and sharply defined powers of observation who might, with untiring and stubborn patience, grasp the subtleties of these experiments, take a firm command of them, and provide a clear explanation'. Hempel might have been describing Mendel, who in fact was born two years after he wrote this. Truly, we can add Knight (at a distance), André and Hempel to the pantheon of Mendel's inspirers. Taken together with the great biologists already cited, his was almost an embarrassment of riches.

Indeed the world at large caught the bug of agricultural science in the late eighteenth and early nineteenth centuries. It appeared as a subject on university curricula. Edinburgh was among the first and has remained in the forefront; giving rise to Roslin Institute, which, in our own day, has produced Dolly the cloned sheep (who is discussed on page 133). In Moravia, the ever-active André suggested setting up a professorship for agriculture in 1808. The first was established at Olomouc in 1811, where Mendel attended the Philosophical Institute, and the second in 1816 at Brno. In 1823 J. K. Nestler (1783–1841), a former colleague of André, began teaching breeding at Olomouc, while in 1824 F. Diebl took the chair at Brno. We met Diebl in Chapter 2 as a friend and associate of Abbot Napp; he was principally a plant scientist. Between 1835 and 1844 he published a five-volume book on agricultural science in which (in Volume 2) he described artificial pollination. With Nestler, he co-wrote *General Natural History* in 1836, and both of them published articles on hybridisation and heredity. In the 1830s Diebl worked with Abbot Napp on the committee of the Agricultural Society and especially with the Pomological Association, when Napp was president. Diebl, then, was also a significant and influential figure.

Nestler, for his part, was interested mainly in sheep. In his writings he refers to Kolreuter and he also discusses progeny testing and consanguineous breeding. In his lectures he speaks both of blending inheritance (where characters combine features of both parents) and of characters that have an 'either–or' quality. Thus cattle tend either to have horns, or not; not somewhere in between. He also refers to sports, which he thought were inexplicable. Whether offspring could inherit features acquired by their parents in their own lifetime as Lamarck had proposed was, he said, 'problematical'. In the mid-1830s he told Brno's Sheep Breeders' Society that 'the most essential thing of all for improved sheep breeding as well as being an urgent question of our time [is] the ability to inherit'.

The science of heredity was undoubtedly advanced by the breeding of sheep. In 1812 Christian André described artificial selection in sheep to increase wool production and his son, Rudolf, published a manual on sheep-breeding in 1816. In 1818 André senior perceived that consanguineous mating would weaken the breed, which, he said, was 'a natural physiological law'. In the same year he asked a renowned Hungarian sheep breeder, Count E. Festetics (1764–1847), to formulate the main principles of interbreeding in breeding practice. The following year, 1819, Festetics published what he called 'genetic laws', *Genetische Gesetze*. The term 'genetic' is generally supposed to be a twentieth-century invention but this, evidently, is not the case. Festetics's term *Genetische* is the same word.

Festetics's 'laws' are not really 'laws' at all: they are observations. But they are sensible observations, which helped to consolidate the subject. First, he observed that the characteristic traits of healthy parents are inherited by the progeny. Secondly, however, the traits of one of the grandparents may also appear in the progeny, even though they may not have been present in the parents. But then again the progeny may exhibit traits that are quite different from either parent; and if these traits do not correspond to the aims of the breeder, but are heritable, then of course they are undesirable. Finally, if you are going to inbreed – indulge in consanguineous matings – then you must, said Festetics, select the stock animals scrupulously. In general, consanguineous mating was necessary to maintain constancy; but it had to be used circumspectly if production was to be maintained. He also observed, as early as 1820, that wool quality was now judged 'with mathematical precision'.

All in all, there has been no better place and time to discuss the breeding of sheep, and all the ideas that may follow from it, than in the Moravia of the 1830s. Nestler boasted that 'Moravia can claim special credit for having become . . . a source of modern, rational sheep breeding'. After that, however, Moravia's sheep industry waned somewhat, out-competed by cheap imports from the British colonies. Nestler himself died suddenly in 1841.

Fruit was Abbot Napp's first love. In 1840 he chaired the fourth congress of German-speaking farmers and foresters in Brno and there discussed hybridisation as a way of creating new varieties, although others said that cross-breeding (hybridisation) merely produced random results. A year later Napp commented: 'Nothing certain can be said as to why production through artificial fertilisation remains a lengthy, troublesome, and random affair.' Truly, breeding and the mechanisms of heredity were the burning issues in mid-nineteenth-century Moravia; the place was on fire. Yet despite all the many advances, all the straws in the wind that can be seen in retrospect, puzzlement reigned.

In the early nineteenth century, too, various learned bodies were offering prizes to anyone who could solve various problems of heredity and breeding. Many of these again were clearly grist to Mendel's mill. Thus in 1822 the Berlin Academy of Sciences offered an award to anyone who could show for all time whether plants are, or are not, sexual beings. One A. F. Wiegmann, an apothecary from Brunswick, was the winner in 1828. He crossed various species of peas and produced some hybrids that more closely resembled one parent or the other, some that combined traits of both and some that seemed to bear no resemblance to either parent. He seems thereby to have answered the main question: plants must be sexual, since both may contribute to the offspring; but again, his studies did not show definitively whether both parents always contribute equally. His experiments have much to commend them, however. Note again his choice of peas.

A similar prize was offered in 1830 by the Haarlem Academy of Sciences, this time won by F. C. Gartner (1772–1850). In the 1830s and 1840s Gartner carried out more than 10,000 artificial fertilisations, in 700 species of plant, yielding 250 different hybrids. He summarised his findings in an extensive monograph in 1849. Gartner cites both Kolreuter and Knight. Like them, he showed that hybrids between different species tend not to be fertile, and in general he reinforced the idea that species are indeed constant and cannot be changed into other species. Mendel bought Gartner's monograph in the year that he wrote it; and again he quoted him in his paper of 1866.

Purkinje's friend and correspondent, R. Wagner (1805–64) at the University of Göttingen, also deserves mention. In 1853 he argued that the rules of heredity might be discerned by analysing a mass of data statistically, although, he felt, this would be expensive and time-consuming. He was right; but this, of course, is precisely what Mendel undertook. Wagner thought that both parents contribute to heredity, an idea he got from Purkinje.

Finally, after 1850, both Franz Unger at the University of Vienna and Carl Naegeli at the University of Munich studied plant hybridisation from a physiological point of view, both trying to make use of physics and chemistry. Unger, as we have seen, was Mendel's teacher and a great admirer of Naegeli; and Mendel, as we have noted, tried to interest Naegeli in his own research, though with miserable results. If only Naegeli had grasped the signficance of Mendel's work the course of science would have been quite different. Genetics would have begun forty years earlier.

In short, by the time Mendel began his own studies into heredity some time in the mid-1850s, probably in 1854, a huge amount of groundwork had already been done. There were so many fine ideas around that it may seem as if he had merely to dot 'I's and cross 'Ts'. The crafts of breeders were well advanced, but many were stressing the need for keen experimentation and, indeed, such experiments had begun with Kolreuter in the eighteenth century. Specifically, these early experimenters stressed the need to explore heredity by hybridisation, crossing plants (or, in principle, animals) that were sexually compatible but had somewhat different characters. They also emphasised the need to work with true-breeding plants – those whose offspring really did resemble themselves when they were self-fertilised – and the garden pea had long since emerged as the favoured subject. Indeed, the garden pea occupied the same niche in early nineteenth-century breeding experiments as the fruit-fly, *Drosophila*, assumed in the twentieth. Finally, Wagner in particular emphasised the need for large-scale experiments and statistical analysis.

Then, as we have seen in Chapter 2, Mendel's own education, predilections and working conditions primed him beautifully for the task in hand (even if he was somewhat overworked). He was born into a community of gardeners and plant-breeders and surrounded by them all his life. But he was a physicist and a passable mathematician: used to the idea that certainty in science depended on quantification. I feel, too (although this is only a feeling), that a physicist would take naturally to the idea that heredity is particulate, digital, in nature: that creatures would pass units of heredity from generation to generation. Biologists are more inclined to think in terms of mixing of inks, or semens, or 'sanguineous nutriments'. Mendel also, clearly, had the appropriate scientist's instinct: to carry out simple experiments that would give clear answers and then work outwards from the areas of certainty into more difficult problems.

Darwin, the greatest biologist of the nineteenth century (and indeed of all time), failed to see the underlying simplicity of heredity partly because he had the temperament of a naturalist, focusing on and relishing the *variety* of nature. As he explains in *Origin of Species*, he spent a lot of time talking to breeders of pigeons. But for all kinds of reasons, it is impossible to see the patterns of heredity in such animals (unless you know in advance what patterns you should be looking for). As we will see in Chapter 4, Mendel was able to see simple hereditary ratios in his peas partly because the peas were true-breeding (for he went to great lengths to ensure that this was so) and partly because they produce enormous numbers of offspring. The simple ratios are of a statistical nature: they are evident only when the numbers *are* enormous. When creatures produce too few offspring, as pigeons or human beings do, and when they are not true-breeding themselves, the simple patterns are not evident at all.

But although in retrospect we can see that Mendel picked up on an enormous backlog of good, solid ideas, confusion reigned nonetheless. To be sure, a great deal of good and necessary work had been done. But the good and necessary results had not been brought together to create a coherent picture; and the good ideas were balanced, almost equally, by traditional notions that were crackpot or just plain wrong. It was still not even 100 per cent clear, at least not to everybody, that plants were sexual; or, if they were, whether each parent (plant or animal) always contributed in equal amounts. These are very basic matters to be uncertain about.

In fact Darwin summarised the prevailing state of confusion in *Origin of Species* in 1859 when Mendel's own experiments were well advanced but not yet published. He wrote:

no-one can say why the same peculiarity in different individuals . . . is sometimes inherited and sometimes not so: why the child often reverts in certain characters to its grandfather, or other much more remote ancestor; why a peculiarity is often transmitted from one sex to both sexes, or to one sex alone, more commonly but not exclusively to the like sex.

Even in 1872 the renowned animal-breeder H. Nathusius still felt constrained to observe: 'the laws of heredity have not yet fallen from the tree of knowledge – that which, as legend would have it, led Newton on the right path to the conception of the Law of Gravity'. In truth, the essence of the laws *was* known then, at least to Mendel; and he had already made them known in lectures and publications. But nobody was looking.

Others made progress of a kind between 1866, the year of Mendel's paper, and 1900, the year of its rediscovery. Chromosomes were described in that period; and in the 1880s the details of cell division, which involve the orderly separation of chromosomes, were first described. In 1886 yet another great German, August Weismann (1834–1914), declared that the germplasm (the tissue that gives rise to the gametes) develops entirely separately from the rest of the body, so that changes within the body cells could not be passed on to the next generation. This assertion effectively showed that Lamarck's notion of 'inheritance of acquired characteristics' was impossible. At least it is impossible in animals: some plants may produce new flowers and hence eggs and pollen from just about any tissue. In 1883 W. K. Brooks summarised the general state of understanding in the second edition of his book *The Law of Heredity*. Brooks was one of one of Thomas Hunt Morgan's early instructors. Francis Galton, too, also working with peas, produced his *Ancestral Law of Heredity* which he published in 1898. This was well received, although, as R. A. Fisher showed twenty years later, Galton's 'ancestral law' in reality merely applied Mendel's principles to characters that are coded by more than one gene (that is, to 'polygenic characters', as discussed in Chapter 4). More broadly, Galton developed the discipline of 'biometrics', which discussed continuous variations between different individuals – in essence, the very characters that Mendel avoided during his studies on peas because of the intractable complexities he knew would ensue. However, Galton's biometrics, carried forward in particular by his disciple Karl Pearson, have formed a parallel tradition of heredity throughout the twentieth century and gave rise, among other things, to the eugenics movement. I will discuss this in Chapter 9, but apart from this will have very little to say about biometrics. This book specifically traces the Mendelian influence. Now it is time to look at his research.

4

From Mendel to Molecules

Mendel is pivotal in genetics in the way that Charles Darwin is pivotal to biology as a whole. Everything before Mendel seems a little primitive: often excellent and much of it crucial, but now mainly of historical interest. The modern age begins with Mendel. Put his ideas and Darwin's together, as was achieved in the early twentieth century, then stir in a little molecular biology (which is the great contribution of the later twentieth century), and we have the core of modern biology: what relativity and quantum mechanics are to physics. Since Mendel's and Darwin's ideas are not in principle difficult, biology emerges as an easy subject. It is also vital. It's all very pleasing.

Mendel conducted his most important experiments – on the garden pea, *Pisum sativum* – in the monastery garden at Brno between around 1856 and 1864; although he seems to have carried out two years' preliminary trials (in 1854 and 1855) to ensure that the peas he was using were pure-breeding (or, to anticipate a term explained later, 'homozygous'). He reported his findings to the Brno Natural Science Society in February 1865 and then again in March 1865; and they were published formally as a paper in the journal of the society in the following year, 1866, with the title 'Versuche über Pflanzen-Hybriden', 'Experiments in Plant Hybridisation'. This is a stunning paper, lucid and thorough – remember how Mendel was praised as a young man for the clarity of his teaching – and must have been seen by the greatest biologists in Europe, most of whom were attached to the Brno Society. Yet it was all but ignored. His disappointment must have exceeded that even of David Hume, who mourned a century earlier that his maiden master work, *A Treatise of Human Nature*, had fallen 'dead-born from the press'. Mendel's work was rediscovered in 1900, but by that time he had been in his grave for sixteen years.

Since his death, insult has been added to the disappointment of his last years. We saw in Chapter 2 how political insults were heaped on his head in Eastern Europe. But even here in the West, where his work has found its home, many have suggested that his research was simply lucky; in fact, it has almost become orthodox to argue this. If he had not chosen to study peas, say the critics, then he would not have achieved such clear-cut results. Given that he did study peas, he still would not have produced such sharp results if he had not singled out the particular characters (physical features) that he happened upon: seed colour, seed shape, and so on. Other factors which we will look at later in this chapter, linkage and polygenic characters, would have confused the picture no end. As the *coup de grâce*, the great British statistician-biologist R. A. Fisher suggested in 1936 that Mendel's results were just too good to be true, indeed that 'most, if not all, of the experiments have been falsified so as to agree closely with Mendel's expectations'. Fisher fully acknowledged Mendel's genius – perhaps it really does take one to recognise another – and never really believed that Mendel had cheated. But others, less scrupulous and far less scholarly, have been all too keen to suggest that he did cheat. In our age, after all, iconoclasm is trendy and profitable.

We will see, however, and the preceding chapters have already established, that his experiments with peas were not 'lucky' at all. Mendel was a fine biologist and had many excellent predecessors – in his paper he cites both Kolreuter and Gartner (and a few others) – and he knew exactly what he was doing. As his paper clearly shows (perhaps none of his critics have actually read it), he *did* confront linkage *and* polygenic characters (in beans) and dealt with both effortlessly. Neither did he cheat. Fisher never thought that he could have done, but remained puzzled; and a new paper by Teddy Seidenfeld, of Carnegie Mellon University and the London School of Economics, perhaps solves Fisher's dilemma well enough. For my part, again I feel inclined to quote David Hume, who said of people who report miracles: 'If the falsehood of his testimony would be more miraculous than the event which he relates then, and not till then, can he pretend to command my belief or opinion.' That is, the idea that Mendel cheated is more incredible than any alternative explanation, even if we don't know for certain what the alternative explanation might be.

This chapter has two objectives. First, I want to describe what Mendel did with his peas and point out the significant features, which often seem to be overlooked. I will not deal in any detail with his later experiments, partly because so little is known about them, but mostly because they divert from the main story. Mendel knew that he could not simply assume that the rules of heredity he found in peas would *necessarily* apply to all other plants, or indeed to creatures apart from plants. As he says in his paper of 1866: 'a generally applicable law governing the formation and development of hybrids . . . can only be arrived at when we shall have before us the results of detailed experiments made on plants belonging to the most diverse orders'. So from the 1860s onwards he set out to work through plants of other families – about seventeen species in all – and in his later life his work with bees showed him both to be a master technician and an extraordinarily accomplished naturalist. But he never finished any of this later work, apart from what he called some 'minor experiments' with *Phaseolus* (kidney) beans, which he carried out at the same time as the work on peas. As he said in his paper. 'It requires some courage to undertake a labour of such far-reaching extent', and there he was talking only about his work on peas. In truth, his grand agenda, to find the basic patterns of heredity in all species, would have required at least a lifetime and a team of senior scientists, post-grads, and graduate students, such as a modern department might bring to bear. Mendel had the peace that many modern scientists crave but not the resources. He might reasonably have expected that someone would have offered him a professorship, but apparently nobody did.

In the second half of this chapter, I want to show how all the modern ideas of twentieth-century classical genetics flow naturally from Mendel's initial observations. There were many twentieth-century greats, among whom we can single out Thomas Hunt Morgan (1866–1945), who at Columbia University in 1908 began the research on the fruit-fly, *Drosophila*, which still continues; and his one-time colleague, the irascible Hermann Joseph Muller (1890–1967), who did most to elucidate the mechanisms and importance of genetic mutation, the process by which genes actually change (and either then do something different or else simply become non-functional). But I will race through classical genetics, pausing only to sketch in the main vocabulary and concepts. The now-standard ideas have often been well described elsewhere. Once the basic notions are in place I want to move as quickly as possible to the issues that mainly concern us now.

So let's begin with Mendel's peas.

Mendel's Peas

Mendel's key experiments were an exercise in hybridising garden peas, crossing different varieties that had clearly distinct physical characters. There was no 'luck' in his choice, either of experimental design or of subject. As we have seen, many biologists before him had stressed that the problems of heredity would be solved only by hybridisation of different, clearly defined varieties, and some – Kolreuter, Seton, Goss and others – specifically recommended peas.

Mendel began his preliminary work in 1854 'with 34 more or less distinct varieties of Peas . . . obtained from several seedsmen'. These were then 'subjected to two years' trial'. Then, 'For fertilisation, 22 of these were selected and cultivated during the whole period of the experiments.' Finally, as he announced in 1865, 'after eight years' pursuit [the work is] concluded in all essentials'. Thus the experiments themselves ran from 1856 to 1864.

Mendel makes it very clear that not all plants would serve his purposes. For, he said:

The experimental plants must necessarily:
1 Possess constant differentiating characteristics

78

2 The hybrids of such plants must, during the flowering season, be protected from the influence of all foreign pollen, or be easily capable of such protection.

He adds as an afterthought, although he might have made it point 3: 'The hybrids and their offspring should suffer no marked disturbance in their fertility in the successive generation.'

So why home in on peas? Well, says Mendel, while acknowledging Kolreuter: 'At the very outset special attention was devoted to the Leguminosae. Experiments which were made with several members of this family led to the result that the genus *Pisum* was found to possess the necessary qualifications.'

Let's look at these qualifications one by one: a pedantic exercise, maybe, but the ghost of 'luck' should be laid for ever. On the first point: as Mendel and about a million gardeners were perfectly well aware, many if not most common plants are *not* particularly 'constant' in their 'characters'. At least, some are too constant: all primroses are yellow, for example, and if all the plants have the same colour, then it is impossible to see any patterns of heredity at all, since there are no variations to analyse. Others, though – lupins, antirrhinums – have very variable colours, and a parent of any one colour seems able to give rise to offspring of many different colours (or, at least, this is how it looks at first glance). When the characters are *so* variable, any underlying pattern is obscured by complexity and indeed by randomness. So to make sense of heredity, the experimenter needs plants that come in several or many different forms, but each of those forms must breed true, unless specifically hybridised. You can assess how round-seeded plants interact with wrinkled-seeded plants by crossing them, but *only* if the round-seeded plants normally give rise to round-seeded offspring and the wrinkled-seeded plants to wrinkled-seeded offspring. If round-seeded plants produce wrinkled-seeded offspring even when self-fertilised, or round-seeded plants produce wrinkled-seeded offspring, then we can learn next to nothing by hybridising the two different types. If either type, when 'selfed', could also produce offspring of quite different types, then it would be impossible to make any sense of the outcome. Peas fit this particular bill, but remarkably few other plants do so. Mendel knew this, but he needed to carry out two years' preliminary work to ensure that the different samples of peas he began with were indeed true-breeding: that plants of any particular type did indeed produce offspring only of their own kind, when left to themselves.

On the second point: 'Accidental impregnation by foreign pollen . . . would lead to entirely erroneous conclusions.' With peas and many other legumes, says Mendel, it is particularly easy to avoid this:

> On account of their peculiar floral structure . . . a disturbance through foreign pollen cannot easily occur, since the fertilising organs are closely packed inside the keel and the anthers burst within the bud, so that the stigma becomes covered with pollen even before the flower opens. This circumstance is especially important.

In fact, Mendel showed that unless his peas were attacked by a particularly pestilential beetle called *Bruchus pisi*, which caused the flower to burst open, then his experimental peas were virtually never pollinated by pollen from other peas that just happened to be in the neighbourhood.

All the fertilisations were carried out either by 'selfing' (leaving the flowers alone, and allowing the pollen to scatter on to the stigmas in the same flower) or by deliberate hybridisation using artificial pollination, the technique which had been in widespread use since around 1820. Of this, Mendel says:

> Artificial fertilisation is certainly a somewhat elaborate process, but nearly always succeeds. For this purpose the bud is opened before it is perfectly developed, the keel is removed, and each stamen carefully extracted by means of forceps, after which the stigma can at once be dusted over with foreign pollen.

Finally, on his third point, Mendel says: 'Reduced fertility or entire sterility of certain forms, such as occurs in the offspring of many hybrids, would render the experiments very difficult or entirely frustrate them.' Putting the matter crudely, it would be very difficult to produce worthwhile statistics on patterns of inheritance if a proportion of the experimental plants refused to breed at all, or did so only in a fitful way that defied analysis.

Once he had identified 'lines' (as a modern breeder would say) of peas that he knew were true-breeding, he deliberately selected characters for study that he knew would give comprehensible results. There was no luck in this. He was simply aware of the principle that Sir Peter Medawar made explicit a century later: 'Science is the art of the soluble.' Again, Mendel clearly describes why he chose the features he did:

The various forms of Peas selected for crossing showed differences in length and colour of the stern; in the size and form of the leaves; in the position, colour, size of the flowers; in the length of the flower stalk; in the colour, form, and size of the pods; in the form and size of the seeds; and in the colour of the seed-coats and of the albumen [by which he means the seed-leaves or cotyledons]. Some of the characters noted do not permit of a sharp and certain separation, since the difference is of a 'more or less' nature, which is often difficult to define. Such characters could not be utilised for the separate experiments; these could only be applied to characters which stand out clearly and definitely in the plants.

So which particular characters did he choose to study? Again, in his own words (though the passages in square brackets are mine):

The characters which were selected for experiment relate:

1 To the *difference in the form of the ripe seeds*. [They were either round or wrinkled.]

2 To the *difference in the colour of the seed albumen (endosperm)*. [Either pale yellow, bright yellow and orange, or intense green.]

3 To the *difference in the colour of the seed coat*. This is either white, with which character white flowers are constantly correlated; or it is grey, grey-brown, leather-brown, with or without violet spotting, in which case the colour of the standards is violet, that of the wings purple, and the stem in the axils of the leaves is of a reddish tint. The grey seed-coats become dark brown in boiling water.

81

Note here – we will discuss the point again later – that in this instance he is clearly observing the phenomenon of 'linkage': the fact, that is, that sometimes characters are not inherited entirely independently of all other characters, but are often (or always) associated with other characters. As he says here, particular pod colours tend to be associated with particular flower colours: for example, white pods go with white flowers. In truth this might not be linkage: it might simply be an example of one gene producing two different effects. Again, though, my point is that Mendel did not achieve the clear results just by striking a lucky course through all the difficulties. He perceived the difficulties, and dealt with each one sensibly. To continue:

4 To the *difference in the form of the ripe pods*. [Either 'inflated', or 'deeply contracted in places'.]

5 To the *difference in the colour of the unripe pods*. [Either light to dark green, or vivid yellow.]

6 To the *difference in the position of the flowers*. [Either axial – meaning along the main stem, in the angles of the leaves; or terminal – meaning at the end of the stem.]

7 To the *difference in the length of the stem*. [This was 'very various in some forms'. But it was constant enough when plants were grown in constant conditions. Mendel differentiated between very tall ones – six to seven feet long – and markedly short ones – between 9 inches and 18 inches.]

This, then, was the basic set-up: twenty-two varieties of well-selected peas which he knew were true-breeding, and seven carefully selected characters to study which 'stand out clearly and definitely in the plants'. For the next eight seasons he studied various hybridisations between the different types. In all, he studied about 10,000 different plants minutely. He knew that the patterns he would be looking at were of a statistical nature, and unless he looked at a lot he would not achieve valid results. This was the mathematician in Mendel coming to the fore.

In the following, I will not look at all Mendel's experiments in detail: they become complicated as the generations pass and

Mendel takes at least 10,000 words to describe them. I will look at just a few, to make the main points. After much deliberation, too, I have decided to cheat a little here and there, and to employ twentieth-century vocabulary to make it easier to see what is going on. In particular, Mendel makes clear his realisation that characters are passed on from generation to generation in the form not of inks but of discrete 'factors', sometimes known as 'Mendelian factors'. We now call these factors 'genes'. But although the term 'gene' was not coined until 1909 (by Wilhelm Johannsen), I will use it where appropriate in the following account. As we go through, too, I will pick out the truly essential features, and comment on significant details that sometimes seem to be overlooked.

To begin with, Mendel simply crossed plants with each kind of character with other plants that had the corresponding but different character: round-seeded with wrinkled-seeded; yellow cotyledons with green cotyledons; white seedcoat with grey seedcoat; inflated pods with contracted pods; green pods with yellow pods; axial flowers with terminal flowers; long stem with short stem. With each cross he found that *all* the offspring had the character that is cited first in the above list. Thus when true-breeding round-seeded plants were crossed with wrinkled-seeded plants *all* the offspring had round seeds, and so on.

From this, Mendel derived one of his most significant principles, which has resonated through all genetics ever since:

Henceforth in this paper those characters which are transmitted entire, or almost unchanged in the hybridisation, and therefore in themselves constitute the characters of the hybrid, are termed the *dominant*, and those which become latent in the process *recessive*. The expression 'recessive' has been chosen because the characters thereby designated withdraw or entirely disappear in the hybrids, but nevertheless re-appear unchanged in their progeny.

Doubtless you are familiar with the idea of 'dominant' and 'recessive' genes. Here, in Mendel's paper of 1866, is their first clear mention. Specifically, he says:

Of the following characters which were used in the experiments the following are dominant:

1 The round or roundish form of the seed.

2 The yellow colouring of the seed albumen [cotyledons].

3 The grey, grey-brown, or leather brown colour of the seed-coat, in association with violet-red blossoms and reddish spots in the leaf axils.

4 The simply inflated form of the pod.

5 The green colouring of the unripe pod.

6 The distribution of the flowers along the stem.

7 The greater length of the stem.

On this last point, Mendel observed the phenomenon we noted in Chapter 3 – 'hybrid vigour'. The pure-bred tall plants were never more than seven feet tall, while the hybrid ones, those crossed with short-stemmed plants, were up to seven-and-a-half feet tall. We will look more closely at the phenomenon of hybrid vigour a little later. Note, though, that *sometimes* when two individuals with contrasting characters are crossed, the characters of the offspring average those of the parents. But sometimes, emphatically, they do not. In this case, because of 'hybrid vigour', the offspring are *taller* than the taller parent, even though the other parent is extremely short!

In general, Mendel says:

Experiments which in previous years were made with ornamental plants have already afforded evidence that the hybrids, as a rule, are not exactly intermediate between the parental species. With some of the more striking characters, those for instance which relate to the form and size of the leaves, the pubescence of the several parts, etc, the intermediate indeed is nearly always to be seen. In other cases, however, one of the two parental characters is so preponderant that it is difficult or quite impossible to detect the other in the hybrid. This is precisely the case with the Pea hybrids.

Now, perhaps remembering his bad experience with Fenzl when he failed his teaching exams for the last time, a note of triumph seems to creep into his paper:

It was furthermore shown by the whole of the experiments that it is perfectly immaterial whether the dominant character belongs to the seed plant or to the pollen plant; the form of the hybrid remains identical in both cases. This interesting fact was also emphasised by Gartner.

Fenzl, you will remember, was a latter-day spermatist, clinging to the idea that in plants all the inheritance comes from the pollen, the male parent. Mendel was delighted to demonstrate clearly what he had known all along: that this simply is not the case. The contributions of male and female are equivalent (except of course in beastly organisms like *Hieracium*, which practise parthenogenesis, as noted in Chapter 2). Actually, as we will see later, there are caveats here. In particular, research from the 1980s onwards has shown that in some cases, at least in mammals, the father or the mother puts their own stamp upon particular genes. But the usual, default position is entirely as Mendel says: it really doesn't matter which parent contributes which genes.

Mendel now allowed the hybrid offspring to self-fertilise, as peas do when they are left alone. He then observed and counted the resulting offspring in each case. Again, in his own words:

Expt 1. Form of seed: From 253 hybrids 7324 seeds were obtained in the second trial year. Among them were 5474 round or roundish ones and 1850 angular wrinkled ones. Therefrom the ratio 2.96:1 is deduced.

Expt 2: Colour of albumen: 258 plants yielded 8023 seeds, 6022 yellow, and 2001 green; their ratio, therefore, is as 3.01:1.

So he worked through all seven pairs of characters, which led to the grand conclusion:

If now the results of the whole of the experiments be brought together, there is found, as between the number of forms with the dominant and recessive characters, an average ratio of 2.98:1, or 3:1.

This 'three-to-one' ratio is another crucial Mendelian finding. Mendel describes how he thought it was arrived at; and as always, it seems, his instincts and reasoning were spot-on. (It is easy to say this in such a patronising way 150 years later, after many generations of geneticists have retrodden the same ground!) Mendel does explain the reason for this ratio,* but it seems reasonable to précis the argument in a more modern form. Herein lies the crux of classical genetics.

For imagine, now, that each *simple* character, characters such as round-seededness in peas, is conferred by a single factor (which we now call a gene). So now we have merely to surmise that the complete set of all characters in any creature is conferred by its genes. Now imagine that each individual contains *two* complete sets of the genes appropriate to its species. One set has been inherited from one parent and one from the other. Now imagine what happens when the individual reproduces. It produces gametes – sperm or eggs. We merely have to suppose that each gamete contains just one set of genes. Then, when the genes in the sperm combine with the genes in the egg during conception, the resulting embryo again contains two complete sets of genes: one from each parent.

So now let's look in genetic terms at what happens when a round-seeded pea is crossed with a wrinkled-seeded pea. I will use my own nomenclature, R for the gene for round-seededness and Wr for the gene for wrinkle-seededness, simply because I think this makes things easier.

A pure-bred, true-breeding, round-seeded pea contains two copies of the R gene: we can call them RR. A pure-bred, true-breeding, wrinkled-seeded pea contains two copies of the Wr gene: we can call them WrWr. So far, so easy.

---

* In fact, Mendel does describe different forms of gametes, though the sentence in which he does so lacks some of his usual lucidity. Perhaps it works better in German:

> Since the various constant forms are produced in *one* plant, or even in *one* flower of a plant, the conclusion appears logical that in the ovaries of the hybrids there are formed as many sorts of egg cells, and in the anthers as many sorts of pollen cells, as there are possible constant combination forms, and that these egg and pollen cells agree in their internal compositions with those of the separate forms.

Note, though, how confidently he talks about egg cells and pollen cells. In Mendel's day such ideas were new. As noted in Chapter 3, the fusion of egg cells with sperm cells was observed in plants only in the 1850s, not in flowering plants but in algae.

All the gametes – pollen or eggs – produced by the true-breeding, round-seeded pea contain the R gene; and *all* the gametes produced by the wrinkled-seeded pea contain the Wr gene. Still very easy.

The hybrids produced by crossing true-breeding round-seeded plants with wrinkled-seeded plants will *all* contain one R gene and one Wr gene. These can be called RWr. All the hybrid, RWr individuals have round seeds because the R gene dominates the Wr gene.

So now we allow RWr plants to cross with other RWr plants (or rather, we allow them to self-fertilise, which amounts to the same thing).

Now, *each* kind of plant produced *two* kinds of gamete: some containing an R gene, and some containing a Wr gene. That is, some pollen and some eggs contain R genes and some pollen and some eggs contain Wr genes.

So now there are four possible kinds of combination, each of which is equally likely to occur. An R pollen may combine with an R egg, to produce RR offspring. An R pollen may combine with a Wr egg to produce RWr offspring. A Wr pollen may combine with an R egg to produce WrR offspring. Or a Wr pollen may combine with a Wr egg to produce WrWr offspring.

However, the RWr offspring are genetically the same as the WrR offspring because it does not matter which gene comes from which gamete. So now we have three genetically distinct kinds of offspring: RR, RWr (or WrR); and WrWr. Since each combination is equally likely to occur, we can see that for every four offspring – on average – we can expect one RR individual, two RWr (or WrR) individuals and one WrWr individual. Thus these different genetic types occur in the ratio 1 to 2 to 1, generally written 1:2:1. This is another famous Mendelian ratio. Of course, because mating occurs randomly, we won't expect to see this ratio of 1:2:1 if we produce only four offspring. We will see such ratios only when we produce a great many offspring, which Mendel knew perfectly well (and as some of his predecessors emphasised) and which is why he set out from the beginning to produce large numbers.

But finally, as we have also seen, the RWrs and the WrRs both have round seeds, because the R gene dominates the Wr gene. Hence the RWrs and the WrRs look exactly the same as the RRs. Hence the ratio of three-to-one that Mendel observed when he crossed round-seeded plants with wrinkled-seeded plants (or, indeed, crossed any pair of plants with contrasting dominant or recessive characters). You can't tell that the RRs are genetically different from the RWrs or the WrRs until you do further breeding experiments. The offspring of self-fertilised RRs will all have round seeds; but, as we have seen (and indeed is obvious), *some* of the offspring of the self-fertilised RWrs or WrRs will have wrinkled seeds. Mendel's two-year preliminary experiments were to ensure that all the plants he began with were RRs rather than RWrs or WrRs.

Already, albeit explained with some reference to modern terminology, we have most of Mendelian genetics. There is one further vital principle. In general (though not invariably in practice), different characters are inherited *independently* of each other. Mendel showed and described this. Later geneticists called this 'Mendel's law (or principle) of independent assortment' (although Mendel himself did not formally present this 'law' as such).

Thus, among other combinations, he crossed plants that had round seeds with yellow cotyledons with plants that had wrinkled seeds with green cotyledons. The hybrids then all contained genes for round seeds and for yellow cotyledons *and* genes for wrinkled seeds and for green cotyledons. He then allowed these hybrid offspring to self-fertilise. Then, as always, he counted the offspring of this self-crossing. This is what he reports:

In all, 556 seeds were yielded by 15 plants, and of these there were:
    315 round and yellow
    101 wrinkled and yellow
    108 round and green
    32 wrinkled and green.

If you examine these figures you see that they give us another famous 'Mendelian ratio: 9:3:3:1, or 'nine to three to three to one'.

To describe in words why we obtain this ratio would take too many pages. You can probably see the reason intuitively, but as an aid to thought we can present the whole thing as a Latin square, as favoured by fixture secretaries of squash clubs. We simply write all the possible gametes along each axis, and see what the combinations look like. As we see, there are four possible kinds of gamete, giving us sixteen possible combinations. Nine of out of the sixteen contain at least one gene for roundness, and at least one for yellowness, and so the seeds appear round and yellow. Three contain two genes for wrinkliness and at least one gene for yellowness, and so emerge wrinkled and yellow. Three contain at least one gene for roundness and two genes for greenness and so are round and green. Finally, a miserable one out of the whole sixteen contain two genes for wrinkliness and two for greenness, and so is wrinkled and green.

Note again, too, that these figures are simply ratios. You might well produce sixteen offspring – or, though this is less likely, 160 offspring – and produce no wrinkled and green offspring at all. This is why some combinations of characters seem to disappear and re-appear so capriciously in the family trees of creatures which do not have huge numbers of offspring. Human beings have few offspring, which is why, as Darwin noted, it is very difficult indeed to see the Mendelian ratios within any one family tree. Of course you can see Mendelian patterns in human families if the genealogical tree is large enough and you know in advance what you are looking for, which is why genetic counselling works. You can work out for yourself how complex the genetic patterns and ratios become if you consider combinations of three, or four, independent characters at once. You need a very large Latin square to do this and if you were to consider, say, five or six characters, you would need a two-year prison sentence with nothing else to occupy your time to do full justice to the possibilities. In short, Mendel's very simple rules readily produce immensely complicated outcomes. Mendel was well aware of this. His genius was to trace back from the surface complexity to the underlying simplicity and then work outwards again.

I hope we have now dispelled most of the charge of 'luck'. Clearly, Mendel knew exactly what he was doing, and why, and states his reasons with exemplary clarity. Yet one last crumb of calumny remains to be teased out. For some critics say how fortunate it was that Mendel never apparently encountered any characters of a polygenic nature, that is, the kind that are shaped by more than one gene. For such characters are not generally inherited in the 'all-or-nothing' pattern on which Mendel based his rules.

But of course Mendel did encounter such characters. In his initial pea experiments, he describes them and then deliberately puts them to one side because he knew they would introduce unnecessary complications before he had acquired the theoretical equipment to deal with them. Such polygenic characters would have included at least some of those that he said were of a '"more or less" nature, which is often difficult to define'. But in what he calls his 'minor experiments' with two species of *Phaseolus* beans he confronts this problem head-on. Thus he found that when beans of different colours are crossed, the results are complicated:

> Apart from the fact that from the union of a white and a purple-red colouring a whole series of colours results, from purple to pale violet and white, the circumstance is a striking one that among 31 flowering plants only one received the recessive character of the white colour, while in Pisum this occurs on the average in every fourth plant.

A blow to the theory worked out in peas? Not at all; for with remarkable anticipation of twentieth-century ideas he writes:

> Even these enigmatic results, however, might probably be explained by the law governing Pisum if we might assume that the colour of the flowers and seeds of *Ph multiflorus* is a combination of two or more entirely independent colours, which individually act like any other constant character in the plant.

What could be clearer? But of course, Mendel, being Mendel, knew that such easy explanations have to be explored in greater depth: 'It would be well worth while to follow up the development of colour in hybrids by similar experiments, since it is probable that in this way we might learn the significance of the extraordinary variety in the colouring of ornamental flowers.' As we have noted several times above, the typical flowers of cottage gardens – lupins, antirrhinums, stocks – are multicoloured, and seem at first sight to follow no hereditary rules at all. But Mendel saw that by investigating beans, which are harder than peas to keep track of, but not quite as capricious as some others, he (or others) could find the underlying principles even in the hardest cases. Thus we see him edging step by step from the simplest cases to the most difficult; exactly as any modern philosopher of science would recommend.*

Here, then, is Mendel's contribution to the science of genetics. He hypothesised that characters are conveyed from generation to generation by individual Mendelian factors (which we now call 'genes'). The parents possess two complete sets of such factors, the gametes contain only one set, and the genes contained in the gametes are recombined in the next generation to form an individual who resembles both parents, but is uniquely different from either. It makes no difference whether any one gene is inherited from the male parent or the female: they both behave the same. If an individual inherits two different kinds of genes from each of its parents from any one character, then one kind may be dominant and the other may be recessive. As a rule (though not invariably), each gene is inherited independently from all other genes; so that, for example, a pea may have seeds that are round and yellow, or wrinkled and yellow, or round and green, or wrinkled and green.

Those are Mendel's basic ideas. Clearly, though, he already appreciated some of the necessary refinements. He saw that sometimes two different characters may seem to travel together, as white seeds and white flowers go together in garden peas. Clearly, too, as he shows in his 'minor experiments' with *Phaseolus* beans, he appreciates that some characters might be conferred by consortia of genes, working together. He was correct in this and

---

* Mendel also saw another reason why the flowers in cottage gardens are so multicoloured: they are planted close together and interbreed, so that most of the offspring are in fact hybrids. As he says: 'It is only the Leguminosae, like *Pisum*, *Phaseolus* and *Lens* [the lentil] whose organs of fertilisation are protected by the keel, which constitute a noteworthy exception.'

recommended that the point should be followed up, though he never had sufficient time or resources to do so himself.

As we will see in the second half of this chapter, these ideas have been refined and expanded throughout the twentieth century; and with the refinements and expansions they form what is known as 'classical genetics'. Grasp Mendel and the rest falls naturally into place, intricate though it may sometimes be. In short, as the title of this book suggests, all genetics is 'footnotes to Mendel'.

Mendel was indeed a genius; but he was not the only outstanding intellect of the mid-nineteenth century, nor was he the only one interested in heredity. How did he manage to get it all right, effectively to define the subject in a few brief growing seasons, with a few pots of homely garden plants, when other great thinkers were all at sea? It is probably fatuous to erect league tables and to pit Mendel against Darwin; but if we were to do such an invidious thing, I would agree with the majority, that Darwin was the greater, for nothing quite compares to the majestic sweep of his vision. Yet it was Darwin who lamented in 1859: 'no one can say why the same peculiarity in different individuals . . . is sometimes inherited and sometimes not so: why the child often reverts in certain characters to its grandfather, or other much more remote ancestor'; and it was Mendel who, by 1865, had said all that really needed to be said to resolve such issues and a great deal more besides. (There is no excuse for Nathusius, who observed in 1872 that 'the laws of heredity have not yet fallen from the tree of knowledge', because by then they very definitely had.) So what did Mendel bring to the problem that the other great minds did not?

Well, there was, of course, his background, which we have looked at in Chapters 1 and 2: how he was born into a gardening community, brought up among people obsessed with the problems, both practical gardeners and intellectuals, and spent his professional life in a monastery which was, in effect, a research station and as a member of a society (the Brno Natural Science Society) that seemed to include most of the great biologists of mainland Europe. The same kinds of point apply to Darwin, however. At least, Darwin was not born among peasant farmers, but he did consort with gardeners and pigeon fanciers, trying to pick up the same folklore that was in Mendel's bones.

The key difference, though, surely lies in Mendel's approach. First and foremost, he was by inclination a physicist and mathematician. As a physicist it was his instinct to seek out the simplest possible rules that lie behind all natural phenomena and during his formal education at Vienna and elsewhere he was surrounded by people, like Doppler, who emphasised the need for this. As a physicist, too, he was inclined to think of digital mechanisms: in this instance, the notion that heritable characters might be conferred by corresponding, discrete 'factors', and not through the messy mixing of inks and semens. As a mathematician, he knew that if he wanted to make sense of anything in nature he had to quantify and to apply statistics. Again, many of his teachers specifically stressed this. Darwin, by contrast, was innumerate, as he confessed in a letter to a friend when he left school at Shrewsbury in 1828: 'my noddle is not capacious enough to retain or comprehend Mathematics – Beetle hunting and such things, I grieve to say, is my proper sphere.'

Darwin was more than a beetle hunter, of course. He was the greatest naturalist of all time. But herein lies the final and most important distinction. Naturalists seek out and admire the variety of nature. No one has ever known more about nature's variousness than Darwin, but this is the trouble. For every simple case he knew, for every phenomenon, he also knew a hundred exceptions; and as a naturalist, a glorifier of diversity, he could not resist the exceptions. Mendel knew that to get to the core of heredity he had to put aside the exceptions: to identify the simplest possible cases, explore them in full and then work outwards. Darwin's broad vision was perfect, indeed indispensable, for the grand task he set himself: that of teasing out the underlying mechanism of evolution. Mendel's more 'reductionist' and numerical approach was ideally suited to the job that he undertook. They complemented each other perfectly. We have inherited the fruits of their complementary genius. Mendel knew about Darwin, and understood him. Darwin, evidently, did not know about Mendel (though he did recommend to a friend a book which contained references to Mendel's work).

But there is one final ghost to lay to rest.

R. A. Fisher – and Why Mendel Did Not Cheat

R. A. – Sir Ronald – Fisher was one of the great brains of the early twentieth century: a mathematician turned biologist (not dissimilar from Mendel himself, though a better mathematician). As a third-year undergraduate in Cambridge in 1911 he suspected that Galton's ideas of 'biometrics' could and should be reconciled with Mendel's genetics, although most biologists seemed to suppose they were naturally opposed; and by 1918 he had shown how the two sets of notions could be aligned. He made it all clear in 1930 in *The Genetical Theory of Natural Selection*. Fisher was, in short, a key figure in formulating 'the modern synthesis', the harmonisation of Mendel's ideas with Darwin's, which is discussed in Chapter 6; and he remains one of the principal scholars of Mendel's work and one of the elite who truly understood, and could improve upon, Mendel's statistical deliberations.

It was a shock, then, when in 1936 Fisher published an essay entitled 'Has Mendel's Work Been Rediscovered?', in which he argued that Mendel's wonderfully clear statistics – so clear that anyone can see the 3:1 and 9:3:3:1 ratios which underpin his theory – were too good to be true.

The point can be demonstrated by tossing a coin. On average, if there is nothing wrong with the coin or with the toss, heads and tails should occur with equal frequency: 50 per cent each. We all know, however, that if we tossed the coin only twice then we are quite likely to get two heads or two tails. If we tossed it half a dozen times, we might still get half a dozen heads, or half a dozen tails. English captains of cricket tend to call the same every time, which is as good a strategy as any, and in recent years have proved wonderfully adept at losing half a dozen tosses in a row. If we tossed the coin 100 times, however, we would be surprised to get 100 heads, or 100 tails. We would probably be a bit surprised if the ratio of one to the other was greater than, say, 70 to 30. (I believe, in contrast to what most scientists are inclined to say, that human beings are very good at assessing odds intuitively. Most of us would not be surprised if 4 tosses produced 3 heads and one tails; but we would be surprised if 100 tosses produced 75 heads and only 25 tails).

In short, although there is a 50:50 chance of producing heads (or tails) on any one throw, we would not expect to achieve an exact 50:50 ratio in any one series of throws. But we would expect the ratio to move closer and closer to 50:50, the more throws we made. If we made a million throws, we would not expect the discrepancy to be more than a few thousand, which is a very small proportion of the whole million.

Most of us, as I say, know this intuitively; the more throws you make, the closer you are likely to get to the theoretically expected 50:50. Professional statisticians, however, are able to be far more precise. They can say that the chances of getting six heads on the trot are 1 in 64 (one in $2 \times 2 \times 2 \times 2 \times 2 \times 2$); whereas the chances of getting 100 heads on the trot are, well, very small indeed (one in $2 \times 2 \times 2 \ldots$ etc, 100 times). With a little more manipulation they can also work out what the chances are of getting, say, a 90:10 ratio, or an 80:20 ratio, or a 99:1 ratio, in 100 throws – or a 1000, or a million. Statisticians, in short, can work out what the chances are of getting any particular result from a particular experimental set-up.

Mendel demonstrated clearly that in the second generation of self-fertilised offspring the plants with the dominant feature outweighed those with the recessive feature in the ratio 3:1. To be precise, as we have seen, he reported an 'average ratio of 2.98:1, or 3:1'. But, said Fisher, there is very little chance that Mendel could have achieved ratios that were so close to 3:1 with the relatively small samples that he was able to grow in his monastery garden. Indeed, the chances that he could have achieved such fine results are so low as to be incredible. In Fisher's own words:

A serious and almost inexplicable discrepancy has . . . appeared in that in one series of results the numbers observed agree excellently with the . . . ratio which Mendel himself expected, but differ significantly from what should have been expected had his theory been corrected to allow for the small size of his test progenies.

So what did Mendel do? Many people have speculated since. Perhaps some assistant, in a spirit of helpfulness, massaged the results. Perhaps that well-intentioned but misguided assistant transferred seeds somewhat marginal in character from one pile to the other to make the results come out better. Perhaps Mendel was simply too old-fashioned and did not realise that his experiments were actually meant to provide raw data. Perhaps he felt they were for demonstration purposes only and that it was fair game to bend the results so as to make the point more clearly, given that the point was obvious enough. Perhaps, some modern iconoclasts have suggested, he simply cheated. Some, after all, seem very anxious to demonstrate that all scientists cheat as a matter of course; and the fact that Mendel was a cleric reinforces his status as fair game.

Yet it is hard to doubt for one second that Mendel was scrupulously honest. He was a scientist through and through, and knew perfectly well that if data are fiddled then the whole fabric of science collapses. Everything about his life, and the comments of those who remember him, attests to his honesty. He knew he was presenting his results to the greatest scientists in Europe (it wasn't his fault that they ignored them) and in his paper he stresses how necessary it is to repeat his work. Even a cynic must acknowledge that it would be very risky to cheat in such circumstances. Neither did Fisher ever doubt Mendel's probity. For example, in a paper of 1955 Fisher praises Mendel's excellence (as he had done throughout his life) and never mentions the caveats he raised in 1936. Perhaps he was simply tired of the subject. Perhaps he was irritated that others had used his arguments to cast a shadow on Mendel's work and genius.

I do not claim to know the answer. If Fisher couldn't solve it, I certainly am not going to try. I recommend, however, an excellent paper by Teddy Seidenfeld of the Department of Philosophy and Statistics, Carnegie Mellon University, and the LSE, called 'P's in a Pod: Some Recipes for Cooking Mendel's Data'. Seidenfeld makes two main points. First, he suggests that Fisher's analysis is unjust. The essence of his argument is that Mendel anticipated the kinds of objections which Fisher, much later, homed in upon, and designed his experiments in ways that overcame them. This subtlety of design is not directly evident from Mendel's 1866 paper, but it is there if you look. This, says Seidenfeld, answers some of Fisher's criticism, though not all of it.

So what of the rest? Intriguingly, the answer here may be botanical. As we will see later, each 'germ cell' gives rise to four gametes, which, in the case of flowering plants, means four eggs and four grains of pollen. In a hybrid plant each pollen grain has an equal chance of containing a dominant gene (for any particular factor) or a recessive gene (for the same factor). Because the pollen grains are produced in fours, there would then be a chequerboard pattern of grains on the surface of the anther: dominant-gene grains alternating with recessive-gene grains. Peas are self-fertilising, which is why Mendel chose them. Mendel's reported results also show that his own particular peas were low-yielding: he obtained only 30 seeds per plant, while most growers would expect 100 or more. Seidenfeld suggests that in low-yielding plants of the varieties which Mendel grew pollination would *not* be quite random – because the pollen grains were arranged in the chequerboard fashion on the anther. If fertilisation was not random then the results would be biased. In fact, the results would be more or less as Mendel reported them.

Seidenfeld points out that his hypothesis could be tested by repeating Mendel's experiments precisely: growing the same varieties under conditions in which the yields were poor. It would be good to do this. But even if the peas failed Seidenfeld's test, I still would find it impossible to believe that Mendel was in any way to blame. His results may not seem plausible as they stand, but the idea that he cheated is even less plausible.

However, I have said enough about Mendel to make my point: that he was great; that everything since is extrapolation. It is not possible to discuss all the ideas that have emerged since with the same detail. Instead, I shall rush with indecent but I hope useful haste through the main ideas of classical genetics as they unfolded in the twentieth century. Some of them extrapolate from Mendel and some merely provide vocabulary for his own ideas.

A Lightning Overview of Twentieth-Century Classical Genetics

Mendel's work was effectively lost to view from the time he presented it in his lecture of 1865 until 1900 when Carl Correns in Germany, Hugo de Vries in Holland, and Erich von Tschermak in Austria, independently brought it to light. The science of genetics, then, properly begins with the twentieth century. Mendel *might* have lived to see his work revived and vindicated – he would have been seventy-eight in 1900 – but, sadly, he did not.

Mendel, as we have seen, was anxious to show that the rules he had found in peas apply elsewhere; and others soon found the necessary proof. In 1902 William Bateson in England showed from his work on fowl that Mendelian rules apply to animals. Bateson also coined the term 'genetics' in print in 1905, although, as we have seen in Chapter 3, the German *genetische* had already appeared in 1816, albeit, of course, with a pre-Mendelian meaning. In 1909 Bateson's friend Wilhelm Johannsen proposed the term 'gene' to replace the somewhat clumsy 'Mendelian factor'. After that, things moved apace. As we will see in Chapter 5, Archibald Garrod in England began the process that was to link the study of genes – 'genetics' – to biochemistry, and hence into molecular biology; in other words, the study of what genes are and how they work. In the rest of this chapter, however, I will look at the study of how genes behave to produce different patterns of heredity: the study known as 'classical genetics'. For brevity, the account can take the form of an extended glossary of notions.

'BEADS ON A STRING'

When scientists don't really know what things *are*, or even when they do, they like to build 'models' of them: sometimes simply in their heads and sometimes literally. In classical genetics, genes are viewed in a quasi-literal light.

At the end of the nineteenth century microscopists became aware that cells contain 'chromosomes': peculiar thread-like structures that appear when cells are preparing to divide (but disappear again when division is complete and the cell nucleus re-forms). The idea grew that these chromosomes are concerned with heredity. Following the rediscovery of Mendel's work at the start of the twentieth century, biologists began to think of hereditary factors as discrete entities – that is, as 'genes'. What more natural, then, than to think of chromosomes as strings of genes, like beads on a necklace? Now, of course, we know that each chromosome consists of a giant 'macromolecule' of DNA. But in truth the genes *are* positioned end-to-end along the DNA; so the rough-and-ready model that sees chromosomes as necklaces and genes as beads works very well for many purposes. We can say that each creature has as many strings of beads as it has chromosomes.

Indeed, we can hang a great many useful concepts and much accompanying vocabulary on this model. For example, you and I are both human beings, but we are not identical twins. Because we are both human we both in a sense have the same 'genes', but if our genes were literally identical in every detail, then we would be identical twins. So what's going on?

Well, we can simply say that what you and I have in common as human beings is *positions* where particular genes fit on our chromosomes. Each position is known as a 'locus': plural 'loci'. But each gene, in any one locus, *might* come in two or more different forms. Each form, each variant of any one gene, is known as an 'allele' (an abbreviation of Bateson's proposed term, 'allelomorph'). So you and I have the same loci, but we have different alleles, in at least some of those loci. In fact we have about 100,000 loci each, and the genes that are positioned on many of those loci do indeed occur in two or more alleles: some of them in many different forms. Thus the *combination* of alleles that each of us possesses is unique to each human being (except in the case of identical twins); and the number of possible combinations, when you have different alleles at any or many of the 100,000 loci, is effectively infinite.

Human beings are genetically different from, say, oak trees because we have different loci from them; but human beings differ from other human beings, and oak trees from other oak trees, because they have different versions of particular genes, different alleles, in at least some of the loci. In fact, since human beings and oak trees shared an ancestor in the distant past (around a billion years ago) we should not be entirely surprised to find that *some* of the genes that we possess are the same as some of those in oak trees. But they are quite likely to be positioned differently: on different loci.

The total apportionment of genes in any one individual is called its 'genome'; and the study of all the different genes in any one species (or individual) is called 'genomics'. Genes which exist in two or more different allelic forms are said to be 'polymorphic'. Populations of creatures that exist in two or more different forms are also said to be 'polymorphic'. 'Polymorphic', after all, simply means 'many forms', so there is no reason not to apply the term in several different contexts. A gene that exists in only one version in any one population is said to be 'fixed'. This is a breeder's term. It means that no matter what you do, the feature ('character') brought about by that gene cannot vary since there is only one version of the character in the population. The total apportionment of alleles contained in all the genomes in all the individuals in any one breeding population is referred to as the 'gene pool', although it would be more accurate to call it the 'allele pool'. The total number of different alleles within the gene pool is called the 'genetic variation', though, again, it would be more accurate to speak of 'allelic variation'. Scientific vocabulary isn't always as sharp as it ought to be.

Finally, Mendel was keen to emphasise that any character could be recombined, in the offspring, with any other character: a principle sometimes called 'independent assortment'. But when two genes are located close to each other on the same chromosome, they often are passed on as a duo. Then the two are said to be 'linked'; the overall phenomenon is called 'linkage'. Indeed, classical geneticists have been able to work out whether two genes are or are not on the same chromosome, an exercise in 'gene mapping', by seeing whether or not they tend to be inherited together. Then they can work out just how close any two linked genes are to each other by seeing how often they are passed on as a duo.

Darwinian natural selection affects the position of genes on the chromosomes, just as it affects which genes actually survive. Thus we commonly find that genes tend to be linked when they are all contributing to the same physiological system. The most spectacular example of linkage is provided by the hox genes, which control the total layout of an animal body. The different hox genes are closely linked, one to another.

HOMOLOGY, HOMOZYGOSITY, HETEROZYGOSITY, AND MUCH THAT FOLLOWS

Mendel inferred that each adult individual plant contains two sets of heritable factors, or, as we would say, two sets of genes. In fact, as can clearly be seen under the microscope, each cell of each plant or animal contains two complete sets of chromosomes, each one of which may be envisaged as a string of genes. One set is inherited from the mother, the other from the father. The two sets are said to be 'homologous'. Any one gene at any one locus on any one chromosome is also said to be 'homologous' with the equivalent gene on the same locus on the homologous chromosome.

With these very simple ideas, derived from Mendel, we can tighten the vocabulary that Mendel applied to his own experiments and clear up much of the confusion that existed among breeders and biologists before Mendel.

Thus, sometimes, two homologous genes on two homologous chromosomes are identical, one to another. This is because the individual has inherited the same version of that gene, the same allele, from each parent. Then the individual is said to be 'homozygous' for that particular gene. Sometimes, however, an individual will have inherited two different versions of the same gene from its two parents. Then it will have one allele on one chromosome, and a different allele on the equivalent locus on the homologous chromosome. Then the individual is said to be 'heterozygous' for that particular gene. To Mendel and his contemporaries, the term 'heterozygous' was essentially synonymous with the term 'hybrid'.

So now we can apply these notions and terms to Mendel's experiments. Round-seededness in his peas was conferred by one kind of allele; and wrinkled-seededness was conferred by a

101

different but homologous allele. Individuals may be homozygous for either of the alleles; containing either two round-seed alleles or two wrinkled-seed alleles. All the gametes that come from a round-seeded homozygote are bound to contain a round-seed allele, so all the offspring produced by two round-seeded homozygotes are bound to have round seeds. Similarly, all the offspring of two wrinkled-seeded homozygotes are bound to have wrinkled seeds.

However, we must now distinguish between 'genotype' and 'phenotype'. The 'genotype' refers to the genes that an individual contains; and the 'phenotype' refers to its appearance (or chemistry, or behaviour). A pea that is heterozygous for the gene that determines seed shape, an individual with a round-seed allele on one chromosome, and a wrinkled-seed allele on the homologous chromosome, clearly has a different genotype from one that has a round-seed allele on both homologous chromosomes. But because the round-seed allele dominates the wrinkled-seed allele, the heterozygote finishes up with round seeds. Phenotypically, the heterozygote is identical with the round-seed homozygote. In other words, you cannot tell just by looking at a round-seeded pea whether it is homozygous or heterozygous. You can tell only by breeding it and looking at its offspring. Homozygous round-seeds are 'true-breeding' because all their offspring are bound to inherit two copies of the round-seed allele. But heterozygous round-seeds are not true-breeding because they produce some gametes that contain the wrinkled-seed allele; and if two of those wrinkled-seed alleles get together they will produce a wrinkled-seeded offspring. Of course, a wrinkled-seeded plant is bound to be homozygous for the wrinkled-seed gene. If it was heterozygous, containing a round-seed allele as well as the wrinkled-seed allele, it would have round seeds, since the round-seed allele dominates the wrinkled-seed allele. 'Dominant' and 'recessive' are terms introduced by Mendel himself.

The notions of homozygosity and heterozygosity, and of dominance and recessiveness, take us into vast and intriguing territory. For sometimes genes change: that is, they 'mutate' (sometimes under the influence of identifiable 'mutagens' and sometimes, it seems, simply through imperfect copying). If they

102

did not mutate, then there could be no polymorphism. Genes may exist in several or many different allelic forms because, at some time in the past, there has been mutation.

However, mutations are chance events, and only a minority of such events can produce advantages. Most mutations are harmful, or 'deleterious'. Any one population is bound to contain at least some mutant, 'deleterious alleles' (which are sometimes perfunctorily referred to as 'bad genes').

Sometimes deleterious alleles simply kill the creatures that contain them. At least some deaths which occur in the womb or the egg must be caused by such 'lethal mutations'. Sometimes, however, deleterious alleles persist within the gene pool. But how are they able to persist if they are harmful or even lethal? The answer is for three different kinds of reason.

First, and most commonly, many persistent deleterious alleles are recessive. Individuals that are homozygous for such alleles suffer their ill-effects. But in individuals that are heterozygous for such a gene the deleterious allele is silent; the normal, homologous allele dominates. In modern parlance we say that the dominant allele is 'expressed' and the recessive one is not. Natural selection would generally eliminate genes from the population if they killed their possessor every time they appeared. But natural selection cannot eliminate potentially harmful genes if the harmful gene is recessive and so, usually, is simply unexpressed.

Thus potentially harmful alleles lurk in the gene pool, within the genomes of heterozygotes, who are then said to be 'carriers' of the particular gene. However, they *do* cause disease when they are inherited from both parents, to produce an offspring who is homozygous.

During the twentieth century medical scientists have identified at least 5000 different deleterious alleles in human beings which, when present in double-dose in homozygotes, cause obvious and sometimes fatal disease. They are commonly known as 'single gene disorders'. The frequency' (another technical term) with which particular deleterious alleles occur varies from population to population. Among north Europeans the most common single gene disorder is cystic fibrosis. Among people of African descent by far the most common is sickle-cell anaemia. Some Mediterranean peoples and south-east Asians commonly suffer from a family of similar inherited anaemias known as 'the thalassaemias'. Ashkenazi Jews are particularly plagued by Tay–Sachs syndrome; and so on.

With modern medicine, sufferers from these and many other diseases can be helped to live fulfilled lives and may indeed live to have children of their own. Without therapy most would have died before reaching sexual maturity. Some people who might loosely be called 'eugenicists' (more of this in Chapter 10) have suggested that it is a bad thing for the future of the human species to enable, or allow, people suffering from single-gene disorders to breed. This (they argue) simply allows the 'bad genes' to spread, and in the end would be bad for the human species.

Fortunately, this argument is fatuous as well as cruel. First, we may simply observe that ever since these bad genes first appeared in the human gene pool, which in some cases may have occurred hundreds of thousands of years ago, natural selection *has* been eliminating the homozygotes. Without modern medicine the sufferers often could not survive. Yet the bad genes persist. Clearly, mere elimination of homozygotes does not work. Why doesn't it? Because for any one allele, the heterozygotes are bound to outnumber the homozygotes many times over, so the mere elimination of homozygotes makes virtually no difference to the total frequency.

We can see the point by reference to cystic fibrosis. The deleterious allele is present – remarkably – in about 1 in 20 Caucasian people; that is, 1 in 20 are heterozygous 'carriers'. There is thus a 1 in 400 (20 × 20) chance that two carriers will mate together to produce children. Only one in four of those children (on average!) will inherit two copies of the cystic fibrosis allele, so only one in four will actually suffer from the disease. Thus the incidence of cystic fibrosis in the Caucasian population is 1 in 1600 (1 in 400, divided by 4). Thus if we cruelly prevented people with cystic fibrosis from having children (assuming they were able to), we would be tackling only a very small proportion of the people who actually carry the gene; one in 1600, as opposed to 1 in 20. If a deleterious allele is present only in about 1 in 1000 carriers, then the incidence of homozygotes would be 1 in 4 million. That is, the rarer the allele, the greater the discrepancy between the number of heterozygous carriers, and the number of homozygous sufferers. The ratio between homozygotes and heterozygotes is determined by the 'Hardy-Weinberg' principle, another twentieth-century contribution, of great use to genetic counsellors and breeders, which it would not be appropriate to discuss in detail.

Note, finally, that *each* human being is estimated to carry an average of five deleterious alleles that would cause disease if any two carriers produced offspring together. So to eliminate *all* deleterious alleles from the human gene pool we would have to wipe out the species. Adages involving bathwater and babies spring to mind. In general, however, we need have no fears that humanitarian medicine will lead to the decline of the human race. More of this is Chapter 10.

The second reason why apparently deleterious alleles may persist is that at least some of them, and probably more than we know, bring some benefit when present in the heterozygous form. Recessiveness and dominance are not necessarily absolutes. Sometimes the recessive gene is expressed to some extent: the degree of expression is known as the 'penetrance'. Sometimes, therefore, the heterozygotes are a little different, phenotypically, from the homozygotes. And sometimes the heterozygotes have an advantage.

Such reasoning explains why the sickle-cell allele and the thalassaemias are as common as they are. These genes affect the form of the haemoglobin, the red pigment in the blood that carries oxygen. People who possess two copies of the 'normal' gene have normal haemoglobin and do not suffer from inherited anaemia. But people with normal haemoglobin are extremely susceptible to malaria if they live in a malarial region. People who are heterozygous for the sickle allele of one of the thalassaemia alleles, however, are less susceptible. When the malaria parasite invades their red blood cells, the cells collapse and the parasite dies. In Africa, and to a lesser extent in the tropics worldwide, malaria is rife. In such areas, people heterozygous for sickle cell or for thalassaemia have some advantage: a built-in form of protection against a parasite which the immune system seems virtually powerless to ward off. To be sure, the homozygotes tend to die young from inherited anaemia; but this disadvantage, cruel though it is, is outweighed by the protection afforded to the heterozygotes. And, of course, the heterozygotes greatly outnumber the homozygotes. So natural selection positively favours the sickle-cell and the thalassaemia alleles in malarial regions and the alleles are more common than might otherwise be expected. Of course, if the sickle-cell allele became positively common, then natural selection would come down hard upon it, since then too many people would die from inherited anaemia. Thus the level of the sickle-cell allele is higher than expected, but is still low. This is called 'frequency-dependent selection': natural selection favours a particular allele until it becomes too common (too frequent), at which point it is selected against. Frequency-dependent selection produces 'balanced polymorphism': different alleles of the same gene maintained in a more or less constant ratio, one to another.

However, both the above arguments refer to deleterious alleles which are recessive. A few 'bad genes' persist in the human population, even though they are dominant. The most famous example is the one that causes Huntington's chorea, a dreadful disease which inexorably incapacitates the nervous system, and of course curtails life. How can it possibly persist? Because it is not expressed until late in life, after the individual who possesses it has reproduced, and passed the gene on to the next generation. Thus natural selection sometimes (usually) allows deleterious mutant genes to persist by encouraging recessiveness, so the gene is not normally expressed; and sometimes, as in Huntington's, simply by postponing its expression.

The example of cystic fibrosis and sickle cell (and any one of 5000 other examples we might have given) are specific instances of a much broader generalisation; that far more often than not, heterozygosity is a good thing. Darwin noted the phenomenon of 'hybrid vigour', which was already well known to breeders. Creatures that are 'outbred' often tend to be more 'vigorous' than those which are more inbred. We noted in Chapter 3 the case of 'mulattos' or 'half-castes', who may have been despised historically, but often seem extra bright and athletic. In this chapter we noted Mendel's outbred peas, which tended to be taller than the taller parent, even when the other parent was a dwarf (this being the technical term). From the discussion of human single-gene disorders, we can easily infer the reason. Although only a few of our alleles are obviously deleterious, some do not do their job as efficiently as others. If we inherit two doses of an allele which, though not actually *bad*, is not the best, then we will not be as well off as we would if we inherited two different alleles of the same gene, one of which might be a superior type. Thus *in general* heterozygosity is favoured. 'Hybrid vigour' is more generally known these days as 'heterosis'.

This is why some plants have evolved specific 'mating barriers' which prevent inbreeding – mating with other individuals which are genetically too similar. This would lead to excess homozygosity. Some plants, however, are adapted to inbreeding, and can tolerate high degrees of homozygosity. We must assume that such plants do not have too many deleterious alleles in their gene pool. Peas are of this type, of course, natural 'inbreeders'. So are wheat and barley. Maize and millet, by contrast, are natural 'outbreeders', and tend to be severely compromised if they are allowed to become too homozygous. But as we saw from Mendel's extra-tall cross-bred peas, even natural inbreeders benefit from a little extra heterozygosity now and again. However, as discussed in Chapter 2, before the mechanisms of homozygosity and heterozygosity were understood, indeed before the concept of the gene was formulated, the caprices of inbreeding and outbreeding were extremely confusing.

SEX LINKAGE

Darwin asked why inherited characters sometimes appear more in one sex than in the other. Among such characters are haemophilia, which is far more common in boys than in girls (and plagued many of the men and boys in Queen Victoria's family). The reason is that in mammals and birds and many other animals (though not for example in all reptiles) the sex is largely determined by the possession, or non-possession, of particular chromosomes. Female mammals have two X chromosomes, both of which are much the same size as the other chromosomes; while male mammals have one X chromosome and one Y chromosome, and the Y is diminutive. If a deleterious allele occurs on the X chromosome then, in females, it is likely to be balanced by a normal homologous allele in the other X chromosome. But if the same allele occurs on the X chromosome in a male, then it may well find itself unopposed by any homologous allele, since the diminutive Y chromosome may not contain any homologue. The allele that leads to haemophilia in humans occurs on the X chromosome and has no homologue in the Y. So whenever it occurs in the males it leads to disease. Female haemophiliacs are possible, but are produced only when a haemophiliac male mates with a carrier female: a rare event. Incidentally, the X and Y chromosomes are called 'sex chromosomes' and the rest (which are the same in both male and female mammals) are called 'autosomal chromosomes'.

POLYGENIC AND PLEIOTROPIC

Mendel deliberately homed in on characters that clearly had a simple hereditary basis; what twentieth-century geneticists called 'single gene characters'. However, as Mendel well knew, only a minority of characters are determined so simply, by 'single genes'. Most are influenced by whole batteries of genes, working in concert. Such characters are said to be 'polygenic'. In humans the general character of the hair and skin are each influenced by whole batteries of genes.

It also became apparent in the twentieth century that many genes, perhaps most, affect more than one character; and that the different characters that may be affected may be very different and apparently have very little connection. Thus the deleterious allele of cystic fibrosis affects, principally, both the lungs and the pancreas. Such many-actioned genes are said to be 'pleiotropic'.

If, to Mendel's simple rules of heredity, we now stir in the notion that many (perhaps most) characters are polygenic in origin, and that many (perhaps most) genes are pleiotropic in action, then we can quickly see intuitively how those simple rules, when applied in practice, can lead to endlessly complex results. This does not mean that Mendel was a simple man, unable to grasp complexity. It means instead that he was a genius, able to see the simplicity that lies beneath the astonishing complexity of nature.

THE MATTER OF PLOIDY

Finally, we noted earlier – Mendel implied as much – that creatures like us and oak trees and fungi (though not all creatures) contain two sets of chromosomes in each of their body cells. Such creatures are said to be 'diploid'. Gametes, however – and some adult organisms – contain only one set of chromosomes, and they are said to be 'haploid'. In general, the number of sets of chromosomes in an organism is referred to as its 'ploidy'.

However, before a diploid cell divides, it doubles each of its chromosomes. After this doubling has occurred, a normally diploid cell is, in fact, 'tetraploid': containing four sets of chromosomes. But in some organisms, including a great many plants, the cells are normally tetraploid (and after the chromosomes have divided, as a warm-up to cell division, they are octoploid). Organisms with more than two sets of chromosomes are said to be 'polyploid'.

The ability of plants to become polyploid enables them to produce new species, apparently out of the blue. Thus when creatures of different species mate, they often cannot produce viable, fertile hybrids because their chromosomes are incompatible. The chromosomes need to co-operate with their homologues in order to produce gametes; and if the two sets of chromosomes inherited from the two parents are different, then no one chromosome has a convincing homologue with which to team up. Sometimes, however, a haploid gamete from one kind of plant combines with a haploid gamete from another, related but different, kind of plant, to produce a diploid, hybrid offspring; and then all the chromosomes in that diploid offspring double *without* subsequent cell division, to produce a tetraploid organism. By doubling, each chromosome acquires an instant homologue. So the tetraploid offspring of two diploid parents can produce gametes and so can be fertile. But the tetraploid offspring cannot now interbreed with either parent and so has formed a new

109

species. Thus swedes are perfectly fertile tetraploid hybrids formed by the mating of turnips and cabbages, although turnips and cabbages are different species. Speciation by tetraploidy seems to be common in plants, both in the wild and in cultivation. It can be seen in whole series of wild aloes, for example (which are succulent plants that grow in Africa). The domestic European potato is a tetraploid, produced by doubling the chromosomes in a South American diploid ancestor. Bread wheat is a hexaploid hybrid, containing six sets of chromosomes, the complete genomes of three wild ancestral grasses. Animals are clearly much less tolerant of polyploidy.

It would be possible to go on discussing such ramifications more or less indefinitely. Twentieth-century geneticists were busy and many were exceedingly brilliant. I maintain, however, that *most* of the principal ideas are outlined in the thirty or so preceding paragraphs, and that if you can see the point of them then you would be able at least to start to comprehend the vast corpus of twentieth-century genetic scholarship. I also maintain that most of the ideas outlined above extrapolate quite readily from the ideas of Mendel.

At this point the story bifurcates. Some twentieth-century biologists asked what genes actually are and how they work; and out of this came the practical crafts of biotechnology, with all its present-day, extraordinary power. Others, in more theoretical and philosophic vein, sought to reconcile Mendel's ideas of heredity with Darwin's theory of evolution, to see where that would lead. I will discuss these two threads in the following chapters.

5

What Genes Are and How They Work

At the start of the twentieth century the newly defined concept of
the 'gene' was still an abstraction: a 'factor', as Mendel had said,
which affected the phenotype of a creature – the way it looked and
behaved – in particular ways. The whole of 'classical' genetics,
which came of age in the early decades of the twentieth century,
treats genes as abstractions, or at least as beads on a string. Yet
early in the twentieth century, thanks to the insight of an
outstanding English physician, Sir Archibald Garrod, biologists
gained some insight into what genes actually *do*: to whit, they
make proteins. The best part of another half-century passed
before anyone could be sure what genes actually *are*: they are
stretches of DNA. The three-dimensional structure of DNA was
made clear in the 1950s and this insight gave rise to a new
discipline of science known as 'molecular biology'. For the past
half century (as they surely will for centuries to come) the new
molecular biologists have sought to understand how DNA works
its magic, with many a surprise along the way.

So now at the start of the twenty-first century biologists can
still think of genes in abstract terms when it suits them to do so,
but they can also think of them as chemical entities, involved in
complicated chemistry. It is often appropriate for biologists of
many kinds – breeders, physicians, conservation biologists,
evolutionary psychologists – to think of genes as beads on strings:
classical genetics is alive and well and always will be. Increasingly,
however, classical genetics may cross-refer to molecular biology
and then approach genes as an exercise in chemistry. The two in

111

combination are powerful. Classical genetics underpins the crafts of agricultural breeding and genetic counselling; and molecular biology has generated the technology of genetic engineering. This chapter traces the shift in understanding that took place during the twentieth century and which still continues: the perception of genes *qua* beads to genes *qua* discrete chemical entities that carry out specific tasks (and can be manipulated by genetic 'engineers').

First Stirrings: The Late Nineteenth Century

The hiatus between Mendel's announcement of his pea experiments in the 1860s and the rediscovery of his work at the start of the twentieth century is regrettable; but there were important developments nonetheless. First, in the 1860s, chromosomes were discovered. Biologists watched living cells dividing. Before they do so the nucleus, the most conspicuous feature of the cell, simply disappears; or, to be more precise, the membrane that surrounds the nucleus breaks down, so that the nuclear contents suddenly become continuous with the surrounding cytoplasm. When this happens, a small battalion of strange entities swim into view that will absorb coloured dyes, hence their name: 'chromosome' is Greek (or at least Greek-ish) for 'coloured body'.

Soon it became clear that these 'chromosomes' come in pairs: each one has a 'homologous' partner. It was clear, too, that each species has its own characteristic number and pattern of chromosomes. Human beings, for example, have 46 chromosomes: 2 homologous sets of 23. Chimpanzees have 48: 2 homologous sets of 24. Fruit flies have 4 chromosomes. Cabbage has 18: 2 sets of 9. There is no particular rhyme or reason (or at least, none that is known) why any one species should have any particular number.

Then in the early 1900s three American biologists working independently, Clarence McClung, Nettie Stevens and Edmund Wilson, found that in grasshoppers and other insects the different sexes had different chromosomes. At least, *most* of the chromosomes in the males and the females were the same. But whereas the females had two X chromosomes – the name 'X' was conferred by Nettie Stevens – the males had only one. Clearly the number of X chromosomes correlated with the sex. But was it possible, asked McClung, Stevens and Wilson, that the number of X chromosomes did not merely correlate, but actually *determined* sex? Nowadays we know that in many animals (though not all), one pair of chromosomes does indeed determine the sex (although many other factors influence secondary sexual characteristics). These are the 'sex' chromosomes. The rest, the majority, are the 'autosomal' chromosomes. Thus in mammals, females have two X chromosomes while males have one X matched by a diminutive Y.

Even more exciting, though, was the behaviour of chromosomes during cell division, which was first described in detail in the 1880s. The division is conducted with military precision. We need not bother with the details, they are in all the textbooks, but a few salient points are in order. First, when the chromosomes first appear (as the nuclear membrane breaks down) they appear to be *doubled* structures. Thus each of the 46 chromosomes of a human being appears to be shaped like a cross or like a pair of scissors, each chromosome appearing as two distinct entities joined at one point (which is called the *centromere*). In fact, each entity in each doubled chromosome is at this point called a *chromatid*, as if it was a diminutive, a half-chromosome. But it is not. Functionally, each so-called 'chromatid' operates as an entire chromosome and the two chromatids are exact copies of each other. Anyway, cell division begins when the centromeres break down and each pair of chromatids are separated – and once they are separated, the chromatids are called chromosomes again. So after the chromosomes have split neatly down the middle we have two complete sets of chromosomes (two complete sets of 46, in the case of human beings). These two sets now separate (they are pulled and pushed apart by strands of protein in the cytoplasm) and each collection of 46 chromosomes now acquires a new nuclear membrane. So now we have a cell with two complete nuclei. Now the cytoplasm divides between the two nuclei to produce two complete cells.

The method by which the chromosomes divide ensures that both daughter cells finish up with identical sets of chromosomes. This kind of chromosome division is called *mitosis*.

(Gametes are produced by a more elaborate method of cell division known as meiosis; but description of this had to wait until the twentieth century. Meiosis roughly resembles mitosis, but is a two-stage process. In the first stage ['Meiosis-I'] there is no separation of chromosomes: already doubled structures seek out their homologous partners and they cleave together. Then they essentially intermingle: bits of each chromosome interchange with equivalent bits from its homologue. This interchange of chromosomal material is called 'crossing over'. The result is to produce a new complete set of 'recombined' chromosomes, each of which contains material from *both* the parent homologues. These two paired sets of recombined chromosomes now separate in the phase known as 'Meisosis-II', or 'reduction division'. Without further doubling of chromosome material, each set of chromosomes from each pair separates from its homologue. The final result of meiosis is to produce four cells, each of which is haploid, containing just one complete set of chromosomes; and each of those chromosomes is a unique new entity, combining genetic material from both parent homologues. Each of the four haploid cells now matures to become a gamete, a mature sperm or egg.)

But why would the cell go to such lengths to divide its chromosomes so precisely unless the chromosomes were supremely important? If they are important, then for what? The great August Weismann suggested in the 1880s that their role might be to pass on hereditary information. This suggestion is the perfect complement to Mendel's own observations. Mendel suggested that hereditary information is passed on in the form of discrete particles with numerical precision; and in mitosis we can see physical entities dividing as precisely as could be required. Many have said what a shame it was that Darwin did not know of Mendel's work. What a pity it was, too, that Weismann was apparently unaware of it.

But when Mendel's work resurfaced in the 1900s, biologists did not immediately perceive how neatly his ideas on hereditary factors chimed with the real, observable physical behaviour of the chromosomes. William Bateson, though a pioneer of the new genetics, seemed positively distraught by the thought that the

114

chromosomes might actually carry the genes (for reasons I confess I cannot fathom). Some scientists like to suggest that science is unswervingly logical, but that simply is not the case. It requires counter-intuitive, wild leaps of imagination (which in turn requires creative genius). It is even less true that the history of science is unswervingly logical, with brick placed neatly on brick to create an edifice of undisputable truth. Science is a human activity and its history is as messy and perverse as that of all human dealings.

These were the first stirrings of the physical basis of heredity. There is one more thread in this story, again from the nineteenth century. In 1869 a Swiss biochemist called Johann Friedrich Miescher working at Tübingen in Germany discovered DNA in pus cells. He didn't know what it was, of course, and simply called it 'nuclein' (the name 'nucleic acid' was coined much later, in 1889, by another scientist, named Richard Altmann). Then in the 1870s Miescher studied nuclein in the sperm of Rhine salmon and concluded that it might be 'the specific cause of fertilisation'. Note again how even at this late date it was difficult to differentiate between factors that have to do with fertility and those that have to do with heredity. Miescher was clearly on to something, however. He perceived, at least, that his 'nuclein' could be highly significant. But he died in 1895 aged only fifty-one, never knowing what his discovery would lead to.

Thus at the start of the twentieth century there were some solid pieces of information: Mendel's genetic rules, Weismann's insight into the possible significance of chromosomes and Miescher's discovery of DNA. Of course it was not obvious at the time how these threads of information fitted together. That is always the way in science. I hate the metaphor which says that science is a 'jigsaw', waiting for bits to be brought together, but sometimes it is appropriate. Sometimes it seems that some bits are stashed in a file somewhere in Germany, and other bits are tucked in drawers in England, and other bits again may be in some engineer's head in the United States; each one able to make sense of the others, but with no obvious way to bring them together. In practice, another half century passed before these key observations of nineteenth-century genetics (or what we now call genetics) were brought properly together. Yet early in the twentieth century, remarkably early, biologists gained insight into what genes really do; although it would be some decades before they knew what genes actually *are*, or how they operate at the molecular level.

What Genes Do

Again, we can begin this part of the story with two key discoveries from the nineteenth century. First, early in that century chemists became fully aware that the chemistry of living things is not completely different, qualitatively, from the everyday chemistry of the laboratory. There is continuity between the two; between 'living' and 'non-living'. The compound urea, a principal excretory product of mammals, was analysed and found to contain nitrogen and carbon. Thus 'organic chemistry' was born: the chemistry of organisms, but more to the point – and less restrictively – the chemistry of carbon. This was one of the first serious nails in the coffin of 'vitalism', the ancient notion which held that life requires some extra vital 'spark' quite beyond the bounds of normal chemistry. (Clearly, life *might* require extra forces, over and above those of mere chemistry, but even if that were so it was clear that much of what living things do can be analysed in terms or ordinary chemistry. But there was certainly no *a priori* reason to assume that life *had* to partake of some extra 'vital' spark).

Later in the nineteenth century biologists became aware of catalysts within the cells known as 'ferments', later known as 'enzymes', which drive and control the metabolism. In 1897 yet another great German, Eduard Buchner, was studying such 'ferments' in yeast. These, after all, were the agents that turned grapes into wine and malted barley into beer. Buchner ground up the yeast to release the cell contents for further study. He decided to store the yeast juice overnight and to do this he added sugar as a preservative, just as a cook adds sugar to fruit to make jam. When he came back in the morning, however, the juice of the yeast had fermented the sugar, just as the whole yeast organism was known to do. This was the first demonstration that 'ferments' could function perfectly well even when they were separated from the cells that contained them. Buchner's discovery may be taken to mark the birth of biochemistry and dealt another blow to the ancient conceit of vitalism.

The idea of the enzyme as the catalyst of metabolism was widely established in the early twentieth century when Archibald Garrod, at St Bartholomew's Hospital in London, was studying the peculiar disorder known as alkaptonuria. Patients with alkaptonuria have peculiar urine, which turns black on exposure to air. This does not matter in itself, though it is important in diagnosis. What does matter is the arthritis that patients tend to suffer later in life.

Anyway, Garrod and the energetic William Bateson showed that alkaptonuria runs in families and is most common in families where cousins marry each other. Effectively, although the numbers were too small for statistical significance, they showed that the disease followed a Mendelian pattern of inheritance. Garrod then showed that sufferers from alkaptonuria excrete homogentisic acid (HA), which is the material that turns black in air. HA is present in food, but in people with 'normal' enzymes it is broken down chemically before excretion. In a lecture to the Royal College of Physicians in 1908 Garrod suggested that alkaptonuria was an 'inborn error of metabolism'. Later, he described three more such 'inborn errors'.

Garrod hypothesised that the failure to break down homogentisic acid must be due to a defect in a particular enzyme. Since the disease seemed to have a simple genetic basis – that is, the pattern of inheritance suggested that a single recessive gene was at work – he deduced that the failure in the enzyme must be due to a defect in the gene. Thus he coined the brilliant adage 'One gene, one enzyme'. This was a wonderful insight, a resounding inference from a simple observation that was worthy of Mendel himself.

Garrod's adage was confirmed in the 1940s by George Beadle and Edward Tatum at Stanford University, California. They worked with the orange breadmould, *Neurospora crassa*, which normally can live on an irreducibly modest diet of inorganic salts, sugar and the vitamin known as biotin. Beadle and Tatum irradiated the *Neurospora* with X-rays and then crossed the resulting mutants with healthy *Neurospora* that had not been irradiated. The offspring of such a cross could no longer live on the simple diet. They needed extra nutrients in order to survive. Beadle and Tatum inferred that the genetic mutations caused by the X-rays had robbed the mould of its ability to produce the enzymes they needed to synthesise an adequate diet from simple ingredients. Garrod studied a naturally occurring genetic defect in humans and Beadle and Tatum studied an artificially induced defect in a fungus, but they both reached the same conclusion: one gene, one enzyme.

This seminal observation was then extended. Chemically speaking, all enzymes belong to the grand class of organic compounds known as proteins. Many thousands of proteins function as enzymes. Others are primarily structural – all cell membranes consist of proteins interwoven with fats. Fingernails, hair and muscles are proteins. Others function as hormones, including insulin. The pigments within the blood that carry oxygen – haemoglobin in vertebrates and some other animals, haemocyanin in molluscs and others – consist mainly of protein. Antibodies, which the body produces to ward off anything foreign, including pathogens, are proteins. Proteins, in short, run the show; they form the structure, they direct the metabolism, they run messages, they form the defensive forces. We may see the genes as the central directors of the cell's activities, but the proteins are the players; the operatives.

In the 1950s the American chemist Linus Pauling made an observation directly analogous to that of Garrod. He perceived that sickle cell is caused by a defect in haemoglobin; and that the disease is inherited, apparently in a simple Mendelian fashion (insofar as can be inferred when the number of offspring is too low for rigorous statistics), so that it is probably brought about by a single Mendelian gene. So just as Garrod had inferred that a defective gene produces a defective enzyme, Pauling surmised that a defective gene leads to defective proteins in general. Garrod's 'one gene, one enzyme' became 'one gene, one protein'.

'One gene, one protein' should not be taken too literally. Many proteins, at least in their finished form, require several genes working together: sometimes different genes make different parts of the protein; often oligosaccharides (middle-sized sugars) or metals need to be added before the protein is fully functional; and although proteins largely fold themselves into their finished shape, they are often given a helping hand. The helping hands are typically supplied by other proteins produced by other genes. Most phenotypic characters, too, are polygenic, requiring many different genes; and most genes are pleiotropic, affecting more than one character. But the central observation 'one gene, one protein' is the simple case that encapsulates the essence. All other cases (albeit the majority) are elaborations.

After Garrod, then, biologists knew what genes do; and Beadle and Tatum, and then Pauling, sewed the matter up beyond reasonable doubt. Until the 1940s, however, when the age of classical genetics was well advanced, it was not at all clear what they actually *are*.

What Are Genes?

Biologists tend to say as a form of shorthand that genes 'make' proteins but no one ever supposed this is literally the case. What they do (as was inferred from a very early stage) is to provide the code on which particular proteins are based.

But just as proteins are astonishingly versatile in function, so they are correspondingly variable in structure, for their structure determines their function. Structurally, in fact (or at least in effect), they are infinitely variable. So the underlying genetic code must be correspondingly versatile. If genes themselves are chemical entities, and no serious biologist in the twentieth century supposed otherwise, then the code they provide must be as versatile as the things they code for. But what, in all of nature, is as versatile and various as a protein? For a time it seemed that the answer was 'Nothing – apart from another protein.' Small wonder, then, that biologists in the early twentieth century tended to suppose that genes, too, were proteins. Erwin Schroedinger was a particle physicist rather than a biologist, but nonetheless, in 1944, he wrote a book called *What Is Life?* which was highly influential and in which he assumed that genes were themselves made of proteins.

The known biology seemed to support this idea. By the 1940s it was beyond reasonable doubt that the chromosomes are involved in heredity, that indeed they carry the hypothetical abstractions known as 'genes'. So what in practice do chromosomes contain? Chemical analysis revealed only two components: proteins and the stuff which Miescher had discovered in the 1860s, nuclein, *alias* nucleic acid. Protein was already known to be astonishingly various; but nuclein seemed to be rather boringly uniform. It was reasonable to conclude that the genes resided in the protein component of the chromosomes and that the nucleic acid was simply a helpmeet, or perhaps merely provided a suitable environment.

But let us look at proteins more closely and seek the source of their variousness. The properties of a protein – whether it behaves as an enzyme and, if so, which one; or whether it can function as piece of fingernail or a muscle fibre – depend, in the end, on its three-dimensional, sculptural form, which chemists call its 'tertiary structure'. But whatever strange and intricate form a protein finally assumes, it begins life in the form of a one-dimensional chain. The finished protein is like a ship's cable, lying in a heap on the dockside, except that the finished shape is far from random; it is moulded as precisely as a Henry Moore sculpture. The chain is folded into the finished form partly by 'self-assembly' – it folds the way it does partly because that's the way it is – and partly with the help of subsidiary proteins (known as 'chaperonins') and other enzymes. In the end, though, however the folding is carried out, the tertiary structure of the finished, functional protein depends absolutely on the 'primary' structure of the initial chain.

So of what does the basic chain consist? Emil Fischer of Germany (where else?) showed in the early 1900s that proteins are strings of sub-units known as amino acids. Each amino acid is a molecule in its own right; so a protein 'molecule' can properly be called a 'macromolecule'. Since proteins are infinite in structure, you might suppose that there is an infinity of amino acids. Organic chemists, in the laboratory, can indeed make as many different kinds of amino acids as they choose: but nature, it turns out, makes do with about twenty. All the many millions of different proteins in all the many creatures on Earth are compounded from that basic twenty or so (most of which, though not all, occur in the proteins found in human bodies). In fact, the amino acid is to the protein what the letter is to the word. All 415,000 or so English words in the *Oxford English Dictionary* are compounded from just twenty-six letters; and those same letters, with a few accents here and there, also code adequately for the many thousands of other languages and dialects used throughout the world.

The task, then, for the gene, is simply to ensure that amino acids of around twenty different kinds are lined up in the right order. The infinity of different forms of protein that are seen in nature (or can simply be imagined in our heads) will then follow naturally.

So let us look again at nuclein, to see if it might be up to the task after all. Miescher showed that nuclein was an acid and further analysis quickly showed that it contained a sugar, which, in the 1920s, turned out to be deoxyribose. Hence nuclein was given the name deoxyribonucleic acid, or DNA for short. Miescher had shown that DNA is confined to cell nuclei, but in the 1920s Robert Feulgen of Germany went one step further and showed, by judicious staining, that it was exclusive to the chromosomes. But then another, similar 'nucleic' acid turned up, which in fact was found in the cytoplasm at least as much as in the nucleus. This second acid contained a similar but different sugar, called ribose. Hence it was called ribonucleic acid, alias RNA.

We must still ask, though, could DNA provide the variety needed to code for the infinity of proteins? The chemical evidence, at first sight, suggests not. It became clear in the first few decades of this century that the two nucleic acids consist of chains of smaller molecules, just as proteins do: not amino acids, in this case, but nucleotides. But whereas there are twenty different kinds of amino acids within protein chains, there are only *four* kinds of nucleotides within DNA or RNA. Furthermore, the different nucleotides all seem much of a muchness.

Each nucleotide has three components: a sugar (deoxyribose in DNA, ribose in RNA); a phosphate radical; and a base, which was either a purine or a pyrimidine. The sugars and phosphates are the same in every DNA or RNA nucleotide. The only source of variation lies in the four bases. Each nucleotide of DNA either contains one of the two purines: adenine, A, or guanine, G; or else it contains one of two pyrimides: cytosine, C, or thymine, T. RNA is much the same, but the bases differ slightly: uracil, U, a pyrimidine, is substituted for thymine. How can a DNA chain, with only four different kinds of component, provide an adequate code for a protein that has twenty different kinds of component?

It still doesn't seem to make sense that DNA, apparently so boring chemically, can provide the code for proteins, which are infinitely various. Yet the twentieth century provided a succession of experiments that first hinted and finally demonstrated beyond doubt that DNA is indeed the stuff of genes, and that proteins are merely the products. In the 1920s an Englishman, Frederick Griffith, set the ball rolling with his work on the bacterium pneumococcus. The normal, 'virulent' form of pneumococcus causes disease in mice, but it loses its virulence if it is first killed by heat. There are also nonvirulent strains that do not cause disease at all. But Griffith showed that if nonvirulent living pneumococci were injected into mice together with killed virulent pneumococci then the mice died, *even though neither form alone was capable of causing disease*. In other words, the two kinds of bacterium, though each deficient in some way, could combine their strengths and between them reacquire the quality of virulence. There was thus an exchange of 'information' between the two kinds; an exchange which, as is now evident, is analogous to sex in animals and plants.

Then in the 1940s Oswald T. Avery and his colleagues at the Rockefeller Institute Hospital in New York found that there was a specific material that was transferred from the virulent pneumococcus to the nonvirulent type, and could 'transform' the nonvirulent type into the virulent type. So what was this transforming material? He treated it with a protease, an enzyme that breaks down protein, but it did not lose its ability to transform. Therefore, the transforming material was not a protein. Then he treated it with an enzyme that was known to destroy DNA and the ability to effect transformation was lost. Thus, he concluded, the transforming material was DNA. Avery announced these results in 1944.

The second significant line of enquiry that effectively proved the role of DNA in conveying hereditary information involved viruses of the kind known as *bacteriophage*, usually shortened to *phage*. Phage comes from the Greek for 'eat', and phage viruses do in fact make their living as parasites of bacteria (illustrating Jonathan Swift's adage that 'a flea/ Hath smaller fleas that on him prey;/ And these have smaller fleas to bite 'em,/ And so proceed *ad infinitum*'). In particular, biologists studied phages that multiply within the bacterium *Escherichia coli*, which lives in the guts of animals. Inside an *E coli* host, a single phage can produce several hundred replicates of itself within twenty minutes, but by the 1940s microbiologists already knew that they can do a great deal more besides. They can also exchange genetic information. Thus, if different mutant phages are allowed to infect a single *E coli*, it isn't long before *normal* types of phage begin to appear: different individuals have evidently combined the 'good qualities' from two or more otherwise defective phages. The parallels with Griffith's and Avery's pneumococcus experiments are obvious.

Viruses are structurally much simpler than bacteria. By the middle of this century, phages were known to consist of a central core of DNA and an outer coat of protein. In 1952, at Cold Spring Harbor, Long Island, Alfred Hershey and Martha Chase showed that only the DNA of phage entered the bacteria that they attack. The protein coat remained on the outside. Thus the subsequent reproduction of entire phages within the bacterial host was orchestrated by DNA alone. Presumably, the exchange of information between phages was also enacted through DNA.

In short, more and more evidence showed that hereditary information – genes – was in fact encapsulated in DNA. So now the question is: 'How can a molecule that apparently has a rather boring basic structure, being made of only four basic components, provide a code for molecules that have a much more complicated structure? This can be answered only by describing the structure of DNA in more detail. Some biologists, though by no means all, realised at the start of the 1950s that this was one of the key issues of biology. The answer did not come easily.

The Structure of DNA

The general model of DNA that is now accepted was first proposed in 1953 by the English physicist-turned-biologist Francis Crick and the young American chemist-turned-biologist James Watson, who worked together at Cambridge. Crick and Watson were the great synthesisers. Their strength lay not in performing key experiments, or in compiling crucial data, but in making sense of the observations of others. Biology needs its craftspeople, who can manipulate delicate cells and instruments; but it also needs its thinkers, who can make sense of the data thus provided. Sometimes manual dexterity and depth of insight are combined in one person. Some great scientists are also great craftspeople, just as some (surprisingly many!) composers are virtuosos. But dexterity and imagination do not always go together. Crick is a great thinker, but never claimed to be manually adroit.

The data from which Crick and Watson synthesised their model came first from analytical and physical chemistry, and then from attempts to describe and measure directly the physical structure of the DNA molecule, both with the electron microscope and, most important of all, by X-ray crystallography.

We have already looked at the early chemical findings, that DNA consists of chains of nucleotides. Two outstanding pieces of chemistry after the Second World War enriched the picture enormously. First, by 1953 the British chemist Alexander Todd had shown that the nucleotides are joined together via the phosphates. In fact, the phosphates linked sugars in adjacent nucleotides, always joining the number 3 carbon in one deoxyribose to the number 5 carbon in the next one along. This observation alone gives a rough insight into the overall form of the finished molecule. At least it shows what shapes the complete molecule *cannot* assume.

Observations elsewhere revealed subtleties in the proportions of the four bases in DNA. Biochemists of an earlier age assumed that all four types – A, G, C and T – would be present in equal amounts: in other words that DNA was just a boring polymer, like polythene, with long chains of identical units. But after the Second World War it became clear that the four bases were *not* present in equal amounts, so DNA was not like polythene. Furthermore, a highly intriguing finding, the proportions of the four nucleotides differed in DNA from species to species.

Then in the 1940s Erwin Chargaff, an Austrian biochemist working at Columbia University, added one further and highly pertinent insight. He showed that, whatever the total amounts of the four bases, the amount of A always equalled the amount of T; and the amount of G always equalled the amount of C. We might think of several entirely uninteresting reasons why this might be so. But in fact the real reason proved to be very interesting indeed, as became evident in the early 1950s and will be revealed in a few paragraphs' time.

In addition, twentieth-century scientists were able increasingly to explore the structure of complex molecules directly. The electron microscope, in general use after the Second World War, showed that DNA molecules were thread-like: many thousands of angstroms long, but only 20 angstroms thick (an angstrom is one 10-millionth of a millimetre). Since individual nucleotides were only 3 angstroms thick, DNA was obviously compounded from many thousands of them.

But the crucial technique was X-ray crystallography, developed in England from the start of the First World War first by William Bragg and then by his son Lawrence, for which they both received Nobel Prizes. The general idea was to deduce the arrangement of atoms in crystals by firing X-rays at them. The atoms scatter the X-rays, and from the pattern of the diffractions (as revealed on a photographic plate) the position of the atoms can be inferred (the necessary calculations having been done). Early work was carried out on very simple compounds such as sodium chloride, but even before the Second World War W T. Astbury of Leeds University felt confident enough to begin such work on DNA. It is remarkably easy to extract DNA – this has become a standard exercise in school laboratories – and it manifests in a form like fluffy cotton. But, when wetted, it becomes tacky and can be drawn into long threads in which the macromolecules line up in parallel: a regular arrangement that is crystal-like. However, to prepare crystals good enough for X-ray is no mean technical feat.

The final phase was begun after 1949 at King's College, London, by Maurice Wilkins and Rosalind Franklin, using DNA prepared in Bern by Rudolf Singer. Crucially, they showed that the DNA chains are arranged in a helix, with the purines and pyrimidines on the inside and the sugar-phosphate backbone (more of a scaffold than a backbone) on the outside. They also showed that each purine or pyrimidine occupied 3.4 angstroms, and that each turn of the helix was 34 angstroms deep, so there were 10 nucleotide molecules per coil. But the diameter of the helix (as was already known) was 20 angstroms, which was too large, if the DNA helix contained only one chain. Perhaps, then, it contained two chains; or perhaps (as Linus Pauling hypothesised at one point) it contained three.

There was one further, highly intriguing line of thought: not a piece of evidence but an idea, put forward in 1940 by Linus Pauling and Max Delbruck at Caltech. Perhaps, they said, the replication of genes involved a splitting, with each half of each gene acting as a template for the re-creation of a complementary half.

Finally, in Cambridge in 1953, James Watson and Francis Crick put everyone out of their misery by proposing that the DNA macromolecule in fact consists of two helical chains that run in opposite directions, 'head to tail'. This was the famous *double helix*, now the favourite symbol of every institution which has anything whatever to do with molecular biology.

The two DNA chains in the double helix are held together by weak chemical bonds (hydrogen bonds) between the bases that run along the centre: adenine in one chain joins to thymine in the other; cytosine in one links with guanine in the other. This explains the ratio observed by Chargaff. One chain thus complements the other precisely: if there is a sequence of bases running CATTG in one chain, then it will be matched by GTAAC in the other. In principle, though not of course in detail, this is more or less the same kind of mechanism suggested more than a decade earlier by Pauling and Delbruck.

Watson and Crick described their wonderful vision of DNA in the international journal of science, *Nature*, in 1953. Their paper occupied a mere 800 words: tight as a sonnet. It ended with a wonderfully disarming sentence: 'It has not escaped our notice that the specific pairing we have postulated [between A and T, G and C] immediately suggests a possible copying mechanism for the genetic material.'

This was the turning point. Molecular biology and all that comes from it ('genetic engineering', DNA fingerprinting and all the rest) begin here. Crick, Watson and Wilkins shared the Nobel Prize in Medicine in 1962 (Rosalind Franklin having died at the tragically early age of thirty-eight in 1958).

Nowadays, too, the structure of chromosomes is perfectly understood. It transpires that the long, long double helices of DNA are wound around a central core of proteins known as histones. The histones have several functions, but one very obvious one is to provide a robust scaffold that allows the DNA to be hauled bodily about during mitosis and meiosis. Each chromosome contains just one continuous DNA double helix, wound round and round the central histone core. The chromosomes appear during cell division and disappear at other times because when the cell is not dividing the DNA macromolecules are released from the binding core of histones and spread themselves out throughout the nucleus. They can function much more freely in this spread-out form than when they are packed up tightly ('condensed' is the technical term) for the purposes of division. But when the macromolecules are spread out, they are not visible individually through the light microscope.

So now we know the structure of DNA; and we know that it makes proteins. How can we put these two kinds of information together? How, in fact, does DNA work?

127

How Does DNA Work?

Here there are several sub-questions. The first, perhaps, is: how does DNA replicate itself? The second: how in practice are the protein chains put together according to the DNA's instructions? And the third is the one we have posed before: how do the four different nucleotides in DNA code for the twenty different amino acids in protein?

In the event, Pauling and Delbruck had already guessed the principle of DNA duplication and Watson and Crick hint at it in the last line of their *Nature* paper. In practice, one strand of DNA splits away from its partner and, from the moment the splitting starts, nucleotides within the surrounding medium begin to line up against their complementary opposite numbers. As they do so, they are joined one to another by an enzyme, DNA polymerase. Note, a point crucial to the later development of genetic engineering, the extent to which the assembly and disassembly of DNA depend upon teams of enzymes, of which DNA polymerase is one.

The fact that DNA really does duplicate in this way was first shown experimentally in a highly ingenious experiment by Matthew Meselson and Franklin Stahl at Caltech in 1958. They grew cultures of *Escherichia coli* in a medium that was highly enriched with the heavy isotopes 13C and 15N. (The more common isotopes of carbon and nitrogen have atomic weights of only 12 and 14 respectively, so DNA built from the heavier forms is significantly more weighty). Meselson and Stahl then transferred the *E coli* with their heavy DNA to a medium containing only light isotopes of C and N, and allowed them to divide for one generation. After one generation they found only one kind of DNA in the new *E coli* cells, and that had a molecular weight that was intermediate between that of heavy *E coli* DNA and normal, 'light' *E coli* DNA. So the newly formed DNA clearly consisted of one strand of heavy DNA and one strand of light. Clearly, then duplication was achieved first by splitting the original double-stranded DNA into two single strands, followed by the replication of each one. (The fact that the replication begins as soon as the splitting begins, and does not wait for a complete separation, was established only later).

Next question, then: how does DNA make protein? It was clear from the start that DNA could not itself act as the manufacturer of protein. DNA is (mostly) confined to chromosomes within the nucleus; but it can be seen that proteins are synthesised in the cell cytoplasm outside the nucleus. Clearly, there had to be some kind of intermediary ferrying the DNA instructions to the sites of protein manufacture. This is where the second nucleic acid, RNA, enters the scene.

That RNA was in fact the intermediary between DNA in the nucleus and the sites of protein manufacture in the cytoplasm seemed likely from before the time that Watson and Crick proposed their DNA model. For example, cells that make a lot of protein always have a lot of RNA in their cytoplasm; and the sugar-phosphate 'backbones' of DNA and RNA are similar, which suggests some kind of liaison between them. (As we have seen, RNA contains ribose rather than deoxyribose, and uracil rather than thymine. But uracil forms a *base pair* with adenine just as thymine does.)

Even as early as 1953, then, the picture was envisaged: a strand of DNA, once separated from its partner, *either* can begin to make a complementary copy of itself, and so replicate, *or* can begin to make a complementary strand of RNA, which then leaves the nucleus and supervises the manufacture of appropriate protein in the cytoplasm. The creation of RNA complementary to a piece of DNA is called *transcription*. In the cytoplasm, the code now carried upon this RNA is made manifest in protein by the process of *translation*.

In practice, the manufacture of protein is somewhat complicated. It involves three different kinds of RNA, each of which is created by different parts of the DNA. The RNA that ferries the message out of the nucleus is called *messenger* RNA, or mRNA. But messenger RNA does not make protein directly. Instead it cooperates with RNA which resides permanently in the cytoplasm (though it is initially manufactured in the nucleus) in bodies known as *ribosomes*, and thus is called *ribosomal RNA* or rRNA. In addition, each amino acid which is lined up for incorporation into protein is chaperoned into the ribosome by a short length of RNA known as *transfer* RNA or tRNA. Each tRNA chaperones a specific amino acid and links up to a particular place on the mRNA, with rRNA acting as a kind of workbench for this linking to take place. Enzymes again are needed to push this process along.

So we have what looks like a hierarchy (although, as we will see, appearances can be deceptive, and the 'hierarchy' should probably be re-interpreted!). On the face of things, however, the DNA acts as the administrator, snugly cocooned in its office within the nucleus. The various kinds of RNA are the executors, ferrying the DNA's instructions to the protein workshops, the ribosomes, in the cytoplasm. The proteins themselves are the all-purpose functionaries, which form much of the structure of the body and make the metabolism run. Francis Crick summarised the whole process in what he called the 'central dogma' of molecular biology: 'DNA makes RNA makes protein'. I like to think of DNA-RNA-protein as the Trinity: the three molecules which, by their dialogue and interaction, form the basis for all life on Earth (unless we consider that prions, the agents of scrapie and BSE, represent an alternative life form). In truth, it *must* be possible for life to operate in ways other than this, for DNA, RNA and proteins are highly evolved molecules, and they must have had predecessors, and those predecessors almost certainly cobbled together some form of metabolism and replication that deserves to be called 'living'. But on Earth, at least, the Trinity has won the day; and all living creatures (prions and a few other oddities aside) partake of it.

So now for our third question: how does a particular piece of DNA – a gene – code for a particular protein?

One obvious and known fact was that protein consists of linear chains of amino acids (even if the final shape of a protein is far from being a linear chain) and DNA consists of linear chains of nucleotides. Somehow the sequence of nucleotides has to determine the sequence of amino acids. This raises the problem we posed before. There are roughly twenty kinds of amino acids in protein, but there are only four kinds of nucleotide in DNA. So how does four code for twenty?

In combinations, of course, is the answer. If nucleotides lying side by side acted in pairs, then four different kinds could produce 16 different combinations: 4 × 4. If they operated in threes, they could produce 64 different combinations: 4 × 4 × 4. If they operated in fours, they could produce 256 different combinations: 4 × 4 × 4 × 4. Clearly, they cannot operate in pairs, because 16 is too few. Two hundred and fifty-six is far too many. If nature is logical (and nature is sometimes logical, though this cannot be guaranteed), then the nucleotides should operate in groups of three. Sixty-four possible combinations is more than seems to be needed; but it is not absurdly too many.

Sydney Brenner and Francis Crick it was, at Cambridge in 1961, who showed that the genetic code did indeed operate through triplets of nucleotides in DNA. They worked with mutant forms of the T4 phage, which infects *E coli*. They found that if just one nucleotide was added to the T4 gene the protein which resulted was nonfunctional. If two nucleotides were added nonfunctional proteins resulted again. But if three nucleotides were added to a T4 gene, the resulting protein *was* functional. The addition of one or two nucleotides simply messed up the reading of the code, threw the whole reading out of sync. But the addition of three nucleotides added a whole new amino acid, which changed the resulting protein somewhat, but not enough, necessarily, to disrupt its activity significantly. Each trio of nucleotides that codes for a specific amino acid is now known as a *codon*.

Brenner and Crick's work also illustrates immediately the nature of mutation. If a gene operates, as it does, by providing successive trios of nucleotides, then a mutation could clearly be one of three kinds. If just a single nucleotide was added to the sequence, then this would horribly disrupt the reading of the code. If a single nucleotide was taken away, then the code would be interrupted again. But if a single nucleotide was simply changed – one substituted for another – then this might or might not cause a different amino acid to be substituted in the corresponding protein, and might or might not disrupt the function of that protein. In any case, we see that mutations in chemical terms can be tiny changes, but that tiny changes can have huge effects. (I am reminded of the doggerel: 'For want of a

131

nail the shoe was lost, for want of a shoe the horse was lost, for want of a horse the battle was lost.' Of course, most nails lost from most horseshoes don't have such disastrous consequences. But they *can*. Similarly, alteration in, as opposed to removal of, a single amino acid may have no discernible effect at all – many mutations are 'neutral' in their effects – but it could render the entire creature non-viable.)

Exactly which sequence of three nucleotides coded for which amino acids was worked out in the early 1960s, beginning with the work of Marshall Nirenberg and Heinrich Mattai, who showed that artificial mRNA consisting exclusively of chains of uracil produced a protein that contained chains of the amino acid phenylalanine. So UUU codes for phenylalanine. Similar experiments in other laboratories followed, and by June 1966 it was known that *all* codons contain three successive nucleotides, and that 61 of the 64 codons code for amino acids (some amino acids clearly have more than one corresponding codon), while the other three (UAA, UAG, and UGA) serve as punctuation marks to indicate that a particular protein should be brought to a close. In short, the genetic code was 'cracked'.

Thus did genetics take on the additional discipline of molecular biology, and thus has 'molecular genetics' emerged as a discipline in its own right.

This, then, is the detail: DNA makes RNA makes protein. But how does the collective of genes in an organism, its genome, produce a complete creature with all its many different tissues and organs? And how does the genome provide the instructions that turn an embryo into an infant and then into an adult (which then grows old and dies)? How does the nuts and bolts mechanism – 'DNA makes RNA makes protein' – translate into the grand life plan?

From Nuts and Bolts to Grand Plan: A Matter of Expression

Rudolf Carl Virchow it was who declared in 1858, 'Omnis cellula e cellula': 'All cells derive from (pre-existing) cells.' Thus the single-celled embryo (the 'zygote') divides to give rise to a multi-celled embryo, whose cells continue to divide until the organism reaches its final size (although some cells, like those of nerve and muscle, stop dividing before this point while others, like those which produce the skin and stomach lining, continue to divide throughout life). This was a fine insight when the idea of the cell was still new, but of course it raises a problem. For the zygote does not divide simply to produce more cells identical to itself. As the daughter and granddaughter cells are produced so they change their character: some become liver cells, some skin cells, some muscle cells, some blood cells, and so on and so on. This specialisation of cells is called 'differentiation'. How can one kind of cell, the zygote, give rise to cells of many different kinds?

August Weismann provided an answer in the 1880s. He suggested that as the cells divide and differentiate, so they lose some of their genes. Thus the zygote contains all the genes needed to produce an entire body, but the liver cells that derive from it contain only the genes needed to make livers, and the nerve cells contain only those genes that are appropriate to nerves, and so on. Of course, in the 1880s the term 'gene' had not been coined, so Weismann did not express the idea in quite this way. Nonetheless, he envisaged a steady loss of hereditary material in each kind of specialised cell line as differentiation proceeded.

Weismann was, beyond doubt, one of the greats. He was right about most things and he should be better known to the world at large. But evidence throughout the twentieth century increasingly suggested that in this particular regard he was wrong. In particular, in the 1960s the English biologist John Gurdon produced clones of frogs by the technique known as 'nuclear transfer'. Specifically, he took nuclei from the intestinal cells of frogs, placed them in 'enucleated' frog eggs (that is, eggs whose own nuclei had already been removed) and grew the resultant 'reconstructed embryos' into tadpoles. Thus he showed that the nuclei of the intestinal cells, highly differentiated cells, *are* able to give rise to entire creatures. However, the absolute, final copper-bottomed demonstration that Weismann was indeed wrong did not emerge until 1996, when Ian Wilmut and Keith Campbell at Roslin Institute near Edinburgh cloned Dolly the sheep. They took cells from the mammary gland of a sheep (so the cells were already differentiated); then multiplied those cells in culture (which inevitably produces more differentiation); then transferred the nuclei from those cells into enucleated sheep eggs to produce a number of embryos, which they transferred into surrogate mothers. One of those embryos developed to become Dolly. (In fact, the two ewes produced in the previous year, Megan and Morag, made the point just as cogently as Dolly. But Megan and Morag were made from cultured embryo cells and the fact that those cells were already highly differentiated was not so obvious to the world at large as it was in the case of Dolly).

In modern vocabulary we say that the zygote is 'totipotent': that it is able to give rise to all the cells of the creature it is destined to become. In animals, at least, it seemed until John Gurdon's experiments that differentiated cells could not recover their totipotency. For three decades after Gurdon most biologists doubted whether differentiated cells from *mammals*, as opposed to Gurdon's amphibian frogs, could recover totipotency. But Dolly (and before her Megan and Morag) show that if conditions are right, then they can. This also proves beyond all doubt that differentiated cells have *not* lost genes, as Weismann proposed. But if an intestinal cell or a mammary gland cell has not lost any of the genes that were present in the original zygote, how come those cells are not the same as the original zygote? How is differentiation possible?

The answer, of course, is that although genes are not physically lost as cells differentiate, many of them are switched off. Each cell in the body contains a complete genome, copies of all the genes characteristic of the species. But in a liver cell all the genes are switched off except those required to produce a liver cell, and in a lung cell only the genes needed to make lungs are 'expressed'. (The most obvious exception to this generalisation is in the red blood cells, 'erythrocytes', of mammals, in which the entire nucleus, genome and all, is lost in the final stages of differentiation.) So how are genes turned on and off?

The first mechanism to be demonstrated was in bacteria, by the French biologists François Jacob and Jacques Monod in the late 1950s (for which they shared a Nobel Prize in 1965). Specifically, they worked with *Lactobacillus*, which forms lactic acid from sugars and is involved in the fermentation of milk to make cheese and milk. By various ingenious means they showed that each stretch of DNA which serves as a gene has a corresponding control region 'upstream' of it (that is, further along the DNA molecule). Each control region has various components including a *promoter*, a *regulatory gene*, and a *terminator*. The promoter instructs the regulatory gene to produce a protein which acts as a *repressor* and shuts down the activity of the gene it is supposed to regulate. Now it's clear that organisms such as animals and plants (collectively known as 'eukaryotes': organisms with a distinct nucleus in each cell) have many mechanisms for controlling the expression of genes, some of which repress particular genes, and some of which turn them on. But the basic mechanism shown in *Lactobacillus* makes the general point. A gene may be present in a cell, but it remains silent and non-functional unless it is switched on; and there are many fine control mechanisms for ensuring that each one is turned on and off just to the required degree.

The general problem of development is related to that of differentiation. All creatures change as they get older: they do not merely get bigger. William Shakespeare's Jaques summarised life's progress in the human male in *As You Like It* (Act II, scene vii). He distinguished the seven ages of man, including 'the infant, /Mewling and puking in the nurse's arms'; then the 'soldier, full of strange oaths'; to be followed by 'the lean and slipper'd pantaloon' who, in the end, is 'Sans teeth, sans eyes . . . sans everything.'

Although the mewling infant is a very different creature in size, appearance and behaviour from the soldier full of strange oaths, the two have the same genes. It's all very strange, just as it's strange that the cells of livers and lungs can have the same genes, although they are so different. But again, once we grasp the notion of gene expression – genes turned on and genes turned off – we can see how it all works. The genome can be thought of as a programme. As time passes, different sets of genes within the genome are activated or switched off. Babies express genes appropriate to babies; adults express genes appropriate to adults. Behaviour is affected just as much as physical appearance. To be sure, human behaviour (and much animal behaviour) is shaped by culture, but babies do not cry for cultural reasons and neither does fashion account for the sexual desire of adolescents and adults (although, of course, it affects the ways in which that passion is expressed: whether men write sonnets or slay mammoths to impress their mates; whether women are sexually expressive or prefer defenestration to deflowerment).

Once we see the genome as a programme, unfolding as time passes, much natural history becomes explicable which is otherwise mysterious. Why and how do caterpillars 'metamorphose' into butterflies? Well, the laws of physics decree that offspring must be smaller at the time of their birth than their parents. Before those offspring can reproduce in their turn, they have to grow (or each successive generation would be smaller and smaller). So in all organisms, in general, early life is dedicated to growth and later life, when the appropriate size is reached, is dedicated to reproduction. But growth and reproduction are very different activities, requiring very different physiological and behavioural adaptations. How can an animal change its physiological strategy as it grows bigger and older? Answer: by switching off some genes and switching others on. You can see the changes most clearly in animals such as insects, which have tight, unyielding exoskeletons like armour which they must moult at intervals in order to grow at all. Of necessity, they progress via a series of 'instars': distinct periods of growth and development between moults. They cannot simply process from infant to adult in a smooth continuum as soft-bodied animals may do, or as vertebrates can with their internal skeletons. Thus, natural selection is able to work on each instar separately and each instar may become highly specialised. In the early life of a lepidopteran genes are expressed that produce a voracious feeding caterpillar, which has no thoughts of sex at all. The last phase is a bright, highly mobile, winged creature dedicated entirely to reproduction. Some adult moths and butterflies (and many other insects from other classes) do not feed at all in their brief, obsessively nuptial phase of existence.

Profound evolutionary changes can be brought about simply by changing the time-switches on the genomic programme: causing some genes to be expressed for longer or for shorter periods;

bringing others forward in the life cycle, or postponing their expression. Thus in many different lineages of animals we see the evolution of neoteny – prolonging infant features into adulthood; or of paedomorphosis – bringing forward the ability to reproduce into childhood. (I have never been able to see any practical difference between neoteny and paedomorphosis, but the two nonetheless are commonly given different names.) One of the most obvious example of neoteny is among the Mexican salamanders known as axolotls. Larval salamanders and newts are aquatic, like the tadpoles of frogs and toads, and have external gills; but when they mature they emerge on to land and lose their gills. Axolotls, however, remain in water and retain their infantile gills throughout their lives. In some other salamanders neoteny seems optional: sometimes they retain their larval gills and stay in the water, and sometimes they lose them and migrate to the land. Some biologists have speculated that axolotls retain their gills because the lakes in which they live are deficient in iodine, which prevents them producing sufficient thyroid hormone and inhibits their maturation. But others point out that axolotls remain larval in form however much iodine they are given. More likely, they say, axolotls would find little to eat in the surrounding desert and so they have adapted to stay in the water. A small shift in the timing of the genomic programme, keeping the genes switched on that produce gills, has done the trick.

Similarly, primatologists used to suggest that the flat face of human beings is a neotenous feature. Chimps have flat faces when they are young and great prognathous (jutting) jaws when they are adult; and so, probably, did the common ancestor that chimps and humans share. Chimps retained the jutting ancestral jaw, but humans retained the infant flat face into adulthood. More detailed study of skull development suggests that this explanation will not do, however. A human skull is not moulded like a baby chimp's. On the other hand, the high foreheads and wide eyes of most domestic dogs *are* a neotenous feature. Dogs resemble the puppies of ancestral wolves in behaviour as well as in looks. They have been bred that way.

Shifts in the timing of gene expression also provide a neat explanation for the otherwise mysterious property of ageing: why we all, in time, become slipper'd pantaloons, if the grim reaper does not call for us first. The notion here is that mutations occur all the time and that most mutations are harmful. One way for evolution to deal with harmful mutations is to suppress the expression of the mutated gene, or to postpone the expression until after reproductive age. Mutations that are postponed until after reproductive age do not get weeded out by natural selection, but they do remain to plague the ageing creature (the principle we saw with Huntington's chorea). In short, as we age, we run into a backlog of accumulated, postponed mutations. You can run, as they say in the westerns, but you can't hide.

In short, the general picture of life's controls that emerged as the twentieth century progressed is wonderfully neat. Archibald Garrod's 'one gene, one enzyme' became Francis Crick's 'central dogma', 'DNA makes RNA makes protein', and proteins, of course (mainly in the form of enzymes), are the body's functionaries, which effectively run the show. The sequence of nucleotides in the DNA corresponds to and codes for the sequence of amino acids in the protein; and the sequence of amino acids effectively determines how the finished protein will fold into its final three-dimensional form and hence how it will behave. Once we see how genes can be switched on or switched off, then the phenomenon of differentiation ceases to be a mystery, and we can see how the whole genomic programme unfolds to produce creatures which change as they proceed from embryo to adult to geriatric: seen in dramatic form in the caterpillar's progress to the butterfly and in all of us as we journey from mewling infant to slipper'd pantaloon.

Note in passing, too, how the experiments outlined in this chapter illustrate the general nature of science. Huge problems, like what a gene is made of, are tested by irreducibly simple experiments: showing, for example, that bacteria cannot transmit hereditary information if first treated with an enzyme that destroys DNA. At least, the experiments may be technically difficult – it is really hard to manipulate individual cells – but they are simple in concept. Then, from a minimal baseline of 'robust' observations the scientists *infer* how life must be. Nowadays, with ultra-modern microscopes, it is possible to photograph DNA molecules in fine detail and to show that they are indeed as Crick and Watson described. But their initial description was based on inference, from a wide range of disparate data. *All* science, when you boil it down, is inference; but it works nonetheless. This is what scientists mean by 'elegance': to build great, robust conceptions of the world on minimalist observations. Mendel, with his rows of peas, showed the principle supremely, and is matched, as I have commented, only by Galileo. But all the people mentioned in this chapter have this quality too (and many others, of course, who should be mentioned if the chapter could be longer).

However, the picture revealed in the early and middle decades of the twentieth century was a little too neat. Biology is rarely neat, at least in all its details. We and our fellow creatures were not, apparently, designed to a specification, in the way that Ford designs cars and Sony designs televisions. Nature evolved; and systems that evolve are messy. Each generation builds on what was there before, without necessarily disposing of its predecessors, so that every living creature – and every system within every creature – is liable to carry legacies from its ancestors, in the form of 'vestiges'. Underlying the neatness, then, and to some extent subverting it, we should expect to find all kinds of diversions, curlicues, accidentals and conditional clauses; and indeed we might find that the true nature of the beast is not as we initially envisaged it at all. As the twentieth century wore on the initial simplicities became a little more, well, *lifelike*.

Life is Full of Surprises

An early surprise was that DNA, including functional genes, occurs in the cytoplasm of the eukaryotic cell as well as in the nucleus. Mitochondria, the small cytoplasmic structures ('organelles') which contain the enzymes associated with respiration, also contain their own genes. So do the chloroplasts, the organelles in plants that carry the photosynthetic green pigment, chlorophyll. Mitochondrial genes account for only a few per cent of the cell's total genes, but they are influential nonetheless. They provide at least some of the information needed to make the respiratory enzymes. Mutations in the mitochondrial genes can lead to definable defects. The presence of mitochondrial DNA supports the idea championed by the American biologist Lynn Margulis, which says that the eukaryotic cell is a coalition. That is, the cytoplasm of the eukaryotic cell came from the bodies of ancient prokaryotes of the kind known as archea; and the mitochondria evolved from parasitic bacteria that lodged within the body of the archae and stayed. Host and lodger then co-evolved, and many of the invader's genes passed to the nucleus of the host (so that mitochondria are no longer able to live independently outside the cell). But the mitochondria have retained some of their ancient, bacterial genes. In practice it is clear that mitochondria do resemble some living bacteria, notably those of alpha-proteobacteria; and their DNA is in some ways more like that of a bacterium than of a eukaryote.

It also came as a shock to discover from the mid-twentieth century onwards that DNA itself is much more untidy than was anticipated. Molecular biologists might have expected to find that each double helix of DNA consisted entirely of genes, strung without interruption from one end of the other, each coding for proteins or for tRNA or rRNA, with occasional codons to provide punctuation and stretches to regulate expression. Not a bit of it. Between the genes there are huge stretches of DNA that do not code for anything at all. Worse: there are similar stretches *within* the genes, known as 'introns' (while the bits of the gene that do actually code for proteins are known somewhat confusingly as 'exons'). Originally, the non-coding DNA was known as 'junk' DNA, although it seems presumptuous to suggest that something is 'junk' simply because its function is unknown. Clearly, at least some of the alleged 'junk' does serve some function. Introns, for example, may be involved in gene expression. Be that as it may: about 90 per cent of the DNA in a eukaryotic cell is now known to be non-coding. The DNA of bacteria is much tidier, with very little non-coding DNA indeed.

The non-coding DNA clearly has various origins. Some is vestigial: old genes which have lost their function but have not been weeded out; old viruses which have become integrated into

140

the host's own DNA. After all, if the non-coding DNA is not expressed then, unlike some positively deleterious alleles, it does the creature no harm. If it does no harm, then it is not visible to the forces of natural selection and remains to clutter up the genome. When genes are transcribed to make mRNA the introns are slavishly copied as well; but these are snipped out when the mRNA exits from the nucleus, so that when the mRNA reaches the ribosomes, it is strictly functional.

One of the greatest of all surprises was revealed in the 1940s, before the structure of DNA was known in detail, by the American geneticist Barbara McClintock. She showed that some genes actually shift their position within the genome. She called them 'mobile elements', but they became also known colloquially as 'jumping genes'; some of which are known more formally as 'transposons'. McClintock first revealed such mobile elements in maize, but they are known to be ubiquitous.

In fact, Barbara McClintock's mobile elements helped to promote a new way of thinking about DNA which has had profound theoretical consequences. For biologists have naturally tended to think, as Darwin did, that the 'unit' of life is the individual: the particular cat or oak tree; the particular human being. If you think of individuals as the basic units, then you assume that the genes, which help to shape the individual, are somehow subservient to that individual. They are parts of the individual, just as carburettors and brake shoes are parts of cars. You expect the carburettor and the brake shoe and all the other component parts to do what is good for the car. But there is something anarchic about a jumping gene, as if bits of the DNA were simply doing their own thing.

Indeed, there is a great deal about the jumping gene that is anarchic. A stretch of DNA detaches itself from its allotted place in a chromosome and then inserts itself somewhere else, and where it lands up seems to be more or less random. A jumping gene may indeed cause mutations in the places where it lands. If it lands in the coding region of the gene (in an exon, rather than an intron) then the mutation it causes could be damaging. In fact, some biologists have been so impressed by the extent of such activity within the genome that they suggest it may be a more important agent of change than natural selection itself. Gabriel Dover of Cambridge University coined the expression 'molecular drive': and suggests that molecular drive, operating at the level of the DNA itself, has largely determined the way we are. Others acknowledge that molecular drive is a fact – the DNA is far more restless and apparently anarchic than might be supposed – but in the end the DNA itself survives only if it manages to produce a creature that can actually function. If the restless DNA produced creatures that could not compete with their fellows, then they would die out, and their unruly DNA would die with them. In short, the mechanisms of molecular drive may cause variations in lineages of creatures, but in the end the different variants are weeded out by natural selection. Molecular drive exists and is important, but as an agent of evolutionary change it seems to offer very little challenge to natural selection.

Out of this realisation, that individual bits of DNA may behave apparently anarchically, has arisen the concept of 'selfish DNA'. The selfish DNA idea is not quite the same as the selfish gene idea, which is discussed in Chapter 6. The concept of the 'selfish gene' encapsulates the notion that we should think of natural selection as a force that operates most forcefully at the level of the gene, rather than of the individual as a whole. As we will see, this notion is much misunderstood and contains the apparent paradox (though in truth it is not a paradox at all; just a natural consequence) that *because* genes are selfish, the creatures that contain them can behave most unselfishly, and indeed altruistically, to the extent of self-sacrifice. Thus the concept of the selfish gene belongs to evolutionary theory as a whole. The concept of selfish DNA belongs to molecular biology. It describes the odd but inescapable fact that individual bits of DNA do indeed do their own thing. If these bits of DNA had any self-awareness (which of course they do not) they would *not* see themselves as servants of the organism of which they are a part. They would see themselves as individuals, free citizens, milling about in the marketplace.

One highly intriguing manifestation of 'selfish' DNA in action is the phenomenon of 'genomic imprinting'. You will recall that Mendel was bedevilled by spermatists and ovists, who had been so slyly lampooned by Laurence Sterne in the previous century. He was at great pains to show that 'factors' inherited from the female line are entirely equivalent to those inherited from the male line, which fact he announced triumphally in his paper of 1865. From the 1980s onwards, however, it has become clear that in this he was not entirely correct. At least, this generalisation applies to most creatures, but in mammals the action of at least some of the genes *is* influenced by the sex of the parent.

Thus in 1980 scientists at Cambridge, notably Azim Surani, found that it was impossible to make a viable mouse embryo which began with two pronuclei that were both derived from sperm, or both derived from eggs. Embryos made with two sperm nuclei developed excellent, lusty placentae, but the body of the embryo itself was feeble and non-viable. Embryos made with two egg nuclei did well at first, but they failed to develop placentae that were able to sustain them. Nuclei from both egg and sperm were needed. Thus parthenogenesis, virgin birth, seemed to be impossible in mammals, at least by this simple route, since a male nucleus was needed. More broadly, it was clear that male and female nuclei were not exactly functionally equivalent. A sperm nucleus might contain the same genome as the egg genome (give or take a few allelic differences), but clearly at least some of the genes derived from the male were behaving differently from their homologues derived from the female.

This is 'genomic imprinting'. In mammals at least, the male (or the female) does indeed impose his or her special stamp on some at least of the genes. The defective allele that causes Huntington's disease is imprinted in just this way. If the allele is inherited from the father, the disease strikes earlier, and in general is worse, than if inherited from the mother. A daughter of an affected father may suffer badly because she has inherited the bad gene through the male line; but she then puts her own stamp on the allele and her own offspring will not generally suffer the disease until they are older.

Huntington's is a pathology, it may be seen as a bolt from the blue, but we must ask *why* the phenomenon of imprinting should have arisen. The question is answerable only in terms of selfish DNA. In mammals, the foetus can be seen (physiologically speaking!) as a parasite. A gene that causes the parasitic foetus to take more than its proper share of nutrient will produce a big, lusty infant, but also stands a good chance of killing the mother. Analysis reveals that genes which are passed on through the male line will spread through the population if they do indeed produce good healthy infants, even if they harm the mothers that bear them along the way; while genes passed through the female line will do less well if they harm the mothers along the way. Hence, broadly speaking, some male-derived genes have evolved to produce greedy foetuses, while female-derived genes produce less voracious foetuses. In any one foetus, alleles derived from the male parent compete with the alleles derived from the female parent. The picture is further complicated because both sexes of foetus of course contain genes derived from both sexes of parent. There are female-imprinted genes in little boys and male-imprinted genes in little girls. All in all, then, the theory of genomic imprinting requires a cool head. The generalisations are as stated, however: that each sex of parent imposes its own stamp on some of the genes; and that this phenomenon is explicable only when we consider genes as 'selfish' entities.

How, then, do 'selfish' DNA, genes battling it out with each other within the cell, manage, between them, to produce a genome that in the end provides the code for a beautifully co-ordinated mushroom, or a horse, or a human being? The answer may be essentially the one by which Adam Smith, that eighteenth-century paragon of the Scottish Enlightenment, explained the way that bloody-minded individual human beings manage, between them, to produce coherent societies. Each individual, said Smith, pulls on his or her own rope. But human beings do not thrive well on their own. They do better as members of society. *Ergo*, individuals who are acting entirely in their own interests thrive best by doing whatever meshes in with what others are doing. Through all the individual acts of selfishness, then, what Smith called the 'hidden hand' produces a collection of human beings who, to all intents and purposes, are co-operating. The selfish individuals form a society because it is in their selfish interests to do so. As Richard Dawkins has said, individual rowers do best when they co-operate with seven others to produce a rowing eight. Eight self-centred rowers fired by personal ambition can produce an eight that functions just as well as one in which each individual thinks only of his team's glory.

Of course, many people, including me, do not believe that Adam Smith should have the last word on the formation of human societies. It is clear, after all, that human beings (and other animals) *also* have a sense of 'society as a whole' and work to make a better society. The point is, though, that Adam Smith's concept of the 'hidden hand' seems to explain well enough how blind and selfish genes finish up by co-operating.

Yet in recent years, many a liberal and socialist has opposed the notion of 'the selfish gene' and 'selfish DNA' on political grounds. Some biologists have allowed their politics to get in the way of their scientific detachment, and attacked biological findings that they ought to realise are rather strong. We might simply point out (more of this in Chapter 9) that science and politics should be kept separate. The task of science is to tell us, as far can be found out, what is actually true: and the task of humankind, as moral creatures, is to decide what kind of societies we want to create and set out to do what we think is right, whatever science tells us is actually the case. But it is tempting rather to point out that socialist objections to selfish genes and selfish DNA are simply muddle-headed. These are the ideas that have explained Darwin's dilemma: that animals often, and in very many contexts, do behave unselfishly and even self-sacrificially. The selfish DNA/ selfish gene concepts show, in fact, that nature is not 'red in tooth and claw' as Tennyson supposed. Of course all creatures, and all genes, must compete with each other: that is life's burden. But in reality, creatures (and individual genes) often survive best by co-operating. Life itself evolved as a coalition; it could not have evolved in any other way. In short, if biological theory showed that we are pressured to be at each others' throats, then we should learn to live with that fact, and override it. Fortunately, however, biological theory shows no such thing. Darwin never said it did.

It is time to look at what Darwin did say, and how his ideas chime with those of Gregor Mendel. It took biologists a few decades to perceive that Darwin's evolution and Mendel's genetics do indeed fit together; but once they did see this then the

145

result, known as 'neodarwinism', became one of the great intellectual insights of the twentieth century. The synthesis of the two sets of ideas is the subject of Chapter 6.

6

Mendel and Darwin: Neodarwinism and the Selfish Gene

Mendel (and others in the German tradition) provided half the foundations of modern biology. Charles Darwin, in England, provided the other half. For Darwin produced the first truly plausible theory of evolution, 'by means of natural selection', an idea which came into the world with the force of revelation. Natural selection may yet prove to be the most fundamental 'force' at work throughout the universe. Even physicists, these days, wonder if their 'fundamental' particles are really so fundamental after all or whether they too, like elephants and oak trees and human beings, have been selected from among a range of candidate particles.

Yet Darwin, like Mendel, is easy to underestimate. People seem to misconstrue his genius, how very great he was, perhaps because he seems so homely (tweedy, rich, amiable, established middle-class, pottering around his garden in Kent, surrounded by children and playing backgammon with his wife) and because he apparently deals in the day-to-day. *On the Origin of Species* was seminal – modern theoretical biology is really an addendum with one significant codicil and many noises off – but it tells of pigeons, orchids, ants and barnacles. Anyone can respond to such exemplars: our brains are geared to natural history. Really clever people, we tend to think, deal in weirdness that most of us will never grasp: Einstein with relativity, Niels Bohr with quantum mechanics and the insubstantiality of the universe. Metaphysically speaking, though, and for that matter in sheer brain power,

Darwin was up with the greats – perhaps, we might whimsically suggest, playing Tolstoy to Einstein's James Joyce. Don't be fooled, either, by his pottering; he just happened to be, by way of a hobby, the finest field naturalist of all time, with a canny line in experiment. Of course, he makes use of other people's observations in *Origin* (and gives them fulsome credit), but it's astounding how many insights are his own: from ants in Hampshire and the 'tangled banks' of Kent to the entirety of South America.

Then again, many of those who continue to underestimate Darwin simply misunderstand history. It is often said that when Darwin wrote *Origin*, evolution was 'in the air'. Darwin himself acknowledges many of his predecessors in his introduction. Jean-Baptiste Lamarck was among several biologists in the late eighteenth-century and early nineteenth-century France who expounded evolutionary ideas. We have seen that in Moravia, Mendel's teacher Unger wrote in evolutionary vein, as did Mendel, during one of his unsuccessful attempts to qualify as a teacher. In England Darwin's own grandfather, Erasmus, wrote in the eighteenth century of creatures emerging from earlier creatures. In Scotland in the 1830s Patrick Matthew summarised the gist of natural selection somewhat bizarrely in the appendix to a book on naval architecture.

But none of these apparent predecessors hit the jackpot. Many (like Erasmus Darwin) felt that living things had changed over the years, but proposed no mechanism and, in particular, they could not explain how creatures are clearly adapted to the places where they live – shaggy where it's cold and smooth where it's hot. Lamarck proposed a mechanism, 'inheritance of acquired characteristics', but it failed to convince at the time and is now known to be wrong. German biologists, like Unger, tended to conflate evolutionary change from generation to generation with the development of an embryo. Matthew (and others) who did think in terms of natural selection failed to develop their ideas. Perhaps they simply did not perceive, as Darwin did, that to produce a theory of evolution that could be applied universally and was robust it was necessary to look at the natural history of the whole world. It was also necessary to take account of palaeontology (fossils played a large part in Darwin's thinking), embryology and the homely craft of livestock breeding (the 'artificial selection' that gave Darwin the clue to 'natural selection'). Darwin, like Matthew, conceived of natural selection in the 1830s; but, unlike Matthew, he realised that a single flash was not enough. Darwin knew that he could not make the case that was needed unless he brought to bear a huge weight of evidence, and thought through the minutest caveats, which is why it took him twenty years to publish. The only other biologist to grasp the full idea was Alfred Russel Wallace, who summarised the notion convincingly and succinctly in 1858, but Darwin is rightly acknowledged as the greater man.

Yet when Darwin wrote *Origin* the dominant belief among educated people, and also among the uneducated, was of 'special creation'. God had simply made the creatures that we see around us in their present form and placed them in their present locations. Adaptation was not perceived as a problem; of course God had matched the creatures to their environments. Neither was there any crude division of belief between churchmen and scientists. Most of the influential scientists of the day were creationists, including Adam Sedgwick, who was Darwin's own teacher, and the great Richard Owen, who in the early nineteenth century was Britain's leading biologist. Owen coined the word 'dinosaur' and his ideas in anatomy are still cited. Even those who did think of evolution tended to reject the notion that any one lineage could be branched. At best they envisaged that God had created a range of primordial creatures some time in the past (and the world was commonly perceived to be only about 6000 years old) which had then all 'evolved' quite independently, up a series of separate evolutionary ladders.

So, as Ernst Mayr describes in *Towards a Philosophy of Biology*, Darwin needed to undertake three conceptually separate tasks. First, he needed to show that evolution was a fact, the route by which all existing creatures had assumed their present form, which emphatically was not the common view. Secondly, he had to provide a plausible mechanism to explain how change over time led to adaptation, which he did by proposing the mechanism of natural selection. Thirdly, he had to establish what to us now seems obvious (now that Darwin has pointed it out) but in the nineteenth century decidedly was not: that species can change. 'Species', in the mid-nineteenth century, was still essentially a Platonic concept: even biologists still felt that the creatures they saw about them were mere material copies of some heavenly ideal. It was inconceivable that they could change into different creatures, and that the lineage could branch, with any one species giving rise to many different ones. Indeed, 'transmutation of species' was virtually a blasphemy. As Mayr says, Darwin's principal battle was not with God but with Plato. But you cannot have branching of lineages without transmutation of species; and once you have branching of lineages, you can, as Darwin made explicit in *Origin*, envisage all creatures united in one great universal tree of life that sprang from a single, common ancestor. Thus eagles and oak trees are our relatives, and, in fact, it now transpires, even the oaks are not so distant from us as you might suppose. Many other creatures, including the homely amoeba which every biology student draws at some time, are far more distantly related to us than plants are.

'Natural selection' was the notion that carried the day: the mechanism which made the idea of evolution plausible. The bones of the idea, as with all the greatest ideas, can be stated in a paragraph. First, all creatures are engaged willy-nilly in what Darwin called a 'struggle for existence'. The English economist Thomas Malthus had pointed out at the end of the eighteenth century that if the human population continued to grow as it was doing, then it would soon exceed resources; and Darwin saw that this principle applied to all species. Every creature could, if unconstrained, produce enough offspring to cover the entire Earth within a few hundred years, and the fact that they do not do so shows that they are indeed held back. Many more are born than live to reproduce themselves.

Secondly, creatures which are of the same general type, nonetheless, vary. No two kittens in a litter are exactly the same. Inevitably, some of the variants will be better adapted to the prevailing conditions than others. The better adapted will be more likely to survive and reproduce. Herbert Spencer, good friend of George Eliot, coined the expression 'survival of the

150

fittest', where 'fit' has the Victorian sense of 'apt': and Darwin later adopted this form of words. The survivors' offspring will resemble themselves because 'like begets like', although the resemblance is not exact for all the reasons we have already outlined in this book (not that Darwin knew the reasons). Hence, over time, lineages of creatures become better and better adapted to their surroundings.

Darwin did not stop with natural selection, however. Indeed, it has been said that after *Origin* he seemed to lose interest in it. After all, he had already been living with the idea for some decades. He went on to consider another possible mechanism of evolutionary change, sexual selection, which he presented in 1871 in *The Descent of Man and Selection in Relation to Sex*. Here he emphasised that sexually reproducing creatures (including most animals and plants) cannot reproduce unless they find compatible mates; and that, most obviously in the case of sentient and mobile animals, they first have to attract mates. Therefore, he argued, selection will favour individuals whom potential mates find most attractive. Hence, for example, the peacock's tail.

Often, the features that are most attractive to mates detract from the creature's ability to withstand the rough and tumble of everyday life: the peacock's tail does not do much for his agility. Yet sexual selection may also encourage the evolution of characters that are of enormous value in other contexts – and Geoffrey Miller of University College London argues in *The Mating Mind* that only sexual selection can explain the extraordinarily rapid evolution of the human brain. All in all, biologists are only now beginning to appreciate the full significance of sexual selection. But Darwin saw it first: and it took the rest of the world more than a century to catch up.

Darwin, who was his own best critic, perceived the two most important flaws in his evolutionary thesis. First, he had no plausible mechanism of heredity, nothing convincingly to explain how 'like begets like' and yet gives rise to variations. Secondly, his ideas were unquantified. He was aware of his mathematical deficiency at a very early age. Maths is crucial in the development of science, of course, as Mendel showed, but science also needs creative imagination and Darwin showed that those who have an abundance of it may make pivotal contributions even without maths. To be sure, very few great scientists were non-mathematical; but Darwin was one of them. Michael Faraday, intriguingly, was another. However, in the 140 years since *Origin* the deficits that Darwin perceived in his own work have been made good. In that 140 years, too, biologists have also made just one, enormously significant, adjustment.

The first of the great problems, the mystery of heredity, was, of course, effectively solved within a few years of *Origin* by Mendel. But we have seen that although Mendel had many good friends, he did not seem able to gain their serious attention. Darwin certainly did. Thus he leaned heavily on the great geologist Charles Lyell, who was older than himself, and on his juniors, Thomas Henry Huxley, Joseph Hooker, John Lubbock and others, who assumed the role of critical disciples, supportive but sharp in equal measure. Contrast Mendel's dismal correspondence with Carl Nägeli. So it was that Darwinian evolution emerged as the great obsession of the late nineteenth century while Mendel's genetics was left to become the science of the twentieth century.

You will see intuitively that Mendel's genetics and Darwin's ideas on evolution fit together beautifully. Oddly, however, when Mendel's ideas on heredity were first rediscovered, they were felt to be *at odds* with Darwin's theory. The history of science is the history of human beings; it is not the logical outworking that non-scientists and bad philosophers of science suppose it to be. The problem was (or was perceived to be) that Mendel's rules were based on patterns of inheritance of simple characters which (as we would say today) were coded by single genes. If all characters were of this kind, then evolution would surely follow a very jerky course. Any one character would have, as Mendel said, an 'all or none' quality. But Darwin had stressed that the characters of all creatures tend to change gradually, step by step, over many millions of years.

The answer to this apparent contradiction now seems obvious and would have been obvious to Mendel, if he had lived long enough to be consulted. Mendel deliberately set out to study very simple, single-gene characters because, as he well knew, these alone would give clear results that could be analysed statistically, reveal the underlying patterns and hence suggest the underlying mechanisms. But he also knew full well that most characters in most creatures do not have an all-or-none character. Most, as he certainly realised, are in modern parlance 'polygenic', coded by consortia of genes. A character that is polygenic obviously can be changed gradually as the generations pass simply by changing one gene at a time. So there is no irresolvable conflict. Indeed there is no conflict at all.

All this became obvious during the first decades of the twentieth century and by the 1940s Mendel's genetics was fully reconciled with Darwin's idea of evolution by natural selection. The reconciliation is known as 'the Modern Synthesis' and the result of this synthesis is called 'neodarwinism'. Neodarwinism is the cornerstone of modern biology and can properly be seen as one of the intellectual triumphs of the twentieth century. Stir in molecular biology, which came on-line after the 1950s, and you effectively have a summary of modern biology. In practice, however, the true significance of the modern synthesis seems under-appreciated, at least by non-biologists. Physicists are more impressed by quantum theory and non-scientists are more impressed by physicists.

Be that as it may, neodarwinists perceive essentially that natural selection affects the gene pool as a whole. As time passes, duplication of genes and genetic mutation tend to increase the total variety of alleles within the gene pool and hence the total variation of the creatures themselves. Natural selection then weeds out the individuals which contain the least favourable combinations of alleles. As time passes, some alleles get weeded out totally. Thus, as the generations pass, the composition of the gene pool – the frequency of the different alleles within it – changes. As we will see, late-twentieth-century neodarwinists tend to argue that although natural selection in practice appears to operate most directly upon individuals – it's the individual creatures who die or live to reproduce – that it is better, in general, to think of natural selection acting upon individual genes. But we will come to that. The general point is that by the action of natural selection the composition of the gene pool is altered over time. (We will also see, especially in Chapter 8, that natural selection is not the only force tending to alter the composition of the gene pool. Chance plays a large part as well.

Darwin's second great *desideratum*, the need to manipulate his evolutionary notions with the precision of maths, began to be tackled seriously in the 1920s and 1930s by the great British biologist-mathematicians R. A. Fisher and J. B. S. Haldane. But the maths that has proved truly appropriate was initiated only in the 1930s by the Hungarian John von Neumann: the notion known as 'game theory'. Von Neumann himself did not apply game theory to problems of biological evolution; that was done by the British biologist John Maynard Smith, who showed how with game theory it is possible to measure and compare the effects of different survival strategies, effectively to measure aspects of 'fitness'. It has occurred to me that, although Darwin was embarrassed by his own poor numeracy and impressed by mathematicians such as his cousin Francis Galton (whom we have met; and more of whom in Chapter 10), perhaps he felt deep down that the maths of his day was not able to tackle the kinds of problems he was posing. In practice, in the absence of game theory, his ideas were hijacked by dull statisticians (like Galton and Pearson), with their cocked-hat curves of normal distribution and the rest, a line of thinking which has led many biologists and sociologists to emphasise the differences between different human beings and has helped in some circles to give Darwin a bad name. In fact, all those decades of grind can be seen as a diversion, not to say an aberration. I am sure Darwin knew in his bones that this was not the way to go.

These two twentieth-century innovations, genetics and appropriate maths, can be seen as a fleshing out of Darwin (although of course both Mendel and von Neumann must be seen to be great in their own right). The third twentieth century, innovation is truly an adjustment. It concerns the level at which natural and sexual selection operate. For Darwin supposed that selection operated upon individuals: the cheetah is favoured which runs more quickly than other cheetahs; the peacock with the largest tail catches the hens. But since the late twentieth century, Darwinians, first the *avant-garde*, then the mainstream, have thought of selection as acting upon individual genes. In the present simplistic examples, a gene which promotes swiftness is favoured in the cheetah, a 'gene for attractiveness' is favoured among peacocks. This is the concept which Richard Dawkins has encapsulated as 'the selfish gene'. Whole organisms, he says, are merely vehicles for genes. Often there is no practical reason to distinguish between selection 'at the level of the individual' and selection 'at the level of the gene'. After all, a gene which makes a cheetah swift also helps the whole animal to survive and reproduce; and if the gene fails, it's the whole animal which dies without issue. But whereas thinking at the level of the individual works some of the time, thinking at the level of the gene works all the time; it is like the difference between Newtonian mechanics and Einstein's relativity.

The expression 'the selfish gene' is wonderfully arresting. But when Richard Dawkins made it the title of his brilliant book in 1976 he did not anticipate that so many people would read the cover line but skip, ignore or otherwise misconstrue the text that followed. On the face of things, after all, the idea of the 'selfish gene' seems to imply that the possessor of such a gene must itself be selfish. Since all genes are supposed to be 'selfish' this implies that all creatures are selfish, including all human beings. This would be a dismal thought and this is what many people evidently think Dawkins intended to imply.

In fact, as Dawkins is at pains to explain, the complete opposite is true. Darwin wondered, in *Origin*, how it was that ants could co-operate in the way they do, apparently sacrificing themselves for the good of their peers. This apparent 'altruism' did not seem to square with the notion that creatures are condemned to compete, one with another. But in the 1960s and after, Bill Hamilton, who became professor in the zoology department at Oxford, solved Darwin's dilemma by reference to the concept of what Dawkins called 'the selfish gene'. The point is that *because* the gene is 'selfish' it is 'concerned' only within its own replication; and a gene which sacrifices its owner in some act of altruistic foolhardiness will nonetheless be disseminated if, through the apparent self-sacrifice, it thereby enhances the survival of other individuals who contain copies of itself. Hence animals, including humans, will sacrifice themselves for their own relatives – and especially for their own children, whom they know are likely to carry copies of their own genes. This is 'kin selection': simple in principle, but once you start to apply it remarkably powerful.

We cannot really see the full power of Darwin's idea of natural selection until we apply it directly to genes. For the word 'selfish' is merely meant to be an intriguing slogan: a flag to entice people to look at the ideas. It does not literally mean 'selfish', of course, because 'selfishness' implies some underlying emotion, and genes are simply bits of DNA when you boil them down and have no emotions. This is the point: they are without emotion and without senses. Their role in life, their *raison d'être*, is simply to replicate. Those that replicate remain in the population and spread, from generation to generation; and those that do not, die out. That, at bottom, is all there is to it. It is a circularity: nothing succeeds like success; only success succeeds. It is *meant* to be a circularity. Once perceive the circularity of natural selection and you begin to feel the weight of this relentless force, certainly shaping living creatures and possibly shaping the whole universe down to what are thought of as fundamental particles and even the apparently immutable laws of physics.

Darwin had two other great and pervasive ideas. The first was that behaviour could be and is shaped by natural and sexual selection just as physical features are. A peacock's tail is simply a waste of energy if the peacock does not strut his stuff – and if the hen does not respond to his strutting. The cheetah's beautiful shape and extraordinary physiology are merely caprices if the cheetah does not care to give chase. Behaviour must evolve too.

Darwin's final great and revelatory idea, which offended many of his contemporaries and successors even more than the idea of evolution itself, is that there is continuity between human beings and other creatures. Everyone knows that he proposed that human beings have indeed evolved, just as other creatures evolved. The story of Adam and Eve has been, in its literal form, another casualty. Everyone knows, more particularly, that he proposed in *The Descent of Man* that human beings are most closely related to chimpanzees and gorillas and that we and they shared a recent common ancestor who lived in Africa. The weight of evidence since then suggests that in all these details he was absolutely right, just as he was uncannily right in almost everything he looked at (from sex in barnacles to the labours of earthworms and the propensity of some flowers to track the path of the sun).

Put these two thoughts together – that behaviour has evolved by natural selection, and that human beings have evolved, just like every other creature – and it becomes reasonable to contemplate the evolution of human behaviour. There have been several false starts in this area, notably by Herbert Spencer in the late nineteenth century who first, and prematurely, devised the notion of 'social darwinism'. But biologists of the late twentieth century, informed by the notion of 'the selfish gene' and restrained by the discipline of game theory, have been able to make a much more orderly and convincing attack. The moderns, in short, produced the discipline of sociobiology, out of which emerged evolutionary psychology. We will see where this is leading in Chapter 7.

7

'Genes for Behaviour': The Promise of Evolutionary Psychology

On an ancient wall in Delphi is inscribed the injunction: 'Know thyself!' It does not follow that if we 'know ourselves' then we will necessarily behave better, yet self-knowledge should surely enable us to behave more appropriately. On balance, it seems to be a good thing. Evolutionary psychology is an attempt to obey that Delphic command: it is an attempt to explore our own minds and thoughts and behaviour; to ask *why* we feel, think and behave as we do. It is an attempt to pin down that elusive quality which we refer to casually as 'human nature'.

Of course, *all* psychology aspires to do at least some of this. But the specific approach of evolutionary psychology is to apply *evolutionary* ideas to what we know about our own thoughts and social interactions, to see what light this may throw. Evolutionary psychologists do not for the most part seek to sweep aside all other kinds of insight into the human psyche, from other fields of psychology, from sociology, or indeed from literature. But they do lay their own insights alongside other kinds of idea and feed them into the discussions, in the hope that understanding will be nudged along. Evolutionary psychology is a young subject – so far, there are not many extensive, robust studies – but already the signs are that it has a great deal to offer. Some of its ideas are not politically correct, prompting some of its critics to protest far too loudly, sometimes with some cogency, but usually without revealing anything that would qualify as understanding. When the nonsense has died down, evolutionary psychology will surely prove to be one of the most significant intellectual and moral legacies of the late twentieth century. Most of the chapters of this book could be expanded into fat books of their own, but this chapter more than most. In fact, though, this account will have to be a telegrammatic run-through of the main ideas: not exploring them in depth, alas, but trying to show how the different notions fit with each other and with ideas from other fields.

But is there really such a thing as 'human nature'? The idea was certainly fashionable in the eighteenth century; indeed it is a key theme of the Enlightenment. David Hume published his *Treatise of Human Nature* in 1739 and 1740; Alexander Pope commented that 'the proper study of Mankind is Man' and Dr Johnson, Rousseau and Voltaire all offered their own accounts of what human beings are really *like*. But others, notably John Locke in the seventeenth century, argued that the human mind is, as he said, a *tabula rasa*, a blank tablet; many have taken this to mean that human beings can be shaped absolutely by their environment. Bring a girl up as an Irish Catholic and she may become a nun; raise the same young woman as a Soviet atheist and she will raze the convents to the ground. If Locke's idea is taken literally, then we are all of us protean creatures, able to be moulded every which way, and it hardly seems reasonable to speak of 'human nature' at all. We simply become as life shapes us to be, unless, of course, we say that it is 'in our nature' to be infinitely flexible.

However, nobody (I presume not even Locke) would care to argue that human beings are *infinitely* flexible. There are many tales in mythology of human babies raised by animals, from Romulus and Remus the founders of Rome, who were nurtured by wolves, to Edgar Rice Burroughs's Tarzan, brought up by apes. All learnt some of the tricks of their adoptive parents' societies, but all broke away. This is fiction, but it undoubtedly reflects what is the case. If you were brought up by giraffes you would learn to browse from high places, but you would always feel – would you not? – that this was not quite your *métier*. When tourists appeared in the savanna you would at least be intrigued, just as Tarzan was when people finally came his way. At least, you would not turn so disgustedly away as the giraffes would do. You would want to say to the chief giraffe, 'Hang on a minute! Let's see what's going on here!'

In such discussions we may choose to refer to texts and authorities (if such there are), but it is hard to improve on common sense and observation, which should at least provide the initial hypotheses. They tell us that we are flexible creatures, both physically and – much more importantly – in behaviour. The same person born in different places and circumstances really might develop in a whole variety of ways: labourer or aristocrat, Geordie or downtown Cantonese, faithful husband or polygamous despot, pillar of society or Mr Big, shrinking violet or charismatic leader. Great actors show how easily, in principle, a single individual may slip from role to role. Literature again is full of examples (from Cinderella to Mark Twain's *The Prince and the Pauper*).

Yet we *know* that however many 'roles' we may adopt, however our talents and even our personalities may be moulded by our experience, we remain recognisably human. A Martian, taking a long view of humanity, as it is difficult for humanity to do of itself, would surely be much more impressed by the similarities between us all than by the differences. Some qualities that human beings have in common with each other they also share with other species. Human beings, for example, are obsessive child-rearers; but then so are virtually all mammals and birds. Sometimes the mother shoulders the burden alone, but among humans the fathers generally share at least some of the work, and this is true too of most birds. Other qualities are uniquely human, including language, at least of the kind which is underpinned by syntax and is, apparently, open-ended and infinitely flexible. Of course, different people speak different languages and the range of accents and dialects within any one language can be truly staggering. It used to be possible in Britain (and perhaps still is) to trace a person's origins to their particular village, and to track all the changes in social fortune which life has imposed upon them, just by listening to their voice. The flexibility, the subtleties of ear and larynx, and the processing of information that goes along with them, surpass understanding.

Even more striking, however, is that all those different people share the ability to learn their own language, with all its quirks of accent and dialogue, within the first few years of life, given only a minimum of always rather scrappy clues. *All* human beings can do this in the absence of gross pathology. No other creature can. What we all share, too, is an almost total inability to acquire a second language, later in life, with the same degree of surety that we once learnt our own. We may speak a foreign language correctly; but the languages that are truly ours we can abuse, and re-invent on the hoof, which is a much more cogent skill.

So, yes, human beings are supremely versatile creatures; much more so than giraffes, who merely browse from the tops of trees, or even wolves or apes, although their lives are highly various and differ in tradition from time to time and place to place. Yet all human beings are recognisably human beings and not something else. Different individuals and different societies do things in different ways, but at a not particularly deep level they also all do the same kinds of things, some of which some other animals do as well and some of which are uniquely human. It seems reasonable to call the things that all human beings do 'human universals': and reasonable to suggest that the sum of human universals together forms this elusive quality of 'human nature'.

But of course, *pace* Locke (although this is really just another common-sense observation), the concept of 'human nature', defined by 'universals', does not imply, not for one second, that each individual or each society is *bound* to do particular things in particular ways. The point is merely that, although our behaviour may seem infinitely flexible, in reality it is not. In the end, we all finish up doing the same *sorts* of things, although individually, and as a society, we all do those things in our own particular way. We all look after our children – or at least, when people do not do this we say they are sick, or wicked. Even if we do not necessarily remain monogamous for life we all form enduring man-and-woman relationships of one kind or another for the purposes of procreation; or at least, the cases where this does not happen are again considered pathological, as in rape. We all acquire language, inventing a new pidgin if there is no common language to hand, and converse. More abstractly (as explored in recent years by Professor Ken Binmore of University College London) all human individuals and societies, from the school playground to the chambers of the United Nations, have a highly developed sense of justice and fairness and of individual dignity. Again, modern studies are beginning to show that other animals may also share such sensibilities: cats illustrate the importance of personal dignity, while many primates have a fine sense of social acceptability.

In short, each individual does things in his or her own way; each society has its own mores and traditions; and yet, once you get past the superficial differences, the similarities come roaring through. Again this is a common theme of literature: as people who thought they were quite alien to each other discover their shared humanity (like the Japanese soldiers, brutalised by too much war, and their prisoners, in Nevil Shute's *A Town Like Alice*). Yet the question – is there really something called 'human nature', or are we all just modelling clay? – has been a key theme of Western philosophy and politics for centuries. It has led to wars and, right now, leads to unseemly spats in otherwise polite company.

The debate in its many forms is commonly summarised as 'nature *versus* nurture'. No harm would result if the 'nature–nurture' debate was simply a matter for philosophers. Alas, however, the discussion has become extremely politicised. On the one hand, those who suggest that there is indeed something called 'human nature' have often been accused of 'biological determinism', or, if we assume for a second that 'biological' in this context means 'genetic', of 'genetic determinism'. Enthusiasts for 'human nature' are accused of suggesting that each of us is merely a slave to his or her own genomes, slavishly behaving, minute by minute, according to the *diktat* of our genetic programmes. The accusers suggest that all ideas of free will or human conscience thereby go by the board. As free will is cast aside, so too is personal responsibility. How can we be held responsible if we must simply do what our genes tell us, since we did not prescribe our own genes?

The notion of 'genetic determinism' has perverted much of our history. It can be seen in the Old Testament in the story of Noah, as his various sons are decreed to be fundamentally different, with the descendants of Ham condemned to be slaves (Genesis 9:25). The church of South Africa justified the policy of apartheid by reference to Noah. 'Genetic determinism' is thus the stuff of racism; it includes the notion that people of a different skin colour (denoting different genes) are of a different clay and *ipso facto* inferior. It has also been the stuff of class distinction, which, as Marx said, has perhaps been the most divisive human proclivity of all. People born of poor parentage have commonly been assumed to be of no worth. Such notions underpinned the feudalism of Europe and Asia and have played a far greater part in the history of the United States than many enlightened Americans would be happy to admit, and of course still do. The notion that we are shaped ineluctably by our genes does not realise its full awfulness until it is combined with the notion that some genetic combinations are better than others, that light skins are better than black or brown, blond hair better than brunette (or worse, in some societies), 'high birth' better than 'low birth'. But human beings have a great (I am inclined to say 'innate') ability to attach value judgements whenever they detect differences. The willingness to say *vive la différence* is a refinement of civilisation, advocated by the French though not necessarily practised by them. 'Genetic determinism' is indeed foul.

On the other hand, those who have taken the *tabula rasa* position most literally have produced some of the most hideous and cruel societies ever perpetrated. For, as Christopher Badcock of the London School of Economics is wont to point out, the counterpart of 'biological' or 'genetic' determinism is 'environmental determinism'. Stalin's USSR was founded in the idea (crudely derived from Marx) that human beings would grow up happily as perfect communists, casting off their own personal desires and ambitions in favour of the State, provided only that they were brought up in a perfect communist environment. Those who for recidivist and entirely reprehensible reasons did not find it quite so easy to conform to the State machine were seen to be anomalous, pathological, and were suitably disposed of.

In short, both the 'biological determinist' and the 'environmentally determinist' positions are hideous, although at the time of writing (at the start of the twenty-first century) the former seems

163

to be receiving the worse press. After all, we like to believe that we can influence the way we are and the fate of others (including our children) by manipulating the environment, so perhaps we are less alert to what can happen when the environment is manipulated to an extreme degree.

Fortunately, however, both extremes are a nonsense. The sensible position is intermediate. Yes, of course we have 'human nature', which in the end is rooted in our genes; but our genetic programmes do not *prescribe* our particular actions and they cannot. After all, modern Darwinism sees our genes as 'survival machines': and they would be very bad survival machines indeed if they simply promoted inflexibility! Yes, of course we are shaped by our environment, but only within the (albeit broad) constraints of our innate biology. In all creatures there is constant dialogue between the genome and the environment: each proposing, each disposing. In human beings the dialogue is particularly complicated because our genes, over evolutionary time, have produced great brains, which give us a degree of individual flexibility which far exceeds that of other creatures. But each of us is a dialogue, nevertheless, between genome and environment.

Since Darwin's (and Mendel's) day there have been several distinct attempts to discuss human nature, or at least human behaviour, in evolutionary and genetic terms. These attempts have given rise to a series of quite different schools, with different premises, approaches and ambitions. Critics of evolutionary psychology, or what they seem to imagine is evolutionary psychology, tend to conflate the different schools. They tend to be remarkably bad scholars. Before we begin, it seems worthwhile to outline the distinctions.

First, there is a school that derives from Francis Galton's biometrics. This school has sought to explain *differences* between human beings in genetic terms. It has, for example, given rise to the various exercises to rank people's intelligence, measured as IQ. Evolutionary psychology is not concerned with this. It is concerned with universals: the qualities that human beings all have in common. Thus an evolutionary psychologist would study the human ability to acquire language – contrasting this extraordinary skill with the language abilities of other species – but would have no interest in producing league tables to see whether some people are more linguistically adept than others. However, by seeking out the biological roots of language, evolutionary psychologists have managed to show that some specific inabilities, like dyslexia, have specific causes. Teachers and parents of dyslexic children, and the children themselves, are not distressed by this. On the contrary, the revelation of specific dysfunction has been liberating: removing the blame and charges of 'idleness' which have often dogged sufferers in the past, removing the guilt from the parents, and also (which is ultimately the point) suggesting new approaches to treatment.

Where evolutionary psychologists are concerned with differences between human beings, it is between men and women, or boys and girls, or children and adults. It is cruel and destructive to assume (as many societies have) that the rights and desires of one particular category of people should prevail: typically, the rights of ageing males. But it is also cruel and destructive to begin with the premise that all human beings are the same and to assume that everyone in society really does have the aspirations and propensities of an ageing male – or would have, if only they were given the chance. It seems far more sensible and humane to recognise differences where they exist, and then to build societies which enable all aspirations and abilities to flourish.

Then, in the mid-nineteenth century, Herbert Spencer proposed the philosophy known as 'social Darwinism', though he had begun to develop it before Darwin published *Origin of Species*. He attempted to explain the structure of society in terms of natural selection, but he made two mistakes. First, his view of natural selection was crude and Victorian, and nothing like the modern view. It saw nature as one long battle. Spencer, not Darwin, initially coined the expression 'survival of the fittest'. Secondly, he supposed that since nature itself leads to the survival of the fittest, then that is how human societies ought to behave. Thus he slides seamlessly from a description of how life *is* (not that it really is, but he thought it was): to a recommendation of how life *ought to be*. David Hume pointed out that philosophers often do this – slip without pause from 'is' to 'ought' – and that it is a very sloppy thing to do. There is no necessary connection, he said, between 'is' and 'ought'. In *Principia Ethica*, in 1903, the English philosopher G. E. Moore took the point further. He coined the expression 'the naturalistic fallacy', meaning that it simply is not permissible to argue that what is natural is what is right. We have to frame ethical principles *without* reference to what nature happens to do. Lions practise infanticide on a massive scale, but that does not make it right. So Spencer's 'social Darwinism' was wrong on two counts: its view of nature was misguided (the 'Darwinism' he applied was crude), and he fell foul of the naturalistic fallacy. It is amazing, however, how many modern critics of evolutionary biology apparently conflate it with Spencer's social Darwinism.

We might note in passing, however, that G. E. Moore's 'naturalistic fallacy' need not be taken as the last word. In truth we *do* take nature into account when framing ethical principles and it is not unreasonable to do so. In the debates on human cloning or *in vitro* fertilisation, for example, we tend to begin with the premise that it is acceptable for young women to want babies because it is 'natural'. If we did not feel that childbirth is good because it is 'natural', we would not debate those technologies at all.

'Sociobiology' is the late–twentieth–century attempt to apply evolutionary ideas – *modern* evolutionary ideas, not those of Tennyson – to human behaviour. E. O. Wilson suggested the term in the early 1970s; indeed it was the title of his book. Evolutionary psychology is the direct descendant of sociobiology and in most respects is indistinguishable. The change of name is largely for political reasons. For some early enthusiasts of sociobiology simply forgot, or were never aware of, Moore's naturalistic fallacy. They pointed out that men are able to produce more offspring than women and then went on to argue that therefore it was permissible for men to philander because it was 'in their nature' to find as many mates as possible. By contrast, women could not physically produce more than a few children in the course of their life, so needed above all to find men to help them bring up the children and therefore should be monogamous. As in Spencer's case, much of the underlying biology is suspect, for the discrepancy in fecundity between men and women is

166

nothing like so great as might at first be expected (see page 185). Much more importantly, however, the naturalistic fallacy must apply. Even if it is in a man's biological interest to impregnate as many women as possible, this does not make it right.

Because of this philosophical lapse, sociobiology in its initial form gave itself a bad name. The renaming, as 'evolutionary psychology', was an attempt to continue the good work that was implicit in sociobiology but to shake off the bad philosophical impendimenta. Modern evolutionary psychologists commonly begin public lectures by acknowledging the naturalistic fallacy: 'The way I suggest that human beings *are* is not the way I necessarily think they ought to be.'

There are none so deaf, however, as those who don't want to hear. So the old *canards* such as 'genetic determinism' continue to be published, almost gleefully, in attacks on evolutionary psychology. It is all very sad. I believe that evolutionary psychology will prove to be one of the greatest intellectual legacies of the twentieth century. In the twenty-first century and beyond, it surely will prove to have immense implications for all human affairs, including psychology, of course, but also medical practice, sociology, moral philosophy and politics. So we should put aside the excesses of unscholarly critics and ask what the subject is really about.

The Essence of Evolutionary Psychology

All ideas in science prompt us, or should prompt us, to ask three questions. Is it plausible? Is it testable? And, if it were true, what difference would it make? We will look at these issues as they arise but the answers for evolutionary psychology are, I suggest, 'Yes', 'Yes', and 'In many contexts, a great deal'.

At present, many different and often apparently unrelated notions are being discussed under the general heading of evolutionary psychology, for it is still a young subject and all subjects take time to settle down. But the idea as a whole is rooted in four fundamental premises that are worth looking at one at a time.

Premise one.

The first, and obviously crucial, premise is that *genes do, to some extent, underpin the way we behave*.

Some people find even this most basic proposition implausible, or at least they affect to do so. One well-known biologist points out that genes are merely strands of DNA while behaviour is, well, behaviour – and why should one lead to the other?

What, though, is the price of this biologist's incredulity? In truth, people in general and scientists in particular tend not to take ideas seriously unless they find them plausible. The crows in Walt Disney's *Dumbo* were quite right to dismiss the rumour that an elephant might fly. It just is not plausible. Their ears could never be big enough. They could never generate the power. Cartoons are weightless, but real elephants must respond to the call of gravity.

Yet we should not set too much store by plausibility. If we did, we would still be in the Middle Ages. Much of science's role has been to show that unlikely ideas are true: that the universe is not always as it seems. Thus Darwin made the idea of evolution respectable largely because he provided a mechanism – natural selection – which seemed to make it plausible. With natural selection it was possible to see how intelligent creatures could evolve from less intelligent creatures, and less intelligent creatures might evolve from entities that had no intelligence at all. Many biologists before Darwin had proposed that evolution was a fact, but none had provided a plausible mechanism. After Darwin, most biologists believe that evolution is indeed true and that natural selection is the most powerful shaping force within it. But is it the plausibility of natural selection that makes evolution true? Of course not. Animals and plants were happily evolving for hundreds of millions of years before Darwin, even though no one had yet conceived a plausible mechanism.

Similarly, in 1915 Alfred Wegener proposed the idea of 'continental drift', the notion that the continents have shifted around the surface of the globe, such that South America, for example, was once joined to Africa. At first geologists were intrigued, but then they laughed the idea out of court. They simply could not see how this could happen. Continents could not plough their way through the oceanic crust as a ship can plough through the ocean's waters. *Ergo*, they said, continental drift is a silly idea.

Then in the 1960s geophysicists formulated the notions of plate tectonics: showing that the crust itself is divided into sections and that these move relative to each other, carrying the continents with them. This made continental drift plausible and now, of course, it is accepted as scientific truth. But is it the plausibility that makes the idea true? Not at all. Continents were drifting in 1915, even though Wegener did not suggest a plausible mechanism. Indeed they have been shuffling across the surface of the globe for more than four billion years, when the Earth itself was first consolidated.

In short, we are right to demand plausibility. The criterion of plausibility saves us from an uncritical pursuit of flying elephants. But we have to be prepared to be surprised. Sometimes what we find implausible turns out to be the case. All the best ideas in science, including that of the gene, seemed implausible at some point to somebody. So when a professor of biology tells us as a matter of dogma that genes *cannot* underpin behaviour because, well, genes are merely chemistry while behaviour is behaviour, we might remind him that plausibility, in the end, is a poor criterion of truth.

Indeed when we look more closely we realise that, implausible or not, *of course* genes influence behaviour. Chimpanzees do not behave like dogs, or dogs like blackbirds. Of course they are anatomically different, so they cannot all behave identically. Yet anatomy is part of the point: no one doubts the genetic basis of anatomy and of course it influences behaviour. But animals which are very similar anatomically may still behave quite differently. Some birds are monogamous (or nearly so) and some appear so but are highly unfaithful, while others of similar constitution may be polygamous and others are communal breeders. They are all anatomically capable of adopting each others' *modus vivendi*, but they do not do so. Have their genes really got nothing to do with this?

Of course, some people like to think that human beings are not subject to the normal rules of biology. In essence, this is an ancient idea: it is the anthropocentric Judaeo–Christian notion that we alone, of all creatures, are made in God's image, and so are qualitatively distinct from all the rest, which are merely his creatures. Nowadays, orthodox Judaeo-Christianity is less fashionable than once it was, but the idea persists in new guises, one of which is the notion that any suggestion of genetic influence is a species of 'genetic determinism', which is *ipso facto* bad. This view is now politically correct. Biologists who choose for whatever reason to go down the politically correct route point out that human beings have enormous brains which, they suggest, can override the cruder input of the genes.

Are they suggesting that those brains were made *without* input from the genes? Presumably not. Presumably, as biologists, they must accept that genes make brains in the same sense that they make stomachs and pancreases; and that the function of a brain (just like the function of a stomach or a pancreas) is influenced by the way it is put together. This is all that an evolutionary psychologist would claim, or needs to claim. Genes make brains. Nobody claims, or needs to claim, that the DNA itself tells the person who contains it what to do. That really would be implausible. Nobody claims, or needs to claim, that the layout of each and every synapse in the brain is prescribed by some particular, pre-assigned gene. But then nobody claims that the release of every single red blood cell in the bone marrow is prescribed by its own particular gene. Genes do not work like that. No one ever said they did. Genes work at longer range. They set processes in train by making proteins which initiate chains of metabolism. In the case of animals (including humans) evolutionary psychologists merely claim that genes make brains which can think and initiate actions. That is not implausible. That is simply what happens. Deny that and you are denying the essence of all biology.

Finally, who would reject the notion outlined at the head of this chapter, that a human brought up by giraffes would never feel quite at home? That he or she would never quite master the behavioural repertoire of the giraffe, and yet would feel constrained by it? Would anyone really want to deny that the sense of discomfort would derive, at least in part, from the genetic difference between human beings and giraffes?

In short, the first premise should not be controversial. Of course our genes influence the way we behave. The general question is, 'To what extent do they do so?' More particularly (although evolutionary psychology is more concerned with human universals than with human differences), 'To what extent can behavioural differences between, say, men and women, or children and adults, be ascribed to genetic differences?' Then again, 'How do genes influence our behaviour – what are the mechanisms?' And, 'To what extent, by the exercise of what we like to call "free will", can we override the influence of our genes?' These are all legitimate questions. But the premise on which they are all based – that our genes are in there somewhere – is, when you think about it, simply undeniable.

Premise two.

The second premise is that of *the selfish gene*.

I said at the end of the last chapter that 'the selfish gene', an expression coined by Richard Dawkins, although he never laid claim to all the ideas behind it, is the most significant idea to emerge in evolutionary theory since the modern synthesis was put together. It is relevant in all evolutionary contexts, but we can perhaps see its power most vividly in the context of behaviour.

Natural selection is the mechanism of evolution, but at what level does it operate? Darwin had no doubt that natural selection picks out the individuals which are best adapted to the prevailing circumstances. The 'fittest' individuals are the ones which are most likely to survive and to produce offspring that resemble themselves.

Others, later (as Darwin himself had done), observed much behaviour in creatures of all kinds that did *not* seem necessarily to favour the individual who was doing the behaving. Often creatures seemed to behave unselfishly. The most obvious example is the way that parents of all species, plants as well as animals, often sacrifice themselves on behalf of their offspring; but this example is so obvious that most biologists overlooked the

171

innate oddness of it – the fact that an individual can sacrifice himself or herself for some other individuals. But there were many examples, too, of apparent sacrifice for individuals other than one's own offspring. If natural selection favoured the individuals who strove most effectively to survive and reproduce, how could it ever favour unselfishness?

The problem seemed solved in the early 1960s by a British zoologist, Vero Wynne-Edwards, in *Animal Dispersion in Relation to Social Behaviour*. Most famously, he described the behaviour of red grouse. The males compete fiercely for territory, but if they fail to obtain a territory after a reasonable time they simply give up, sit on the margins of other males' territories, and (usually) quietly pass away. Why? On the face of things they have nothing to lose by continuing the fight. If they go on challenging for more territories they might acquire one and go on to raise families of their own, but if they simply give up they are bound to die without issue. Therefore, it seems, natural selection ought to favour red grouse males that are prepared to fight to the death, rather than the quitters who obviously have been favoured.

Wynne-Edwards proposed the notion of 'group selection'. Natural selection, he argued, does not in fact operate at the level of individuals, as Darwin proposed. It works primarily at higher levels; in effect, at the level of the breeding population as a whole. Male grouse which fought all-out, beak and claw, for territory might indeed succeed sometimes and might indeed be favoured over males that simply gave up. But if all males always fought to the death then the breeding population as a whole would be wrecked. Every male which had a territory would have go on fighting and fighting until the last dispossessed individual had been slaughtered. By that time the breeding season would be over, even if anyone had any energy left to look after the babies. No: it would surely be much better all round if animals tempered their behaviour to the group as a whole, assessing how many could breed, fighting their own corner for as long as there was a reasonable chance of winning and giving up when the game was obviously over. Natural selection, then, would surely favour creatures that were alert to such subtleties.

But this idea, grand, ennobling, ingenious and for a time

influential as it was, finally fell at the hurdle of plausibility. It was easy to see how such a 'group selection' mechanism would have advantages; how, once it was in place, it could help the population to survive better than it would if nature really was as red in tooth and claw as Tennyson had proposed. The idea seemed to fit the facts, but it was impossible to see how such a mechanism could evolve in the first place. To be sure, if all the individuals in the group played the game in the way that Wynne-Edwards proposed, the system would be efficient and would surely persist. But what if some mutant grouse were born who really did prefer to fight to the death? Surrounded as he would be by such gentlemanly grouse, he would have a relatively easy time. If he went on battling while others gave up, he would acquire territory and produce offspring like himself, battling bruisers. Soon the population of gentlemen would be overrun by hooligans. To be sure, the hooligans would probably die out. To prevent this happening, however, natural selection would have to be able to look ahead; it would have to include mechanisms which said: 'Don't behave in an ungentlemanly fashion, for if you do you will eventually endanger the group as a whole, including your own children.' But a grouse that thought in this way would lose out to one that said: 'To hell with that! If I fight my way in now I can have children of my own, and if I just lie down and die I won't!' Thus the ungentlemanly behaviour would win in the short term; and unless you win in the short term, there is no long term.

So now biologists were back where they started. If natural selection operated primarily at the level of the individual, as Darwin argued, then it was extremely difficult to explain all the many cases in which animals (or other organisms) seem to behave self-sacrificially or self-effacingly, as with the male red grouse. But Wynne-Edwards's idea that natural selection operated on the group as a whole did not seem to work. Self-sacrificial behaviour, loosely classed as 'altruism', seemed impossible to explain, but thousands of observations proclaim that it is common. Once we perceive that parental investment is an example of altruism, with or without additional childcare, then it becomes universal.

The answer was worked out in the 1960s primarily by Bob Trivers and George Williams in the United States, and by

William Hamilton in England. Again we must envisage a shift in the level at which natural selection operates most forcefully. Paradoxically, though (at least it may seem a paradox), we should not shift the focus of our attention upwards – from individual up to group. Rather we must shift it downwards – from the individual to the individual gene. The message that came ringing from the 1960s, in short, was that *natural selection operates primarily at the level of the gene.* Individuals can be seen merely as vehicles for the individual genes that they contain. This is the idea which Richard Dawkins summarised and developed so cogently in *The Selfish Gene* in 1976. The shift of focus from individual to gene is the most significant intellectual advance in evolutionary theory since the formation of the modern synthesis itself.

The paradox, or the apparent paradox, is that if genes are 'selfish' then it becomes easy to see how the individuals that contain them can behave unselfishly; or, as biologists say, 'altruistically'. Suppose there are two female rabbits. One possesses a gene which tells her, 'If your babies are attacked, fight with might and main to defend them!' The other possesses no such gene. When the polecat comes to the first rabbit's burrow she fights like mad and drives him away. Her eight babies all survive and each of them has in turn inherited the gene which says, 'If your babies are attacked, defend them!' When the polecat comes to the other rabbit's burrow she sneaks away, and all her babies perish. Of course, sometimes the first rabbit will be killed and so will her babies. But in general we can see how defence of young beyond the normal course of duty must enhance their survival and that risk of death is a reasonable price to pay for this. We can also see, which is much more to the point, that a gene which told its possessor to fight for the survival of the offspring would spread through the population. Such a gene would, after all, be inherited by the survivors. A gene that simply favoured cowardice would die out as the children were slaughtered.

Of course, the above case is simplistic. Genes do feed into behaviour but no one gene operates alone, and all in practice underpin mechanisms that have conditional clauses built into them. So a gene that encouraged its owner to fight for her children's lives would not normally be expected to say: 'Sacrifice yourself at the drop of a hat on every occasion!' We see in nature how mothers of all species effectively weigh up the cost and the risk of fighting against the option of conserving their own lives and producing more babies later. We can see the appalling dilemma in the body language of any lapwing as she attempts to lure predators away from her chicks at great personal risk, but usually falling short of sacrifice. On the other hand, birds in general are long-lived creatures which reproduce more than once. Other creatures, less liable to reproduce more than a few times, might do more to defend any one litter. These are refinements, however. The general points remain. First, a gene that tells its possessor to defend her young will spread through the population. That is what is meant by being favoured by natural selection. Secondly, once we see that natural selection operates on genes more powerfully than on individuals as a whole, we see how natural selection can indeed favour unselfish, altruistic behaviour. Thus the problem that Darwin felt so acutely is solved at a stroke.

Of course, the sacrifice of parents for their offspring is a special case, albeit an almost universal special case. In practice biologists have identified three main sets of circumstances in which altruistic behaviour would be favoured by natural selection.

The first is *kin selection*. The care of parents for offspring is the principal but not the only example of this. The basic point is that a gene will promote its own replication if it prompts the creature that contains it to lay down its own life to save other creatures that also contain the same gene. Of course, a few conditions have to be fulfilled for this to work. First, the number of individuals saved has to exceed the number sacrificed. Secondly, the creature that is sacrificing itself has to be pretty sure that the creature for which it is it is making the sacrifice really does contain the gene that is promoting the behaviour. There is a 50 per cent chance that any one gene contained in the parent is also contained in any one offspring; and a 50 per cent chance that a gene contained in any one sibling is contained within another sibling. There is a one in eight chance that a gene contained in any one individual will be contained within a cousin. In general, then, we would expect individuals to sacrifice themselves for their offspring or for their siblings – and also for cousins, but to make less effort. In general, we would expect individuals to behave in ways that promote the welfare of their own families. Bill Hamilton extrapolated from this the idea of *inclusive fitness*. Natural selection will favour a gene that promotes acts which maximise replication of that gene. Replicates of that gene are found in the individual's relatives – offspring, siblings, cousins, aunts. The sum total of benefit to all the copies of the gene in all the relatives is called 'inclusive fitness'.

Kin altruism, leading to inclusive fitness, is a one-step operation. By promoting a particular kind of behaviour in the individual that contains it, the gene in effect replicates itself. Other mechanisms which promote altruistic behaviour require some measure of reciprocity. An individual is nice to another individual (or group of individuals) who in some measure returns the favour. The gene that promotes the altruistic behaviour does not automatically become replicated by doing so (as is the case with kin altruism). But it does help to create conditions that enhance its own chances of survival and replication.

The two well-recognised examples of this are mate selection and reciprocal altruism. Animals might well be nice to other animals whom they hope to mate with, or indeed have already mated with. The mating partner, after all, provides the means for the replication of their own genes. The apparent unselfishness is well worth it. 'Reciprocal altruism' implies exactly what it sounds like: a creature does a favour for another creature in the hope and expectation that, on some future occasion, the favour will be returned. There are several prime examples in nature. One involves vampire bats. They feed by lapping blood from other animals, such as donkeys and cattle, which is a somewhat precarious way to live. Sometimes the bats get too much to eat and sometimes too little. On any one night those that have too much will regurgitate some of the surplus for their less fortunate nest-mates who have got too little. The expectation is that on some future night when fortunes are reversed, the favour will be returned. Another involves the co-operation of subdominant males in some apes and monkeys. One of the co-operators engages the attention of the alpha male while the other one mates with one of the females. Again it is expected that on future occasions the favour will be returned. Finally, grey whales practise co-operative matings. Copulation in open water is not too easy and one male will help another to a successful conclusion. He expects the favour to be returned, however.

All in all, though, as Matt Ridley points out, convincing examples of reciprocal altruism in nature are not very thick on the ground. He prefers a more general suggestion, which at least applies to human beings: that natural selection ought to favour trading. There are not many circumstances in which any one creature is liable to be able to repay a favour *exactly* within an interval of time short enough to remember. But if the animal that had once been favoured were simply to return some equivalent – some quid pro quo – then this would be trading of a kind.

My own contribution to world wisdom is to suggest that natural selection ought generally to favour 'genes for conviviality'. The logic is as follows. Natural selection clearly favours social life, at least in many creatures. If it were not so, there would be no social animals. Given that many animals are social, they need to get along with their fellows; and indeed in social animals a huge proportion of the behavioural repertoire (and, very often, of the brain itself) is occupied with social behaviour. It seems to me self-evident that natural selection should favour social creatures who invest at least some of their time in being nice to other members of their society, whether or not they expect any immediate favours. In the end, this is simply a way of lining your own nest without having to try very hard. Life is certainly a lot easier if you are surrounded by friendly people than by unfriendly. Friendliness breeds friendliness and enmity breeds enmity. In short, a gene that favoured general friendliness (unless otherwise provoked) should surely be favoured.

Premise three.

That behaviour has indeed evolved by natural selection; and that many aspects of our behaviour were adaptive once, even if that no longer seems to be the case.

This is where the term 'evolutionary' comes in. We begin with the first premise (that genes may underpin behaviour) and then ask why a particular creature should find itself with the genes that it in fact has. As good post-Darwinians we assume that at least a significant proportion of a creature's genes have been selected through the course of evolutionary history because they conferred some survival or reproductive advantage. A horse has legs that equip it for long-distance travel because a life as a grazer on the open plains would be aided by such equipment; a peregrine is sharp in beak and claw because this favours life as a predator. The assumption in the present context is that we have genes that shape our behaviour in particular ways because *sometime in our evolutionary past* natural selection favoured such genes. In accord with premise two, we would assume in general that natural selection would favour genes that promoted behaviour which favoured their (the genes') own replication.

Two interesting and perhaps somewhat contrasting points follow from this. This first is that our behaviour, or moods and thoughts, may well have some adaptive advantage even when this is not obvious to us. But the second is that particular sets of genes have in general been selected in conditions that prevailed in the past, but no longer prevail. In other words, some at least of the genes that shape our behaviour may have been adaptive once, but now no longer confer any advantage, or indeed may now be maladaptive.

Simple examples of 'behavioural genes' that were favoured by conditions in the past but are no longer pertinent include some that influence our dietary preferences. Thus (the hypothesis has it) in the Pliocene and Pleistocene epochs (between five million and, say, 40,000 years ago) our ancestors lived in the savanna and woods of Africa. There it would have been difficult for them to obtain enough energy for day-to-day life, or indeed enough sodium, normally eaten as sodium chloride (which is common salt). Natural selection therefore favoured individuals with a particular liking for high-energy foods and for salt, and who would go to considerable lengths to seek them out. In the wild, high-energy foods include honey and fat and not much else. Both are relatively rare (wild game is not generally very fatty) and well guarded. Bees guard honey and wild animals do not give themselves up easily. But in a modern agricultural/industrial society we find it very easy to produce fat livestock (in fact we throw a great deal of fat away), we produce sugar by the megatonne and mine salt. In short, modern people are surrounded by plenty, but they have inherited the appetites of ancestors who lived for many generations in extreme austerity. Here then is an evolutionary explanation for the common observation that human beings, given the chance, so readily eat to excess even though, as a result, they suffer all the 'diseases of affluence' from obesity to heart disease and diabetes.

There are parallels among 'behavioural' genes, too, for the many cases we noted in earlier chapters: of genes that are useful in some genetic contexts and less useful than others. The classic case is the sickle-cell gene which protects against malaria in single dose, but leads to damaging anaemia in double dose. It now seems clear that autism has a genetic basis. It also seems to be the case, however, that the gene 'for' autism also enhances its possessor's spatial sense.

The notion that the genes that shape our behaviour have been selected through our past experiences is of course at the core of evolutionary psychology. Clearly it has given rise to the name of the discipline. However, this key idea offers leverage for criticism. Once you get into the rhythm of the idea, it can be very easy to think of 'evolutionary' explanations for just about any kind of behaviour – or any other quality, behavioural or not! – that we possess. Stephen Jay Gould in particular, who criticises evolutionary psychology on various grounds, has coined the expression 'just-so-stories' to encapsulate all those *ad hoc*, apparently 'evolutionary' ideas that people dream up to 'explain', well, just about anything.

However, serious evolutionary psychologists are serious thinkers. They are fully aware that science is not science until it produces specific hypotheses that are testable. So its practitioners do not merely think up 'just-so' stories. They frame their speculations as testable hypotheses and they undertake the specific tests. But there are two snags. First, evolutionary psychology is not yet fashionable and so it does not attract an enormous amount of grant money – and you cannot do research these days without grant money. Secondly, there are so many variables to be tested

179

when trying to explore human behaviour that it can take many years to produce robust results. Margot Wilson and Martin Daly have taken more than twenty years to demonstrate beyond any reasonable doubt that step-parents are at least a hundred times more likely to kill their stepchildren than 'natural' parents are to kill their own children, and that the critical problem is not one of poverty, or social class, or general social instability, or any one of a dozen other possibilities which have often been mooted, but is primarily one of genetic relationship. Since the whole discipline of evolutionary psychology is new, and good studies can take such a long time, it is hardly surprising that, so far, so few have been done.

So long as ideas remain untested you might reasonably call them 'just-so-stories'. However, there is a significant difference between a serious idea that could be tested in the fullness of time, given the resources, and one that is merely intended to amuse (like Kipling's original *Just So Stories*), and perhaps is not testable at all. It is mischievous to place serious ideas which have not yet been tested in the same category as ideas that may not be testable and, even if they were, were only intended to be frivolous in the first place.

The fact is, though, that the most crucial thread of the thesis – the idea that our behaviour has been shaped by natural selection and was adaptive once even if that is no longer the case – is in principle the most difficult to demonstrate. That is simply a cross that has to be borne and, in the fullness of time, overcome.

Premise four.

Quantification.

Strictly speaking, of course, 'quantification' is not a 'premise': it is merely a *modus operandi*. But it is fundamental. Evolutionary theory has grown on the back of a series of mathematical advances that make it possible to measure, compare and assess different behavioural strategies. The general notion is that natural selection will favour the strategies most likely to enhance survival and reproduction (meaning the survival and replication of the gene that promotes the behaviour).

180

Mathematicians use various devices to assess the value of different behaviours, but two particular kinds are outstanding. First, there are various optimisation models, whereby the scientist first seeks to work out what the creature is actually trying to do, works out mathematically how it might best solve that problem and then tries to see how closely the animal's behaviour conforms to what the maths says is ideal. The scientist does not simply assume that if the animal is not carrying out what the maths says is ideal then the animal has got it wrong. Probably, and much more to the point, the animal knows more than the analyst does and in fact is trying to do more than one thing at once. Optimum foraging theory is a good example of the genre – asking what an animal needs to do to maximise its food intake in a given time. If you watch, say, blackbirds feeding from cotoneaster berries, then they seem to hop from branch to branch, or from bunch to bunch, more frequently than they strictly need to and you may feel this is a gratuitous waste of time and energy. Consider more closely, however, and you realise that the blackbird also needs to avoid its own predators, including cats and hawks. So the blackbird stays on the move as it feeds. Optimum foraging theory, then, properly applied, not only helps us to see how efficiently an animal is functioning, but also helps us to perceive more clearly than we otherwise might the nature of its problems. We can reasonably assume that all creatures, including humans, operate in large part according to optimising strategies of one kind or another. It is hard to see how we would still be around if that were not the case.

The second kind of model that is proving particularly instructive is game theory. This pits a creature not simply against its own environment, as optimisation theory does, but against others of its own kind. One example of game theory in action is the prisoner's dilemma, in which two players gain maximally if they betray the other and both lose maximally if they are betrayed; but each does reasonably well if only they both co-operate. The question is, if you don't know how the other is going to behave, should you begin by co-operating or by betraying? If you betray and the other person plays fairly, then you win everything and the other loses everything. If you co-operate and the other player cheats, then you lose everything. On balance, it seems safest to co-operate – but not necessarily.

The prisoner's dilemma in a sense encapsulates much social life. Should we set out to co-operate with our fellows and risk being done down completely? Or should we 'get our retaliation in first', as villains like to say, and operate a policy of hit-and-run? In reality, of course, few confrontations with our fellow human beings are one-offs. In normal social life we meet the same people (or some of them) over and over again. So we acquire reputations. If we acquire a reputation as a cheat, then nobody will co-operate with us and we can never pull a fast one on anybody else. If we acquire a reputation as a soft touch – as someone who never retaliates, no matter what the provocation – then we will always be done down. In general it seems best to be known as someone who is fundamentally honest and co-operative, but is not to be trifled with. All this emerges from simple application of game theory. It is remarkable how closely it conforms to the way human beings behave in practice and how carefully they build and guard their own reputations.

These four ideas, then, lie at the root of evolutionary psychology: that genes influence behaviour; that natural selection operates primarily at the level of the gene; that our fundamental behaviour patterns have evolved through natural selection and are likely to have conferred an adaptive advantage at some time in the past, even if they do not seem to do so in the present; and the attempt to predict likely behavioural strategy according to various mathematical modellings. However, the notion that our behaviour has deep and analysable roots in no way denies what is obvious: that we also have brains that enable us to remember, to think and to communicate; and that whatever we do has heavy cultural overlay. What remains fascinating, however, is the extent to which apparently huge cultural differences tend to emerge as variations on underlying, universal themes: language, childcare, courtship strategies and mate choice, and so on. To understand human beings, surely, we need to see both the cultural differences and the underlying biological similarities, and to see how each plays upon the other. Anthropologists and psychologists in the twentieth century have focused largely on the cultural differences. The attempt by evolutionary psychologists to describe the underlying similarities can be seen as an attempt to restore the balance, no more, no less. It is not, innately, a threatening pursuit, nor is it a fatuous one.

These, then, are the basic premises and *modus operandi* of evolutionary psychology. Out of the subject, so far, a number of key themes have emerged. We can place these themes in three general categories: general strategies for living; how the brain works; and specific quirks and pathologies.

Strategies for Living, Mating and Reproducing

The essence of life is to survive and reproduce and to both these ends most creatures have evolved some measure of sociality. Evolutionary psychology is, of course, concerned with all three components of life: survival, reproduction and social life.

Most creatures which reproduce sexually evolve two distinct sexes. (They may evolve more than two different 'mating types', but on theoretical grounds alone, two is the most likely number). Males (by definition) produce a great many very small gametes that are highly mobile (spermatozoa); and females produce a much smaller number of big gametes, laden with nutritious yolk, that are immobile (eggs).

This difference in physiological output immediately suggests, and prompts, a difference in reproductive strategy. Each spermatozoon is capable of giving rise to a new individual, so that each male even of unfecund animals such as cattle or humans could (so crude arithmetic suggests) produce hundreds or even many thousands of offspring.

Females, on the other hand, must invest a great deal more in each individual egg than a male does in each individual sperm. An egg, typically, is many thousands of times larger (in weight and volume) than a sperm. Simply because she invests so much in each individual egg, the female *must* invest far more *per individual offspring* than the male is bound to do; but also (as a result of this) she cannot produce anything like so many per lifetime as the male can.

Given these raw, physical facts we would *expect* males and females to have different behavioural (and emotional) approaches to reproduction. Broadly speaking, we would *expect* males to focus on quantity. Crude arithmetic alone suggests that a male which produces a thousand offspring spreads its genes more effectively than one which produces only two; or, more to the point, that a gene which prompted its owner to be as fecund as possible would be more likely to spread through the population than one that encouraged its possessor to exercise restraint.

On the other hand, we would *expect* females to focus on quality. A female human being living as a hunter-gatherer probably produces only five babies in the course of a lifetime. Other very large animals – rhinoceroses, elephants, orang-utans – probably manage about the same number. Some of the babies will die at birth, some will suffer accidents, but with luck two out of the five will survive to have offspring of their own. Obviously, if each female produces two successful offspring which survive to reproduce, then the population is sustained. (This is not *why* females tend to produce two successful babies per lifetime. But if they do not, then their lineage becomes extinct.) With only five or so babies in the course of a lifetime we can expect enormous care to be lavished on each individual; far more than a male might consider worthwhile.

Common sense suggests that the difference in innate reproductive strategy should operate at two levels. First, we would expect different mating strategies. Broadly speaking, we would expect males to seek to impregnate as many females as possible and so to pay less attention to the perceived quality of each one. But we would expect females to be as choosy as possible. In the course of a lifetime they will entrust their genes to only five partners at most, or five, that is, who will actually furnish them with offspring. So they want the best possible partners. Furthermore, we would expect females to be looking for qualities in their partners which would be likely to bring the greatest reproductive success in their children. The question is often asked, in life and in literature, 'Why are women so often attracted to "rotters"?' – where rotters are defined as men who treat women badly, on a 'love-'em and leave-'em' basis. The answer is that the son of a

184

rotter inherits the rotter's genes and is comparably promiscuous. So a gene which encourages promiscuity in a man is (by and large) spread more widely; and if a women hitches her own genes to the genes of such a man, then her genes will be widely spread as well. Genes are indeed 'selfish' and do not care about the happiness of their possessors.

Secondly, we would expect mothers to invest more in their babies after they are born than a father commonly does. Of course, there are many extremely indulgent fathers, in birds as well as among humans. But we comment approvingly when males are indulgent fathers. We *expect* mothers to be devoted. When they are not, we feel this is 'unnatural'.

When musing along these lines, it is easy to fall into deep philosophical traps. Some advocates in the history of evolutionary psychology have done so But the critics commonly accuse the advocates of falling into the traps even when they demonstrate conscientiously that they have avoided them, such is the zeal of the critics. The first trap is that of over-simplification. To critics of this chapter let me observe that I am myself drawing attention to this problem; and kindly note that this is an extremely abbreviated account. So although I point out how 'crude arithmetic' suggests that a male should be promiscuous, I do not suggest that this is, in practice, the best thing for a male to be. In fact, among humans it is really very surprising how *few* offspring men have in the course of a lifetime, even when absolutely everything is lined up in their favour. Thus middle-Eastern potentates sometimes ran reproductive industries, with fertile young women selected and primed nightly for their attentions. Surely they could easily produce thousands of offspring in a lifetime's endeavour, several hundred per year for thirty years or so. Yet the highest recorded number is around 800 (while, much more amazingly, the highest number of offspring for a woman is over 60!). In short, common observation shows us that 'crude arithmetic' does not apply crudely in nature.

We know too that among human beings, the species which interests us most, it generally pays a father to look after a few offspring well rather than produce bastards in the far-flung corners of the Earth, who may come to sticky ends for want of parenting. So we should not be surprised if, in fact, human fathers in modern societies behave towards their offspring much as the mothers do: indulging each one and *not* spreading their seed indiscriminately. More broadly, we find that rape – forced promiscuity – is not a particularly common reproductive strategy in nature, even though crude arithmetic might suggest that it would be. But monogamy, including faithful mating for life, is relatively common, especially among birds. In reality, then, a great many complicating variables override the crude arithmetic (even before we add any ethical considerations).

Yet we should acknowledge that the crude arithmetic exists and that the many apparent exceptions in nature are modifications of the default position. The default position is *not* one of equal input by both sexes. So long as there are two sexes – one producing small gametes and one large – there cannot be equal input per offspring. Furthermore, despite the coalescence of interest between males and females in so many species, the underlying differences still persist. It is an observed fact of life (commonly recorded in literature) that young women often choose old, rich husbands like bankers – looks don't matter – and vice versa; whereas younger men only rarely choose significantly older women. What is perceived to happen conforms precisely to predicted reproductive strategy. A young fertile woman needs resources to raise her children, which the old banker can supply (even if he dies on the honeymoon). She wants offspring who in turn will spread their own genes, which of course include her own genes, so she chooses a man with a proven ability to attract mates. The old banker, on the other hand, wants nothing from his wife except fertility, or, rather, he also wants status among his peers, which again, in the end, serves a reproductive purpose. Young men do not, by and large, greatly enhance their own reproductive potential by hitching up with women near the end of their fertility, or gain much kudos with their peers. Indeed they are derided, as toy-boys and gigolos. In short, in reproductive relations the permutations and the conditional clauses can be infinite (and if it were not so, then life and literature would be far less interesting than they are), but the underlying logic is ever-present, and is not to be denied. This account is simplistic (in the interests of brevity), but the subject itself is not.

The second trap, outlined above, is that of 'the naturalistic fallacy'. We must acknowledge the arithmetic that underpins evolutionary theory, but it is crude in the extreme to allow the arithmetic to shape our morality. All serious evolutionary psychologists acknowledge this. To deny that they do so is simply misrepresentation.

In truth, we seem to face a dilemma. On the one hand, many a society simply applies stereotypes and then for good measure falls foul of the naturalistic fallacy. That is, putting the matter crudely, men are perceived as nature's feckless idlers, boozing, philandering and gambling; while women are perceived as natural Marthas, faithful, house-proud, washing nappies and buffing the front step with donkey-stone. In contrast, it has become politically correct simply to maintain that there *are* no innate differences between men and women, that all perceived differences are 'contingent' (as the fashionable word is) on circumstance. If only girls were treated like boys, this fashion has it, then they would grow up more boy-like, and vice versa, and that is assumed to be a good thing. Of course, upbringing has an influence. On the other hand, it is simply undeniable that boys left together tend to wrestle and compete, while girls more generally converse and co-operate. A billion children's bedrooms and a million school playgrounds worldwide really can't be wrong. To be sure, it is cruel and crude to assume that boys should all behave like Wild Bill Hickock, and girls like Little Dorrit. But it is at least as cruel, and certainly procrustean, to assume that both should necessarily behave like some synthesis between the two. A good and humane society, surely, is one that recognises differences, including those which are innate, and reflects and accommodates the abilities and predilections of all.

Helena Cronin, biologist at the London School of Economics, and author of *The Ant and the Peacock*, has suggested how the dilemma can be resolved. The point, she says, is simply to expunge all traces of the naturalistic fallacy from the discussions – and, more broadly, all the accompanying value-judgements. For example, many studies (and common observation) suggest that women bring different values to the workplace. They do not place such store as men do by status and income. This is not a criticism (either of men or women), but it is a fact, insofar as facts about people's attitudes can be assessed by asking them what they think. If anyone (man or woman) places less store on status and income then they will compete less vigorously for the high-status, high-income jobs. In some sectors the high-income jobs are also the most risky, which is why they are highly paid; and evolutionary psychology predicts (and observation confirms) that women in general take fewer risks than men and so are less likely to compete for the highest-risk, highest-income tasks. If we want more women in politics and industry, which we may decide is a good thing precisely *because* they should bring different values to bear, and if we want them to have influence at the highest level, then we have consciously to change the rules so that influence is *not* linked simply to competitiveness, as is the case at present.

In short, if we want a society that is good both for women and for men, and one in which female values are represented at least as much as male, then we should not pretend simply that women and men are identical creatures. We should recognise the differences and then create societies in which both sets of values are properly reflected. Otherwise we will finish up creating more traditional societies, in which male values prevail absolutely; and/or in which women can succeed only by behaving like men. We can achieve this end not by denying biology, nor by making biology the basis of our ethics, but by recognising our biology and then applying ethical principles to the facts of the case.

We should look more closely too, as evolutionary psychologists do, at the essential prerequisite of mate selection and all that goes with it.

Choosing Mates and Being Chosen

We see differences in reproductive strategy in the way that each individual – human and otherwise – chooses a mate. In very broad terms the adage applies: the man's arithmetically ideal strategy is to find a quantity of women who are, above all, fertile, 'hoping' to have as many offspring as possible. The woman's arithmetically ideal strategy is to find partners of the highest possible quality, to ensure that the relatively few offspring they are able to have possess the best possible genetic start in life (and, more to the point, provide genes that are good partners for the female's own genes). Females who belong to species whose males are simply big and polygamous and do not take part in child-rearing are advised to mate with the biggest, toughest males whose big, tough genes will be passed on to the sons who in turn will achieve enormous mating success. Females of species whose males practise child-care, including human beings, of course, are advised to find males who are good, steady, and will provide resources over long periods.

Unfortunately, of course, cheating plays a large part in the affairs of all animals (and of other creatures as well!) and DNA studies among birds which are apparently monogamous are showing more and more that the chicks in any one nest have more than one father. An early study of dunnocks (hedge sparrows) was among the first to show this, but more are coming on-line. By the same token, of course, the apparently devoted fathers have youngsters dotted here and there in more than one nest. In a sense, the policy suits both partners in any one relationship: each spreads its genes, but each ensures that youngsters are raised safely and that at least some of them belong to the attendant father. On the other hand, Matt Ridley points out that the arithmetically ideal strategy for women is to become pregnant by a rogue (defined here as a man who is good at attracting sexual partners), but to ensure that the child is brought up by somebody nice (in traditional terms) who is prepared to be a loving husband and father. DNA studies have also shown that plenty of human women (more than the investigators suspected) do follow the arithmetically ideal course. Many more women than is socially comfortable have taken their lead from hedge sparrows.

Given that the females *must* place such store by quality of mate, it follows that they must be as choosy as possible. If they are too choosy, they will not find a mate at all; but they ought to set their sights high. Male conceit over the centuries has decreed that men 'choose' a wife – this is a common expression in literature – and of course they do. For many men in many kinds of society monogamy offers the surest strategy of reproduction, even if the arithmetic says otherwise; and when men enter such a relationship they are, in effect, adopting a female reproductive strategy and must be as choosy as the females. But men need to be especially choosy only when they live in particular kinds of society: those which favour monogamy. Women, as female animals, should *always* be choosy. That is their inescapable default position. In general, then, throughout nature, the males compete for the females' attention – they lay out their wares and credentials – and the females choose. Despite the human predilection for mono-gamy, and other cultural overlays, the same does apply in humans. As a broad generalisation, men display and women choose.

The first person to spell this out clearly was, inevitably, Charles Darwin. In *Origin of Species*, published in 1859, Darwin spelled out the idea of natural selection: the notion that lineages of creatures are shaped by their environment over time as they adapt to its vicissitudes. In 1871, in *Descent of Man and Selection in Relation to Sex*, he described a second powerful force that shapes evolution: sexual selection. The notion here is that all creatures fail in the end unless they attract mates – so theory and common sense suggest that any creature *ought* to invest a very great deal in features of anatomy, and in behaviour, which will secure it a mate. The peacock's tail, he pointed out, was inexplicable except as a device for attracting hens. It certainly did not enhance the cock's ability to survive day to day. It was, however, beautiful (in the eyes of the hen) and it certainly attracted her attention. Twentieth-century studies have confirmed what Darwin took to be the case: the peacocks with the brightest tails (in general, those with the greatest number of 'eyes') attract the most mates.

Nowadays Darwin's notion of 'sexual selection' is one of the hottest topics in evolutionary research. It has launched if not a thousand, then at least a hundred research projects. Yet as Helena Cronin pointed out in *The Ant and the Peacock*, the idea was all but neglected for a hundred years after he published it. *Anyone* in science, it seems – even the greatest of the great – can be overlooked. Apparently the late Victorians in particular felt that whereas natural selection was serious since it seemed to focus primarily on the grim business of competition and survival, mate selection and choice were altogether too frivolous to be a serious shaping force. The fact that no sexually reproducing creature can pass on its genes *unless* it finds a mate seemed to escape them: mating is as deadly serious as eating or combat (and indeed involves combat). So, too, did the fact that peacocks demonstrably do have tails that clearly encumber them day to day, and that stags grow the most enormous antlers requiring enormous inputs of energy, which they employ, not to fight off wolves or to compete for grazing rights, but purely to impress and fight off rival males in the rutting season. *Of course*, mating is serious; and so, therefore, are the evolutionary pressures that improve the chance of mating.

One biologist who took sexual selection seriously was R. A. Fisher in the early decades of the twentieth century. He enhanced the notion with an idea known as 'Fisher's runaway'. For the truth is that a peacock's tail by itself will not enhance mating. It does the trick only if the peahens are psychologically attuned to respond to such a tail. So now we must ask how this cosy dialogue could have arisen in the first place: on the one hand, the wondrous tail of the cock and, on the other, the hen's predilection for such wonders.

Well, said Fisher, imagine that long ago, when peafowl still resembled chickens, one particular cock did indeed have a slightly longer tail than the average and one particular hen was attracted by that tail. Imagine, too, that both the tail itself, and the predilection for such a tail, were heritable features; each underpinned by a hypothetical gene. The offspring of that particular cock and hen inherit *both* the gene that produces a big tail *and* the predilection for such tails. Of course, as we have noted in earlier chapters, genes are expressed only when they find themselves in an appropriate context; so we must hypothesise that the long-tail gene is expressed only when it finds itself in a cock, and the predilection gene is expressed only when it occurs in a hen. But there is nothing exceptional about such a suggestion. A great many genes that are carried by both sexes are expressed only in one of them (including genes that contribute to milk yield in mammals).

All we have to suggest finally is that the offspring of the original long-tailed cock and of the tail-loving hen thrive; indeed that they thrive particularly well and produce many lusty chicks of their own. Those chicks too will inherit genes for long tails and genes for a love of long tails. Soon we have a sub-race of peafowl possessed with genes that code for long tails and for the love of long tails.

So now the long-tailed cocks are surrounded by other long-tailed cocks and must compete with them for mates. The hens in turn, imbued with a love of long tails, must compete with others with the same preference. Among the cocks, those with the longest tails attract the most mates because they appeal most strongly to the hens' innate preference. Among the hens, those with the strongest predilections pursue the long-tailed types most ardently. Thus, with each generation, both the long-tailedness and the preference for long tails are enhanced. Always those in whom the tendency is strongest are selected. This is 'Fisher's runaway'. The proposal is that once the trend is established – a showy feature in one sex and a preference for that feature in the other – then it will become increasingly exaggerated in each generation. All that will stop the trend in the end is natural selection. A peacock with a tail twenty feet long would find it hard to survive. Note, in passing, how natural selection and sexual selection can (and probably generally do) operate in opposition.

Why, though, should the peacocks with the showiest tails (and the hens which preferred them) have thrived in the first place? Why didn't the first pair who indulged this fancy simply die out? This is where the original idea needs some refinement. We need to suppose that the tail by which the peacock draws attention to himself in fact reveals, advertises, some serious quality which really does enhance survival. What could such an advantage be? What other quality, apart from the mere beauty of the tail, could the peacock's tail connote?

Well, the beauty is largely the point. A cock that can grow such a tail as that has to be vigorous. It must be well nourished, showing that it has the ability to gather food. It must be free of

192

parasites, for birds beset by worms and ticks are dull and mangy. A big, bright tail says in short to the hen: 'I am a lusty, healthy bird! If it were not so, I could not grow this tail!' This, for a hen who wants to hitch her genes to the best mate, and give her offspring their best chance in life, is valuable information.

So the advertisement must reveal something real. But it requires one other quality if it is truly to be effective. It must *cost* something. After all, if it was easy to produce a big, bright tail, if it required no energy at all to make such a thing, and if parasites had no adverse effect, then the meanest, wormiest, most stupid peacocks could grow and parade enormous plumes and the symbol would mean nothing at all. Hens who preferred big tails would find themselves mating with ne'er-do-wells and their offspring would suffer accordingly and so the lineage would die out. In short, fake symbols (and a predilection for them) quickly die out.

These simple and straightforward lines of thought lead us directly to one of the most extraordinary evolutionary insights of the late twentieth century: the Handicap Principle, first proposed by the Israeli biologist, Amotz Zahavi in the 1970s.

Zohavi formalised the notion, first, that it pays animals to send signals to other animals about their state of health and well-being; secondly, that such signals will not serve their purpose unless they are real (or they will soon be disbelieved); and, thirdly, that such signals will soon be seen through unless they are to some extent costly to the sender. A signal that costs the sender nothing is not worth the feathers it is printed on.

Put all these thoughts together, said Zohavi, and we see – astonishing though it may sound – that a creature which wants to signal something serious about itself ought to show the world (or some specific receiver) that it is able to incur some *handicap*. The signal itself should *be* the handicap. The peacock's tail says, 'I am a big strong peacock', precisely because it handicaps its possessor. In effect the complete message reads, 'I can survive, despite the presence of tigers in the woods and ticks and worms absolutely everywhere, and outsmart my fellow peacocks, *even though* I am carrying this enormous tail. In fact I can spare a significant proportion of my diet to grow this tail even though I have to compete with predators, and parasites, and others of my own kind. What a fellow I must be!'

Because the idea on the face of things seems so bizarre, some biologists were reluctant to accept Zohavi's idea. But in the early 1980s Alan Graffen at Oxford University quantified the idea – fed it into mathematical models – and showed that it still worked perfectly well; and so (such is the modern faith in maths, and why not?) the idea has caught on. Now, indeed, the handicap principle is seen to be one of the most powerful in modern evolutionary thinking.

At the risk of being accused of 'just-so stories' (but in the interests of brevity), we can see how this idea applies to human beings. It lies, indeed, at the root of all conspicuous consumption. Those who sport gratuitous fur coats and huge thirsty motor cars are saying, 'Look! I am so rich I can afford to throw the stuff away – and still be richer than you, or anybody else, come to that!' The man who rushes to pay for the drinks is pursuing the same strategy: 'Look! I can still afford a taxi home even though I am squandering £20 on ten ghastly pints of undrinkable lager!'

We might even apply the handicap idea to the paintings of Anthony van Dyck, presented in the summer of 1999 in a brilliant exhibition at London's Royal Academy. Van Dyck shows various beautiful young men from the court of Charles I in the 1630s and 1640s, with long curly wigs, lace trimmings, huge cuffs and high-heeled boots with tops like big, floppy ice-cream cones. Their expressions are insolent, louche and contemptuous. They seem the ultimate popinjays: self-indulgent, androgynous. That is how I have heard fashionable people describe them. 'Decadent' is the common epithet and their sexual proclivities are the usual topic of discussion. And what of the painter's role? Does he approve of their corruption? Is he complicit? Or is he mocking them – exaggerating their conceit for the world to scorn?

None of the above, I think, is closest to the truth. In reality, the young men at the court of Charles were warriors. They lived in dangerous times and they knew it. They were seeking to defend Catholicism (whether they were devout or not is not the issue: Catholicism was their cause) against what seemed an inexorable tide of Protestantism. They sought to defend the divine right of kings in an increasingly secular and republican age. The civil war was not far away, as they were well aware. They knew it would be their job to lead the armies and that they had a fair chance of losing. They were, however, good at what they did. Some at least were competent field officers and all were accomplished swords-men.

In truth, their effeteness was a double bluff, a handicap. It said, 'We are *such* accomplished warriors, and so far above you in technique and intelligence, that we do not need to dress up as fighting men. Even when we are weighed down with feathers and trimmings and in danger of tripping over our own boots, we can beat you, or anything that those commoners might care to throw at us!' Such feigned effeteness is a common strategy among fighting men. You see it in Dumas's three musketeers; in the British cavalry regiments of the mid-nineteenth century – when the soldiers feigned lisping, childish and effeminate accents, to throw their prowess into sharper relief; and in many of the arch-villains of fiction, like Ian Fleming's Dr No, with his soft furnishings and furry pussy-cats. You also see it in many modern boxers. Some, like Mike Tyson, prefer always to look tough. Others, like Britain's Chris Ewbank, disport themselves as dandies, as though butter wouldn't melt in their mouths.

Indeed the chief problem with the handicap principle is that it seems to explain too much. It can be employed to explain just about every extravagance of human and animal behaviour. Ideas that explain too much are innately suspect. It is for such reasons that evolutionary psychologists must rescue themselves from the charge of 'just-so stories', turn their grand speculations into testable hypotheses and then test them. Evolutionary psychologists are aware of the need to do this, however. Many are among the sharpest thinkers in modern biology. Pointing out to them that they need to test hypotheses is like telling Olympic athletes that they should tie their shoelaces before they attempt the 200-metre high hurdles. Absolutely, yes, it's just a question of getting round to it.

The explanatory power of the sexual selection idea (refined by the handicap principle) has been startlingly demonstrated in the 1990s by Geoffrey Miller of University College London. He has argued that the enormous growth of the human brain between two million years ago and 100,000 years ago – brain size more than doubled between the late *Australopithecus* and the anatomically modern *Homo sapiens* and *Homo neanderthalensis* – should be explained by sexual selection; and indeed that it can be explained *only* by sexual selection. Furthermore, he says, the things that human beings, particularly male human beings, do with their enormous brains are best explained as sexual attractants. Why did human beings develop the skills of dance? Not to impress the mammoths they were trying to kill or the bears they sought to avoid, but to attract mates. Why develop painting to the level displayed by van Dyck? Initially, to show off to potential mates. And so on and so on.

I think this idea is right, but that there is more to it. The alternative, traditional view is surely right as well: that the human brain co-evolved alongside the human hand. With the hand, the brain could turn its ingenuity into useful action. The presence of the brain provided selective pressure, encouraging greater dexterity. Greater dexterity in turn provided preconditions that would encourage greater brain power, to exploit the manual skill more fully. So, as the generations passed, the two organs, hand and brain, egged each other on. That is the traditional view.

The traditional view explains the human brain in terms of survival selection – straightforward natural selection. Perhaps Geoffrey Miller is right; perhaps this is not enough to explain why human beings also developed so many extravagances, from dance to fine art, which do not seem directly to enhance survival. Perhaps we need sexual selection as well, superimposed.

But this is the point. Commonly, as with the peacock's tail, natural selection and sexual selection work in opposition. The handicap principle effectively demands that this should be the case. But in the case of the human brain, natural selection and sexual selection seem to work in harmony. Sexual selection prompts the brain and the body to work more subtly than mere survival seems to demand. But the extra skills, though perhaps not strictly necessary, could certainly be useful when out hunting. By the same token, the skills that enabled a hunter to fashion a better arrow would also enable him to shape the jewellery to win some Stone Age affection.

In truth, it seems worthwhile to stir in the third possible component: social selection. Human beings survive best when living in groups and the bigger the group, and the more intelligent its members, the greater the social skill that is required to live sociably. About 60 per cent of the human brain is occupied with social skill. But again, the ability that underpins sociability also, surely, underpins simple day-to-day survival and also can enhance the refinements that win mates. In humans, then, it seems, survival selection, sexual selection and social selection work together in ways that have not been the case in other lineages. This is why we have developed the way we have, while pigs, dogs and elephants, bright though they certainly are, have not gone on to develop the abilities which lead to civilisation.

This, then, is a glance at one of the categories of ideas which occupy evolutionary psychologists. Broadly speaking, it is concerned with 'Why' questions: why animals (including human beings) behave the way we do. The second great category is concerned with what primarily are 'how' questions: notably, how the brain works.

How the Brain Works: Specific Quirks and Pathologies

Unsurprisingly, evolutionary psychology has attracted two main groups of thinker: evolutionary biologists and psychologists. The former have been mainly interested in behavioural strategies, the latter in how the brain works.

The great shift has been from a view which sees the human brain as a giant, all-purpose calculating machine, applying general rules to all problems, to the idea that the brain is a 'modular' structure, with a variety of specific abilities only loosely grafted together. This latter idea has been summarised (primarily by John Tooby and Leda Cosmides) as the 'Swiss army knife' model.

The modular idea seems to have begun with the attempt by Noam Chomsky, in the 1960s, to explain the human propensity for language. At that time the prevailing idea ('paradigm') in psychology was that of the behaviourists, who suggested (in effect) that people learn language by associating particular sounds with particular events. Chomsky pointed out that for various reasons such a 'model' of learning could not account for the fact that all human beings learn their own local language more or less unerringly in the first few years of life. First, children seem to acquire far more insight into their own language than they seem to be exposed to. Thus nobody formally explains to small English children that to put a verb into the past tense you should add '-ed' to the end. Yet they learn this rule. Indeed, they apply this rule even when the local rules of the language say that it should not be applied. Thus small children invariably at some stage of their lives say 'runned' instead of 'ran'. As pompous adults we can see this as a mistake and chuckle indulgently. If we think about it, however, the child's brilliance is stunning. Thus the child *infers* that the past tense of 'run' ought to be 'runned' from the fact that other verbs follow such a rule. Indeed the child invents the word 'runned' without ever having heard it, since it is not used, except by other small children. Typically, small children first learn the 'correct' form, 'ran', parrot-fashion; and *later*, as they infer the general rule (add '-ed' to make the past tense) they impose the 'mistake', 'runned'.

Furthermore, our own ears tell us that different people speak different languages (there must have been many hundreds of thousands of different languages since human beings first evolved speech), and the textbooks tell us that different languages have different syntactical rules. Yet even cursory inspection shows the underlying similarity. In all languages, for example, there are nouns, verbs and adjectives; and all, despite the many variations, have an essentially hierarchical structure, with subsidiary clauses nesting within main clauses.

In short, the languages of human beings might be infinitely variable, but the ability to learn one's local language rapidly, effectively and unerringly, and with a minimum of clues, is a human universal; and beneath the surface variations, the 'deep structure' of all human languages (the syntax) is essentially the same. Language, in short, said Chomsky, is not just one more task to which the generalised, all-purpose brain can turn itself. It is a very special task indeed, which all human beings learn in a very special way. It is as if we all had a 'language module', a specific part of the brain that is finely attuned to this particular task.

Cosmides's and Tooby's 'Swiss army knife' model applies this basic notion to virtually all the tasks that human beings do. However, we cannot simply see the Swiss army knife as an extrapolation of Chomsky's language module, for the paradoxical reason that Chomsky rejected the idea that the language module could have evolved by natural selection. He could not see how such a module could have evolved and so denied that it had done so. But, of course, modern evolutionary psychologists take it as a premise that all the many modules of the brain (including the hypothetical language module) have indeed evolved. It may be difficult to see how, but it is less implausible to believe that the different modules have evolved than to believe that they have not. For how else does any living creature acquire its various attributes?

The module model is proving to have great power. Within the specific ability of language itself, for example, it now seems that the ability to spell, say, is coded by a different 'sub-module' or 'sub-programme' than the ability to infer grammatical rules (for example, to infer that '-ed' must be added to verbs in English to put them into the past tense). Different people show different and highly specific defects, which are often proving to be heritable, in their ability to process language. At the same time, however, more and more psychologists doubt whether the different 'modules' of the brain are really as separate as the blades and corkscrews in a Swiss army knife. Different parts of the brain do seem able to borrow abilities from other parts and to adapt skills learnt in one area to other areas. In short, brains seem to operate in ways that in part, and at times, are reminiscent of the Swiss army knife, but which at other times suggest that they operate as general all-purpose calculators. There's a long way to go before we can claim to understand the brain.

This, then, is the briefest and cruellest possible outline of the main ideas in evolutionary psychology. What use are such speculations?

What Use is Evolutionary Psychology?

Since I believe evolutionary psychology is offering worthwhile insights into human thought and attitudes, and since it is worthwhile to 'know yourself', I am convinced that it will prove in the future to be one of the most significant contributions to civilisation. The general point is *not* that we *should* strive to behave in the ways in which we think we have evolved to behave. We must respect the naturalistic fallacy: we must, as a separate and independent exercise (insofar as this is possible), contrive to develop systems of ethics that explore the fundamental ideas of fairness, justice, kindness, responsibility and guardianship, and all the other traditionally acknowledged components of good attitudes and behaviour. Then we should adjust our behaviour to those ethical principles, whatever ways our inbuilt proclivities may be urging us.

Evolutionary psychology provides three vital addenda, however. First, it can help us to see when the thoughts and passions that we think are noble may in truth be no such thing; may in fact be mere expressions of some primitive drive that may not be noble at all. Thus people in war experience extreme passions of patriotism, which often incite them to do things which in peacetime they would think horrible: set fire to villages, urge their sons and brothers to commit suicide in some foul trench. If people could recognise the primitive roots of what they perceive to be their own nobility they might take pause. What is 'patriotism' except a kind of extended tribalism? And what is that but the 'desire' of some gene to spread itself by an extreme preference for kin? Why is this 'noble'? Why is it worth dying for, or sending others to their deaths for? *Decorum est pro patria mori*, said Horace, 'It is meet to die for one's country', and many a young man has acted on this adage, of his own volition or someone else's. An evolutionary psychologist would say, 'Nonsense!' Kipling said much the same, after his son was killed in the First World War.

Secondly, however, which may be the opposite point, we may want to build societies that are fair, responsible and so on, but we also want them to be *robust*. Many societies in the past have tried to impose a crude idea of what justice and the rest are all about.

200

Virtually all of them suppose that one particular group – the military, the aristocracy, the church, industry, the working class – should dominate all others. Some civilisations powered by such rules have lasted for centuries, though most, when we look back on them, seem to have been fairly horrible. Even the Greeks, whom we feel had some nobility, kept slaves and were constantly at war (city-state against city-state), and although they coined the term 'democracy' they never supposed that it should be extended beyond the circles of patrician males. But all societies throughout history have felt that they were 'just' and 'right', after their fashion. The unhappiness of most of the citizens was just the way of the world.

Surely we can do better than that. A society that is truly worth fighting for would indeed be just (as defined by the best thoughts and feelings we can bring to bear), but would also conform to the real desires and aspirations of its people: a just society that was truly in line with our own psychology. This must be a worthwhile aim; perhaps, indeed, it is the ultimate aim of civilisation (although we need not assume that 'civilisation' need be the ultimate aim of each individual human being). The idea that 'human nature' is real, and that societies work best when they are in line with human nature, is certainly not new. Hegel, for instance, said something very similar. But we cannot achieve this unless we 'know ourselves'.

Present-day laws provide a small example of the principle. In Britain (as in most countries) we have laws that forbid murder, and others that urge us not to drive our motor cars too quickly. On the whole we obey the first, but, at least when the road is clear, we ignore the second. Why? The point is not simply that murder is serious and speeding (*per se*) is not, although that is one way of putting the matter. The point is that deep down, as if at the level of our genes, we *know* that murder is bad. Most of us know that if we murdered anybody, no matter how we might hate them, we would feel remorse for the rest of our lives. Even if we killed our worst enemy we would probably spend much of the rest of our lives praying for forgiveness (or the secular equivalent thereof). But we have no such built-in antipathy to speeding. The opposite applies: we have a built-in predilection for thrills and risk.

Law-makers recognise this distinction. They acknowledge that a bad law is one that cannot be enforced, no matter how reasonable it might seem; and they acknowledge, too, that laws are especially hard to enforce if, deep down, people do not *feel* the point of them. In practice we don't need a law to forbid murder. We know that murder is bad and the law merely provides formal endorsement. We do need laws to forbid speeding because without them we might well drive twice as fast. But even so this law is widely flouted. Our society would surely be more stable if in general we framed laws – or, more to the point, social policy in general – which reflected how we *are*, and not as some law-maker would want us to be. This is not to say, however (and this is where we invoke the naturalistic fallacy), that how we are is how it is good to be. But the principle does acknowledge that if we can devise laws and mores that conform to how we really are, then they are much more likely to succeed and the society that results is much more likely to be tolerable and to endure.

The final general lesson of evolutionary psychology is that if we allow our societies to go with the flow – to conform as far as possible to how human beings really are – then we should create much better societies than we have managed so far. For evolutionary psychology tells us (I believe) that most people, most of the time, are 'nice'. We all of us behave badly some of the time – selfishly, aggressively, viciously – and some people behave that way most of the time. But most of us, most of the time, are fairly unselfish, reasonably kind, not particularly pushy, and have a sense of fairness and justice and of the need to respect other people's dignity. The fact that most *societies* through history, including most nations, have behaved selfishly, aggressively and often murderously is an unfortunate oddity that can be explained perfectly well by a little game theory. Perhaps when this fact, and its cause, are more widely recognised, we can do something about it.

The point is easily made by reference to one of the simplest models in game theory: that of hawks versus doves. The hawks and the doves are metaphorical, of course: they refer to individuals (let's say people) who behave selfishly and aggress-ively, versus people whose mien is more passive, who never pick a fight, and indeed do not retaliate when provoked.

The following story can be told mathematically, ascribing numerical values, 'scores', to perceived gains and losses, but it can equally well be understood intuitively. Suppose, first of all, we have a society that consists only of doves. These metaphorical doves can be human beings or they can be ciphers in a computer game. For present purposes it doesn't matter. They are simply symbols of dovishness, which behave dovishly.

An all-dove society wastes no time on fighting. Where appropriate, every task is undertaken co-operatively, with all the gains that thus accrue. All energy is thus expended towards useful ends, or to sheer enjoyment, and all tasks are undertaken with high efficiency. The sum total of wealth and happiness within such an all-dove society is as high as it could possibly be. If all the wealth and happiness is shared equally, then each individual would do very well.

Game theory (and common sense) reveal, however, that such a society, though in some ways ideal, is unstable. For suppose, in the midst of such a society, a hawk appears. In genetic terms, we might say that a mutation occurs: a gene that hitherto encouraged co-operative peacableness mutates into one that promotes aggres-sion and self-centredness. Such a lone hawk has an easy time. He grabs whatever is going without working for it and his dovish neighbours simply stand aside. The overall productivity, happi-ness and general well-being of the society go down because the hawk is taking without giving back. But the hawk himself is doing well. Indeed he is doing better than any of the doves did before he arrived, when they simply shared everything equally. The overall cake is smaller than it was, but the hawk grabs most of it.

In short, an all-dove society, enviable and unimprovable though it may seem, is vulnerable. A hawk can prey upon it.

So what happens next? The hawk grabs plenty of mates and produces plenty of offspring. Unfortunately, both for the hawk and for the society as a whole, the offspring inherit his hawkishness. So soon the society contains a great many hawks.

But now the circumstances are changed. When the hawk was

203

on his own, or when there were only a few hawks, they could swagger about taking what they wanted without fear of redress. Now there are plenty of hawks and every now and again – in fact, more and more frequently – the swaggering hawk meets up with another hawk. Now, when he simply demands, he finds himself in a fight. Soon, there are fights everywhere. Everyone is suffering. The fact that the overall efficiency of the group goes down is true but not relevant; the hawks at least are not thinking in terms of overall well-being. What bothers the hawks is that their unalloyed hawkishness no longer pays. They keep running into trouble. Indeed, in a society shot through with hawks, the doves start to do better. They get involved in *fewer* fights (since they do not provoke any) and when they do meet another dove, co-operativeness results.

So although the hawks do well at first, and multiply, the time soon arrives when they start to do badly. Too much hawkishness may drive the society to extinction, but what *cannot* happen is that the hawks will eventually produce an all-hawk society. An all-dove society is vulnerable, but so long as it remains uninvaded, it works very well. An all-hawk society cannot function at all.

It turns out, then, that the only society that is truly stable is one that contains both doves and hawks. We need not assume that any one individual within the society is *always* a dove or *always* a hawk. More probably, as in human societies, any one individual will behave like a dove some of the time and a hawk some of the time, depending on circumstance and opportunity. At any one time, however, some will be behaving like doves and some like hawks. This is the only stable position, long-term; and is what John Maynard Smith called the 'evolutionary stable strategy', or ESS. The idea of the ESS is one of the most important late-twentieth-century contributions to evolutionary theory (together with that of the selfish gene). Note that in the evolutionary stable state the society is *mixed*. It *cannot* consist only of hawks or of doves. It must contain a mixture.

Note, too, though – and this I find encouraging – that in an evolutionarily stable society the doves seem bound to outnumber the hawks. However, and this is the snag, because the hawkish minority are aggressive, they rise to become the leaders. This, in a nutshell, seems to me to be the central dilemma of all civilisation, not to say of humankind. Most people are nice (where nice = dovish), but nice people are bound to be ruled by nasty (= hawkish) people. Thus societies may contain a huge majority of sociable, hospitable, unselfish people and yet be ruled by leaders who are by all reasonable standards dangerously mad, and the kind, sociable, unselfish people follow their mad leaders into war and atrocity just because they are easily led. Democracy ought to solve this problem. It ought to ensure that the majority of nice voters elect nice leaders. There are at least two snags, however. One is that hawks can prevent democracy happening at all (and the doves find it difficult to resist such hawkish ambitions); and the other is that in reality, hawks put themselves forward as candidates in an ostensibly democratic election, while doves do not. Doves seem condemned by their dovishness to be overridden.

The overwhelming task for humanity, I suggest, is to devise systems of government which make it possible for doves to rise to the top; and, having risen, to conserve their dovishness. There is, clearly, a paradox here and so the problem is innately difficult. Always, however, the first requirement in solving problems is to define the nature of the task. This, I suggest, *is* the nature of the task; to overcome the central dilemma that is illustrated by the most elementary game theory.

This kind of thinking surely explains why the world has had so few truly great leaders, or rather, so few of dovish mien. Of course, it has had many larger-than-life, hyper-aggressive Superman-style leaders: Alexander, Julius Caesar, Genghis Khan, Napoleon, and so on and so on – classic hawks to a man. All had greatness of a kind, but all were fundamentally killers. The twentieth century suffered from scores of such people, of greater or lesser magnitude: Stalin, Mussolini, Hitler, Franco, Salazar, Idi Amin, Saddam Hussein, Milutin Milosovich, and so on and so on. Great doves, however – leaders who preached and practised co-operativeness and restraint – have been far rarer. From the twentieth century, Gandhi, Nelson Mandela and the present Dalai Lama come most easily to mind. There have been others, like Archbishop Tutu and Václav Havel, but it is difficult to extend the list much further. Note, too, that none of the great doves has truly held power. All fought, throughout their lives, against some greater power. All in effect have been rebel leaders. We need not be cynical about this. We need not suppose that if Gandhi had ever had real power, he would have behaved like Stalin. Mandela was elected as undisputed president yet continued, magnificently, in dovish vein, helped by the redoubtable Tutu. It seems most likely, however, that unless Gandhi, Mandela, Havel and the rest had first been cast in the role of rebel leader, then they would never have achieved power at all. In a straightforward run for power, they would surely have been outgunned and outsmarted by nature's hawks.

Jesus Christ was the archetypal dovish leader. At least, he may have been somewhat fiercer in real life; more of an anti-Roman, fiercely pro-Jewish zealot. But the Jesus of the New Testament, as portrayed in the Gospels, is the apotheosis of the dove. As a political leader he is in the same category as Gandhi and the others: leader of a group that was itself answerable to a more powerful oppressor. He also, of course, is the world's greatest and most unequivocal advocate of dovishness. Effectively he says (in the vocabulary of modern game theory) that the prize of an all-dove society is *so* great that is it worth living with the short-term insults that are bound to accrue as the hawks begin, inevitably, to muscle in. An all-dove society, he says, is nothing less than 'heaven on Earth'. The insults of the hawks are a small price to pay for that. Besides, he says (which is perfectly good game theory), hawks can only get so far. Before long (when there are too many of them) they will see the error of their ways. This, history tells us, is precisely what many Romans did. In fact, we could analyse Christ's philosophy formally: the attempt to push society from its evolutionary stable state, in which there are both doves and hawks, to one in which there are no hawks at all. Since the mixed society (hawks plus doves) is the stable state, to which societies subtend unless coaxed otherwise, the all-dove state requires obvious and constant effort. But that, nonetheless, is what Jesus asked us to aspire to. Game theory alone suggests that this is not a bad aspiration. Even if the ultra-dovish Jesus was

206

invented by the authors of the Gospels, he is still a remarkable invention, worthy of his place in the world's collective memory.

There are lesser, more immediate targets for evolutionary psychology. It is already beginning to influence medical practice as some doctors begin to rethink their patients' 'illnesses' in evolutionary terms. Much of the world's medicine (Western and otherwise) has been devised to suppress fever. But evolutionary thinking (not in this case psychological, but never mind) says that fever is an adaptive response, evolved to suppress infection: quite simply, most pathogenic bacteria prefer low body temperatures to high. By suppressing fever, therefore (at least too much), the doctor may be siding with the pathogen. Many psychiatrists, too, are beginning to take a longer, more biological view of mental 'disorder'. Grief and sadness are seen as evolved, adaptive responses: the mind's way of disengaging itself from relationships that once were taken very seriously indeed, but have now come to an end. Depression is surely a pathology when taken to the extremes often seen in modern life: totally disabling. But pathologies in general are increasingly seen as extreme manifestations of responses which, in more moderate form, are adaptive. Mild 'depression' can be seen as the mind's attempt to take its possessor out of circulation, to regroup: which can be a useful tactic, from time to time. Constant peak social activity (or the attempt to maintain such activity) is, almost beyond doubt, an inefficient and self-damaging strategy.

Critics of evolutionary psychology suggest that if we seek genetic bases for behaviour then we are *ipso facto* subscribing to 'genetic determinism'. Confusing the modern science with Victorian 'social Darwinism' they then manage to conclude that a society that acknowledges the genetic roots of behaviour is *ipso facto* red in tooth and claw, and can have no respect for human individuality and freedom. The critics thereby manage to conclude that the arguments from evolutionary psychology must be illiberal and inhumane; contrasting with those of the politically correct, which of course have everyone's best interests at heart.

The deep mistake in such thinking – and the *sin* of allowing ourselves to think simplistically and merely follow fashion – is nicely illustrated by contrasting approaches to the perceived 'problem' of teenage pregnancy.

Thus in 1998 the British government commissioned a report to analyse the problems of, and threats to, family life in modern Britain. There is a lot to be said for families, and a great deal of unhappiness in the world, so this was surely a worthwhile thing to do.

However, the solutions that the government's committee suggested might politely, at best, be called banal; but their banality was culpable in its cruelty. The report took it to be self-evident that pregnancy among fifteen-year-olds was bad. They also observed (the data are undeniable) that such pregnancies occur mainly on poor housing estates. Middle-class unmarried teenagers also become pregnant from time to time, but they are more inclined to resort to abortion than are poorer girls. In short, poor girls get pregnant more often and are more likely to continue with the pregnancies. Middle-class girls, if they get pregnant at all, are more likely to abort the pregnancy and have children later, when they are married and have careers.

The government report took a hard line on the poor girls who have babies. The words 'feckless' and 'irresponsible' do not actually appear, but the tone echoes precisely the moral outrage of a century earlier. The 'solution' to this unequivocal 'problem' was more 'education'. Education, however, in this context, meant more education in the crafts of contraception, since it was taken to be self-evident that young girls become pregnant primarily through 'ignorance'. The fact that children these days are taught about contraception when they are barely out of nappies was not allowed to influence the case. Clearly the girls needed more instruction or they would not behave that way. It was even suggested, in the report of this modern, enlightened, democratic government, that the recidivists who would insist on getting pregnant should be sterilised. Temporarily, mind: but sterilised nonetheless.

At the London School of Economics Helena Cronin and Oliver Curry applied a little evolutionary thinking instead. They pointed out that among *all* creatures – not just human beings, and not just animals either, but plants as well – reproduction is a kind of last option. That is, for the first phase of their lives *all* creatures concentrate on growth and on consolidating their position in life: their own physical and mental strength; territory and resources. They reproduce when there is nothing more that can reasonably be done in the way of self-improvement.

This strategy makes perfect sense, whether analysed mathematically or simply intuitively. All creatures have the greatest chance of reproducing successfully when they have consolidated their own strength and resources. If they reproduce too early, before they are up to the task, then they will miss out to those who take a longer view. But – and this is at least equally important – if they delay too long, wallowing in their strength, then they will be beaten by others who are less self-indulgent. For successful reproduction, in short, ripeness is all. Jump the gun and you will fail. Delay too long and you will miss out. If you survey all living creatures you will find, unsurprisingly, that in all of them reproduction is beautifully timed. Some reproduce within weeks of birth (like mice), while others delay for the best part of a decade or even more (like eagles, dolphins and elephants), but in all, the timing suits their way of life precisely. Almost always we can see why a significant change of timing would reduce their overall reproductive success.

So now apply such thinking to rich girls and poor girls. The middle-class fifteen-year-old readily perceives that she would be well advised to wait until she is thirty or so before she has children. At fifteen she is utterly dependent on parental good will. At thirty she will have a degree, a career, a salary, a well-heeled, stable partner – with the option of complete independence should that partnership fail. She also perceives that between the ages of fifteen and thirty life should be fun; university, holidays, parties, friends' weddings, the whole young adult experience. To get pregnant at fifteen would be a terrible act of self-destruction. If pregnancy should ensue, then end it quickly.

The girl on the housing estate has no such prospects. She will not be significantly better off at thirty. No qualifications, no career, no salary, no stable partner. The thirty-year-olds she knows, including, perhaps, her own mother, are no better off than she is, but are already beginning to show signs of age (at least in the eyes of a fifteen-year-old). So the poor girl won't be any better off, but she will, she thinks, be losing sexual attractiveness. Furthermore, the passage from the age of fifteen to thirty is not particularly enticing: more infinitely tedious school, leading nowhere while treated like a child; more dead-end jobs; a string of pointless relationships. In short, there is nothing obvious to be gained from delaying reproduction. But there is a great deal, perhaps, to be lost from delay. Life in the short term would be *more* interesting as a young mother than as a schoolgirl and supermarket shelf-filler; and in the long term she might herself be left on the shelf. Short-term motherhood is not at all bad, with grandmothers, great-grandmothers, aunts and friends rallying to the cause, with herself as the centre of attention. The middle classes who write government reports may see her pregnancy as a 'problem', but she – very reasonably – sees it as a liberation.

So what is to be done? We could simply accept that for some people childbirth at a young age is a reasonable option, and leave it at that. If we think it is not the ideal option, then the only humane solution is to help to provide a way of life in which it is in the woman's own interests to delay childbirth. 'Education' always seems to be a good thing. But the point is not to teach more contraceptive technique. The point is to improve life's prospects, so that a girl can perceive that at the age of thirty life really will be more comfortable than it is at the age of fifteen. Then there is a *reason* to delay: a reason other than that of pleasing the middle classes who write reports.

Finally we might note that eugenics has now become extremely unfashionable (absolutely not politically correct) whereas, a hundred years ago, it was almost *de rigueur* in some intellectual circles. But the instinct which sees teenage pregnancy as *a priori* 'wrong' is a eugenic instinct. If the generation interval is fifteen years, i.e. women reproduce at the age of fifteen, then in a hundred years there are six generations. If the generation interval is thirty then in a hundred years there are only three generations. Even if all the women in both lineages have the same number of children each, the lineage with the short generation time will still produce eight times as many children per hundred years as those with a long generation time. Telling people to delay breeding, in short, is a way of telling them to have fewer children. I do not say it is *bad* to have fewer children. I do say that we should recognise eugenics when we see it.

I could give other examples. This alone reveals, though, that if evolutionary psychology is applied decorously (and all knowledge needs to be applied decorously) it could bring about significant improvements in our lives at all levels. At the individual level, it could improve our lot through better medicine; at the social level, through more enlightened social policy; and at the political level, by sharpening our insights into the nature of power. It will pay us to know ourselves.

Will we, though, seize these advantages?

The Future of Evolutionary Psychology

There is, as we have seen already in this chapter, a huge amount of prejudice against evolutionary psychology. I have heard people declare, apparently with some pride, that they do not know what it is and then, in the next breath, run it down, and all those who take an interest in it. Expressions like 'genetic determinism' and even 'fascist' inevitably surface among the imprecations.

On the face of it, then, two things are needed if evolutionary psychology is to advance and realise its potential. First, it needs better public relations. It needs to show that it has shaken off its equivocal roots: that it has moved a very long way indeed from the crude, nineteenth-century forays of social Darwinism. I like to argue that the ideas of evolutionary psychology should be seen to be Romantic, with a capital R. It is part of the Romantic ideal, after all – as powerful in Richard Wagner as in D. H. Lawrence – that human beings are 'driven' by 'forces' that well up from their past. The notion that these 'forces' were originally shaped on the plains of Africa as our ancestors strove to survive and come to terms with each other seems to me to be stirring indeed. The fact that those 'forces' are encapsulated in lengths of DNA seems to me miraculous, but not innately threatening. On the other hand, the people who choose to reject the notions of evolutionary psychology out of hand, convinced that Darwinism equals fascism and that's an end of it, must attend to their own education.

On the other hand, evolutionary psychology must smarten up its own act. The speculations must be refined into testable hypotheses; and the testable hypotheses must be tested rigorously and over time. Serious practitioners of evolutionary psychology are well aware of this, of course. Some extremely able students are now being attracted to the field, raring to go. All they need is grants. But the world must be patient. Daly and Wilson's study of homicide, perhaps the greatest study in the field so far (and one of the most significant in all sociology), has taken more than twenty years. Perhaps it will be a good half-century, and perhaps much longer, before society as a whole can and will draw confidently and as a matter of course upon the insights of evolutionary psychology as it frames social and political policy. But, as Mendel said of his own work, this time will surely come.

8

Genes Rearranged and Genes Conserved

'To breed' in the intransitive sense is to obey God's directive in Genesis 9:17: to go forth and 'multiply upon the earth'. 'To breed' in the transitive sense is either to cause other creatures to multiply or – and this of course is the meaning intended throughout this book – to manipulate their genes.

However, 'breeding' in this second sense also has two quite different connotations. One is what Mendel, Napp, Knight and Bakewell did, as did all the other characters we met earlier: take some wild plant or animal, or, at least, a domestic one which is not quite suited to the purpose in hand, and produce a creature which does precisely what a farmer (or a gardener, or a pigeon fancier or a dowager duchess or whatever) requires of it. Wild creatures are adapted to the wild. The gene pools of wild plants include alleles that equip them with spikes or render them toxic. The gene pools of wild animals include alleles that make them swift, agile, lean, shy, or perhaps aggressive, willing and able to produce just as many eggs or babies and milk to feed them as are compatible with survival and no more, because although nature as a whole is notoriously profligate, individual creatures cannot afford to be extravagant. Domestic creatures do what the farmer or the pigeon fancier or the duchess requires. The gene pool is stripped of the untoward alleles, which make spikes and toxins and prompt the baring of teeth (or that, at least, is the intention). Mutations which encourage anomalies – ten times more milk than is needed to raise a calf, or eggs by the basket-load – are retained and encouraged. The gene pool as a whole is typically subdivided:

213

not all the alleles are available to all the creatures; and the subdivisions are commonly called 'varieties' (in the case of plants) or 'breeds' (in the case of animals). Each such subdivision is roughly equivalent to the discrete subgroupings that occur naturally in the wild and are then known as 'races' or sometimes more grandly as 'subspecies'. Wild plants and animals tend to be highly various: not always, but a certain degree of variety is part of the survival strategy. Domestic creatures tend to be uniform, or at least far more consistent. The farmer or the duchess, and the consumer, want to know what they are getting.

But 'breeding' in the transitive sense also has a quite different connotation. At least in recent decades breeding in zoos, reserves and botanic gardens has become a serious and increasingly vital arm of conservation. Of course, breeding in zoos and gardens does not replace conservation in the wild. Nobody has ever said it does, or should. Increasingly, however, it is an essential back-up. A population of wild tigers, for example, is unlikely to be viable in the long term unless it contains several hundred individuals, because of the vicissitudes of the wild, and because the wild populations need to retain some genetic variability if they are to adjust in the future to changing conditions. But, depending on how much prey there is, each individual tiger may require up to a hundred square kilometres. So a reserve big enough to maintain a viable population of wild tigers may well need to stretch over tens of thousands of square kilometres. There are reserves for tigers in the wild, notably in India, but none is as big as that. India is a crowded country. So, we can be reasonably sure, none of the present populations of wild tigers can be considered viable.

In the fullness of time, however, things could get better. The human population seems likely to stabilise in the twenty-first century and within a few centuries' time our numbers may start to diminish, not through coercion but because people worldwide tend in general to have fewer children as they grow richer and more secure. That at least is the hope and hope is a necessary component of conservation strategy. As populations go down and agriculture becomes more efficient it might be possible to re-create reserves that are big enough for tigers and elephants, and the thousands of other creatures which are now endangered. But if we care about their long-term survival, then we have to keep them going during the next few difficult centuries, when there is too little room for them in the wild. In reality, too, wild populations are always liable to require some back-up. This is the purpose of 'conservation breeding'.

However, the goals and hence the strategies of conservation breeding must be quite different from those of the farmer or the breeder of domestic dogs. The latter has an ideal in his or her head, some vision of what the perfect apple, or cow, or poodle should look like; and as they move towards that ideal, they talk about 'improvement'. The breeder of domestic apples or sheep deliberately reduces the gene pool of the wild creatures, retaining only those alleles that serve the commercial purpose in hand. The conservation breeder, in absolute contrast, seeks to conserve *all* the alleles that are present in the original wild population: or, since this is liable to prove impossible, at least to retain the highest possible proportion. The term 'improvement' can have no meaning in the context of conservation. The purpose of conservation breeding, however, is not simply to maintain creatures in their present state. The purpose is to retain enough genetic variety to enable the creature in hand to resume its evolutionary path when, at some future date, it is returned to the wild. (Contrary to what the critics often say, it is possible to return zoo-bred creatures successfully to the wild. This has not been done very often, because serious conservation breeding is a new craft, but it has rarely failed when carried out conscientiously and no biologist ever expects 100 per cent success. We may also note in passing how many *domestic* creatures – bred through many generations simply to be succulent or handsome and compliant – have taken wonderfully to the wild as soon as the cage door is opened!)

Very obviously, the breeding protocols required to reduce the variation in a gene pool, and to produce different subgroups that contain some of the species' alleles and not others, should be very different from those that are needed to retain all the original alleles. It is remarkable, however, how often the two kinds of enterprise tend to be conflated. Thus zoos in the past have sometimes tended to breed giraffes or tigers as if they were domestic animals, seeking to produce the tallest or the brightest or whatever. The present worldwide fashion for white tigers is a manifestation of this. Such practices are highly pernicious. They are not exercises in conservation, although they sometimes pretend to be, and they waste space. Similarly, aviarists with cages full of rare parrots are sometimes mistaken for conservationists just because they produce six individuals where before there was only one. Well, there is safety in numbers. But if all the individuals in the flock are genetic replicas of each other (which is often virtually the case) and if the rarer alleles are allowed to disappear (which is highly likely), then, again, such activities have nothing to do with conservation. Beware, in short: do not assume that a 'wildlife park' that produces an annual crop of baby animals to amuse the visitors is necessarily involved in serious conservation. It may be a serious institution, but babies *per se* do not make a conservation programme. Neither, emphatically, does a zoo or a reserve which breeds antelope as if they were prize cattle contribute anything worthwhile at all.

It is worth looking briefly at what each of these two strategies of 'breeding' really implies. Both are vital. We could not support a human population of six billion people without domestic crops and livestock, without creatures which are often quite different from their wild ancestors; and a steadily increasing catalogue of wild creatures will become extinct if we do not, in some measure, undertake conservation breeding. Furthermore, when we come to consider our own species – the past and present attempts in 'eugenics' and the future possibilities of 'designer babies' – we can learn a great deal from those who deal with other creatures. Indeed, as we will see in Chapter 9, people who aspire to breed better human beings have a great deal to learn from breeders of millet or maize, although it never seems to have occurred to them that this might be the case.

Breeding to Specification: The Craft and Science of 'Improvement'

One problem in the 'improvement' of crops and livestock is that the goalposts keep moving. Thus in the eighteenth century British farmers wanted the fattest possible pigs. Eighteenth-century labourers working hard in God's fresh air needed plenty of calories and fat is the most concentrated source. Traditional Yorkshire bacon was nearly all fat, and much prized. (Yorkshire is a cold county.) Even today very thin slices of pig fat known as 'lard' (literally spelt 'lard') feature on Italian menus and very fine it is too. Eighteenth-century breeders accordingly imported Chinese pigs, which veer to the spherical, to cross with the lean, native Tamworths and what you will. Then, in the twentieth century, when people discovered nutritional theory but also began to forget what food once tasted like, leanness was again *de rigueur*. Modern bacon as approved by the European Community is all but uneatable, bulked out with water measured to the milligram: a legalised adulteration. But that is a diversion.

The goals of domestic breeders are both aesthetic and functional, with criteria which sometimes are in opposition, but are sometimes complementary. Many an otherwise fine Berkshire pig has been turned into pork chops before its time because it lacked the four white feet favoured in the breed (which is otherwise black). Perverse, you might think, for white feet have nothing obvious to do with performance. Yet the white feet showed, in an age before ear-tags and computerised records, that a particular pig was indeed a Berkshire and not something else and that it had all the more practical, excellent features of that breed, including good mothering, a love for the outdoors and a diet high in grass. The 'white socks', apparently whimsical, were in practice a badge of authenticity.

Sometimes such badges detract from performance, however, at least in principle, though not necessarily in practice. It takes energy to produce horns which otherwise could be used to build muscle, so the long droopy horns of Britain's traditional longhorn cattle were presumably costly, although the cost was not great when set against the massive bulk of the beast. Herefords, however, the great commercial beef breed of the nineteenth and early twentieth centuries (and still going strong), had stubby horns. The vast crescent horns of Africa's domestic ankole cattle are almost pure aesthetics. Yet in context those adornments make perfect sense, for cattle, in much of traditional Africa, serve as currency rather than as food (and as such they are highly convenient, if only because you don't have to carry them).

Nowadays though, in general, the breeding of livestock is all about measurement: milk yield, rate of growth, number of eggs, and so on and so on. Europe's farmers (as opposed to the professional breeders) began keeping records of pedigree round about 1800. Now pedigrees, routinely maintained by computer, show who should be crossed with what to maximise the chance of the perfect genetic combination. On the other hand, some animal breeding is almost pure whimsy, like the breeding of dogs specifically for show. The snooty, narrow-headed collies which win the rosettes are not, on the whole, the tough little packets of energy that round up sheep so efficiently in the cold mists of Wales.

Whatever the targets for improvement, breeders both of crops and livestock adopt one or both of two main strategies.

When breeders (or farmers) are beginning with a population of wild creatures, or of domestic creatures that have not yet been 'well-bred', then the only sensible route at first is *mass selection*. The breeder simply decides what features are required and then, with each generation, breeds again from that proportion of the population which meets the required criteria most closely. Thus it was that the earliest farmers developed (and subsistence farmers worldwide continue to develop) the informal 'varieties' known as 'landraces'. The farmer plants a field of, say, barley. Many of the plants subsequently die, some of drought and some of late frost, while a great many are killed by fungi ('rust' and all the rest) and by viruses. Some of the survivors are consumed, of course (that's what the crop is for), but some are saved, and replanted the following season. Generation by generation, by a process that resembles natural selection more than modern breeding, the farmer thus selects a population of plants more and more closely adapted to the particular conditions. After all, the individuals which are not so well adapted simply die out, taking their alleles with them.

Typically, landraces vary from area to area, each one finely tuned to the particular slope of the ground, the pests that emanate from the local woods, and so on. Typically, over time, the landraces begin to differ markedly from their wild ancestors: less poisonous, more juicy, and so on. Typically, although each landrace will have a distinct character, the individual plants within it are highly various – some tall, some short, some flowering early and some later. This variousness is helpful in a primitive context: an invading pathogen or a late frost will kill some individuals, but not all. 'Monocultures', by contrast (where all the individual plants are genetically virtually identical), may be wiped out completely by any one epidemic. But variability has its drawbacks, too. Ideally, it would be good if all the plants in the field performed as well as the best ones do. Furthermore, although variation confers some protection against pests, such protection is rarely absolute. Effective, specific resistance (requiring specific resistance genes) is better. Subsistence farmers commonly lose at least half of their crop to pests before it is consumed, meaning they must do twice as much work, and use twice as much land, as ought to be necessary. *Sometimes*, then, landraces are the best option, but as conditions improve and the farmer gains more control, more tightly defined varieties bred for particular qualities tend to prove superior. It is important not to jump the gun, however. Modern varieties need back-up: pesticides, fertilisers, marketing and bankers to underwrite the costs. Imposition of modern varieties in economies that are not geared up to them has sometimes proved very destructive.

At the genetic level, mass selection simply weeds out many of the alleles from the gene pool as the generations pass: the ones that lead to thorniness or sourness, or coarseness of fleece or whatever. Soon (and mass selection can produce significant changes within a few seasons) the farmer *qua* breeder has produced a new gene pool which is much less various than that of the wild ancestors, with many of the polymorphisms reduced to 'fixed' alleles. But, as the seasons pass, more and more of the remaining alleles are of the kind which produce the characters that suit the grower.

Clearly though, mass selection has limitations. In general it lacks precision. In addition, the breeder (or farmer) makes use *only* of those alleles that were present in the initial, wild gene pool. Often, extra qualities are required and new genes – the livestock breeder would say new 'blood' – must be brought in from elsewhere. Thus English breeders of horses produced fine strong animals by mass selection, but then introduced Arab 'blood' for extra speed; and thus, too, England's eighteenth-century breeders of pigs turned to China for extra fat.

So we come to the second main strategy: 'crossing and selecting'. In general, this works best when the parent lines are already well-bred, with gene pools already refined and narrowed to the task in hand, producing predictable phenotypes. The breeder begins with two parental 'lines' or 'strains' (or sometimes with full-blown varieties) that seem to have complementary qualities and crosses them. Some of the progeny will combine the good qualities of both parents. Some will combine the worst features of both. Most will be somewhere in between. Breeders of wheat in the British government's old Plant Breeding Institute at Cambridge typically used to make 800 or so different crosses every year, each one a different marriage of different strains, to produce literally millions of offspring, of which just a few were then selected to be bred on to the next generation. Typically, after the initial cross, the desirable would be allowed to reproduce and then the best of their offspring would be selected. Then these offspring would reproduce again, and they were again selected, and so on and so on until, after about twelve generations, a new variety – of high quality and 'breeding true' – was ready to be passed on to the farmers.

Each individual plant, of course, inherits half of its genes from one parent and the other half from the other. Often, however, breeders require most of the characters from one parent and only one character from the other. Commonly, for example, they will cross a well-established variety, beautifully suited to the conditions (let's call it A), with some wild or primitive relative that, for example, just happens to contain some particular gene which confers extra resistance to some pest (which we'll call B). The primitive parent confers its valuable allele, of course, but also donates thousands of others which are far less desirable. So then the breeder undertakes a series of 'back-crosses'. The F1 generation contains 50 per cent alleles from A and 50 per cent from B. The breeder then crosses F1 plants with As. The consequent F2 generation has now derived 75 per cent of its genes from A and only 25 per cent from B. Another back-cross reduces the contribution of B to 12.5 per cent. In each generation the breeders ensure that the plants they retain are the ones that contain the required allele. If the allele in question is one that confers pest resistance, then they can pick out the appropriate plants simply by exposing the whole lot to the pest in question and seeing which survive. The plants that remain after half a dozen or so back-crosses will contain almost no B genes at all, apart from the required resistance allele.

All these general principles apply both to animals and plants. Plants, however, present an extra complication (although it is one that is also evident in less dramatic form in animals). Thus as discussed in earlier chapters, most creatures benefit from some measure of 'outbreeding'. It is not wise to cross creatures that are too closely related (which is 'inbreeding'). There are specific benefits in heterosis (having different alleles on particular loci); and several possible disbenefits in too much homozygosity. Many a dynasty of plants and animals has been killed off by too much inbreeding.

However, some plants are specifically adapted to inbreeding. Often, in such 'inbreeders', the female flowers are fertilised by pollen from the same plant, or indeed from the same flower. Mendel's garden peas were natural inbreeders, as we have seen: the sexual parts of the flower are entirely enclosed within petals so that pollen neither leaves nor enters. Wheat and sorghum are also natural inbreeders. Biologists speculate that the ancestors of such plants were thinly scattered through the landscape, so that their chances of being fertilised were reduced: and in such circumstances, it was better to forgo the advantages of heterosis and settle for pollen produced at home, so this was the strategy favoured by natural selection. We must assume, however (and experiment generally confirms this), that the gene pools of natural inbreeders do not include too many deleterious recessive alleles, which would otherwise cause trouble.

Other plants, however, are fully committed outbreeders. Some,

221

including apples and plums, have 'specific mating barriers' which prevent pollen from the same plant, or from genetically similar plants, from fertilising the flowers. Thus we find that, in general, two apples of the same variety will not fertilise each other. Since fruit is produced only when the ovum is fertilised (except in plants like domestic bananas which produce fruit parthenogenetic- ally) growers get no fruit at all unless they raise compatible varieties within a bee's flight of each other. It is bizarre that two creatures of the same species cannot breed together; but in plants this is often the case. Other natural outbreeders do not have specific mating barriers but they will suffer severely nonetheless from excess homozygosity. Maize and millet are of this kind and so are many pulses.

Consumers like crops that are reasonably uniform: they like to know what they are buying. Modern farmers also prefer reasonable uniformity; first, because they want to please the consumers, but also because they want to be sure that all the plants will respond equally and eagerly to the extra expensive fertilisers that they apply to the fields and that they will all be ready for harvest at the same time, whether by machine or by gangs of hired labour. Breeders, in their turn, have to supply the farmers with seed that is correspondingly uniform. They also have to supply that seed in vast amounts.

When the plants are natural inbreeders, like wheat, it is relatively easy to produce uniform seed in large amounts. Natural inbreeders do not suffer excessively from homozygosity. Thus the breeder could in principle start with just one, highly homozygous, parent plant and multiply it up by self-pollination, and all the offspring would be genetically the same as the parent and as each other (or at least very similar). Those offspring would be highly homozygous, but as inbreeders they would not be unduly affected by this.

However, when the species in turn is a natural outbreeder, simply multiplication of a single self-fertilised parent is not an option. Natural outbreeders need to be heterozygous. But heterozygous plants do not 'breed true' for all the reasons discussed in earlier chapters. How, then, can the breeder reconcile the two requirements of high performance and uniformity?

In many crops asexual reproduction comes to the rescue. Thus the breeder of potatoes may produce an excellent plant by the normal methods of mass selection, followed by crossing and selection; and then simply multiply that plant by tubers. The tubers are all clones, genetically identical to each other and to the parent. Similarly, fruit breeders multiply their favoured varieties by cuttings. Thus it is that all the Cox's orange pippin trees in the world have been cloned by cuttings from the first Cox, which was bred by normal sexual means in the nineteenth century. Each of the many different varieties of grape, from Aglianico to Zinfandel, is also a clone. Each vine plant or apple tree may be highly heterozygous, yet all the different plants of any one variety are genetically more or less identical.

But cereals and pulses, the world's most important crops, cannot be multiplied asexually. They reproduce only by seed. When the cereal or pulse is an outbreeder, it becomes extremely difficult to reconcile the two opposing demands: for uniformity on the one hand (which the consumer and farmer require); and for heterozygosity (without which the crop itself will suffer).

There are two main ways round this problem. The first is to produce a population of plants whose gene pool (a) is as purged as possible of frankly deleterious alleles, (b) contains just enough polymorphism to ensure reasonable heterozygosity in each plant and (c) in which the different alleles that may occupy any one locus are indeed different, and yet produce much the same phenotypic effect. Thus two different individuals in the same variety may look and behave much the same, but may nonetheless contain different alleles. At the molecular level, which is where it counts, the need for heterozygosity is thus satisfied, yet the phenotypes are reasonably uniform. Overall, however, the approach is essentially one of compromise. The different traditional varieties of runner beans, say, have gene pools of this kind.

The second strategy is to produce first-generation, F1, hybrids. Each of the two parents of the F1 hybrid may be fairly homozygous and, therefore, since the plant is an outbreeder, may well look rather feeble. But when the two are mated, the resulting first-generation offspring are highly heterozygous: and if the parents are themselves well-bred (despite being phenotypically feeble) and are well matched, then the F1 hybrids could be very vigorous indeed. In short, such F1 hybrids are highly hetero- zygous *and yet* are uniform. Of course, F1 hybrids do not themselves breed true, so farmers and growers cannot simply save F1 hybrid seed and hope to get the same results again. They must buy fresh F1 seed each year. For commercial growers in developed economies, however (or indeed for weekend gardeners), the F1 hybrid is an excellent option. More and more crops are grown as F1 hybrids. It transpires, too, that even inveterate inbreeders benefit, after all, from some heterozygosity: so even wheat, these days, is increasingly grown in hybrid form.

Livestock farmers play comparable games. Thus British dairy farmers typically raise Friesian (Holstein) cows, which give plenty of milk; but cross the cows with a bull of a beef breed – traditionally with a Hereford but increasingly, these days, with one of the big European breeds like Charolais – to produce an extra beefy calf. Britain's sheep farmers ring endlessly complex changes, commonly keeping F1 hybrid ewes on the hills (generally of medium body size) which they cross with big meaty rams (like Suffolk or Leicester) to produce fast-growing 'triple-cross' lambs, which are then fattened in lowland pastures.

For my part, I love agriculture, at least in its more traditional forms before so much of the countryside became a sprawling, rural factory. In all parts of the world it is good to look into fields and ask what exactly is going on. No cow ever stood on a hillside without a reason. Why that particular breed in that particular place? There are many pleasant surprises in modern Britain, away from the prairies and the big sheds, where more and more hobby farmers are raising Highland cattle which look like musk-ox, or Belted Galloways, jet black with broad white cummerbunds.

If you don't share this obsession, you may be asking, 'So what?' Well, the key aim of this book is to explore current ideas: including the notion that human beings might be 'improved' genetically, at first by 'eugenics' and in the future by genetic engineering. I will discuss this further in Chapter 9. Here, though, I would ask you simply to ponder the problem of producing a 'better' human being, cleverer, more handsome, more athletic, in the light of the above comments about wheat and cattle. Wheat breeders produce millions of offspring to get the right combinations. The millions that do not come up to scratch are simply thrown out. Breeders of maize know they must conserve heterozygosity. It seems to me almost beyond question, even in the absence, as yet, of any firm data, that human qualities such as intelligence, insofar as they are influenced by the genes, *must* operate best when they are highly heterozygous. For good genetic reasons, a great maize plant may be the heterozygous offspring of feeble homozygous parents (and it is the job of the breeder to recognise the genetic merits of the parents beneath the unprepossessing phenotype). Similarly, we might commonly expect human geniuses to arise out of the blue, as the genes of each rather ordinary parent click in some magical but never to be repeated combination. Beethoven and Newton, both of irredeemably ordinary birth, seem to illustrate that principle perfectly (though Mendel's parents were obviously bright). In truth, some measure of mass selection might well produce significant changes in human dynasties within a few generations (although, of course, each generation in humans lasts a great deal longer than in wheat; twenty-five years as opposed to one year, or six months if you use greenhouses). But Adolf Hitler's ambition to breed better people by crossing and selecting can be seen immediately to be ludicrous. Science cannot tell us what is right, ethically and politically; but it can tell us what is feasible. We may rant against Hitler's eugenic policies as some extroverts still contrive to do. But why bother, when that particular balloon can be pricked simply by reference to runner beans?

Breeders of plants employ other tricks, too, which are not available to breeders of animals. We have discussed one of them: the creation of brand-new species by crossing different types, followed by polyploidy. Thus the swede arose as a polyploid hybrid of cabbage and turnip. We have seen, too, how August Weismann finally put paid to Lamarck's idea of inheritance of acquired characteristics. He pointed out in the late nineteenth century that the germ cells which produce the gametes develop quite separately from the somatic (body) cells, so mutations or other changes in the latter should not affect the former. However, the same does not apply in plants. In many plants, virtually any

225

tissue might redifferentiate to produce flowers and hence seeds. Thus a mutation almost anywhere in the plant (at least in some plants) might find itself in a seed and be passed on to the next generation. Breeders make use of this phenomenon in many ways. One is to grow plant tissues in culture, when some mutation inevitably takes place, leading to what is called 'somaclonal variation'. Then entire new plants may often be generated from the mutated tissue, to produce entire new lineages. Modern breeders of crops also induce a great many mutations artificially, in their search for new variations.

However, the details of breeding would require an entire book. (I wrote one once and perhaps it is time to update it.) We should move to the art and science of breeding for conservation purposes. In almost all respects the strategies are quite different.

Breeding for Conservation

The world's first breeders of dogs, beginning perhaps 100,000 years ago, started with the gene pool of the wolf and, after many a summer, their successors have produced a catalogue of show dogs which extends from the Pomeranian and the chihuahua to the mastiff and the Leonburger, with dachshunds, Dandy Dinmonts and German shepherds in between. It seems an astonishingly creative process: that so many varied creatures should emanate from an ancestor that all seemed much of a muchness.

But the modern dogs, astonishingly various though they are in phenotype, contain very few alleles that are not present in wolves (or, at least, were present in the wolves of 100,000 years ago). A few novelties must have been added to the gene pool by mutation, but for the most part each modern breed merely teases out, and emphasises, a small proportion of the alleles that made up the gene pool of the pristine wolf. In short, whenever you breed to a prescription – whether for show dogs, dairy cattle or field crops – you must narrow the initial gene pool. Individuals produced along the way that do not perform as the breeder requires are simply cast aside – castrated, sold for cats' meat, thrown on the compost heap; and any esoteric alleles that they may contain, however valuable they might have proved in the wild, are thrown out with them.

But conservation breeders aim to retain *all* the alleles that were present in the initial gene pool. In practice, compromise is necessary, for it is rarely possible to conserve every one of the initial alleles. Serious modern zoos which take part in co-operative breeding programmes have widely agreed an arbitrary but sensible goal – to conserve 90 per cent of the initial genetic variation for 200 years within each of the species in their care. In 200 years, after all, it might be possible to re-create safe environments in the wild for the animals to return to; either that, or the zoos of the twenty-third century will simply continue the programmes. The protocols adopted by the conservation breeder are absolutely different from the ones followed by those who seek to 'improve' livestock and crops. When conservation breeders adopt the techniques of the livestock breeders, as they sometimes have in the past and may still, inexcusably, do today, then their animals are in deep trouble.

Conservation breeding is an exercise in population genetics. The particular qualities of individuals are not of prime importance: what matters is the total allelic variation within the gene pool as a whole. Some quirks of population genetics are very much against the conservation breeder, but others are serendipitous. In breeding for conservation, there are (a few) unexpected sources of happiness.

The great enemy of conservation breeding is genetic drift. Small populations have an inexorable tendency to lose alleles. (So do big populations. But the likelihood of loss is greater in small populations, and there is far less opportunity to acquire new alleles by mutation because there are fewer individuals in which those mutations can take place.) There are various reasons for this. One is that some animals in any generation will die without producing offspring and their genes die with them. If alleles are rare then, by definition, they are contained within only a few individuals. If the population is small then some at least of the rarest alleles may well be contained within only one individual. If he or she dies without issue, then that allele is gone from the population for ever.

But there is a more constant cause of loss by genetic drift. Each individual passes on only half of his or her alleles to each offspring. If the individual belongs to a species which habitually produces huge numbers of offspring in the course of a lifetime – a fly may have thousands, for example – then there is a very good chance that each individual will pass on all of its alleles to its collective offspring. But if the animal is a rhinoceros, say, or an orang-utan, and normally produces only half a dozen offspring in the course of its life, then there is a fair chance that at least some of its alleles will not get passed on at all. If the total population is large, then any one allele ought to be contained within more than one individual, and there is a very good chance that between them the breeding animals will pass on all the alleles that they contain between them. But if the population is small and the rarer alleles are contained within only a few individuals, then again, there is a good chance that some of them will be lost as each generation reproduces.

Thus we find that the rate of loss by genetic drift increases as the population goes down or decreases as the population goes up; so if you want to conserve genes, you need to maintain the biggest possible population. On the other hand, alleles are lost by drift only when the animals reproduce. So the rate of loss by drift *in a given interval of time* depends on the number of generations within that time. Thus the longer the interval between generations, the lower the rate of loss by drift. The generation interval of a mouse may be as little as nine months, so in our arbitrary but sensible period of 200 years it will fit in more than 250 generations. But an elephant may have an average generation interval of around 30 years, and fit in only six generations in 200 years.

Thus loss by genetic drift is less in big populations, and in animals with long generation intervals; and greater in small populations and in animals with short generation intervals. It follows, as night follows day, that *the shorter the generation interval, the bigger the population of animals needs to be in order to minimise genetic drift*. Now if we do some maths (the details of which need not delay us, though they are standard fare to conservation geneticists), we find that we would need to keep a breeding population of more than 1000 mice if we are to conserve

90 per cent of the allelic variation over 200 years. But we could retain the same proportion of allelic variation over the same period with as few as 35 or so breeding elephants.

That, I feel, is an astonishing thought: that with as few as 35 breeding elephants, we could retain 90 per cent of the allelic variation of the founding population for 200 years. It is also encouraging. Many countries, especially if they worked co-operatively, have the wherewithal to maintain a breeding herd of 35 elephants, and any one such effort could effectively save the species. In truth, life is not quite so simple. The 35 elephants would all have to be ready and able to breed; but a real herd of elephants would contain some that were too old, some that were still youngsters, and some that were simply not required for breeding purposes (because they might be genetic duplicates of others). The 35 that were required for breeding are called the 'effective population' and in practice you would need at least 100 elephants to maintain an effective population of around 35. Still, 100 is not many. This, then, strikes me as a serendipity.

There are other serendipities, too. Thus it transpires that two highly heterozygous individuals, male and female, chosen from different parts of an animal's range, could between them typically contain around 75 per cent of the total allelic variation of the wild population. Six well-chosen individuals should easily contain more than 95 per cent of the total allelic variation of the wild population. These figures apply in a rough-and-ready way *whatever* the population. So if we began a herd of Asian elephants in Europe with six 'founders' well chosen from the wild, then that herd could in principle contain 95 per cent of the total allelic variation of the entire species.

Even when they get the numbers right, however, and begin their herds with well-chosen founders, conservationists still need to adopt fairly strict breeding protocols to maximise the propor-tion of alleles that are passed from generation to generation. The sex ratio matters, for example. Thus a breeder of prize cattle might happily keep one stud bull with, say, twenty cows. This is fine for farming purposes. The bull would be an outstanding animal, and all the calves would partake of his fine qualities. But the genetic variation of the offspring would clearly be limited, since every one of them would obtain half of its genes from the same parent. A conservation breeder, interested in maximum diversity, would clearly need to keep more than one male. In fact it transpires – the maths proves this, but the point can be seen intuitively – that diversity is maximised when the sex ratio is equal: the same number of males as of females. Ideally, in any one generation, all the males would mate with all the females. This is rarely practical, and not vital, but equalisation of sex ratios certainly does matter.

This can raise all kinds of practical problems, however. In the case of elephants, the males are very big and often dangerous. An effective population of thirty-six elephants would be a handful if eighteen of them were bulls. Bulls can be kept safely and with kindness: but it takes a lot of money to provide safe, adequate quarters. With gorillas, and many other animals, one male tends to dominate the breeding even when there are several males. The females prefer to mate with the dominant (alpha) male. It is very difficult to arrange all the genetically desirable matings without severely overriding their natural behaviours. In such cases, judicious sterilisation of the dominant animal and artificial insemination can help; but again this is difficult in practice and some curators find such interventions distasteful.

It is important, too, that each individual should pass on the same proportion of its alleles to the next generation as every other. So family sizes should be equalised. But in any one population, some individuals will be more prolific than others. Breeders might feel that this simply shows natural selection in action; and that they should simply continue breeding from the animals that breed best. Again, though, this would be a mistake. Among other things, the animals that breed best in one situation (in captivity, say) may not be the ones that would fare best in another situation (back in the wild, perhaps). The aim must always be to minimise the loss of variation by drift and the theory shows (as again is intuitively obvious) that this is best achieved by ensuring that each individual has the same number of offspring. But this means that if one female tiger, say, produces five cubs, and another produces two, then only two of the cubs from the more prolific family should be allowed to breed. In real life, where space is

230

limited, the three cubs not required for breeding might have to be culled. It seems perverse to kill individuals in what is supposed to be a last-ditch breeding programme, but simple theory says that this is necessary, if we really want to conserve animals long-term. Again, though, many curators find such requirements distasteful.

All in all, then, conservation breeding is not easy. I discussed the ins and outs in an earlier book, *Last Animals at the Zoo*; and although the examples have changed since its publication in 1991, the principles are the same.

It may well strike you that all the above comments seem to apply to animals bred in zoos. But surely it is better to conserve them in the wild? The answer is that, in principle, of course the wild is preferable. But for some animals, as things are at the moment, conservation in the wild is simply not sufficient. We have noted one reason, that for some species, such as tigers, the wild reserves simply cannot be made large enough to accommodate large populations. To be sure, with slow-breeding animals, which in general means big animals, it is possible to maintain a high degree of genetic diversity even in remarkably small populations. But it is also clear that this can be done only when the animals' breeding is orchestrated. Wild animals make their own mating arrangements. Among wild gorillas or black rhinos a few males dominate the breeding. With wild animals, too, some individuals really will breed much faster than others and there are no curators around to equalise the numbers. So when populations grow small among wild animals, the rate of loss by drift can be horrendous.

If the population remains small for several generations, the remaining animals will be almost homozygous. Populations that are greatly reduced – and stay reduced for several generations – are said to pass through a *genetic bottleneck*. Modern-day populations of cheetahs in Africa, of elephant seals worldwide and of the lions on the Serengeti are extremely homozygous, indicating that at some time in the past each of them passed through a bottleneck and lost allelic variation by drift. All of those creatures are lucky to have survived, for extreme homozygosity often leads to extinction through inbreeding depression. They remain vulnerable. All the cheetahs of Africa would be roughly equally vulnerable to the same pathogens and one epidemic could in principle wipe them all out.

Note, though, that breeding in captivity does not necessarily contribute significantly to the survival of species. A captive population of, say, fifty parrots could well maintain a very significant proportion of the total genetic diversity of the particular species (given that parrots can have a long generation interval) if the founders were well chosen, the sex ratios and the family sizes were equalised, and so on and so on. But fifty parrots who are all descendants of the same founding pair and are being allowed to breed randomly – or are being selected for the brightest feathers or the shiniest beaks or whatever, as if they were prize chickens – would probably contribute nothing worthwhile, especially if the flock was isolated and not exchanging genes with other flocks elsewhere. In short, the breeding of exotics is not necessarily conservation; and if the founders have been caught from the wild, as still may be the case, then it can be the opposite of conservation. On the other hand, if a good zoo takes animals from a wild forest that is destined to be devastated in the ensuing months by a timber concession, and integrates them into a serious breeding programme, then that is conservation. It is important to know the difference.

Finally, many people who are interested in wildlife conservation see it as essentially a 'romantic' and certainly a spiritual exercise. So it is. Take away the romance of it, and the emotion, and it loses its point. The economic arguments in favour of wildlife conservation are necessary, but not sufficient. Unfortunately, many people who feel the appropriate emotions tend to see high technology as the natural enemy of spirituality. However, several of the modern biotechnologies, including cloning, have a great deal to offer the conservationist. Conservationists should not eschew high-tech. As the Reverend Rowland Hill put the matter rhetorically: 'Why should the Devil have all the best tunes?'

But I will come to this. It is time to move beyond the ideas and methods of classical genetics and breeding protocols to discuss the family of new technologies centred around genetic engineering.

The Roots of Genetic Engineering

Many modern commentators are fearful of genetic engineering. The power it offers, they feel, is just too great. It frightens people at the practical level, with threats of novel life forms out of control. More broadly, critics often argue that transgenesis is 'unnatural'; and as such raises the spectres of blasphemy and hubris, which go far beyond mere practicalities. Advocates of genetic engineering reply that such misgivings are muddle-headed. Any day-to-day problems can be contained and, on the broader front, genetic engineering is no more 'unnatural' than the ancient crafts of breeding, which farmers and dealers in horseflesh have practised for centuries.

For my part, I am sure that we should continue with the science and technology of genetic engineering. It has so much to offer on so many fronts: insights into how life works; the treatment of human disorder; clean, neat agriculture; wildlife conservation. But since its potential is enormous the criticisms must be taken seriously.

In particular, the argument which says that all interventions are 'unnatural' and that genetic engineering 'merely' extends traditional crafts, is at best disingenuous. There is a brief but cogent catalogue of qualitative differences between the changes wrought by genetic engineers and those made by traditional breeders.

First, and crucially, traditional breeders in general can make use only of those genes that are within the sexual compass of the organisms. In general, animals or plants can be cross-bred only with others of their own species: maize with maize, mice with mice, and there's an end to it. In fact, there are many exceptions. Modern breeders induce novel mutations with the aid of mutagens, and thus create alleles which have never existed before. By various manoeuvres plant breeders in particular have organised many a cross between different species. Plants form new species from interspecific crosses by polyploidy. Modern bread wheats are hexaploid, meaning in effect that they contain more chromosomes than they need, which enables breeders to produce 'lines' that lack one or more chromosomes, or have one too many, and by judicious crosses breeders can shift whole chromosomes from one lineage to another. Viruses, too, transmit genes between organisms that may be quite unrelated. The extent to which viruses bring about such 'horizontal transmission' is unknown, but it may be significant. Such transmission, however, is beyond the direct control of the traditional breeder. In general, the gene pools that traditional breeders can work with are bound by more or less impregnable biological boundaries.

The genetic engineer, by contrast, can in principle take genes from any organism and put them into any other: human into sheep, fungus into mouse, cabbage into human. Charles Darwin proposed that all the creatures now on Earth descended from the same common ancestor and that we all, therefore, belong to the same vast family tree. With the aid of genetic engineering all organisms now on Earth belong to the same gene pool. A mushroom, potentially, becomes a fit mate for a human being.

Secondly, a traditional breeder who crosses two creatures to combine the desirable features of both, in fact creates a hybrid which contains 50 per cent of one parent and 50 per cent of the other. Any one offspring may or may not contain the good features of either or both parents, and is at least equally likely to combine all the bad features. But genetic engineers, in principle, can simply introduce the required genes *ad hoc*. If they want to introduce a disease-resistance gene from some wild grass into a cereal, they do not have to make an unhappy hybrid, and then undertake half-a-dozen generations of back-crossing to dilute out all the bad features of the grass – the low yield, the inability to respond to fertiliser, and all the rest. They can simply pick out the required resistance gene and, in principle, pop it in. In principle, in time, they might create crops like Christmas trees. The species will hardly matter. The initial plant will merely provide a framework, on which desired features are hung like parcels, to the growers' orders.

Yet this is not the limit of the engineers' potential. They can remove genes, too. Or they can take them out, alter them and put them back. In principle (and increasingly in practice) they can make fresh genes from scratch. They can arrange the nucleotides in the order required to produce a protein to a precise prescription, and protein chemists are increasingly able to predict how a given protein will fold (that is, to predict the tertiary structure that will result from a known primary structure) and hence to predict how that protein will behave. Through genetic engineering, the ancient craft of breeding is meeting the modern science of pharmacology. We have the basic techniques required to reconstruct and redirect the fundamental mechanisms of metabolism, even if, at present, we lack the knowledge to apply those techniques in more than a few simple contexts.

In short, traditional breeders, albeit helped by serendipitous tricks of nature, such as the plants' propensity for polyploidy, operate within strict biological boundaries, which in general are the reproductive barriers that divide each species from all the others. By contrast, the genetic engineer need acknowledge no constraints at all except those imposed by the laws of physics. That, truly, *is* a qualitative shift. It is much better to recognise it as such, and to frame laws and mores accordingly, than to obscure the distinction. In the long run fudging is never a good idea.

'Genetic engineering' became a reality in the 1970s, but the first stirrings can be traced back to the 1950s, even before Crick and Watson had worked out the three-dimensional structure of DNA. Then the Italian-American biologist Salvador Luria showed that bacteria could ward off invading phage viruses by chopping their DNA into pieces with the aid of enzymes. These enzymes were called 'restriction enzymes' because they restricted the virus's attack (though this does not seem a particularly appropriate name, now that their *modus operandi* is better understood). Then in 1970 Hamilton Smith at John Hopkins University isolated one of these restriction enzymes from a bacterium, *Haemophilus influenzae*. This particular enzyme attacked, not phage viruses, but another bacterium, the ubiquitous *Escherichia coli*. *H influenzae* escaped attack by its own restriction enzymes by protecting the vulnerable points of its own DNA with methyl radicals.

The *H influenzae* restriction enzyme, it turned out, attacked the *E coli* DNA only at specific points. That is, the enzyme recognised particular sequences of bases. When it perceived such sequences, it latched on to them, and cut the DNA at that point. The particular sequence that attracted this particular enzyme was

G, T, any pyrimidine, any purine, then A then C: six in all. The bits of DNA that result after a restriction enzyme has had its way are called 'restriction fragments'. Clearly, each macromolecule will yield its own particular pattern of restriction fragments when exposed to a particular restriction enzyme, and since the fragments can be separated by various means (in general involving migration through an electric field) the fragments provide a 'signature' for any one kind of DNA.

Nowadays hundreds of restriction enzymes are known, produced by many different organisms. Each has its own preferred site of attack. Some latch on to particular sequences of four bases, some on to five-base sequences, and some on to eight-base sequences. Clearly, there is more chance of encountering a particular four-base sequence than a particular six-base sequence, so those which attack four-base sequences produce smaller restriction fragments than those which attack six-base sequences. When any one kind of DNA is exposed to a variety of restriction enzymes (one at a time) it yields a series of restriction fragments that start and stop in different places and which overlap. The sequence of bases in each fragment can be analysed and by matching the overlaps it becomes possible to construct a complete base-by-base sequence of an entire DNA macromolecule – in fact, of an entire chromosome. Repeat the process chromosome by chromosome and you finish up with a print-out of the entire genome. This is the basis of genomics: the endeavour first to map all the genes in a genome and then (or simultaneously) to plot the sequence of bases within each gene, and of the non-coding regions within and between each gene. Several organisms have now been sequenced in this way and even as I write these words the Sanger Centre near Cambridge is publishing the first rough draft of the sequence of bases in the entire human genome. All this results from the ability to cut up DNA into pieces by means of restriction enzymes.

But I am running ahead. Genetic engineering is not primarily a matter of analysing the sequence of bases in DNA. It's about joining different bits of DNA together to make *recombinant DNA*: lengths of DNA that contain material from two different sources,

which may be two different, totally unrelated organisms. So how are different bits of DNA joined together?

Well, some restriction enzymes simply cut the DNA straight across, leaving 'blunt ends'. But some make a staggered cut, typically leaving two bases poking out from each of the two cut ends. These spare bases are known technically and concisely as 'sticky ends'. They are sticky because they have loose chemical bonds and so are highly prone to attach themselves to other samples of DNA which happen to be around, provided they too have sticky ends. If two samples of DNA from different sources are mixed and exposed to the same restriction enzyme to create sticky ends, then they will immediately join up again with other sticky ends; and each kind of DNA is just as likely to rejoin with the bit of DNA of the different kind as it is with its own kind. The rejoining is mere chemistry and chemistry is blind, whatever its biological consequences. This initial, passive rejoining is weak, however. The join must then be consolidated – 'annealed' is the technical term – using another enzyme known as a ligase, which is normally concerned with DNA repair. Thus the genetic engineer employs the agents and the mechanisms that nature has already provided. The first recombinant DNA to be created in such an orderly fashion was made by Janet Mertz and Ron Davis in California in 1972.

Note, too, that DNA and enzymes (which of course are proteins) are in dialogue. DNA provides the code that shapes the proteins, to be sure; but some of those proteins are then required to form the DNA. So which came first? This is a chicken and egg problem. Neither came first is the only sensible answer. The primitive precursors of proteins and DNA surely arose separately, neither at first requiring the other. Then the two co-evolved into their present, wonderfully sophisticated modern forms. Thus life is not innately hierarchical. It is inveterately dialectic (where 'dialectic' simply means 'in the nature of dialogue'; I am not making any Marxist points here).

The creation of recombinant DNA is not 'genetic engineering' by itself. Genetic engineering implies that a piece of DNA – in fact, a functional gene – is stitched into a chromosome within a new host organism. Conceptually, the simplest way to do this is to

237

inject the novel DNA into the nucleus of the recipient cell, which, until the mid-1990s, was almost the only method of getting new genes into animals. 'Engineers' of plants, however, generally employ vectors, which carry the novel DNA into the new host and supervise its integration into the chromosomes. Viruses are often employed as vectors. Otherwise, the most common vector employed in plants is the bacterium *Agrobacterium tumefaciens*, which in nature is a pathogen, causing 'crown gall'. Bacteria typically practise a form of sexual exchange, in which they pass packets of DNA known as plasmids between each other. *A tumefaciens* normally passes plasmids into plant cells to induce them to form the galls on which the bacterium then feeds. Genetic engineers modify the *A tumefaciens* plasmids to act as vectors. Herbert Wayne Boyer and Stanley Cohen in California first introduced novel DNA successfully into new hosts in 1973. Thus recombinant DNA technology was born in 1972 through Mertz and Davis; and 1973 saw the birth of 'transgenesis', the transfer of genes between organisms, by Boyer and Cohen. These are the basic techniques of what is colloquially called 'genetic engineering'.

Now, nearly thirty years on, genetic engineering has still not transformed the world's economies in the ways that have sometimes been predicted. In truth, many of the predictions have been unrealistic: greatly exaggerated not by the much-maligned 'media', but primarily by the scientists and biotech companies themselves as they bid for grants and venture capital. Technologies of this power and significance take far more than thirty years to unfold. In three hundred years our descendants will still be exploring the possibilities. But although these are still early days in the history of genetic engineering, a great deal has happened nonetheless.

Where We're At: The Trinity of Biotechnologies

The ability to isolate genes, and to stitch them into new hosts, raced ahead in the 1970s, 1980s and 1990s. From the beginning, however, the engineers felt frustrated. Only in a few, rare cases

did they know which genes, which particular stretches of DNA, they should be transferring into the organisms they wanted to transform. So they might know that one particular potato might contain a gene that conferred resistance to, say, mildew because that particular potato was indeed resistant. But that was a fact of classical genetics, the kind of genetics which treats genes as abstractions. As engineers, they needed to know which particular piece of DNA corresponded to the resistance gene.

The act of finding out which bits of DNA in an organism correspond to which genes is called genomics. It has three connotations: first, to map the positions of all the genes on their various chromosomes; secondly to work out the sequences of bases within the functional genes, and within all the bits in between; and thirdly, to show what each gene actually *does* – whether making proteins, or making transfer RNAs or ribosomal RNAs. Genomics has been the grand pursuit of the 1990s and will surely continue well into the twenty-first century and beyond. The genomes of a few simple organisms have already been mapped and sequenced. The human genome is well on the way. The principal farm livestock will follow soon, and so will the world's major pathogens. In the fullness of time, as the methods of sequencing become ever more automated, rapid and routine, biologists will surely sequence genomes from representative species across the entire tree of life. These are exciting times. Among other things, this work will give us many surprising insights into the evolutionary relationships, the phylogeny, of our fellow creatures.

However, some of the claims made for genomics are a little overstated. It is not true, for example, that the print-out of the human genome will enable biologists to 'read the book of life' in the sense that we can now read, say, *Hamlet*. If we compare genes to words, then we should compare the genome as a whole to literature. The individual words interact, the meaning of the whole lies in the interactions and the genome, like literature, is full of historical allusions, puns, nuances, caprices, abbreviations, colloquialisms and what you will; and like any book that comes straight from the author, it has many a typo as well. The print-out of the genome will provide the equivalent of a dictionary, a lexicon. But truly to 'read' the genome we need to know its syntax and all its quirks of dialect. We could not understand *Hamlet* if all we had was a dictionary. It will be hundreds of years before we can interpret the human genome in the way that we can interpret *Hamlet*. Some already talk of 'designer babies', implying that the human genome might be manipulated to produce people to prescription. Would anyone undertake to edit *Hamlet* if all they had was a dictionary that sketched out the rough meaning of individual words? Would anyone, to make the analogy more cogent, undertake to edit an epic poem written in Linear B? Not if they were sane, is the short answer.

Genomics, nonetheless, is the necessary handmaiden of genetic engineering. Without it, the technology of recombinant DNA remains a laboratory exercise.

So far, too, genetic engineering has advanced most rapidly in bacteria (for example, to produce novel antibiotics) and in plants (to produce a wide range of new crops of the kind known as 'GMOs', 'genetically modified organisms'). There have been only a few successful manipulations of animals and very few of direct commercial significance. One of the first is 'Tracy', a sheep which was fitted with a human gene that produces the enzyme alpha-1 antitrypsin or AAT, which is used to treat cystic fibrosis and emphysema. Tracy produced AAT in her milk; and her descendants are now producing AAT in amounts that should soon prove to be of huge medical significance. That, at least, is the realistic hope of the biotech company PPL, based near Edinburgh, which owns and is developing Tracy's descendants.

The transgenesis of animals has lagged behind that of bacteria and plants for various reasons. One is welfare. At least until recently, novel genes had to be introduced randomly into the genomes of the host animals, and such importunate introductions can cause changes in other genes, with untoward effects. Then again, some genes have highly circumscribed effects – for example, inducing resistance against a particular pathogen. But others – those which affect overall growth rate, for example – influence the whole metabolism and so may throw the whole organism out of kilter. In general, most genes are pleiotropic to some extent and so again can produce unexpected side-effects.

For all these reasons, genetic introductions can produce very distressed-looking organisms. If the recipient is a plant, then the distress does not matter. Most of us assume that plants do not have feelings. But if an animal is distressed – a monster, a later abortion, neonatal death – then we should take pause. This is another reason why the genetic engineering of humans looks less promising than some enthusiasts seem to suppose.

The second reason is more technical. In some ways, it seems easier to get novel genes into animal cells than into plant cells. Plant cells, after all, have thick walls of cellulose, and most of the inside tends to be water, with the nucleus tucked away to one side. Animal cells lack walls and are much more compact, with the nucleus occupying proportionally more of the space. This is why it is possible simply to inject novel DNA into animal cells, while plant cells require vectors.

But plants have one huge advantage. Since the 1960s it has been possible to multiply plant cells in culture, as if they were plates of bacteria, and then regenerate entire new plants from single, cultured cells. This is not possible with all species, but it is becoming possible with more and more. Thus it is possible to introduce DNA into hundreds or thousands of cells at a time as they lie in culture. Then, by attaching suitable markers, the biologists can pick out the cells that contain and express the introduced gene, and make new plants from them. Thus they can easily make thousands of attempts to produce just one good, functional, transgenic plant.

But until recently, the only way to make transgenic sheep, such as Tracy, was to inject DNA directly into a one-cell embryo *in vitro*, then implant that embryo into the womb of a surrogate mother. Sometimes this worked, but usually it did not. It took a lot of embryos to produce one that really worked. The technique was expensive and time-consuming, and hardly practical. Tracy was a rare success.

This has now been changed by the techniques of cloning developed at Roslin Institute near Edinburgh, which is a government laboratory, together with its neighbouring biotech company, PPL. First, in 1995, Keith Campbell and Ian Wilmut at Roslin produced two sheep, Megan and Morag, which they grew from embryo cells they had multiplied in culture. The following year, 1996, they produced the famous Dolly, who was grown from an *adult* cell (taken from the mammary gland of an old ewe) which had been multiplied in culture. Such cloning alone is a tremendous achievement. All animal cells differentiate in culture and the mammary gland cell from which Dolly was cloned was, of course, highly differentiated to begin with. The fact that whole adult animals were produced from these cultured cells demonstrated beyond all doubt that the genomes of differentiated animal cells *can* be reprogrammed, provided the conditions are appropriate.

Most commentators at first assumed that cloning was the point of the Roslin and PPL experiments. Not so. The real point was and is that once the cells are in culture, then genetic engineers can work on them just as they already can with cultured plant cells and bacterial cells. They can add DNA to hundreds or thousands of cells, not by injecting it, but effectively simply by pouring it over the top (though there are refinements). Then the engineers can pick out the cells that have taken up the required gene and are expressing it. Now they too can have hundreds or thousands of attempts for every transgenic animal they produce; a far cry from the days when they had to inject one-cell embryos, and had only one try per animal.

In 1997 this technique was taken to completion with the birth of the ewe Polly. She was produced from cultured foetal cells that were transformed genetically in culture; the first mammal to be both cloned *and* genetically engineered. She carries the gene which produces human blood-clotting Factor IX, which she secretes in her milk (just as Tracy's descendants secrete AAT). Factor IX is used to treat the form of human haemophilia known as Christmas disease. At present Factor IX is obtained from human blood, with all the attendant disadvantages of expense and possible transmission of infection. Production of therapeutically useful protein in the milk (and potentially in other tissues) of livestock has been called 'pharming'. Pharming, at present, is one of the most promising uses for the techniques of cloning and genetic engineering.

Or, to put the matter the other way round: cloning by cell

culture and nuclear transfer is the technique that was required to make the genetic engineering of animals into a feasible technology. Biotechnologists will soon be able to produce transgenic animals as readily as they now turn out transformed plants and microbes.

Thus, genetic engineering is coming of age by virtue of two subsidiary biotechnologies: genomics and cloning. These three, genetic engineering, genomics and cloning, are the modern trinity.

Of course, cloning is an intriguing technology in its own right, even without genetic engineering. Many have envisaged that humans might be cloned, although this may well remain a fantasy, as it probably should. American researchers in particular have sought to clone 'elite' cattle, to raise the general standard rapidly.

I feel, however, that the most significant role of cloning may be in animal conservation. Even in the best-managed programmes herds of endangered animals will have lost at least some of their genetic diversity in a hundred years time. Suppose, though, biologists now rushed around the world as fast as they can, gathering tissue samples (just a few cells will do!) from well-chosen samples of all the animals they can lay their hands on, both from zoos and from the wild. (The wild ones can be trapped and/or anaesthetised in the field and then released, as is commonly done these days for all kinds of reasons.) These tissue samples can then be cultured and then deep-frozen in liquid nitrogen. (They have to be cultured *before* they are frozen to produce cultures which are just one cell thick and which can be frozen evenly and quickly, without damage). In a hundred years time, when cloning culture is more efficient, the remaining members of the species, or even from some closely related species, can be given embryos which have been reconstructed using the cells that have been frozen now. With such technology it will not be necessary to pursue the elaborate protocols that are now required to reduce genetic drift. Virtually all the alleles that now exist within any species could be kept permanently in store; and all that will be needed to turn them back into whole animals are healthy females of the species in question. Conservation zoologists, including all zoos, ought to be collecting tissue samples now, as a matter of urgency. To my knowledge, however, few are doing so.

All in all, the power of genetic engineers, aided by subsidiary techniques, is becoming stupendous. As the decades and centuries pass they will be able to create novel creatures to order and at will. Such power is not necessarily bad; but clearly it must not be taken lightly.

Now we will see how all the technologies discussed in this chapter have been essayed in human beings, or might be in the future, if some people have their way.

9

The Shaping of *Homo sapiens*

Could we breed 'better' human beings, just as we have 'improved' our crops and domestic animals? Could we make people who are more handsome, more resistant to disease and more intelligent? Could we, as we develop the science and skills of genetic engineering, finally produce 'the designer baby', specified to the last unit of IQ, the finest tilt of the nose? Many people in recent history, including a significant army of intellectuals, have found such questions enticing. In the light of twentieth-century events, they are more likely to seem chilling. But they need to be asked.

The designer baby must be considered technically possible. We could not at present make new human beings to specification, but as things are there seem to be no absolute barriers, or none at least that are posed by science. Over the past four decades the idea that there are absolute barriers posed specifically by biology has become outmoded. In the 1960s most scientists still assumed it was impossible to transfer genes between unrelated species, yet in the early 1970s we entered the age of genetic engineering. In the mid-1980s a world-renowned embryologist declared in *Nature* that it was 'biologically impossible' to clone a mammal by nuclear transfer, but a decade later scientists at Roslin Institute produced first Megan and Morag by those precise means and then Dolly. The transfer of genes and the cloning of mammals from somatic cells: no biological barriers that have ever been envisaged seem more profound than these, and yet they have been overcome. Nowadays it is most prudent and most honest simply to presume that anything in the realms of biotechnology should be considered

245

possible provided we do not attempt to break what Sir Peter Medawar called 'the bedrock laws of physics', or to defy the rules of logic. There is nothing physically or logically impossible about designer babies. We need to start asking as a matter of some urgency what might really be implied. In Chapter 10 I will look at the ethical issues as I see them. This chapter is about the practicalities.

Even without officious intervention, of course, our gene pool will not stand still. DNA is innately restless. Clearly, too, our own lineage, leading to *Homo sapiens*, has evolved rapidly over the past few million years. So how might our species change in the future if we eschewed all talk of 'improvement' and simply let nature do as nature does?

How Might Human Beings Evolve if We Let Nature Take Its Course?

That human beings did evolve, and that we share a common ancestor with the apes, was one of Charles Darwin's most shocking revelations of the mid-nineteenth century; and now it seems that our lineage separated from that of the chimpanzees only around five million years ago. Our oldest known specifically 'hominid' – human-like – ancestor was *Ardipithecus*. Then came *Australopithecus*, and from those australopithecines, just over two million years ago, emerged the first of our own genus, *Homo*. The genealogical tree of *Homo* has been branched, like all evolutionary trees, but the particular line leading to us seemed to run via *Homo habilis*, then *Homo ergaster* (who was very like the better-known *Homo erectus*), who in turn gave rise both to us, *Homo sapiens*, and to our 'sister species' the Neanderthals, *Homo neanderthalensis*. The various species of *Australopithecus* walked upright but were short, generally not much taller than a metre, and had small brains, around 450 ml. *H habilis* was a little taller (not much), but had a significantly bigger brain of around 700 ml. *H ergaster* was as tall as we are, with a brain of around 1100 ml. Our own brains average around 1400 ml, while those of Neanderthals were bigger still (but then the Neanderthals had bigger bodies as well).

246

It has become unfashionable and politically incorrect to suggest that there is anything resembling progress in evolution (although there clearly is, when once we distinguish 'progress' from 'destiny', but that is another story). Yet the *trend* is undeniable. Since the human line departed from the chimp line, five million years or so ago, our own ancestors have become more upright, taller and distinctly brainier. Our brains are three times as large as a chimp's or an early australopithecine's.

Folklore commonly has it that those trends, particularly the increase in brain size, will continue. The favourite boys' comic in 1950s Britain was *The Eagle*, featuring spaceman Dan Dare, 'the pilot of the future', whose arch-enemy was 'the Mekon': a green homunculus from Venus with a head the size of a dustbin. Are we all on course to become Mekons? Will our brains continue to grow as they have done in the past? Will our legs shrink as we travel more and more by motor car?

The short, quick answer is 'No'. There are many reasons for supposing that, in the past, survival and sexual and social selection combined to drive our evolution from *Australopithecus* to *H sapiens*. The appropriate pressures were there: a big-brained animal with hands to translate its thoughts into action would surely have out-competed its slower-witted contemporaries, attracted more mates with its tricks and jokes, and found it easier to socialise with others who were similarly blessed. In addition, it is easy to see how those with slower wits (reflected in smaller brains) simply died out. In a state of nature the pressures are enormous; and anyone who could not deal with those pressures was pushed aside. Nowadays, extra intelligence still brings clear advantages, including a well-paid job as, say, a New York lawyer. But the people who cannot outsmart the New York lawyers do not fade into oblivion as they might have done when we all competed on the African plain. They are more likely to employ those lawyers to fight battles on their behalf. To be sure, many people are still under enormous pressure and die before their time from disease and poverty. But, genetically speaking, such blows strike more or less randomly. A very intelligent and athletic person living in tropical Africa is probably more liable to die young than a much less alert individual who happens to live in, say, the English Home Counties.

This does not mean that natural selection has ceased to operate. It is a fact of the universe and cannot be escaped. Natural selection is ensuring, for example, that certain forms of disease resistance are increasing among some sections of the human population. But the consistent driving pressure that turned *Australopithecus* into *Homo ergaster* and then into *Homo sapiens* is no longer bearing down on us. Society still favours intelligence but, overall, the big-brained people are not outbreeding those with smaller brains. There is no consistent pressure, at present, to make us more Mekon-like.

However, the Mekon does provide a nice demonstration of biological impossibility – because he really would break various laws of physics. His enormous head was clearly too heavy for his spindly neck, defying the laws of mechanics, but his worst problems were thermodynamic. Brains are incredibly greedy organs: it takes about 20 per cent of our total energy to service our enormous nervous systems. If the Mekon's brain was ten times larger than a modern human's, it would consume at least twice as much energy as an entire person. He would need an enormous gut to feed such a monstrous organ; yet he was a physical weed. Such a brain would also generate enormous heat and would be very difficult to cool. His huge skull would need to include a refrigeration unit.

On a different tack, note that our personal failure to take exercise would not in itself cause our legs to shrink in any heritable way. August Weismann pointed out that changes wrought in our bodies are not reflected so simply in our gametes. More broadly, such an evolutionary progression would be Lamarckian and Lamarckism does not work (or not, at least, in this gross fashion). In practice, we are not growing smaller but a great deal taller. As discussed later, the reasons for this may seem Lamarckian, but they are not.

In fact there are various reasons to suppose that the genus *Homo sapiens* is likely to stay much the same for the next few thousand years, or indeed for the next few million, unless we set out officiously to change it by breeding or engineering. The fossil record shows that many creatures go through long periods when they hardly change at all. Some lineages of clams remained virtually the same for tens of millions of years at a time. Change, when it does come, is often rapid, giving the pattern that Stephen Jay Gould and Niles Eldredge have called 'punctuated equilibrium'. Our own fossil record suggests that we are in a period of stability; certainly, the fossils suggest that our ancestors have hardly changed at all in the past 100,000 years, at least anatomically, although they clearly evolved very rapidly at times in the few million years before that.

Evolutionary change implies alteration of the gene pool, the total inventory of alleles contained in all the genomes of all the population. The total DNA in each human genome includes around three billion base pairs, which in turn include around 100,000 genes. Yet the range of allelic variation within the world's current population of six billion people is remarkably small; less than is known to exist even within the remaining few thousand chimpanzees. The reason, so some suggest, is that the human species went through a severe genetic bottleneck around 70,000 to 80,000 years ago, when the total world population must have been reduced to a few thousand. (One possible cause of this putative reduction was the eruption of Toba, the 'supervolcano' on Sumatra, which is known to have occurred around 74,000 years ago. Huge volcanoes send so much dust into the stratosphere that sunlight is all but excluded for several years, bringing on a severe if short-lived ice age and killing just about everything. However, this particular scenario does not explain why other creatures, who on the face of things were no less vulnerable, did not apparently suffer a similar fate.)

There are good reasons to suppose that our present gene pool is as stable as gene pools are liable to get. Of course, the frequency of some alleles is bound to be changing all the time and some would say that such change is evolutionary by definition. However, we should surely distinguish between the kinds of change that may be temporary, and might in principle be reversed, and those which cause permanent, significant change, perhaps leading eventually to speciation. The first kind of change is bound to happen constantly. Thus Kenyans at the moment are breeding faster than Italians: the Kenyan population is currently on course to double every twenty-five years or so, while the Italian population is, if anything, going down. So the proportion of alleles typical of Kenyans is increasing relative to those typical of Italians. Of course, most of the alleles possessed by Kenyans are the same as those in Italians, so fluctuations in the two populations make no overall difference. But some of the alleles in the two groups are different, for if they were all the same then the two groups would look much more similar than they do. Yet it seems silly to class such fluctuations as 'evolution'. They could, after all, prove reversible. One day, the Kenyan population may stabilise while the Italians could again become pro-natalist. We surely should not speak of 'evolution' unless there is a clear qualitative shift: a loss or gain of alleles that is not reversible (by natural means).

Beyond doubt, some irreversible qualitative changes in the human gene pool must be taking place as well, but on balance these seem too small to be significant. Thus, on the one hand, the human gene pool must now be expanding. New mutations are occurring the whole time and with six billion people now on board – and the population still rising – the increase in mutations must be faster than ever. Some of those mutations are occurring in the germ cells and thus will be heritable. We are also losing variation, as aboriginal tribes who are likely to contain rare alleles dwindle and disappear. But such gains and losses, however sad the losses may be, strike randomly (genetically speaking) and on the whole are marginal. All in all, then, if we do not contrive deliberately to alter ourselves, we seem likely to stay much as we are.

Yet there is no fundamental principle which says that our evolution is bound to come to a stop, even though such a notion remained fashionable among some biologists well into the twentieth century. For although those biologists paid lip-service to Darwin's idea that human beings had evolved from apes they continued to believe in their hearts that we had after all evolved 'in the image of God', as it says in Genesis. Many simply could not bear to believe otherwise. Now that we had attained God-like stature, we surely would evolve no further. Robert Broom, the distinguished palaeoanthropologist who discovered *Australopith-ecus robustus* in southern Africa in the 1930s, thought precisely along these lines. He had found direct evidence of human evolution in the past; but, he said, now that *Homo sapiens* had come into existence we should expect no further change in the future, because God's purpose was already fulfilled.

Such a view is sublimely non-biological. There is progress but there is no destiny and our present condition cannot be taken as our *dénouement*. If the condition of the world changes radically, if there is ecological disaster, then quite new kinds of hominids could arise from among our ranks. Global warming, all-out nuclear war, or some combination of the two, could do the trick. We know that volcanoes can be very effective. There is at present a vast and smouldering supervolcano beneath Yellowstone National Park in Wyoming which apparently is due to erupt at any time. Disaster on such a scale, perhaps exacerbated by a rise in fundamentalist religion with renewed antipathy to science, could destroy modern communications, and break the world's population into fragments, just as it was in Pleistocene times. Each fragment would then be subject to different ecological pressures. If the isolated groups contained sufficient genetic variation, and if the pressures were consistent but not so strong that they caused extinction, then each could re-adapt in whatever way was required to its own novel conditions.

But there is no outstanding reason to suppose that these newly isolated groups would continue to evolve along the lines of the past few million years. Future selective pressures might favour smaller brains that need less energy. Our scattered descendants might also find it convenient to climb into the trees to avoid tomorrow's predators, who surely would be enjoying a field day. Our post-disaster descendants would not turn back into the kinds of apes already familiar to us; but in a general way, they could well become more simian again, rather than less. Or then again, they might go off in new directions altogether. In short, our present form was not inevitable and it cannot be seen to be permanent. We should enjoy ourselves as we are while we may.

Even so, in the absence of global disaster we do seem most

251

likely to stay as we are unless we set out deliberately to 'improve' ourselves. But how might we do such a thing?

The Paths to Improvement

In the paths to the biological 'improvement' of human beings we can distinguish two trends. On the one hand we can envisage a steady increase in ambition. Most basic are the traditional medical concerns of therapy and prevention, the simple desire to alleviate or prevent the suffering caused by deleterious alleles. But after that we may envisage a steady crescendo of endeavours not simply to ameliorate frank disorder, but to improve ever so slightly, notch by notch, on human beings who by reasonable standards are perfectly healthy already. Finally, we might in principle design a human being absolutely to specification, in the way that Ferrari now designs motor cars. This final analogy is not quite accurate, of course, because the designer of living creatures, human or otherwise, must be more like a chef or a gardener than an engineer. In living systems, more than in machines, each individual part interacts absolutely with every other; the organism must be conceived as a whole. Indeed, although chemists use the term 'organic' simply to mean 'carbon-based', in common parlance it refers to systems in which each part depends absolutely on all the others, and the whole is greater than the sum of the parts. In living systems, as in gardens and great recipes, the final criteria of excellence are aesthetic. Of course, designers of fine motor cars would feel insulted by these musings, for they would argue, quite rightly, that it is necessary also to conceive great machines as a whole and to be guided by aesthetic principles (for what works usually looks beautiful). Even so, it is a matter of degree. Living systems are more complex than human artefacts and are more 'organic' in the common sense. Nonetheless, the engineering analogy remains. In principle future biologists might in effect build human beings to the same, precise specifications that now are employed to shape motor cars.

The second trend is in the steadily increasing power of the technology. The oldest attempts to change human beings (or to

252

keep them as they are) pre-date Mendelian genetics, and simply employed common-sense notions as acknowledged by traditional breeders. The twentieth century saw increasing application both of Mendelian genetics and, at least as conspicuously, the parallel tradition of Francis Galton's biometrics. In the second half of the twentieth century, and increasingly towards the end, we saw the steady growth of reproductive technologies which, though not directly intended to alter the human gene pool, are nonetheless vital for any future, high-tech interventions. Artificial insemination came first: in truth an ancient technique, but made feasible in the 1950s when it became possible to freeze sperm (so that donor and recipient did not have to be in adjacent rooms). Then came *in vitro* fertilisation, or IVF, in the late 1970s: conception in a Petri dish (though more usually represented journalistically as a test tube). After that we have seen a flurry of reproductive techniques, culminating in cloning – only of sheep and a few other species so far, but no one doubts that this is applicable to people. Cloning, as discussed earlier, makes it feasible to carry out precise and potentially large-scale genetic engineering in animals (which in principle includes humans). The animal cells can be manipulated in culture, just as is now possible with plants and microbes. In short, the highest of high technologies are already, in principle, in place.

The two trends, in ambition and in technique, are entirely independent of each other. Thus the highest of high technologies are already being used in the interests of orthodox medicine: trying simply to reduce suffering. On the other hand, the most basic techniques of pre-Mendelian breeding could in principle be used to make dramatic transformations – that is, to breed 'better' human beings. This, essentially, is what the Nazis were attempting when they contrived to create a new, more emphatically 'Aryan' human species.

Clearly, it would be possible to write a very large book on the hierarchy of possible ambitions and technologies, but I will just pick out a few salients.

The most obvious target for prevention and therapy is, or are, the 6000 or so known 'deleterious alleles' which can cause 'single gene disorders'. Most of these are recessive; and most of the

253

recessive ones, the ones that are not specifically linked to X chromosomes, cause disease only when inherited in double dose. The easiest way to prevent most of them, therefore, is for carriers – heterozygotes – to avoid having children together. This notion forms the basis for genetic counselling, or at least for much of it.

In fact, counselling can be carried out at a significant level without any science at all. Common sense can do a lot. Any pre-Mendelian nineteenth-century breeder of sheep could have told the royal houses of Europe not to marry among themselves since various of their members suffered what seemed to be heritable diseases, notably porphyria and haemophilia. But who listens to sheep breeders? In the twentieth century knowledge of Mendelian ratios and access to family trees enabled generations of professional counsellors to be a great deal more precise, and in some cases, at least, to work out the odds that particular people might be carriers of particular alleles and the odds that their children might be affected.

Still we are only talking odds, however. The exercise becomes more satisfactory when it becomes possible to detect carriers directly, either by biochemical means (small changes in the phenotype) or (increasingly, nowadays) by looking directly for genetic 'markers' in their DNA. The search for carriers is in turn reinforced by detection of the homozygous state in the embryo itself, at a stage when it is still possible to do something about it. Diagnosis can be made at birth, which is how paediatricians have been diagnosing alkaptonuria, the disease which enabled Sir Archibald Garrod to define the function of the gene. This is worthwhile because alkaptonuria, if detected early, can be treated effectively. After the mid-twentieth century it became possible to detect at least some disorders *in utero*, by looking for loose cells by the technique known as 'amniocentesis'. Now it is possible to detect a wide range of potentially damaging alleles in embryos conceived *in vitro*; with the option of implanting only those embryos that are free from the deleterious allele.

This last approach is very encouraging: to me, it truly looks like high-tech in the service of sensible therapy. It is now becoming possible, after all, for two known carriers of, say, cystic fibrosis to produce offspring in the absolute certainty that their child will not only be free of the disease, but will not even be a carrier. Embryos are produced by super-ovulation and *in vitro* fertilisation. Then the ones that do not contain the deleterious allele are selected for implantation. Some people feel that such an approach is too interventionist, or indeed callous. However, nature herself is extraordinarily profligate with human conceptuses (although, intriguingly, it is much less prodigal with those of animals that breed seasonally, such as red deer). Most human embryos abort within the first few weeks. Abortion in a Petri dish, before pregnancy has even begun, does nothing that nature does not do as a matter of course. More generally, although intellectuals of all kinds, including scientists and moral philosophers, feel it is their job to improve on common sense, I feel that we override common sense at our peril. Common sense says that, given a choice, it is better to give the chance of life to an embryo who has the potential to be perfectly healthy than to one who will be seriously ill from day one. *In vitro* fertilisation, followed by embryo selection, seems to me to be a very good approach to serious single-gene disorders, provided of course that there is no coercion; that everything is done in accordance with the parents' wishes. (The embryo ought to have a say too in a perfect world, but we have to work within the limitations that the world imposes.)

One flaw with all these techniques, from pre-Mendelian counselling to *in vitro* diagnosis, is that they tend to be *post hoc*. That is, nobody would counsel potential carriers of cystic fibrosis, say – and still less would they attempt *in vitro* diagnosis – unless they had good reason to suppose that the people concerned *were* carriers. They would already have a family record of disorder and perhaps already have affected children. In principle it surely would be better to intervene before there is a family record of disease. This, of course, leads us into 'well-population screening': looking for disorder in people who seem perfectly healthy. Already this is possible for some disorders: where there is an straightforward test; where there is good reason to suppose that people might be carriers (even though there may be no direct evidence); and where the resulting disease is serious. Thus, many health authorities offer mass screening for sickle cell within people of African descent. In the United States, Ashkenazi Jews offer screening for the allele that leads to Tay–Sachs disease. As Matt Ridley points out in his excellent book *Genome* (whence I garnered this example), there is no coercion in this. The people themselves have decided what their problems are and proposed appropriate solutions: and no individual is obliged or in any way pressured to take up the available technologies.

In the fullness of time, of course, it will in principle be possible and feasible to screen everybody for all deleterious alleles just by rapid-reading their DNA. In the weeks in which I finished this text the Sanger Centre in Cambridge published the first draft of the entire human genome, showing the sequence of nucleotides in most of it (all but the last, trickiest sections). Over the next few decades it will become possible to 'read' that sequence, and to see precisely which individuals contain which alleles. At the same time, the techniques for sequencing have come on by leaps and bounds even since the Sanger first began its work just a few years ago, techniques that have been developed largely because of the Sanger's endeavour. In less than a century (probably far less) local clinics will be able to offer a read-out of anyone's DNA within hours. Doubtless this will form part of everyone's standard medical records. Then, people who wish to have children together can put their genomic read-outs together (or ask a computer to do this) to see if they share any alleles that could cause disease if brought together. Some may find this chilling. The main point, though (surely?), is that the decision to match a couple's genomes, and about what to do subsequently, should remain with the couple. It becomes sinister only when it becomes the business of the State.

If a child is born with a genetic disability, it is becoming possible – at least in principle – to correct the damage. Therapists envisage, for example, that defective tissues might be removed, the deleterious alleles could be replaced and then the tissue might be restored. Such treatment has been envisaged for cystic fibrosis for at least two decades and will become feasible sooner or later.

This approach, however, correcting damaged genes and hence the tissues in which they are expressed, raises the possibility of a huge conceptual leap. For if a doctor simply corrects the genes (and hence the cells) in, say, the lungs of a person with cystic fibrosis, then only the patient is directly affected. The genetic changes made in the lungs are not transmitted into the gametes for the reason that August Weismann identified more than a century ago. Thus the children of the treated person are not affected.

It would also be possible in principle, however, to correct genetic defects in embryos *in vitro* (provided of course that they were produced by IVF). If this were done, then the genetic changes made could well find their way into the developing germ tissue, and hence into the gametes, and hence would affect all subsequent generations. This is what is known as 'germline therapy'.

Some commentators (myself included) feel that there is no sensible reason to undertake germline therapy, at least in this form. After all, when embryos are conceived by IVF they are not made one at a time. Typically, the woman produced about a dozen eggs after super-ovulation, resulting in about a dozen embryos. It is in principle possible by the techniques outlined above to pick out the embryos which do not contain a double-dose of the damaging allele, or which contain no damaging allele at all. It is certainly easier to do this than it would be to correct genetic damage in the embryo. Thus to me (and many other commentators) it seems perverse even to contemplate germline therapy, at least in this form. Why attempt heroic correction of a diseased embryo, when it would be much easier to offer the chance of life to a healthy one? However, germline therapy of this kind has its advocates, for example to correct cerebral palsy (and indeed to eliminate it from all of the sufferer's descendants). Germline therapy is not yet technically possible, however, so we have time to think about it.

Note, finally, however, that all these attempts to pre-empt or to correct single-gene disorders will not appreciably affect the frequency of those alleles in the gene pool. Counselling, with or without high-tech examination of DNA, prevents carriers from having children together (or at least it gives then the option), but it does not eliminate the alleles that they are carrying. By the same token, treating patients with cystic fibrosis so that they live to be adults and have children of their own does not appreciably increase the frequency of that allele. For one thing, as we have discussed earlier, the number of heterozygotes – carriers – greatly outweighs the proportion of homozygotes. For another thing, by the use of *in vitro* or 'preimplantation' diagnosis, it is possible for sufferers to produce offspring who themselves are free of the diseases. (If the sufferer mated with someone who was not a carrier, then all the children would be carriers but would not be affected. If the sufferer married a carrier, then half the children would be homozygotes, but could be identified *in vitro*. The other half would be carriers. The offspring of those carriers could then be diagnosed *in vitro* – and as we have already seen, some of the offspring even of two carriers should be completely free of the disorder).

Thus the notion that prevention of single-gene disorders significantly 'improves' the human gene pool as a whole is fatuous, at least within a reasonably measurable interval; as is the idea that it will compromise the human race if we treat sufferers humanely and enable them to have children of their own.

This brings us to another great conceptual leap: from attempts to correct or prevent obvious suffering, to attempts deliberately to improve on creatures – human beings – who are perfectly healthy already. This takes us into the realms of eugenics.

Eugenics

Different people seem to mean different things by 'eugenics', but I use it to mean the attempt to improve human beings by adjusting the human gene pool as a whole, and the genomes of individuals. Different people will also differ, of course, in what they mean by 'improvement'. The general approach, however, must be to reduce the frequency of alleles that are seen to detract from the intended goal and to increase the frequency of alleles that seem to lead in the required direction. As with conventional medicine, the methods may be low-tech: simply a matter of arranging some matings and discouraging others. Or they might in future involve the highest of high technologies including all the techniques of genetic engineering, in principle including addition of novel genes synthesised in the laboratory. Thus in principle the idea of eugenics embraces the notion of the designer baby, even if that is not what its founders or its present protagonists necessarily intend.

Some of the practices of conventional medicine may seem to lead us in eugenic directions. Some critics of gene therapy or of prenatal diagnosis, even of genetic counselling, suggest this. Yet, as we have discussed, gene therapy as currently envisaged is merely intended to reduce the suffering of individuals; even if it were extended into germline therapy, it would still merely reduce the suffering in a particular family. Prenatal diagnosis and genetic counselling are intended primarily to reduce the chances of producing babies that are liable to suffer from single-gene disorders. As we have seen, these techniques do not significantly reduce the frequency of those alleles in the gene pool as a whole (even if some counsellors and therapists sometimes imply that this is the case), so they cannot properly be called 'eugenic'. Human suffering is reduced, but the human species as a whole is unchanged.

It is often suggested, too, that we all practise 'eugenics' up to a point because we all practise mate choice and we all have strong views about who our sexual partners should be. Mostly, of course, we are keen to ensure that the other parent of our children is somebody we actually like, since it is necessary to form a relationship with that person. But also, at least subconsciously, we have some concept of how our children will turn out; and any such preference (some argue) is a prescription of a kind, and so has eugenic connotations. In many societies, of course, the elders arrange the marriages of the young men and women; and many other groups, who do not necessarily go that far, nonetheless have strong views on who their children ought to marry. Orthodox Muslims emphatically prefer their young men and women to marry other Muslims. Orthodox Jews discourage marriage to Gentiles. Such exclusivity seems to imply some preconception of how the next generation ought to be, which, again, has eugenic connotations.

Even so, mate choice and arranged marriage seem to differ

259

clearly enough from eugenics, at least from eugenics in its strong form. For orthodox Muslims are primarily concerned to ensure that their own kind is perpetuated (believing this to be the will of Allah). They do not suppose that the next generation should be measurably better than the present one and the one after that better still. But this is implied in eugenics: that the lineage should change over time, steadily moving towards some target that is *different from*, and measurably better than, what exists at present. To be sure, eugenicists may not aim to produce supermen and superwomen, in the way that cattle breeders dream of the bull that puts on five kilos of beef a day and the cow that produces 20,000 litres of milk a year. But the eugenicist does want to produce a greater proportion of people who conform to some preconceived ideal: more people with an IQ of 140; more people who are tall and fair; and so on. Indeed, eugenicists in general seek to shift the entire human species towards some pre-envisioned target. This is clearly conceptually different from the desire of most tribes and societies in the history of the world simply to perpetuate their own kind.

Finally, decisions on genetic counselling or gene therapy should be made by individuals, on behalf of themselves or the children they intend to have. This is not always the case. As we will see, many governments in the twentieth century took such decisions into their own hands. But personal choice, nonetheless, is the name of the game. People also choose their own mates. Even when marriages are arranged, this is usually by parents, or elders who are perceived to have special rights.

We could envisage, too, that changes of a eugenic nature could be brought about by individuals, exercising their own choices on their own behalf. In principle, the free market could achieve this. Women could decide to produce babies who conform more and more closely to some preconceived ideal by buying the semen of Olympic athletes and Nobel Prize winners from elite sperm banks. Professor Lee Silver of Princeton University envisages in *Remaking Eden* that future parents might pay genetic engineering clinics to manipulate the genomes of their offspring. These are possibilities and therefore should be considered.

Historically, however, early attempts at eugenics in the

twentieth century were definitely coercive. Many a government has taken it upon itself to prevent particular marriages and sometimes specifically to encourage others. We cannot in fairness suggest that eugenics necessarily implies coercion. or is necessarily the handmaiden of totalitarianism. There is still a perfectly respectable eugenics society in London, whose protagonists very properly point out that all technologies, and indeed all philosophies, may be misused, and most have been, at some time. We should not condemn eugenics out of hand, just because its ideals have been misapplied. Opponents, however, point out that some technologies and philosophies lend themselves more easily than others to misuse. Eugenics has lent itself to coercion and has sometimes been the tool of despots, partly because it lends itself to such deployment. In the same way, guns and bombs can be used as agents of peace; but we should not be over-surprised when in practice they are used to make war.

In short, it would be hasty to condemn eugenics out of hand and grossly unfair to suggest that everyone who takes eugenics seriously has evil intent. Nonetheless, it seems a dangerous philosophy, and once we move beyond the realms of counselling and therapy it seems hard to justify any concerted effort to manipulate the human genome, or the gene pool as a whole.

Still, though, we should look as the ideas and the history of eugenics as dispassionately as possible. They are important; and they will not go away.

The term 'eugenics' was coined in 1885 by Francis Galton, polymath (up to a point), statistician and, as we have seen, Charles Darwin's cousin. Thus the idea did not arise out of the science of genetics since Mendel had been the only *bona fide* geneticist before 1885 and at that particular time his work had been shuffled to the sidelines. Galton's eugenics had two, more primitive, origins. On the one hand it was rooted in his own 'biometrics', the attempt to measure and quantify the visible features of living creatures and their behaviour; an attempt presaged by phrenology, the analysis of cranial bumps. On the other hand, Galton applied the ideas of traditional breeders. He reasoned that if you could create better cows by selective breeding then you should also be able to breed better human beings. The prefix *eu* means 'good' or 'well'. Thus a eukaryote is a creature whose body cells contain nuclei (*karyon* being Greek for 'kernel', or indeed for nucleus). 'Eugenics' thus implies 'good birth' or 'good breeding'.

For the first few decades of the twentieth century eugenics was very fashionable. It was new on two fronts: Galton had only recently framed the general idea; and as Mendel's ideas became more widely known, they seemed (only seemed!) to root Galton's ideas in robust science. Thus (as Matt Ridley records in *Genome*) Galton's disciple Karl Pearson wrote to Galton in 1907 to say: 'I hear respectable middle-class matrons saying, if children are weakly, "Ah, but that was not a eugenic marriage!"' Eugenicists in the early twentieth century pursued both the options that had long been explored by breeders of livestock: to eliminate what they perceived to be the negative aspects of the human race and to accentuate the positive.

But for the early eugenic enthusiasts, elimination of the negative did not, as now, focus exclusively on obviously deleterious mutants, like the allele that leads to Tay-Sachs disease. Instead, the early eugenicists identified broad phenotypic qualities of the human race that they perceived to be undesirable. The leading target was 'feeble-mindedness'. Winston Churchill, when he was Britain's Home Secretary in 1911, expressed a widespread sentiment when he declared that 'the multiplication of the feeble-minded [is] a very terrible danger to the race'. Churchill had a way of expressing big ideas in fine style, even if, sometimes, they were bad ideas.

As Ridley describes, most of the Protestant countries of the Western world passed laws in the early decades of the twentieth century to enable government to sterilise those identified as 'feeble-minded'. Six US states had passed such laws by 1911; nine more by 1917. Virginia retained its laws into the 1970s. In the twentieth century the Americans, those arch defenders of liberty, sterilised more than 100,000 of their citizens for the heinous offence of feeble-mindedness. Canada, Norway, Finland, Estonia and Iceland passed similar laws. The Swedes, with a much smaller population than the United States, sterilised 60,000 of their sons and daughters. Most notoriously, of course, Germany sterilised 400,000; and at the outbreak of the Second World War, the Nazis murdered 70,000 inhabitants of mental institutions (who had already been sterilised) to make room for wounded soldiers. As all the world knows, too, the Nazis extended the criterion of undesirability beyond 'feeble-mindedness' to include entire races. Genocide has been common in the history of the human species, but has rarely been so systematic.

Britain almost passed eugenic laws in 1911 and 1934. The first bill was vigorously opposed and beaten down by a heroic liberal MP, Josiah Wedgwood, a descendant of the great potter and hence another relative (by marriage) of Darwin. The second law was proposed in 1934, but by then the Nazis were on the scene and enthusiasm was waning. In the early twentieth century, however, among the developed countries of the north, only the Catholic states (or those with a strong Catholic influence, notably Holland) eschewed such laws. Catholics, after all, see the body merely as the vehicle of the soul, which cannot be compromised by the body's infirmities and which, besides, belongs to God.

The Nazis also sought to enact, as a matter of policy, the second of the two eugenic possibilities: to breed better human beings (which in that Teutonic context meant big, handsome, smart and blond(e)) by arranging marriages between suitably lusty maids and beaux. As a matter of honesty I should record that a German friend of mine knows a man, now of course approaching old age, who was born through such an arranged mating. It would be convenient to relate that he is a twisted ugly psychopath, but my informant tells me that in fact he is handsome, athletic and charming; everything the Führer could have desired. Ah well.

It has been customary in the late decades of the twentieth century, to decry the eugenic movement: first, as science gone mad; and secondly, as a blatant, cruel, right-wing plot, the ruling class attempting to beat the lower orders into shape by whatever means came to hand. But history does not bear this out. Many of the most fervent advocates of eugenics in its early days bore the flags of socialism, in its various hues. John Maynard Keynes, Beatrice and Sidney Webb. George Bernard Shaw, Harold Laski. H. G. Wells, generally perceived to belong to the left, wrote, most chillingly and frankly: 'The swarms of black, and brown, and dirty white, and yellow people . . . will have to go.' 'Go' meant 'die': although, he added (doubtless with a kindly twinkle), 'All such killing will be done with an opiate.'

Matt Ridley, whose own politics are patrician – rooted firmly in the idea of personal freedom with personal responsibility – suggests that socialism lends itself particularly to eugenics, since it so readily grants power to the State and places the perceived needs of society as a whole above the rights of individuals. As a matter of history, the USSR, which was the world's first large centralised but avowedly socialist economy, did not pass eugenic laws, though it did of course persecute minorities for essentially racialist reasons (and, as Ridley points out, it did contrive to eliminate raft-loads of intellectuals). As a matter of history, too, the most vociferous opponents of eugenics were middle-aged men with big moustaches and top hats, who are commonly perceived in our age (which is given to caricature) as old-fashioned fuddy-duddies: G. K. Chesterton, Arthur Conan Doyle, Hilaire Belloc. Chesterton wrote: 'eugenicists had discovered how to combine hardening of the heart with softening of the head'.

Scientists, including some of the greatest and of left-wing persuasion, caught the eugenic fervour as well. Indeed, they did much to stoke the fires. R. A. Fisher, critic but admirer of Mendel, was a keen advocate. So was Sir Julian Huxley. So too was J. B. S. Haldane, who for some time was a member of the Communist Party. These biologists turned against the idea, however, partly because they saw its misuse by the Nazis and partly, too, for reasons of science. In particular, both the behaviourist psychologists and the anthropologist Margaret Mead argued from their different perspectives that human beings were hugely influenced by their environment. Both lines of argument seemed to lend weight to John Locke's idea of the seventeenth century that the human mind is a *tabula rasa*. The research on which Margaret Mead based her ideas has since been questioned and indeed ridiculed. She interviewed people in New Guinea and Sumatra (particularly young girls in Sumatra) but, it seems, her nervous and perhaps mischievous interviewees spun her some fine yarns. The behaviourists have often been criticised for insisting too strongly that animal (and human) psychology can be studied rigorously only by focusing on behaviour: that we cannot directly observe thoughts and emotions, so we should not factor them in to our accounts. This idea, among other things, undoubtedly compromised attempts to improve animal welfare. Many people seemed to conclude, after all, that science had effectively disproved the notion that animals think and feel; whereas the truth was simply that some scientists (the behaviourists) had decided for procedural reasons not to take thought and emotion into account since they were not directly observable and measurable.

However, both Mead and the behaviourists helped to dim enthusiasm for eugenics since they suggested that people can change their ways and develop along vastly different lines, whatever their underlying genetic endowment might be. No modern geneticist would deny this. The notion that scientists who are interested in the genetic bases of human existence are 'genetic determinists' is, as we have seen, an absurd *canard*, which is at best lazy-minded. But in the early twentieth century nonetheless, emphasis on environmental influences served as an antidote to eugenic fervour.

Thus for political reasons (largely but not exclusively the example of the Nazis) and for reasons of science (essentially a shift of fashion) enthusiasm for eugenics waned. Several biologists in the late twentieth century wrote books that affect to jump on its grave and to castigate everyone who had ever been involved (or at least to castigate selected targets). The lesson was taken to be self-evident. Eugenics is bad. Anyone who so much as expressed an interest in it, anyone, that is, who did not spit blood at the mere utterance of its name, was held to be self-evidently reactionary. In some circles this has become the politically correct attitude.

But it is the job of science to look dispassionately, to pick out the facts of the case. If the facts seem distasteful it is mete to come to terms with them nonetheless and unsafe to pretend that they do not exist. I do not want, in this brief account, to trot out all the political arguments for and against eugenics, which have already been rehearsed *in extenso*. But I would like to ask a few *faux naïf* questions of the kind that are rarely raised at all and yet seem pertinent.

Why, first of all, were so many people carried away by the ideas of eugenics in the early twentieth century? Its advocates certainly were not stupid: they included leading intellectuals. They were not necessarily bad: Shaw and the Webbs for example are remembered in history as humanitarians and, although Churchill has lately been the victim of iconoclasm, he was certainly no monster. But although, in the early twenty-first century, it seems self-evidently foul to breed human beings like cattle, to our great-grandfathers' generation it did not. There are obvious reasons for the disillusionment: the sobering example of Nazism and the realisation that human beings really are shaped by their environment as much as by their inherited biology. But why did our early twentieth-century ancestors grasp the eugenic nettle so enthusiastically in the first place?

I don't presume to know the answer, but would like to offer two thoughts: one general and one specific. The general answer is that the nineteenth century saw a rising tide of enthusiasm both for science and for the technologies that arose from science. People were excited by the new chemistry and physics – James Clerk Maxwell, J. J. Thomson, Albert Michelson and Edward Morley, who measured the speed of light; and also by the new biology – the Germanic tradition of cell biology and embryology and the philosophical revelations of Darwin. Some of the greatest architecture of the nineteenth century is that of the engineers: from Decimus Burton's palm house at Kew and Joseph Paxton's Crystal Palace at London's Great Exhibition, to the iron- and then steel-framed skyscrapers of Chicago and New York from the 1880s onwards. The enthusiasts (albeit with reservations) included artists renowned for their fineness of feeling: John Ruskin (who extolled the virtues of chemistry), George Eliot (widely interested in chemistry, geology and biology), Gerard Manley Hopkins (fascinated by the new physics, and a contributor to *Nature*). J. M. W. Turner revelled in the visual excitement, and the sheer physical power, of steam.

By the early twentieth century this smouldering enthusiasm had consolidated into a widespread feeling that science could effectively be equated with rationalism and that rationalism – and rationalism alone – could produce a better world: richer, healthier, and in the end more humane. The First World War may have dampened enthusiasm for technology *per se*; but, if anything, it reinforced the notion that human beings should, above all, *think*. They should not allow themselves to be driven simply by old-fashioned emotions, including that of patriotism. The new psychology (behaviourism on the one hand, Freud on the other), the new biology (genetics, biochemistry), the new philosophy (notably logical positivism: the belief that only the questions that could be answered with certainty were worth asking in the first place), the new art (outstandingly that of cubism) and architecture (soon to culminate in Mies van der Rohe and Le Corbusier) combined to produce what Aldous Huxley, quoting Miranda from Shakespeare's *Tempest*, called 'the brave new world'. Eugenics might be harsh in some of its manifestations, but the human species needed to be purged with the same brisk, no-nonsense brush that was sweeping through the muddled, academic corridors of all science, philosophy, religion and art. In short, eugenics belonged absolutely to the *zeitgeist* of the early twentieth century. Neither science nor politics was the leader of events. Eugenics did not belong exclusively to science, nor to the left or the right wing of politics. Unconsciously, scientists and politicians of all persuasion inevitably adjust to the *zeitgeist*.

I suggest, too, that in Britain in particular there was a particular reason for believing that the human species was indeed producing an 'underclass'. In 1900 Britain found it shockingly hard to raise a convincing army to fight the Boers in South Africa. The men who came forward were tiny, sunken-chested and often tubercular. This merely confirmed what was all too obvious on the streets: that the 'lower classes' consisted largely of runts. These people were not necessarily 'feeble-minded', of course. Some of the greatest intellects and noblest spirits have lodged in small frames, from Alexander Pope to Mahatma Gandhi. But the education of late Victorian working people was perfunctory at best, and they were for many reasons dispirited. It is easy to mistake lack of confidence for stupidity. Truly, it seemed that these diminutive, downcast people were an underclass. Yet they seemed to have lots of children, which was not generally true, but their children were on the streets and so were conspicuous. The human race, or, more specifically, the British people, seemed to be 'degenerating': a much-favoured term in those times. For economic reasons alone humanity in general and Britain in particular needed to smarten up its act. Or so it was felt.

Wasn't it obvious, though, that the lack of stature and of spirit had little or nothing to do with inheritance, but that they resulted simply from deprivation? Well, for curious reasons of biology, and without wishing to excuse 'man's inhumanity to man', it could not have been as obvious as all that.

A person's height, at maturity, is influenced by his or her genes. The Masai people are genetically predisposed to be taller than the average Eskimo; the Sudanese on balance are longer and skinnier than native Tyroleans. But several different environmental forces also influence final, adult height. Nutrition during childhood has a huge influence, of course. Nutrition *in utero* also has an effect, although foetuses are very efficient parasites, even of malnourished mothers. Nonetheless, they cannot procure what the mother cannot provide, so maternal nutrition matters too. Much less obviously, adult height is related to height (length) at birth (assuming that the birth is not premature): small babies in general make small adults.

Even less obviously, the length of a baby at birth is related to the mother's own length when she was born. It is as if mothers have a physiological memory of their own gestation and use this memory to judge what size of baby it is realistic for them to give birth to themselves. The mechanism is subtle, but when you think about it it is necessary, or at least very useful. In general, it pays a mother to produce a big baby, for big babies fare better at birth (leaving aside those who are large for reasons of pathology). She should, then, put as much nourishment into the foetus as possible. But if she puts in too much, she herself will die (and so, then, will the baby). It is good, though, to be able to adjust the amount of nourishment provided, according to the prevailing circumstance; for in nature, circumstances vary enormously. How should her body judge the appropriate input? What better than to remember (at the physiological level) her own pre-natal experience?

Thus a person's height is influenced by his or her mother's experiences as well as his or her own; and the mother's experiences in turn reflect her own mother's experiences and so on, all the way back. Undersized children who are well fed will of course grow bigger than they would otherwise, but they may not grow as big as their genes would theoretically allow them to because their own mothers were (probably) deprived as well. Thus it takes several generations of good feeding to restore an undersized population to its 'proper' height; or at least to the height that its genes would allow.

This mechanism looks Lamarckian, since the experiences of the mother (and grandmother and great-grandmother) are apparently inherited by the next generation; but it is not. The genes are not affected by the nutritional status of the lineage. It's just that genes are subtle, as this book has emphasised: they provide mechanisms that can respond to change. But the genes themselves have been selected by Darwinian means.

Be that as it may, the late Victorian upper classes perceived that the 'lower' classes, the third- and fourth-generation offspring of the Industrial Revolution, were small and meek. Furthermore, their smallness and meekness were passed on from generation to generation. It looked as if the runtishness and lack of spirit were truly heritable, in the sense of being brought about by defective genes. So the idea that the British people (and the human race, by extrapolation) could degenerate was not quite so perversely stupid as it now seems. In truth, diminutiveness and dispiritedness merely revealed the flexibility of the genome. But it did not look that way at the time.

Even in the First World War, Britain was obliged to put together 'bantam regiments' of tiny men, who often acquitted themselves extremely well. Now such runtishness is rare. In the end Britain cleaned itself up socially, rather than genetically, and our physical improvement can be seen as a triumph of the Welfare State. But because it takes several generations to outgrow the nutritional shortcomings of earlier generations, Britain's people – and the people of much of the world – are still becoming taller, generation by generation. The poor prostitutes who fell victim to Jack the Ripper, the notorious serial killer of late Victorian London, were mostly around four feet tall. One of them was nicknamed 'Tall Lizzie'. She was a towering four foot six.

Modern girls are typically at least a foot taller than this and six-footers are already becoming commonplace. I am nearly three inches taller than my father was; my son is nearly five inches taller than I am. There is no point dreaming of a career in basketball these days if you are much under six foot six.

How tall will human beings become as successive generations continue on a high nutritional plane? For how many generations will the current trend continue? What would happen if people who are genetically predisposed to be very tall, like the Masai and the native Sudanese, were fed on Texan diets for four or five generations? Will tomorrow's basketball teams consist entirely of eight footers?

We must wait and see. Meanwhile we may reflect that nature is usually more intricate than it looks and that it is dangerous to be carried away by first impressions and by novel theories. It would be naïve (and just plain wrong) to suggest that the early eugenics enthusiasts were all bad people, but they show how easy it is to be misled.

Let's just ask a few biological questions, however. Let's assume for a minute that some regime did adopt a formal eugenics policy, setting out deliberately to 'improve' people. Of course this hypothetical regime would first have to decide what it meant by 'improvement'. What would the human equivalent be of milk yield in cattle or egg output in poultry? Well, perhaps the regime could produce different breeds for different purposes – athletes, musicians, or whatever. But the quality that they seem very likely to seize upon is intelligence. Specifically, then, would it be possible to breed for greater intelligence?

Could We Breed More Intelligent People If We Wanted to?

The answer to this is surely 'yes', but (a) the problem is not quite so easy as it seems (or, apparently, as it seemed to Hitler's eugenicists) and (b) although we might readily raise the mean (roughly speaking, the average) IQ of the population, it is not obvious that we could improve the top end. That is, we might produce more people able to get firsts at Princeton, but it might be very difficult indeed to produce anyone who was significantly cleverer than, say, Niels Bohr. That is a guess, but it seems sensible. (Throughout this discussion I am assuming that the quality measured by IQ tests reflects what most people mean by 'intelligence', but I am also defining 'intelligence' broadly to encompass all the many things that people do which clearly reflect mental ability, from maths to poetry).

Little is known about the genes that influence intelligence most directly – as critics like to point out, there are no known 'genes for intelligence' – but that need not stop us from making general observations, at least to get the ball rolling. Some scientists affect to dislike speculation, but if nobody speculated there would be no science at all. Classical genetics had reached a high stage of sophistication and had become vital in agricultural breeding and in medicine even before anyone knew that genes are even made of DNA: so it is not so damning as some commentators clearly imagine to point out that no particular 'genes for intelligence' are known.

It is clear (on grounds both commonsensical and empirical) that many genes affect intelligence. In general, the presence and importance of particular genes is discovered only when they are polymorphic, a range of alleles possible at any one locus. Often, genes are discovered when mutant alleles cause disease. Many of the 6000 or so known alleles which can lead to single–gene disorders cause what textbooks describe as 'mental retardation'. We all of us know how sensitive our minds, including our ability to think, are to day-to-day insults and stimulants: fatigue, alcohol, nicotine, caffeine, fear, worry, and so on, and so on. Similarly, any gene that affects any aspect of body chemistry, which all of them do to some extent, could in principle affect brain function. Biologists are wont to suggest, as a kind of informed guess, that around 30,000 of our 100,000 genes affect our mental ability. But we might almost suggest that virtually all of them probably have some kind of input (or would do so, if present in mutant form).

Clearly, it is hard to design breeding programmes if there are 30,000 genes to play with all at once; but the picture is not totally hopeless. Beyond doubt, some genes are more directly involved than others. Those that produce particular neurotransmitters, or help to organise particular synapses, are clearly among the most closely involved. It would not be at all surprising, then, if in the fullness of time biologists discovered particular alleles, or combinations of alleles, which are most closely associated with high IQ and which seem to have a particularly positive effect on IQ. Such alleles surely will be identified as geneticists map and sequence the genomes of more and more different people.

Even before such mapping is done we can see in principle, by applying the basic ideas of classical genetics, that human beings would be more likely to have a high IQ if they possessed a greater number of the alleles that most directly boost IQ and fewer of those that depress it. That is obvious: and the principle applies whether we are talking about just one allele which enhances IQ, or half a dozen, or a thousand, or 10,000.

The broad problem, then, is to produce a population whose gene pool contains as many as possible of the helpful alleles to ensure that each individual within the population has the greatest chance of inheriting a good proportion of those alleles. So how, in general, is this done? By the two basic methods discussed in Chapter 8, mainly in the context of plants: crossing and selection; and mass selection.

The time-honoured method of crossing and selecting is harder than it looks, as described in Chapter 8, especially when the required character is polygenic (or has various components, each of which is polygenic). An individual with good looks must obviously possess a fair proportion of the desirable alleles. But his or her fineness of feature also depends critically on the particular combination of those alleles, and the combinations are broken up and rearranged during sexual reproduction. For this reason alone (and there are many others), the offspring of handsome fathers and beautiful mothers can be very disappointing. Nineteenth-century breeders expressed this phenomenon as 'reversion to the mean': the offspring of outstanding parents tend to revert to the average level of the population. Sometimes you may strike lucky, as suggested by my anecdote of the charming and handsome German born in a Nazi breeding programme. But in general you cannot just 'cross the best with the best, and hope for the best'. Furthermore, we saw that plant-breeders typically cross tens of thousands of individuals from the parent generation to produce millions of offspring, from which they may select only one in a thousand. You can get tens of millions of wheat plants in a large greenhouse, and produce the new generations in one year (or less, if you control the conditions). The same exercise in human beings would require a continent, and twenty years per generation. Crossing and selection, then, seem a bad general strategy for breeding brighter human beings by classical methods.

Mass selection is more appropriate to features that are highly polygenic (or to combinations of features) and in species that are naturally outbreeding. At present, by definition, the mean IQ of human beings is taken to be 100, with the vast majority of people being between 80 and 120. We could beyond doubt raise that mean IQ, probably significantly and within a few generations, simply by ensuring that people were not allowed to breed unless they had an IQ above, say, 95. The political control would be draconian and undoubtedly hideous, and many fine qualities might be lost by such a strategy. But it would work. Mass selection involves random breeding and is clearly very different in strategy from the Nazi attempt to produce better people by crossing particular individuals. The Nazis' mass elimination of large groups clearly had nothing to do with any concerted attempt to raise IQ. True, they attacked the people they diagnosed to be 'feeble-minded' (although we might question the diagnoses). But they attacked people on racial grounds with even greater vigour, with no regard at all for their measured intelligence.

But although mass selection would probably produce a greater proportion of clever people, it is hard to see how it could produce super-Einsteins, or super-Shakespeares. The problem lies with the long-understood issue of heterosis. Some alleles do not produce their best results unless they are matched, on the equivalent locus on the homologous chromosome, by a different allele. As a top-of-the-head calculation we might reasonably speculate that people have the potential to be geniuses when they possess, say, alleles at 5000 loci that enhance intelligence (and very few that detract from intelligence), and when, say, 100 of the 5000 are heterozygous, with each heterozygous locus requiring *particular* pairs of alleles. When excellence requires heterosis and when there has to be heterozygosity at several or many different loci, no breeder can guarantee to produce, or reproduce, the quality required. Individuals which possess such combinations of alleles are one-offs; never to be repeated, at least by the methods of classical breeding. This is why breeders of F1 hybrids, which are highly heterozygous, commonly begin with parent populations that actually look rather feeble. The parents are feeble because they are highly homozygous; but if they were not highly homozygous, then they could not produce heterozygous offspring to a reliable specification.

It is fun (harmless fun, I suggest) to apply these simple plant-breeding principles to what we know of human beings. High ability, in many kinds of areas, undoubtedly runs in families. There was a dynasty of musical Bachs; there are many dynasties of painters (the Breughels, the Teniers) and even more of architects and engineers (Barry, Pugin, Nash, Brunel, and so on). Bragg senior and junior both won Nobel Prizes and the grandsons of Thomas Henry Huxley included Aldous, Sir Julian and Andrew, who became president of England's Royal Society. The Medicis produced more than their share of outstanding individuals (with my vote going to Piero the Fatuous, who famously commissioned Michelangelo to build him a snowman). The Brontë sisters are the most famous siblings of literature. It is clear that high ability can run in families, although it seems obvious that environment and opportunity are just as significant as the genetic input.

But although outstanding ability can run in families, it is rare for that extraordinary quality we call 'genius' to run in families. Only one of the Breughels (Peter the Elder) and one of the Bachs (J. S.) are generally taken to qualify. Jane Austen and George Eliot have commonly been called 'geniuses'; but the term is rarely applied to the Brontës, talented though they were. If genius really does depend on a particular combination of particular alleles heterozygously represented, then this is entirely unsurprising. Neither should we be surprised if genius sometimes turns up in the midst of families which seem to have no outstanding talent at all. Beethoven is commonly presented as the prime example. Newton is another.

In short, a draconian regime could almost certainly raise general IQ – by mass selection, rather than by particular crosses – but it would probably have to wait for genius to turn up randomly, just as human societies have always done. Much more to the point, we should learn to treat genius much better than we do. The geniuses who have died before their time because of society's maltreatment make a horrendous catalogue (which of course includes Mozart, the twentieth-century composer Samuel Coleridge-Taylor, and Alan Turing, perhaps the most extraordinary scientific talent of the twentieth century, who committed suicide after harassment by the British government).

Overall, then, it would clearly be very difficult to make significant changes in human beings by traditional breeding methods even if we did introduce draconian policies. The logistics would still overwhelm us. Of late, however, many have claimed that genetic engineering really could produce dramatic changes, and, indeed, that it is bound to do so. The 'designer baby', structured genetically to specifications, is sometimes said, effectively, to be just around the corner. Again, leaving aside matters of desirability, how realistic are such claims?

Will We Ever See 'Designer Babies'?

Genetic engineering is qualitatively different from conventional breeding, although this has often been denied of late. Conventional breeders 'cross' one individual with another to try to combine the desirable alleles of both into the offspring. Too bad if one of the individuals has only one desirable allele, one which confers resistance to some disease, say. Thousands of other alleles are brought along as well (and generally have to be got rid of by subsequent rounds of 'back-crossing'). But genetic engineers are precise. They pick out the one gene (or the few genes) they want and add them *ad hoc*; or they take away or change individual genes. This is a conceptually distinct operation.

A 'designer baby' is one who may have had many genes added by these *ad hoc* methods to produce a human being to a particular specification. Technically, in theory, this must be possible. In principle, it is becoming possible to create genomes with any specified sequence of genes. The rough outline of the human genome will be written out by the time this book is published, and in a few decades' time, or at least within a few centuries, it will be possible to 'read' it, just as archaeologists now read the hieroglyphs of ancient Egypt. The 'meaning' will leap out of the ciphers. It surely will be possible, then, to create a sequence of genes that will produce human beings who can do whatever their designers require of them: anything, that is, that does not defy the laws of physics. Neither should we second-guess what might be physically possible. We might guess that a basketball player ten feet tall would be mechanically unstable, and suffer disastrously from back problems, or faint when he bent down to touch his toes, but don't hold your breath. Such disasters are plausible, but not predictable from first principles.

I have argued, too, that it would probably prove very difficult to produce super-geniuses merely by conventional breeding (by crossing and selection, or by mass selection) even though we might readily raise the average IQ. But by genetic engineering it might indeed be possible to create super-geniuses (with a measured IQ of, say, 400). This presumably would require geneticists to identify the genes which most directly influence IQ (e.g. act upon neurotransmitters and synapses), explore the way they operate and the combinations in which they work most effectively, and then add more that are similar (or work even better) and so on.

My point is not that such outcomes are inevitable, and certainly not that we should go down such routes, but that it is dangerous to discount them *a priori*. Some scientists in recent years, alarmed by their own pending power, have sought to ward off public criticism by suggesting that the various 'nightmare scenarios' are just not possible. Such a stance, to put the matter crudely, is dishonest. Outlandish scenarios *are* in principle possible. If we want to stay in control of our own lives and societies, then it is sensible to spell out the possibilities as clearly as we can and then ask what we are going to do about them: whether those possibilities can be used for benign purposes (and what we mean by 'benign') and how to avoid courses that are undesirable. That is what I am trying to do here and I am labouring the point because, I have found, it is often misunderstood.

However, there can be a large gap between what is theoretically possible and what is in practice feasible. I do think 'designer babies' are possible, but I cannot see that they are feasible. That is, I cannot envisage a technically or politically plausible series of steps by which we might produce them. Over the next few decades we probably will see some forays into human genetic engineering, but these (I suggest) will be of an *ad hoc* and highly circumscribed nature. We will not slide along the hypothetical 'slippery slope' towards the full-blown redesigned human being, simply because there is no such slope. Instead, there is a difficult obstacle course. From an ethical and a political point of view, the obstacles that can already be envisaged are a good thing. They will serve as milestones and we can stop at any one of them.

Transitions, Obstacles and Milestones

We have already identified most of the principal milestones on the road to the designer baby. There is a conceptual difference between therapy – the alleviation of obvious suffering – and attempts to improve upon a system that is already functioning well enough. In some cases it is hard to identify the borderline, but we recognise the broad distinction well enough. It general it is the difference between medicine, which is intended to cure discrete pathologies, and tonics, which are designed to gild the lily. In Western medicine we tend to approve of the former and take a puritanical view of the latter. The same principle can be applied to genetic interventions. We have also distinguished between *ad hoc* interventions, intended to help particular individuals during their own lives; and germline therapy, which is intended to correct (or rather prevent) specific genetic disorder in future generations. Deliberations of eugenics reveal the difference between attempts simply to ensure that future generations are like *us*, and attempts to push the human species towards some pre-envisioned goal. So long as we can identify such distinctions we can frame laws (or at least define principles) which in theory should enable us to call a halt at any particular point. We need not envisage that we will slide willy-nilly down any hypothetical slippery slope.

There are some difficult cases, however. One is offered by all those alleles that do not lead to 'single gene disorders', like Tay-Sachs or cystic fibrosis, but which do predispose to particular damaging conditions such as diabetes and coronary heart disease. Thus modern convention has it that we are liable to suffer from coronary heart disease if we consume large amounts of saturated fat. True, but in fact only some people get heart disease on a high-fat diet. Others can eat lard all day and escape. The sufferers are the ones who possess particular genes that predispose them to arterial damage when the arteries are exposed to large amounts of fat. Similarly, we can find environmental causes of lung cancer, breast cancer, diabetes, emphysema, or indeed any disease you may care to mention, but you will always find some genetic predisposition as well. Should we accept that in the modern world we are subjected to environmental pollutants and exposed to high-fat diets, and regard those predisposing genes as maladaptive? If so, should they become targets for gene therapy?

My own immediate answer is: 'No, they should not', for all kinds of reasons. Part of the reason is puritanical: I think it is incumbent upon us to live sensibly, if we have that option, and not simply to reach for the technological 'fix'. My greater reason, however, is common sense and some knowledge of biology. We have seen the principle in the case of the sickle-cell allele. On the face of things, it looks all bad; but in reality, in context, the allele in single dose saves a great many lives. The same is surely true of the many alleles that seem to predispose us to cancer, or heart disease, or the rest. True, in the context of modern, perhaps too-affluent societies, they seem to be bad for us. But in other contexts they might be very good. Besides, most genes are pleiotropic and the gene that seems to predispose to diabetes might also have a great many effects that are extremely beneficial, even in our present environment. The grand generalisation applies, too. It is one thing to identify a single gene that is obviously life-threatening and try to do something about it. But we should not take liberties. We do not know enough, and never will, to be able to fiddle with genes without risk. If the risks are small, and the dangers are obvious (even if they remain theoretical), then leave well alone.

Still, though, we can envisage test cases that should give pause for thought. In *Remaking Eden* Lee Silver offers a case for germline therapy. Suppose, he says, it were possible to add a gene that would confer protection against AIDS. Would this be justified? Of course, you might argue that AIDS can generally be avoided by behavioural changes, and so is not a good candidate. What, then, of malaria, which kills 100 million people a year and has so far avoided all attempts at vaccination, and for which there are no fully satisfactory drugs; or of TB, which is currently attacking humanity afresh? Either disease in principle might be prevented by adding (or subtracting) appropriate alleles to the human genome. It would be surprising if this were not the case. The malaria parasite, after all, must recognise the red blood cells in which it lodges by their surface properties and subtle alteration could put the parasites completely off the scent. Germline gene therapy might prove the best and cheapest protection against malaria. Could anyone then suggest that it was too equivocal in principle not to be used?

I find such cases difficult. Perhaps they serve to show that we should not dismiss germline therapy out of hand. But even so, such interventions would be *ad hoc*: specific defences against specific diseases which we know can be particularly nasty and intractable in particular environments. The idea of the 'designer baby', produced by genetic engineering, is generally broader than this: greater height, intelligence, beauty. Again, leaving ethics aside for a moment, could we enhance such qualities by genetic engineering?

In principle again the answer must be 'yes'; but it is hard to see how the attempt could be made. One obvious issue, only one, but it makes the point, is safety. Qualities such as intelligence and beauty, and even height, are polygenic. This does not mean that they could not be affected by addition (or subtraction) of single genes, for they certainly could. So, too, by crude analogy, the performance of an engine might be enhanced by introducing any one individual part of higher quality. However, the single introduced genes would have to work harmoniously with all the other genes already in place. There can be no guarantees that they would do so. Adding an extra gene which you think *might* fit the bill might upset the applecart instead. Genes that promote the output of growth hormone produced monsters when introduced into farm livestock. Future manipulators of human beings would be more sophisticated but the same caveat applies.

Then again, *any* gene is liable to prove pleiotropic in its effects. When single gene disorders are corrected, a defective allele is replaced by the normal version; and we know what the normal one does by observation of healthy people. If we added novel genes to people to enhance height or intelligence we could not predict precisely what other effects that novel gene might have. Nature cannot be second-guessed. We would just have to wait and see. This principle also applies, of course, to attempts to try to provide protection against malaria or TB: but at least in such cases the aim would be to save life and we can argue that the goal outweighs the risk (even if we decide, in the end, to reject that argument). But when the goal is simply to add a few points of IQ to give economic advantage we might reasonably feel that the risk is unjustified.

In general, we might suggest that to replace deleterious alleles with normal ones is like proof-reading: correcting the obvious spelling mistakes and removing the blots. But to enhance a genome that already operates reasonably well is an exercise in serious editing: like changing the end of *King Lear*, for example, as it was once fashionable to do (because the death of Cordelia was too sad). The Human Genome Project, when it is finished, will give us a print-out of the human genome that will be analogous to a dictionary: at least we will have listed all the words in the language. However, it won't really be a dictionary, because it will take some time to work out what all the words mean. But even if it was a finished dictionary, and of the finest quality, would it enable us to edit the genome? For if genes are analogous to words, then the genome as a whole is analogous to literature. There are cross-references, puns, allusions, colloquialisms, dialects, redundancies, and nuances of all kinds. Would you undertake to rewrite

King Lear – or to edit a medieval poem in Chinese – if all you had was a dictionary? Would any sane person do this?

There are further, technical points. To be sure, all technical difficulties can in principle be overcome; but again, there is a clear difference between what is technically possible and what is feasible. We have seen in Chapter 7 that germline genetic engineering in animals depends on the technology of cloning by cell culture and nuclear transfer. This technology raises its own hazards. Nearly 300 embryos were required to produce Dolly. Of course, the techniques will become incomparably better as the next centuries unfold, but cloning will still, surely, be more risky than the standard method of reproduction. Furthermore, some of the failures on the route to Dolly and the other cloned sheep ended in late abortion, deformity and neonatal death. In human medicine we tolerate early abortion – nature itself, after all, is incredibly prodigal in the early stages of pregnancy – but late abortion is still most disturbing and deformity and neonatal death are simple horrible. If attempts to produce a 'designer baby' ended in just one such accident, the whole endeavour would have to be called off. Yet it is hard to see how accidents could be avoided. No procedure in medicine or any other field of human endeavour ever leapt straight to perfection. But anyone who offered technology to produce designer babies effectively would have to promise perfection from the outset.

Of course, no one sane would attempt such feats in humans until the techniques had been polished and honed in other species. That is the best scenario, although, in practice, guns tend to be jumped. But even if the experimenters worked conscientiously through the phylogenetic tree – marmosets, macaques, chimpanzees – there would still be a leap of species at the end: and procedures which seem perfectly safe in other species might have ill-effects in humans. No one can say *a priori* that this would not be the case. Besides, many people, myself included, would question whether it is justified to carry out hazardous procedures in other primates (lots of them!) just to further the dubious ambitions of those who seek to produce extra-tall or extra-intelligent humans. Here, then, is another obvious point, at which we may draw our ethical lines.

Then there is the general point, which has been made elsewhere in this book: although we may develop procedures that achieve what we want them to achieve, and although those procedures may be underpinned by convincing and internally consistent theory, we can never *know* that we know everything which needs to be known. It is logically impossible to possess complete knowledge or, at least, to know that we possess it. So however many experiments we did *en route* to the designer baby, and however deep and intricate our theory became, our knowledge would always be imperfect. We would always be operating, to some extent, on a wing and a prayer. That is the general condition of humankind. All physicians and engineers must operate and build in the absence of perfect knowledge. If the prize is obvious – to save life – and the risk is calculable, then the adventure may well be justified. If it were not, then none of us could ever take an aspirin and no one would build a bridge. We know, however, that we sometimes come unstuck even when the science seems well understood and there are a thousand precedents. Every now and again bridges, built to impeccable standards with irrefutable theory, fall down. When the rewards are highly dubious and the risks are all too easy to envisage and are potentially horrendous, then surely we should back away. The point is obvious. There is no slippery slope to the designer baby, simply because in practice there is no logical, step-by-step passage from the conceptually simple correction of single-gene disorders to the totally prescribed genome.

On a final technical point, in a hundred years the very notion of the 'designer baby' might simply seem rather quaint, like most early twenty-first-century science. There is an alternative route through pharmacology. More and more, modern drugs operate at the level of the DNA. In a few generations we will probably have drugs that can control the expression of genes to the nth degree. Why change a gene permanently and irrevocably, if we can simply add some agent that will invoke what is required from existing genes, or mimic the function of genes that are not there?

But of course, prediction in science is hazardous. I cannot see how designer babies will become reality, but neither do I claim to be omniscient. The idea of the designer baby is now on the

282

agenda of humankind and, until science itself comes to an end (or human beings re-evolve along non-intelligent lines), it will remain there for ever. 'Genetic determinism' is only a slogan for the lazy-minded, but it remains the fact that if we redesign the human genome then, *ipso facto*, we will be redefining what we mean by humanity. That would be the most extraordinary, the boldest and most threatening endeavour that human beings have ever undertaken: to redesign ourselves: to declare our present selves redundant.

I hope we do not do this. We may reasonably leave the last word of all to Marvin Minsky, of the Massachusetts Institute of Technology, who has pointed out that we do not give enough credit to our present selves. He suggests that if you really want to appreciate something then you should just try to make a machine that will do the same things. He and his colleagues at MIT have been trying these past few decades to emulate the human brain and have been chastened: staggered by the subtlety and intricacy of the real thing. We extol to the heavens what we call 'genius', says Minsky: Mozart, Einstein, Shakespeare. Yet the difference between any of these paragons and, say, a 'tween-stairs maid is too small to measure, compared to the difference between the maid and an earthworm. Yet an earthworm is not an inconsiderable creature; it is many, many times more complicated than, say, a protozoan. It is easy to programme computers to make music of commendable intricacy, and of course they do blinding maths. Poetry and general creativeness come harder, but the day will surely come when we cannot readily tell if some new sonnet is the work of a person or a machine. By contrast, it would take more computer power than that of the Starship Enterprise to pro-gramme a robot that could carry a tray of tea and cakes upstairs while running mentally through the most tearful scenes of *Brief Encounter*. Such extraordinariness we take for granted: just sitting on a chair; just holding simple conversations, and adjusting style and content according to who is being spoken to (boss, friend, client, grandmother, little daughter). Yet these abilities beggar belief. 'What a piece of work is a man!' exclaimed Hamlet.

And Shakespeare was absolutely right. For reasons of biology alone, leaving aside all issues of ethics and theology for a moment, we surely should not tinker lightly with such a creature. The idea that we can improve on our own good selves by fiddling with our genes like washing-machine repair men seems to me not simply hubristic, as I will suggest in Chapter 10, but ludicrous. We have taken five million years to evolve to our present state and natural selection really does work and has been a hard taskmaster. It is obviously dangerous to override it. We should remember that our apparent successes as breeders of livestock are extremely limited: domestic animals are bred as one-dimensional creatures to give ridiculously large amounts of milk or lay ludicrous quantities of eggs. The qualities their ancestors enjoyed as wild animals may have been squandered. But we cannot afford to squander the thousands of subtleties that evolution has built into ourselves, in particular into our own psyches. We should accept ourselves, as Oliver Cromwell was content to accept himself, 'warts and all'. Or at least, we might contrive to pre-empt the suffering that is caused by the most objectionable warts, the obviously 'deleterious alleles'. Apart from that we should reflect how nobly the genetically pristine human being can perform when given the chance – three square meals a day, freedom from disease, social harmony, education – and focus, as all sensible social reformers have always done, on improving our environment. The rest is rather distasteful and, in the end, silly.

But whether we like it or not, the human clone and the designer baby, the re-invented human being, will stay on humanity's agenda for as long as science itself is practiced. With such power before us, we have to ask as a matter of urgency, what it is *right* for us to do. Some have suggested that these new technologies raise no 'new' ethical issues – a point that largely depends on what is meant by 'new'. They certainly raise the ethical ante. After all, we cannot be held morally responsible for events that we cannot control, but we are answerable for that we do control. In the normal course of events, we cannot control the genetic makeup of our offspring. At least, we do have *some* influence, because we choose our mates carefully; but the process of genetic recombination, during the formation of eggs and sperms, ensures that the genetic details of our offspring are not in our gift. But if we clone children, or engineer their genes, then we are *prescribing* their genome. Our responsibility then, for all that befalls them, far outstrips that of any parent. *Noblesse oblige*. It is too casual by far to say there are no new issues. We must look deeper.

What Should We Do With All This Power?

This book is concerned with fundamentals. I have sought to show how the complexities of modern genetics, and all the ramifications, flow naturally from Mendel's initial notions and his rows of peas: those notions, as well as the chemistry of DNA and the evolutionary insights of Charles Darwin. Most of this book has been concerned with the facts of the case: with what *is*. In this final chapter I want to ask what *ought* to be. But I want to apply the same general approach: using reverse engineering, working back from the complex surface of things to track down the fundamental principles that underpin, or ought to underpin, ethical and economic discussions. As with genetics itself, I feel that the fundamental moral principles are in the end simple. In ethics great truths may indeed spring from the mouths of babes and sucklings. Beware the rhetoricians and arm-wavers. As Mendel himself so abundantly showed, simplicity should not be confused with crudity, or complexity with profundity.

Why Should We Be Concerned?

If creatures, including human creatures, have no consciousness and no power to change the world around them, then ethical issues do not arise. Cows or lions are not morally accountable. *Forgive them, for they know not what they do* – and even if they did, they could not, in practice, make much impact on the world. Human beings, however, are conscious. We can decide what we

286

want to do, or, at least, if choice is an illusion it is one that we do well to cultivate. From the time we first became human, we have surely felt ourselves to be morally accountable to each other, at least, and perhaps (who knows?) to some deity. Furthermore, we have huge technical power. We can change the world around us, do so restlessly, and have already done so from one pole to the other. Our power, like all power, is both destructive and creative. Destruction is much easier and of course destruction and creation overlap. What we build – farms, cities, domestic crops and livestock – largely destroys what was there before.

Our control of the physical world has long been obvious: rapid transport, dams and highways, skyscrapers, and now, spectacularly, the as yet intractable possibilities of electronics, which already have brought us virtual reality and the Internet. So far, our control of living systems has been more tenuous. Modern medicine and agriculture are fabulous by the standards of earlier centuries, but their successes are *ad hoc*. We do what we do, and we think we understand what we do, yet we have been, as Newton said of himself, children playing with pebbles on the beach.

But this state of affairs is clearly changing. Biotechnologists are already at work on 'designer crops'. The present wave of GMOs, 'genetically modified organisms', which have caused such a kerfuffle is only the beginning. It is not too soon to contemplate the 'designer baby', even though the reality (if it is ever realised) must lie many decades in the future. Indeed we might now sensibly consider the creation of life itself: not simply by modifying present life forms, or rearranging them in the way that enthusiasts build custom cars, but from scratch, with the ingredients you might once have found (in less safety-conscious days) in a child's chemistry set. As late as the 1980s the outstanding German biologist Davor Solter wrote in *Nature* that cloning of mammals 'by simple nuclear transfer' was 'biologically impossible'. Never mind the particular issue that he was addressing. The point is that after Megan and Morag, Dolly, and Polly, the expression 'biologically impossible' seems to have lost all meaning.

In short, we are beginning to acquire a power over living systems which will seem, as the next centuries unfold, to be

287

absolute. It is an ancient principle, made explicit in feudal societies, that *noblesse oblige*: those who have power are obliged to act responsibly, and moral responsibility grows in direct proportion to their power. Absolute power implies absolute responsibility. We really do have the fate of our own and all other earthly species in our hands, or soon will have. Morally, there is nowhere to run.

We should, however, add two conditional clauses, though neither reduces the burden of our responsibility and one of them, if anything, adds to it. First, when commentators (scientists and otherwise) consider the future of biotechnologies, they typically underestimate the timescale. Thus experts have been predicting of late (not least on peak-hour British television) that in twenty years human reproduction would be mediated *in vitro* and sex would purely be a social pursuit. What nonsense. First, as I will argue later, there is good reason to suppose that sex will always be the preferred method of reproduction and that *in vitro* methods will always be reserved for special cases. Even if this were not so, however, twenty years is an absurdly short period for such a prediction. Science and technology seem to progress at a bewildering pace. But the universe is big and complicated and there are a lot of problems to get through, so in reality complex technologies take decades or centuries to unfold, especially when, as in this case, they are concerned with the biology of human beings.

Consider the history of genetic engineering. DNA was first discovered in the late 1860s, yet it was another eighty years before its function was properly appreciated and another decade after that before its three-dimensional structure was worked out (its basic chemistry was already clear). Gene transfer was first mooted in the early 1970s, but did not become a truly practical proposition in animals until the late 1990s, when Roslin developed cloning technology. Thus a hundred and thirty years elapsed from the discovery of DNA to the manipulation of DNA in animals. Similarly, Edward Jenner initiated vaccination (using cowpox to immunise against smallpox) in the 1790s and now, two hundred years later, despite many spectacular triumphs including the total elimination of smallpox, vaccines are still a major topic for research, still posing problems. As knowledge of the universe increases, so do the mysteries and perceived opportunities. The same principles will apply to *in vitro* reproduction and designer-baby technologies. They will take many decades to come on-line and will still be posing problems in two centuries' time. That, at least, is a more realistic timescale than two decades. Scientists exaggerate the speed of progress because they need to attract government grants and venture capital, for few would invest in technologies which might easily take a century to yield dividends.

On the other hand, the human species is not, as people seem so often to think, facing Armageddon. The world is not about to end: or at least, we have no reason to suppose that it is. Our descendants will still be here in two hundred years' time – and, given that human beings are living longer, those descendants could include the great-grandchildren of at least some of this book's readers. Indeed, our descendants will still be here in 500 years, or 1000, or 10,000, or 100,000. I suggested in *The Day Before Yesterday* that in thinking about wildlife conservation, a million years is a sensible unit of political time. So yes, technologies take a long time to unfold. But there is an awful lot of time for them to do so in. Present-day technologies may be promising more than they can yet deliver, but they will remain on humanity's agenda for ever, and as the decades and centuries go past the hype will be superseded, more and more, by reality. So the timescale for the future is far longer than is commonly presented; but the future will arrive nonetheless.

The second conditional clause is truly a caveat. As time passes, our control of living processes will *seem* absolute; but seem is the operative word. Our descendants will be able to do anything they may care to conceive, down to and including the creation of novel life and even of intelligent, novel life. But their understanding can never be absolute; that is a logical impossibility. Nature does what nature does. Always we are condemned to trail along behind, trying to work out what is happening. We can never, as a matter of logic, be sure that we have not missed some vital component of the natural mechanisms. Because our understanding will never be absolute we will, as the future unfolds, make mistakes and every now and again some of those mistakes could be serious.

We can look at this issue in various ways, but let us take just one. A scientist may have a theory on how some aspect of the universe works. On the basis of that theory a technologist may build a machine, or devise a procedure. If the machine works or the procedure succeeds, does this prove that the theory was correct?

In practice, we tend to take such success as proof, for what else have we got to go on? At least, a theory that gives rise to a technology which works must surely be correct *in some respects*, and *as far as it goes*. Yet the theory may still be deeply flawed: wrong in highly significant respects, or simply inadequate. To be sure, the theory may be perfectly coherent and intellectually satisfying. It may be perfectly consistent internally, with all components following logically, one from another. But still, the theory may not match reality as closely as the observer may suppose.

We can demonstrate this by analogy. Ancient farmers typically surrounded their cultivations with rituals, some of them highly elaborate: sow your crops only by the light of the full moon; 'red sky at night – shepherd's delight'; dance to make the rain come; and so on and so on. Some of those ancient rituals make perfect sense when analysed in the light of modern knowledge. Modern agriculturalists have increasing respect for traditional farming systems which once seemed to be steeped in superstition. A red sky at night, for example, suggests dust in the air, which in turn implies that the atmosphere is dry, and might remain so. Other rituals, however, like rain-dances, defy all analysis and seem to make no sense. Yet *all* the farmer's procedures derive from the same, coherent theory of how the universe works: typically from some basic idea that the universe is controlled by a deity who needs to be appeased. But the fact that the theory is coherent and seems to work when put to the test does not mean that it is, in fact, correct. Some of the farming procedures that the underlying cosmology demands are helpful, but some are irrelevant, and some that could be helpful (like fertilising the fields) are being missed. In short, the underlying theory may be coherent and satisfying and the procedures that are based on it may work (up to a point) but the latter do not prove the overall validity or adequacy of the former.

We can bring this discussion closer to home. A decade before Ian Wilmut and Keith Campbell produced Dolly by nuclear transfer and genomic reprogramming, several groups of scientists managed to clone various kinds of animals by various other means. All of them had a good idea of what they were doing, and why. All, in short, had coherent theories that seemed effective. In retrospect, however, it is clear that the pioneers of cloning often missed vital tricks: that some of the procedures they carried out conscientiously were not, in fact, necessary at all, while other things they did inadvertently turned out to be vital. It seems at least possible, for example, that in some of the early experiments in nuclear transfer the receiving eggs (MII oocytes) were activated inadvertently before the nuclei were introduced, just by allowing them to revert to room temperature. In such cases, the concentrations of MPF (which otherwise would have been destructive) were already low at the time of nuclear transfer. The scientists involved in these early experiments had no idea that MPF was significant in this context or that it needed to be reduced. They just happened, in passing, to do things that proved helpful.

In short, in modern science as in ancient agriculture, the underlying theory, however coherent and satisfying, may not underpin the resulting technology as accurately as seems to be the case. So the success of the resulting technology does not *and cannot* demonstrate that the underlying theory is correct and adequate in every respect. The theory must have been good enough to succeed in the particular case that was observed; but if the conditions were changed somewhat, inadequacies could well be revealed.

This is not a criticism of science or of scientists. It is simply a point of logic and, as such, it is inescapable. As it has been in the past, so it will be in the future. Future technologists may 'design' babies and may even make new forms of life; their successes will seem to justify the belief that their understanding is absolute, just as their control seems to be. But this will always be an illusion. Even if their understanding *were* complete (which itself is a logical

291

impossibility) they could never *know* that it was complete. Always, there is likely to be more going on than the scientist is aware of. Always, life will pull surprises. As a final illustration, we may note that modern architects and engineers really do have wonderful knowledge – of Newtonian mechanics and the behaviour of every kind of material you might conceive. Yet when they build with novel techniques, their tower blocks collapse and their prestige skyscrapers shed their windows in the swirling winds that the building itself gives rise to. The failures demonstrate the principle: that our understanding can never be absolute and it is dangerous to assume that it can be. But bridges and stadiums are easy. At least, they are fabulously complicated and engineers include some of the world's cleverest people. But they are easy compared to the processes of life. We might look upon the failures, the twisted strands of metal, as Shelley's traveller looked upon the ruins of Ozymandias, and despair. At the least, we should take serious notice.

Nevertheless, we can expect our more bullish descendants to behave *as if* their understanding were absolute, and the biotechnical feats they will pull will truly be wondrous. It will seem as if they can do anything. And if human beings can do anything they choose to do, then what *should* they do?

How Do We Judge What Is Good?

We may reasonably assume that the very first human beings were moral creatures; so we may likewise assume that the questions 'What is good?' and 'How do we know goodness when we see it?' are as old as humanity. I do not presume to provide the eternal verities that have eluded humankind for so long. I would like to offer a few observations, however.

First, speaking in a broad-brush way, the moral principles which philosophers have defined tend to fall into one of two main categories: either absolutist or consequentialist.

Absolutist arguments say that morality is structured into the universe. Such arguments are easiest to frame and to understand if we assume that the universe is run by an omnipotent and omniscient God. Then we can simply say that what is 'good' is simply what God says is good. What God says is *absolutely* right. Our only task as moral beings is to find out what it is that God requires of us. Obey God and you can't go wrong, even if God is asking you to sacrifice your son as a burnt offering, as Jehovah once demanded of Abraham, although, it transpired, he was only testing Abraham's faith (Genesis, 22:2).

Many philosophers, however, have tried to define absolute moral principles which should apply even if there is no God. These again seem to be of two main kinds. The first is exemplified and reached its zenith in Immanuel Kant, in eighteenth-century Germany. He strove to define absolute ethical principles *a priori*: principles that in effect have the same weight as the laws of science. Such principles should outweigh even the will of God: if God does not subscribe to those principles, then God is wrong. Kant called his principles 'categorical imperatives'. This is not the place to argue whether Kant's imperatives achieve what is required of them (modern moral philosophers seem to conclude that his scheme contains flaws, perhaps inevitably), or whether his ambition was realistic. Let us just take it for the moment as a fact: that much moral philosophy has been concerned to define *absolute* principles of goodness or badness, even in the possible absence of a God who gives the orders.

The second principal strand of non-theistic absolutist arguments takes as its premise that what is *natural* is 'right', and what is unnatural is wrong. Thus, to take a very simple example, it is natural for mothers to look after their babies, so this is self-evidently 'right'; and unnatural for them to shun their babies, so this is obviously wrong. But many have pointed out, with various arguments, that we cannot derive 'good' from 'natural' so simplistically. The teachings of St Paul illustrate the dilemma. He condemned sex between men and women out of wedlock, *even though* it is 'natural'. We should, he said, exercise restraint. On the other hand he condemned homosexual relations between men precisely because they were *un*natural. In general he seemed to feel that unnatural was wrong, but that natural is not necessarily right. In the eighteenth century the Scottish philosopher David Hume pithily pointed out that '"Is" is not "ought"' (he never actually used this particular form of words, but this is the usual modern precis) and in the early twentieth century the Cambridge philosopher G. E. Moore coined the expression 'naturalistic fallacy'. This expression summarises and effectively dismisses *all* attempts to equate morality with naturalness. Biology, said Moore, is just as arbitrary as a source of moral guidance as any other body of ideas we may care to invoke. Yet perhaps we should not dismiss the idea that 'good *equals* natural' quite as peremptorily as Moore would have us do. I will return to this point later.

On a psychological point I suggest that, whether or not we are serious students of moral philosophy – whether or not we are committed Catholics or Muslims or followers of Kant – most of us feel, in our bones, that there are absolute moral principles. There may be such principles out there in the universe, or there may not be; but I do suggest that most of us feel that there ought to be. It is hard to find anyone who has no sense at all of absolute good and bad. Even the most hardened members of the Mafia love their mothers and feel this love to be sacred. The feeling that there is, somewhere, an absolute good is presumably what drove Kant and many a theologian to pursue their intellectual quest. Perhaps King Arthur's search for the Holy Grail is a metaphor for this quest. I suggest that whether or not we ever find this grail – define the absolute principles of goodness and badness – that the search for it is worthwhile. We should never stop seeking to define what we mean by 'good' and 'bad'; and the notion that there are absolute standards of goodness and badness is a useful heuristic, a guide to thought. If we lose sight of the notion that there might be moral absolutes then, it seems to me, we could be in deep moral and biological trouble. Many other people seem to share this feeling in their bones (which is where feelings are felt) even if they don't necessarily express the point in these terms.

Consequentialist arguments, by contrast, judge the goodness or badness of an action by its outcome. Perhaps the most famous and straightforward form of consequentialism was 'Utilitarianism', first outlined in the late eighteenth century by the English philosopher Jeremy Bentham. Utilitarianism is often summarised, cavalierly but accurately enough, as 'the greatest happiness of the greatest number'. The implications are obvious: if an action makes somebody happy (albeit only by reducing their pain) then it is good, unless it makes more people unhappy in the process.

In practice, it can be difficult to disentangle absolutist arguments from consequentialist arguments. Thus we might argue that an action is bad even though it makes somebody happy, if the action itself is 'bad'. Sadists are made happy by other people's pain. Is it right to torture people to keep sadists amused? In such a case, of course, the delight of the sadists is matched by the distress of the victim, but if there is only one victim and a hundred whooping lookers-on, isn't the criterion satisfied, of 'greatest happiness of the greatest number?' Bentham was aware of such criticisms, and there are many others, much more subtle, but still the point remains. Human happiness may be a guideline in our search for goodness and badness, but it does not *by itself* tell us all we need to know. Still, we feel there are good reasons and bad reasons to be happy and that the goodness and badness of the reasons must be judged independently of their effect on particular people.

The prickly issues of human cloning contains the two threads of thought, the absolutist and the consequentialist, and shows how they intertwine. Thus many have argued that cloning is justified if it helps infertile couples to have a baby of their own, who is genetically related at least to one of them. There is no more powerful human instinct (the argument has it, accurately) than the desire for a child. If cloning is the only route to reproduction, as in some conceivable circumstances it might be, then who should deny such a demand?

The issue can be argued purely along consequentialist lines and many have attempted this. Just to make sure we have covered all possibilities, we could lay out the possible gains and drawbacks in a Latin square, like the ones used to describe the matings of Mendel's peas. Along one axis we could list all the people involved in the cloning: the donor of the nucleus, the donor of the egg, the obstetricians and technicians, society at large (for we are all involved to some extent in every birth), and so on. Along the other axis we can list the possible gains and losses. Some of the people involved would grow rich by the procedure, which might be seen as a plus, but some might suffer psychologically (like the surrogate mother who gives birth to the cloned baby), and this would obviously be a minus. Then again, as Ian Wilmut has often asked, what psychological traumas might the family suffer as they bring up a baby who is a genetic replica of one parent but not the other? We can certainly envisage some special difficulties: and these too must be listed among the minuses.

But of course the chief player in all this is the baby itself. If the baby were to be deformed or otherwise incapacitated then obviously the procedure is unjustified. We must assume, though, that cloning would not be attempted at all, in animals or in humans, unless there was a reasonable chance of success. So what is a 'reasonable' chance in the context of a human baby? Late abortions, deformities and neonatal deaths of the kind that occurred in the attempts to clone sheep at Roslin would clearly be unacceptable. So would we suggest that a one in a hundred chance of disaster was acceptable? Or one in a thousand? In practice, of course, it is foolish simply to pluck such figures out of the air. We might rather observe that natural births, generated by the time-honoured sexual means, sometimes end in disaster. So perhaps we might suggest that cloning would be acceptable provided the risk (of late abortion, deformity, neonatal death or some later disaster) was no greater than in natural births. That would be a harsh criterion, however, and impossible to judge until a great many babies had been cloned and statistics were available. It is probably more sensible to take some less demanding yardstick. Should we perhaps suggest that the risk of cloning is acceptable if it is no greater than that of some roughly comparable procedure, such as IVF? Since IVF is already widely accepted, many would feel that this would at least be a sensible compromise.

All this, including the vital assessment of risk, is consequential-ism. We are simply asking who might be made happy by the birth of a cloned baby, who might be unhappy and what is the risk of either outcome. The absolutist would go further. Absolutists would, indeed do, suggest that even if everyone concerned is made happier by the birth of a cloned baby it is still wrong. The principle has been well expressed by Prince Charles, not in this context but in that of GMOs. Such intensive biological interven-tions, he said, trespass 'into God's territory'.

Many people in this secular age are appalled by such language or pretend to be. Nevertheless, I contend, many people who are not overtly religious, and would not themselves speak of 'God's territory', empathise with the Prince's misgivings; and would, if pressed, acknowledge 'God's territory' as an apt metaphor for their feeling. Cloning might make people happy (the sentiment has it), but still it is wrong.

We might draw a parallel with a bank robbery. The robbers might be very polite and benign. They might make tea for the staff, make them laugh and help them to complete their crossword puzzles. They might donate the stolen cash to the local hospital. Even if they spent it on Rolls-Royces, which is the more usual course, they would still be doing good in this capitalist age: helping to keep a worthy industry afloat. Nobody loses much: the bank is rich and insured and its customers lose too little per head to bother about. Besides, crime itself provides endless opportunities for respectable employment: insurance companies, builders of safes and burglar alarms, security guards, police, lawyers, prison warders, and all who service all of the above – van drivers, secretaries, and so on. The elimination of crime would make a huge hole in the economies of all organised countries and destroy some of our most respected professions. Lest you feel that such an example is too fanciful, recall that President Nixon once justified industrial pollution on the grounds that it fostered the clean-up industry. Yet we feel that bank robbery is wrong. The ends simply do not justify the means.

Cloning is not, of course, directly comparable with bank robbery. It is not conceived, as bank robbery is, as an offence against society. It is, we may concede, intended to do good. Yet the point remains. The resulting happiness or otherwise of the participants is not the only issue; and neither do any of us, when confronted with a case like this, *feel* that the resulting happiness is the only issue.

In short, whether or not we feel ourselves to be 'religious', we all of us have some respect for absolutist arguments. Some people might not acknowledge this, but when appropriate cases are brought (and I think the cheery bank robbery fits the bill) then even the most sceptical of consequentialists would concede the point that *mere* human happiness is not the only criterion to be taken into account. There remain misgivings that may not literally emanate from some all-powerful deity, and may not (as Kant proposed) be built in to the fabric of the universe, but must still be taken seriously. At least for the short-hand purposes of this argument, those misgivings can be taken to reflect a deep feeling, which all of us share, that in the end there are absolute criteria of good and evil. Even if that is not literally the case, we feel it to be the case; and what we feel to be the case cannot simply be ignored.

Finally, although in practice absolutist and consequentialist arguments are inescapably intertwined, we should at least try to keep them distinct in our heads. Thus I have heard many an ethical committee at loggerheads, with some talking about human fertility and the pain of childlessness, and others talking about the will of God, and neither connecting with the other; while the chairperson simply looks confused. In ethical arguments it is necessary both to propose moral principles, and to ensure that all the arguments are neat and tidy so that we know where we are; but often in ethical arguments, even in high places, one or both of these essentials is lacking.

But let us speak more of absolutist arguments.

Criteria of Good and Bad: What They Are and Where They Come From

Again, I will be accused of extreme presumption: to dare to address, in a few paragraphs, issues that human beings have pondered for 100,000 years, and failed so far to resolve to everyone's satisfaction. But everyone in a democracy ought to consider serious moral issues. I have been considering them with varying degrees of intensity for at least thirty years, and offer the following as a summary of my thoughts so far. I will try to make them coherent and clear, so that if you disagree with them you can see why easily. Clarity ought to be a virtue, even though obscurantism often scores more Brownie points and many a lucrative career has been founded in obfuscation.

Most of all, I like what David Hume said about ethics: that in the end, all our ethical sentiments are rooted in *feelings*. Our personal morality is driven by emotion. That is ineluctably the case. Moral philosophers write huge tracts, arguing this way and that. But different moral philosophers present different arguments, and of course make vastly different recommendations. In the end, inevitably and invariably, we find that among professional moral philosophers, just as among any group of idlers propping up the bar, some are right-wing and some are left, some are authoritarian and some are liberal, some are softies and some are hard as nails. The pages and pages of argument merely serve to justify, albeit with somewhat more rigour than the average barroom lizard, a few basic predispositions and predilections. In fact, the principal role of moral philosophers is not to tell us what is right or wrong, but to take moral propositions – any propositions – and lay them out clearly for inspection. Their role is like that of the lawyer, except that the lawyer is concerned specifically with the interpretation of law whereas the moral philosopher seeks to make explicit the principles upon which laws can be based.

This leaves us with a problem, though. Moral philosophers are supposed to tell us what is moral, are they not? Surely this is their job. Well, actually it is not. Their job is to examine moral propositions: the proposition, for example, that we ought to be right-wing, or left-wing, or authoritarian or liberal. So who puts forward these basic propositions and where do these basic propositions come from?

In a democracy we all ought to frame the initial propositions. Then we would hand them over to moral philosophers who would argue them this way and that, just to see how the arguments pan out. They in turn, if appropriate, might hand over the tidied-up arguments to government to become the basis of law; and the laws would be worded, and later interpreted, by lawyers. That is how democracy ought to work; or at least, according to the interpretation of 'democracy' that I feel is common in Britain.

In reality, however, most of us don't have time to frame basic moral propositions. We have our own lives to live. Societies have been content to leave the business of framing morality to experts, just as they delegate the teaching of children and the laying of drains. Who, though, are the appropriate experts?

Most people would say, if asked, 'moral philosophers', but, as I have suggested, this is not really their job. Their job is to take premises and argue them through, not to frame the premises in the first place. Some people (those who haven't had time to think it through) would perhaps say 'politicians'. Politicians are, after all, often quite well educated and in practice contrive to tell us all how to behave, so why shouldn't they put forward the basic propositions? Well, the main reason is not that politicians are outstandingly evil or amoral (for although newspapers focus on sleaze, some politicians are among the most morally aware of all human beings), but simply that all politicians belong to parties and defend party positions – social democratic, republican, communist, whatever. As seekers after moral truth we need to operate at a deeper level: to ask whether the bases of those parties are right or wrong.

Yet others would put lawyers in charge of moral policy. This is not foolish: many lawyers clearly have a highly developed moral conscience and most are clear-thinking, which is a *sine qua non*. But the criticism which applied to the moral philosophers also applies, with interest, to the lawyers. It really is not their job to say what is right or wrong. It is their job to frame and interpret laws based on their society's notion of what is right or wrong. Lawyers don't become any more satisfactory as moral leaders when they call themselves 'ethicists', as is fashionable nowadays (although 'ethicist' is a barbaric term).

In practice, however, ethical committees tend to be compounded primarily of moral philosophers, politicians and lawyers, with scientists as expert witnesses and a token 'layperson', commonly a housewife, or a member of some minority. There is also, typically, some manner of cleric: a rabbi, a Catholic, a Methodist, or whatever. Such a grouping is supposed to give us a rounded view. It is supposed to be the best we can do.

But the people I think we really need are prophets. Prophets are not the same as moral philosophers, although they may seem to drink from the same trough; and they are not the same as priests. It is the task of moral philosophers to discuss moral premises, but it is the task of prophets to put forward those premises in the first place. It is the task of priests to carry out the rituals and apply the teachings of particular religions, but it falls to prophets to frame the morality which underpins those religions. Of course a prophet may also be a moral philosopher (as was surely true of Christ) or a priest (like St Francis) or even a politician (I would put Gandhi or Nelson Mandela in the category of prophets), but it is not necessarily so. Prophets are prophets. They define the deep premises.

Prophets are children of religion and manifestations of religion: Buddha, Moses, Isaiah, John the Baptist, Christ, St Paul, Muhammad, and so on. You may feel, therefore, that in appealing to them I have sacrificed the attempt to discover deep principles that can serve all humanity. After all, the religious approach to ethics is to seek 'the word of God', is it not? What validity does this have if God does not exist? And why should an atheist, who does not believe in God, take note of God's alleged prophets? Besides, it is clear, is it not, that different religions advocate different moral strategies. Morality based on religion thus becomes entirely arbitrary: a matter of whether we happen to be born into a Christian society, or a Muslim, or a Hindu. How can such particular points of view serve the needs of all humanity, or claim fundamental, universal status?

Well, many people who consider themselves 'religious' nonetheless reject much or virtually all of the theology that attaches to any one religion. Many modern Christians question whether the virgin birth of Christ, and his resurrection, are literally true. Though these two propositions are traditionally taken as the cornerstones of Christianity, some of the doubters even practise as priests. Many people believe, in short, that if you remove the theology from religions, including the central theological notion that God exists and is the Creator of Heaven and Earth, then what is left is still worthwhile, and is, in fact, indispensable; part of the fabric of being human.

So what do religions do apart from promulgate the notion that God exists and/or (*pace* Buddhism, which is not theistic) promote the idea that supernatural forces lie behind the superficialities that we perceive as 'reality'? Well, they do three things. First,

301

invariably they seek to provide a complete narrative: a complete explanation of how the universe works, how it came into being, and why it is as it is and contains the creatures it does, including us. The great religions seek to embrace all possible knowledge and experience. The attempt to provide a complete account seems to me to have a nobility, even if some moderns may doubt its possibility.

Secondly, all the great religions seek to frame systems of ethics. They all ask (or state) how human beings ought to behave; and they seek, furthermore, to weave those ethics into the grand narrative.

But thirdly, and this I feel is truly important in this context, all the great religions adopt the same kind of methods in reaching their ethical principles. None of them, as far as I can see, present moral arguments of the kind developed by moral philosophers and lawyers. Instead the religions, through their prophets, simply state how we ought to behave. These statements are arrived at not by rational argument, but by appeal to emotional response. The great religions, in short, *seek to cultivate and to define emotional response*. Religions have often been criticised for this approach. Yet this is precisely what is needed. Emotion, as Hume said, lies at the root of all ethics. The arguments of moral philosophers, which seem supremely important, are secondary. The underlying emotional response is what counts. As far as I can see, however, only religion seeks to refine emotional response in a formal way and such refinement, I suggest, is the hallmark of religion. Those who seek to modify moral behaviour by appealing directly to the emotions are employing the devices of religion, although, outside the formal religions, they often do so in a disorderly fashion. (I feel, in short, that Hume's idea provides one of the principal justifications for religion; ethics are what make religion valuable even when stripped of specific theology. It is a pity that Hume seemed to present himself as an atheist, and is generally perceived to be so.)

Thus the ethical positions of the great prophets are statements of attitude: of emotional response. Of the great religions, this seems to be least true of Judaism, which is concerned primarily with law, with carrying out what is prescribed, and seems to make least direct appeal to emotional response. Yet the commandments of Moses and the laws laid out in Leviticus do not simply advocate or proscribe particular actions. They too demand particular attitudes: *honour* thy father and mother; *worship* the Lord Thy God; *love* thy neighbour. Jesus, good Jew though he was, tipped the scales a little further, increasing the emotional demands —' 'Love thine *enemy*!' – and sometimes seeming to emphasise emotional response (namely compassion) at the expense of law (as when he effected cures on the sabbath). Yet this was, in the end, just a shift of emphasis. The underlying emotional requirements are already implicit in Judaism.

All the great prophets, in all the great religions, arrived at their perceptions of attitude in the same kinds of way. Notably, they all spent time in contemplation, living ascetically but cultivating mental tranquillity. Long periods in the desert or in the mountains, far from the madding crowd, have been typical, if not *de rigueur*. Many modern leaders who might be classed as prophets, like Gandhi and Mandela, spent time in jail, in solitary: metaphorical deserts. Solitude *per se* surely does not lead to moral enlightenment; but it is clearly part of the technique that may lead us there.

Still we may ask: 'So what?' What in practice do these prophets have to tell us that could possibly be of use? If it were the case, as the sceptics suggest, that they all arrived at different conclusions, then the answer, surely, would be: 'Very little.' If one prophet said we should love our neighbours and another said that all neighbours should be done away with with all possible speed, then we could reasonably conclude that prophets were of no more use than the incumbents of any saloon bar.

But they do not. In fact, as the great nineteenth-century Hindu prophet Ramakrishna observed, all the great moral teachings of all the great prophets of all the great religions can reasonably be summarised in three edicts, all of which describe, not particular actions that we should take, but attitudes that we should seek to cultivate. These are: personal humility; respect for fellow sentient beings; and reverence for the universe as a whole. I have modified the wording somewhat, since Ramakrishna talked of respect for other people rather than for 'fellow sentient beings', and of God

303

rather than of 'the universe'. But the essence is the same, slightly broadened and secularised.

I suggest that most people who think seriously about ethics, from whatever angle, would find it difficult to sustain serious objections to these propositions. Of course they could take quite different stances. They might suggest, for example (as Nietzsche seemed to do), that personal arrogance and self-belief are worth more than personal humility, that it is foolish to care about anybody except oneself and immediate family, that non-human creatures are beneath consideration, and that the universe as a whole, or at least the bit we are in contact with, namely the Earth, is merely raw material for us to treat as we will. Such recommendations might be classed as ethics since they would, after all, be statements of how we ought to behave. But, I suggest, most people who think about ethics would feel that such recommendations are bad. Ethics, most people feel (and how can they be gainsaid?), is about behaving *un*selfishly. Hitler thought he was a splendid fellow, but most of the rest of the world seems to disagree. The plea for personal humility, respect for fellows and reverence for the universe as a whole surely strikes a chord with most people; it seems to provide a reasonable summary of what most of us feel is 'good'. As a grand overview, reduced to the simplest possible statement, I suggest it is difficult to improve upon.

So where is the authority for this summary of ethics? If the prophets are truly inspired by God, and God is indeed in charge, then they have a right to speak out. But if there is no God, then what right do they have? And why should we take notice of them?

Perhaps, in reality, they have no 'right'. Perhaps the commandments of Moses were his own invention and perhaps he had no more right to publish them than, say, Schubert had to compose his *lieder* or Shakespeare to write *Hamlet*. No more right; but no less, either. We, collective humanity who form their audience, have a perfect 'right' to reject all of their inventions. We didn't ask Moses to tell us what our attitudes should be or Shakespeare to trouble us with his plays. On the other hand, we are here, we have to get through life and we cannot survive without the thoughts of other people. It is foolish to reject everything that everybody else says and sensible to accept at least some contributions as worthwhile. Given that we are trying to get through life in the company of other human beings, and indeed that we rely upon the good will of other human beings, we might accept the proposals of Moses on pragmatic grounds. His authority springs from the fact that his comments seem helpful. (In short, even if we rejected the idea that Moses's or Christ's proposals represent absolute morality, we might still accept those proposals on consequentialist grounds. Society would surely be better – kinder, safer, happier – if we acted as he suggested).

These three basic attitudes seem to me to take us a very long way in deciding which biotechnologies should be developed and which we should at least soft-pedal.

For example, the idea that we should engineer breeds of cows that can produce 4000 gallons per year, or pigs that can breed like termites, seem to falter precisely because it shows no respect for the animals. It reduces them to a womb and a sac of milk. The prospect of a 'designer child' with an IQ of 200 and aggression to match, eager and able to outsmart his or her fellows in the courtroom or stock exchange, falters on grounds both of personal humility and of respect. Is such personal success, achieved at others' expense, really desirable? It may seem so in this present age, to people raised in the politics of the past twenty-five years, but the politics of the past twenty-five years need not be the model for humankind.

More broadly, the notions of personal humility and respect for fellow creatures seem to lead naturally to the notion of 'tools for conviviality', framed by the Mexican-based philosopher Ivan Illich in the 1960s. At that time it was fashionable to judge the goodness or badness of technologies according to their perceived sophistication. 'Low' technologies (relatively simple devices such as windmills and bicycles) were typically judged to be good and appropriate for poor countries, while 'high' technologies (the brainchildren of science, such as electronics) were supposed to be more appropriate to the rich.

Illich drew the lines differently. He suggested that a technology might be judged good if it increased the autonomy (independence, self-determination) of the users. These he called 'convivial'.

Examples did indeed include the bicycle, which improves personal mobility, and is largely under the owner's control (not least because bikes are relatively easy to repair); but they also include the telephone, enabling individuals to talk to individuals. Technologies were bad, by contrast, if they served to increase the power of one particular group of people – sometimes the creators of the technology, sometimes governments – over other people. Illich suggested that public broadcasting (at least as it was manifest in the 1960s, typically controlled by a single radio station) was of this type: run by a minority, to influence the majority. Note that the telephone is judged good even though it is 'high-tech'; and in fact bicycles that work properly are also high-tech (since they require modern tyres and metal alloys).

Again, the principle of conviviality seems entirely appropriate in judging the value or otherwise of GMOs. Thus if Indian peasant farmers had access to pigeon peas which had been engineered with genes that increased resistance to mildew, then this, on the face of things, would seem to be a good thing. At least it would help those farmers to continue with their traditional way of life. Of course, it would not be so good if the suppliers of the peas also demanded some degree of fealty as a *quid pro quo*. If the peas were truly to enhance the farmers' autonomy and so pass Illich's test, then the farmers would need, somehow or other, to control the technology that produced them. This is feasible. Genetic engineering, in the future, need not be a horrendously expensive technology, and might well be carried out at a regional level (or conceivably even at village level), with local goals in mind.

By contrast, the present wave of engineered cereals and rapeseed which have recently caused such a furore in Britain do *not* satisfy the Illich criterion of conviviality. They are produced by a few companies to reinforce a system of agriculture that is increasingly monocultural, reducing the range of crops grown and available to consumers, reducing the farmers to subcontractors and focusing profits in fewer and fewer hands. Clearly, they are being deployed as agents of control and for most people they reduce autonomy. Protesters who dug up the engineered crops in Britain gave a variety of reasons for doing so, some of which do not seem to stand up to close scrutiny. Some (as the defenders of the crops were wont to emphasise) were simply Luddite, a general objection to technology. But the political objection was, and is, undoubtedly valid. The new crops, in the context of late twentieth-century Britain, were part of a broad strategy to make agriculture even more industrial and to bring it ever more under the control of big business. That was widely perceived to be bad. Again, the central objection is not that industry *per se* is bad (of course it isn't), or that capitalism is innately evil. But agriculture is important to all of us in many different ways and it is not desirable to place control of it in the hands of a few people, those with entrepreneurial spirit who happen to be good at handling money. It is an important principle of democracy that power should be spread as widely as is practicable. Behind that lies the desire to protect personal autonomy; and behind that, I suggest, lies respect for fellow human beings. In short, GMOs *could* be convivial, in Illich's sense. But the GMOs destined for British fields in the late twentieth century were not designed with conviviality in mind; and people were right to object to them (albeit often for the wrong reasons).

Finally, of course, but crucially, we may observe that the scientists and companies who change the way that crops are produced, by genetic engineering rather than by conventional breeding, have no mandate to do so. They have argued that they do not need one, since genetic engineering is merely an extension of conventional breeding. But that is not the case. The qualitative distinction is clear. In a democracy, anyone who does anything which affects the life of the community as a whole needs a mandate to do so; at least, if 'democracy' is to mean anything at all.

But does the objection to GMOs, or to designer babies who become supercharged billionaires, spring only from the principles of personal humility and respect for others? What of the kind of objection that Prince Charles has raised, that this is 'God's territory'? If we reject the idea of God as is common in this secular age, does such an objection make any sense?

I suggest that it does. Again I feel that we would do well to be cautious on absolutist grounds, to cultivate the feeling that such

307

interventions really are beyond the pale. But again, this point can be made simply by consequentialist arguments.

For consider the point made earlier: that we can never, for inescapable reasons of logic, understand biological systems exhaustively. We may develop wonderful theories that seem to explain the observed facts beautifully and, indeed, we already have many such theories. But we can never know that we have taken all possible factors into account. Bridges and tower blocks still fall down, even though the technologies have been worked out over 10,000 years (at least), and the basic (Newtonian) physics has been developed intensively over 300 years. Still nature springs surprises. *Living* nature is much more complicated than bricks and steel, and surely has many more surprises to pull.

I suggested in Chapters 7 and 8 that if the gene is compared to a word in a language, then the genome as a whole should be compared to literature: and asked whether any of us would risk editing some ancient, sacred text in a foreign language if all we had was a dictionary. It would be reasonable to correct obvious blemishes, to fill in missing letters destroyed by foxing, for example. But to re-cast the text, to change the structure of sentences and the meanings implicit within them, would be presumptuous.

But if we undertook to edit the text of the human genome (as opposed merely to correcting unmistakable blemishes) then the word 'presumptuous' would not do. The appropriate term is 'hubris'. The word is over-used, as so many words are these days. Footballers who attempt to tackle one defender too many are accused of 'hubris'. But for the ancient Greeks, who invented the term, 'hubris' had a chilling quality. It implied that a human being was trying to usurp the power of the gods. All human fortune (according to Greek religion) was dependent entirely on the will and whim of the gods. Success could be achieved only with their help and approval. If ever a Greek hero, flushed with some victory, thought for one instant that his success sprang simply from his own courage and ability, then he was sure to be cut down. To suppose that human beings are truly in charge was hubris and this was instantly and ruthlessly punishable. Hubris, in short, is somewhat different from the Jewish concept of 'blasphemy', an offence against God, but it carries similar weight.

Many people have tried to list the kinds of things that might go wrong if we add genes to plants and grow them in the fields in contact with other plants, or if we try to rearrange and enhance the genomes of human beings. Some of the mooted possibilities seem fairly chilling, although (it is often argued) the most horrendous in general seem the most unlikely. The simple truth, though, is that *we just don't know*: and however much research is done, over however many decades or centuries, that will always be the case. We will never be able to anticipate all the tricks which nature might pull. To suppose otherwise (an ancient Greek would say) is hubris.

Ah, say the technophiles, but if all our ancestors had taken that attitude, then we would still be living in caves! So we might; except that we might not have made it as far as the caves. We might, rather, still be in the trees. But we can (in consequentialist, rather than in absolutist, vein) do a cost-benefit analysis. What is to be gained by growing GMOs? Well, if it helped human beings to continue living as they choose to live (for example, as farmers of pigeon peas in difficult environments), the gains would be quite large. The technology then would be 'convivial'. If they simply allow big companies to take over the world's agriculture, then the gains are at best equivocal. The known risks (that the genes might escape into wild plants and upset the local ecology) must be balanced against the putative gains, though we would have to suspend judgement on the unknowable risk and keep our fingers crossed.

What are the possible gains in producing designer babies? Well, again we might spell them out in a Latin square: who is involved, who gains, who loses. The gains, I suggest, seem entirely selfish and entirely to do with the personal enrichment of the genetically manipulated offspring and the aggrandisement of his or her parents. The risks are horrendous. The ones we can guess at are serious enough. As for the unknowable ones, we have to envisage the equivalent, in a human context, of a bridge falling into a river: what may happen when technology runs ahead of understanding.

For some, though, the possible gains are tempting. What can

outweigh the temptation? Nothing less, I suggest, than the moral conviction that gratuitous manipulation of the human genome is wrong. Consequentialist arguments based on benefit versus risk do not carry the necessary weight. We need the absolutist concept of hubris. This is, of course, a religious concept. It is an emotional response, carefully defined and deliberately cultivated. The concept of hubris (like that of blasphemy) works most easily if we also believe that the world is literally run by God, or by gods. But the feeling that gives rise to it must be cultivated anyway, simply as a matter of policy. Nothing less will do.

The concept of hubris, I suggest, may in turn be seen as a manifestation of the ethical principle defined by Ramakrishna: that we should treat the universe as a whole with respect. 'Universe' can be seen as a secular translation of 'God', or 'the gods'. The point, in both cases, is that the Earth and the creatures within it, including our own physical and mental selves, are not simply commodities for us to manipulate at whim. By the same token, we should not need to ask whether the conservation of wild creatures is a good thing, or worthwhile. Of course it is. If our attitude to the world, which we did not make, is one of reverence, if we feel it is a privilege to live in such a world and have wild creatures around us, then how could it be otherwise?

In short, I suggest that simple ethical principles – simple in the sense of fundamental – take us a long way in contemplating the uses and abuses of modern technologies. These principles are not the creations of lawyers and politicians or even of moral philosophers, but of prophets: people who operate at the level of the emotions. We need to return to these fundamentals and to reiterate them. They will not provide us with off-the-shelf prescriptions in every situation. But they will provide broad guidelines, and without these we are lost. Indeed, since the new technologies could, if we simply stood back, redesign the human body and mind, then the human species as we now conceive it would be lost. There may be no absolute criteria of goodness or badness. There may be no literal God and Kant's ambition to find such criteria without a God may have been forlorn. Even in a secular age, however, we need to pursue the notion that there are absolutes, and to cultivate again the art of thinking in absolute terms.

The task may not be so difficult or arbitrary as it seems. We should look again at the naturalistic fallacy. Perhaps, after all, at least up to a point, the absolutes we seek may already lie within ourselves. Perhaps, indeed, like the rest of us, they are evolved.

The Strength of Human Nature

The naturalistic fallacy does apply. It is naïve simply to propose that what comes naturally is 'right'. It is *not* the case that it is sound Darwinian policy for a man to rape (or at least, not under most circumstances), but if it were, that still would not (most people suppose) justify rape. A woman may well serve her own reproductive interests most efficiently if she becomes pregnant by one kind of man (basically, one who is good at spreading his own genes), but allows another kind (a good, unselfish father) to bring up her children. Yet we tend to feel that the deception that would be involved is unsavoury. Our own brains, our own consciences, tell us that what may seem most expedient for our genes at any one time may not be right.

But what critics of evolutionary psychology commonly suppose to be 'good' Darwinian policy generally turns out to be very crude Darwinian policy: the first approximation, the stragegy that seems to emerge from the simplest kind of arithmetic. Darwinian policies have evolved by natural selection and natural selection, in general, is far more subtle than many commentators seem to suppose. So we hate the coercion and the cruelty of rape, but the revulsion that we feel can itself be seen as an evolved response. We do not approve of the deception when a woman cuckolds her husband, but again evolutionary theorists (notably, in this context, John Tooby and Leda Cosmides) point out that human beings, and indeed all animals, and plants for that matter, have evolved intricate mechanisms for detecting deceptions of all kinds. More broadly, Robert Frank of Cornell University has argued, notably in *Passions Within Reason: The Strategic Role of the Emotions*, that human beings have *evolved* a huge range of subtle emotions and behaviours which have to do with dignity, honour and trust, as well as with the crude passions of anger and fear. David Hume distinguished between the first-order passions (such as anger and fear) and the second-order emotions (such as respect and trust). Most philosophers have tended to assume that the second-order emotions, often seen as 'higher' emotions, are peculiar to human beings and are yet another diagnostic feature of humanity. But modern scholars of animal behaviour perceive that animals, too, recognise concepts such as respect and dignity. These emotional refinements run very deep indeed; and are themselves evolved.

But then, if we put our prejudices aside – the prejudice which says that human beings are qualitatively different from all other creatures, and the prejudice which says that complex behaviours and emotions *cannot* be underpinned by genes – then we would find ourselves asking: 'How could it not be so?' No one doubts that human beings are, by instinct, social creatures. Prolonged solitude in all literature is considered to be unfortunate, heroic, or weird, but it is never considered 'normal'. As social creatures we need a repertoire of behaviour and emotional responses of enormous range and subtlety. Think how many social nuances are involved in the simplest day-to-day transactions, like ordering a meal in a restaurant. No one supposes in these enlightened days that the waiters are literally inferior to the clients, everyone present may feel they want to relax and have a good time, and most of the participants are strangers to each other who often do not share a common first language. Even in such a simple scenario, the roles which each participant must play if all are to relate satisfactorily to all the others have endless ramifications. Yet, on most days, everyone in most restaurants around the world plays their roles perfectly. The waiters are deferential but not servile, the customers are in charge but they are not aggressive, people relax and laugh, but if they overdo it they are condemned by staff and fellow guests alike as oafs and hooray Henrys. A computer that could play such roles so flawlessly would require a much larger programme than the whole of NASA is liable to need for the rest of its existence. Yet most of us breeze effortlessly into restaurants and behave impeccably (or at least well enough) without thinking about it. Indeed if we *did* think about it, we would screw it up. We would become 'self-conscious': thinking about everyday behaviours that ought to be innate. Once we become self-conscious we cease to be 'natural' human beings and become bad actors, unable even to sit down on a chair without fear of disaster.

In short, we can behave as social beings only because we are so beautifully programmed; and the programming has a powerful and essential genetic component. Of course, we learn different manners in different societies and behave differently in different circumstances; very differently with our friends than with our bosses. But our conscious minds, and our learned manners, would be hopelessly at sea if they could not draw upon the deep well of innate responses that has evolved not simply over the last five million years of specifically human evolution, but through all the hundreds of millions of years in which our pre-human ancestors honed the basic social responses.

Psychologists and computer scientists now agree that emotions, which, vitally, embrace the more subtle responses of appreciativeness, kindness, respect and all the other perceived human virtues, play a vital role in framing those social responses. Computer scientists see emotions as a kind of shorthand. They are not detailed programmes telling the brain to carry out strings of particular actions. They are general instructions, setting the tone and drift of the brain's activities. Computer scientists now build artificial emotions into robots, for if they do not the robots cannot make decisions. If the robots simply use their brains, then they spend all their time weighing pros and cons, and in real life there are too many factors to take into account. Without emotions we are paralysed.

In short, we should respect the idea of the naturalistic fallacy: we should not assume that what comes naturally to us is necessarily, *ipso facto*, 'right'. On the other hand we need not assume that what is 'natural' is necessarily brutish and crude. G. E. Moore was writing at the beginning of the twentieth century when the 'natural' emotions were felt to be those of the zoo, and a primitive zoo at that, where the animals are locked up, deprived and behaving pathologically. Aggression and naked fear were felt

313

to be 'natural', while the fruits of human kindness – benignity, respect for others' dignity – were felt to be exclusively human refinements and the stuff of civilisation. Most people, including many biologists, who really should know better, still seem to assume that this is the case: that 'nature' is innately crude and only the human brain is subtle, preferably after a few centuries of civilisation. This, I suggest, is the prevailing human prejudice. But it just ain't so; and a little reflection shows that it *cannot* be so. If human beings, or if any social animal, behaved as crudely as Tennyson's famous adage suggests, then no creature could, in practice, live socially. Redness in tooth and claw simply will not do. Social interactions are bound to be more complex than that. All social animals are socially subtle. Human beings might reasonably claim to be the most subtle of all, for all kinds of reasons. But the subtlety is not the creation of our own vast brains. Our brains build upon, and make manifest, the social subtlety that was already well established in our most ancient ancestors; and that social subtlety includes the repertoire of all the most delicate emotions that have ever been acknowledged by the world's poets.

So yes, we should be prepared to use our brains to override 'nature'. We should seek to ensure that our brains (or at least our 'minds') are the ultimate arbiters. But we should not underestimate nature; our inherited nature *includes* much of what any of us would call morality; it *includes* a respect for fellow creatures. So although we might override nature, we would do well to listen to nature, too. We all know what a 'conscience' is: the 'inner voice' that tells us we are behaving badly. We need not doubt that that 'inner voice' is itself evolved, calling to us from our difficult days on the African plains.

Indeed I am inclined to suggest that the prophets, whom I have extolled, are not tuning in to the voice of God, as they themselves generally believe or at least proclaim to be the case. In reality, they are listening to their own inner voice: to evolved nature. They need tranquillity to do this. Our evolved nature, shaped by natural selection, is not trivial and it is not crude. It is worth listening to.

How do such arguments help us in weighing the new

314

technologies – designer babies, say, or human cloning? Well, some philosophers of my acquaintance take an entirely 'rational' line. For them, the Latin square approach to morality is enough. On the issue of cloning, for example, they are content to list the people involved along one axis, and the pros and cons along the other, add in a Factor X to acknowledge the risks that are yet unknown, and then add up the figures. If the perceived pros seem to outweigh the perceived cons, then (say the ultra-rationalists) cloning should be seen to be acceptable.

Others, though – I am inclined to say 'most people', certainly most of those I have talked to – have additional misgivings which have nothing to do with quantifiable advantages and disadvantages. Many people simply feel uneasy with cloning. It doesn't seem *right*. The rationalists reply that *all* technologies seem awkward when they are new. It's just a question of getting used to them. Many people objected to IVF when it was first introduced even more stridently than many now object to cloning, and yet IVF has become an accepted reproductive treatment. Once people see the advantages of cloning (the rationalists suggest) then they will also, as night follows day, realise the error of their ways and welcome the new advance. The same will surely apply to the designer baby. In a few hundred years, when the technologies are running smoothly, no sensible person will see any objection at all. Those who do object will very properly be sidelined, the flat-earthers of the twenty-third century.

I would like to suggest that we should listen to our misgivings and strive (as the prophets do) to make them explicit. These misgivings are intuitive. They are built into us. They are evolved responses and we should not take our own evolution lightly. Evolution does not necessarily lead to crude results. We should not assume that the thought processes that we call 'rationality' are necessarily superior. Furthermore, the emotional responses that are built into us in a sense *are* us. We are evolved creatures and these evolved emotions are part of the evolved person. Of course, we should apply our rational brains when making moral decisions, for the alternative is simply to shoot from the hip. But we should not assume that our intuitive responses are merely 'primitive', or that because they are primitive we can disregard them. Our primitive emotions are a very important part of *us*, what it means to be a human being, and if we override those intuitions lightly, then we might as well hand over our lives to computers. Some people evidently would like to do that. Maybe if we did, we could run our human affairs more efficiently. It's a big 'maybe'; but in any case, if we did so, then our affairs would cease to be 'human' at all.

So let's return to the ancient and deep concept of 'hubris'. In the manner of evolutionary psychology (at least when EP is in relaxed mode) we might propose that this concept is itself an evolved response and ask how and why it evolved: what it represented to our early ancestors in whom it first presumably arose. I suggest that the root of hubris is dread; and the cause of the dread is, simply enough, the unknown. Every creature, human and otherwise, depends for survival on knowledge of its own environment. It has to *know* (or at least be as sure as possible) what the possibilities and the dangers are and what outcome will result from any particular action. A rabbit needs to know where the burrows are, so it can dash for cover when the fox appears: and it needs to know, too, that the burrow does not contain a snake, which would be just as bad as the fox. If a rabbit is placed in strange territory and does not know where the holes are or if they are safe, you can see its terror. Animals in novel environments first take time to explore them. All animals need to know (or feel) that they are in control.

Dread, I suggest, is the feeling that human beings get (and other animals too, probably, although we cannot speak for them directly) when they are in unknown territory; when they do not know the dangers, or how to respond sensibly to any danger that might arise. Modern human beings seem to have evolved in the open woods and plains of southern and eastern Africa and although many modern people have returned to the forests (which, after all, occupy most of the tropics) many of us have a dread of forest. Forests contribute much to the terrors of Gothic literature. The very word 'jungle' excites a *frisson*, with its implied confusions and hidden threats. 'Jungle warfare' is innately terrifying.

We have all of us felt the dread that comes from circumstances we do not feel we understand and cannot control; lost in a forest, stuck up a cliff, out at sea. In such circumstances one thought is paramount: 'Get out of here!' We may have to abandon all our gear, cameras and wallets and picnic hampers, and be forced to sustain injury. But the priority is clear: get out, because events are overtaking you.

Hubris surely is the formal, poetic expression of that primitive dread; or rather, the directive intended to prevent people getting into dreadful situations in the first place. The Greeks were wonderfully in control of their environment; none had ever been more so. They had excellent technologies and stable societies supported by clear formal laws and moral philosophy. Yet they were also subject to famine, earthquake, invasion and infection; instant, random death from a hundred quarters. Archaeology and written history record several devastating epidemics, including both malaria and the plague. The Greeks knew, then, that for all their rationality and confidence, they were not *really* in charge of the world around them. They were in charge only up to a point, of the bits that immediately concerned them, at least temporarily. They knew full well that they should take no liberties. They had clear ideas about where it was safe to live and who it was safe to do battle with, and – vitally – what behaviours were acceptable and what were not. Those who exceeded the bounds were always liable to be struck down. The concept of hubris kept them on track.

In the context of modern, very powerful biotechnologies I think we are absolutely right to invoke the concept of hubris and to take it seriously. We *know* we cannot understand the world fully, and the more we seek to manipulate living systems the more we are likely to be taken nastily by surprise. The absolute and apparently fully justified confidence of modern engineers and architects, and the disasters which regularly ensue from their confidence, illustrate the principle. But actually, the modern biotechnologies in their extreme form really do present us with a 'no-win situation', as the modern jargon has it. For if we take the new technologies to their ultimate conclusion (and if, by good luck, we fail to encounter disaster along the way), then we will finish up redesigning humanity. Human beings, *as we know them*, will be superseded. Whatever the qualities of the new race which may come after us, that seems to me like a form of suicide. There is a lot wrong with humanity. But we are not trivial creatures; and the fact that we have *evolved* to be as we are, far from being a drawback, is one of our greatest assets, for natural selection over long periods can operate very subtly and produces subtle creatures. The possible gains that biotechnologists might make by changing our genes are entirely hypothetical and the risks are clear (or unknowable, which is worse). We might well try to avoid the ill-effects of the more obvious blemishes – the pathologies like Tay-Sachs disease, which lead to such distress – but to attempt a wholesale editing of the human genome is simply not sensible. More than that: such an attempt would misconceive our abilities. It would indeed be hubristic. We should accept ourselves as we are, warts and all. Beneath the warts, after all, there is much to be pleased with.

The belief that this is so springs from an emotional response and the emotional response can be seen to have primitive roots, nothing more nor less than the dread of the unknown. But it is misguided to ignore our instincts. We have good reason to suppose that our instincts are good precisely because they are evolved; hammered out over many thousands of years by natural selection and 'designed' (loosely speaking) to help us survive in the rough, tough world as social creatures, alongside others of our own kind. It would be hard to improve on that inheritance. Besides, our instincts are *us*; and if we betray them, we betray ourselves.

Suppose, then, that some readers agree with this analysis, or at least with its conclusion: that we should leave well alone and seek simply to make life better for ourselves and each other (and other creatures) while we are on this Earth. What are the chances that such fine sentiments will be acted upon? In practice, are we human beings truly in command of our own technologies? Or are they running away from us, driven by forces that are already beyond our control?

What Can Control the New Technologies?

Lee Silver, professor of biology at Princeton University New Jersey and author of *Remaking Eden*, suggests that human beings in the future *will* practise cloning, and *will* manipulate the genomes of their offspring to the point where they will, in effect, produce a new stratum of society. These will be the 'Genrich' people, as opposed to the rest of us who are content (or stuck) with the genes we inherited by normal means. Indeed he suggests that the 'Genrich' might eventually evolve into a new species: able to mate successfully with each other, but not with the unmanipulated hoi polloi. In truth, the biological technicalities may be somewhat questionable. Thus, a young lad fitted with genes that confer some outstanding quality (such as speed of thought) might be well advised, genetically, to find himself a wife with an untampered genome. Among other things, the offspring of such a union might benefit from the resulting hybrid vigour. Be that as it may, Professor Silver presents a crucial issue with admirable clarity: not *is it right* to clone people or to produce designer babies, but *will these things happen*, whether or not we think they are 'right'?

Silver is in no doubt that they will. What will drive these biotechnologies, he suggests, are market forces; and market forces cannot, in the long term, be gainsaid. There is pull and there is push: demand on the one hand and an eagerness to satisfy demand on the other. There is no stronger emotion that the desire to reproduce and people seem, at least in the first instance, to prefer offspring who are genetically related to themselves. One in eight couples suffers from some reproductive problems (and there is news, early in 2000, that the figure might be rising closer to one in six). Many have already shown their willingness to undergo and to pay for exotic and time-consuming technologies. By the late 1990s an estimated 150,000 children had been born by IVF and by 2005 there could be half a million. In some cases the cloning of one or other parent will seem to offer the only means to produce a genetically related baby. Besides, in this flexible age, same-sex couples are becoming commonplace and for them (or of course for parents who really want to remain single) cloning seems

319

to offer the only feasible option. Cloning is more exotic than IVF, but, as the decades pass, the technology (at least in other animals) will become more or less routine. *Of course*, then, the demand will be enormous. People will be prepared to pay, too. Already they may pay $50,000 for IVF, without guarantee of success. Cloning (when the problems are ironed out) should be more sure-fire, and the fees could well be even higher. People will pay.

Similarly, American parents these days commonly spend $100,000 on their children's university education. Would they not spend another $20,000 (say) on a few genes that would enable their offspring to make better use of that education? Go to Harvard with an IQ of 130 and you should do well. Start with an IQ of 140 and you should do even better. That is the logic. Where's the harm?

There will be no shortage of willing suppliers, either. Even if personally we may disapprove of cloning or designer babies, we should not assume that those who might supply such services are necessarily cynical or evil. Many do not disapprove. Many do not find the objections convincing. The case made above, for conservatism and acknowledgement of hubris, has yet to be widely tested in the public arena. Besides, many clinicians argue that it is not their job to judge the requests of their patients – patients whom they see, very reasonably, as clients. It is their job as physicians to reduce human suffering. If people are suffering because their reproductive instincts are frustrated (and no human suffering is more keenly felt), then they should do what they can to help. If cloning seems the most feasible option, then so be it. Furthermore, those who supply such services know that they can command high fees; indeed that a successful clinic offers a legitimate route to fortune. Financial return may not be the prime motive for a physician. But it helps.

Silver is right to suggest, in short, that market forces are tremendously powerful and no more so than in the field of human reproduction or (perceived) human improvement. Furthermore, in the present world climate, the free market is seen to be innately, morally, desirable. It is (so many feel) the natural expression of democracy. It supplies what people say they want. That is its *raison d'être* and its sole route to survival. Furthermore, the collapse of centralised economies in the latter half of the twentieth century seems to demonstrate that of all the economic systems devised so far *only* the free market can efficiently supply what people want. If the things that people want do no harm to third parties, if the market does not trade in weapons of mass destruction, for example, then how can the market be criticised? What is better, in theory or in practice?

The moral defence of the free market runs even deeper than this. The United States and Western Europe have long seen themselves as the world's proponents and defenders of democracy and so indeed they are, if anyone is. Yet there are many interpretations of 'democracy'. In Britain we seem to stress majority rule (albeit, in these multi-cultural days, paying significant attention to the special demands of minorities). On the whole, if 60 per cent of the people say they want such-and-such a thing, then the remaining 40 per cent, albeit with reluctance, accept that this is the way society is and put up with it. The citizens of the United States put more store by the democratic principle of personal freedom: indeed, some at least of the politicians who advocated America's secession from Britain in 1776 specifically condemned what they saw as the oppressive principle of majority rule. The *point* of creating their brand-new country, they felt – this brave new world – was to enable men (the eighteenth-century word for 'people') to do their own thing. If they merely kowtowed to the majority, then they were no better off than they would be in a quasi-feudal society ruled by aristocrats. Personal freedom remains the battle cry of modern American Republicanism. The free market is seen as the expression of that freedom, which on the face of things is a reasonable point of view. On such grounds, good American Republicans (or indeed liberals) could perfectly well defend the right of others to indulge in cloning, or to create designer babies, even if they themselves disapproved of such procedures. Thus in the United States in particular, the free market is well protected by layers and layers of moral philosophy, history and law. Such an institution cannot easily be overridden; and nor (many would say) should it be.

So is that the end of the matter? We might pontificate as moral

321

philosophers, and even appeal to religion as I have done (albeit in a non-theistic form), but what can anybody say that can divert the market? What *should* they say? But if moral philosophy and religious conviction (and the laws that may derive from them) cannot in practice override the market, what can? Does this not mean that *whatever* misgivings some of us may have, the market will drive inexorably forwards? Note again, too, the timescale. The market might lose the first few rounds of discussion, over the next few decades, but the technologies will still be around, steadily becoming more and more efficient, in 200 years time, or 500, or 1000; and the market will still be there, too. Why don't we just give up now, and lie back and enjoy the changes that are bound to come about?

But the 'battle' is not yet lost. Even if it is lost eventually, we should go down fighting. It is difficult to doubt after the history of the twentieth century that the free market does have advantages and it is surely foolish at this stage of history to mount any political revolutions.

Yet does the market really reflect the will of the people, or most of the people, all of the time or most of the time? In truth, for all its apparent power and precision, the free market is a limited and blunt instrument. It supplies commodities to people who can pay. The richer they are, the keener it is to meet their desires. It contains no innate mechanisms of social justice. There is nothing in market forces to cater for those who cannot pay at all, to bring them up off the floor. If anything, the free market left to itself reinforces *in*justice. The rich grow richer and the poor grow poorer. A society which dislikes poverty and injustice has to modify the free market. In all civilised societies, for this and all kinds of other reasons, markets have to be constrained by laws (or at least by acknowledged codes of practice). Nobody seriously doubts this. The argument is primarily about the *degree* of control that society at large should exercise over the market; and (in these days of the European Union and the World Trade Organisation) of what 'society' actually means. Is the 'society' the nation, as was once taken to be self-evident, or is it the entire quasi-federated continent, or indeed the whole world? These points are highly pertinent, but we can put them to one side for the minute. What matters is the general principle. The free market is here to stay and we should probably be grateful for that, but the market should be the instrument of society (whatever society is) and should not itself dictate the shape and mores of the society. (Of course it may seem to do so already – *vide* the supermarkets and the chains of eating houses – but the game is not over yet.)

What, though, in a democracy, especially one committed to personal freedom, can prevent the supremacy of the market? What has the moral right to override it?

Well, people at large, of course, have the moral right to constrain the market, to tell it what it can do and what it cannot. The means by which they exercise that right are twofold: through the law and through the market itself. Despite the apparent attractions of cloning and of designer babies people may decide, after all, that they do not want what is on offer. A few people might welcome the new technologies, just as a few opt to have their breasts reshaped or their lips made plumper. The law alone could not prevent such minorities from indulging their desires, for whatever is made illegal in the United States or Western Europe could become a cottage industry on some far-flung island with no particular affiliation. But if cloning and genetic manipulation remain minority pursuits – perhaps somewhat looked down upon, considered *infra dig* – then they will not dramatically affect the evolution of the human species. They will still be important, since they would affect individuals; but their importance would not, as has sometimes been mooted, be of seismic significance.

How we make laws to constrain the market, and what should be in those laws, of course raises all the issues argued in the first part of this chapter. I have suggested that whatever we do we must dig deep, invoking and leaning heavily upon our inherited emotions.

But then, if we do that, we might find that law is to a large extent superfluous. People might yet decide, as it were spontaneously, that they simply do not want what these new biotechnologies seem to offer. To be sure, some exotic procedures, like IVF, have caught on; initial revulsion against such technologies has tended to give way to acceptance. But people in various societies have also shown that they can and do reject particular technologies simply because they feel uneasy with them. Somehow, for whatever reason, the technologies seem threatening. Advocates of those technologies invariably argue that whoever rejects them is simply perverse or 'ignorant': such discussions quickly become acrimonious. I am inclined to suggest, though, that our instincts can be far more sensible than the ostensible 'rationality' of the advocates. The latter, after all, are merely pitting their professional knowledge against five million years of evolved wisdom. Thus many people have rejected nuclear power and some societies have banned it, and although the advocates proclaim its safety (even after Chernobyl and various near-misses) this widespread rejection seems eminently sensible. In Britain, too, the tower blocks which the ultra-rationalist planners saw as the answer to the postwar housing shortage are now being knocked down. For families, at least, they are a disaster, as the families themselves said at the outset would be the case. In short, technologies may come into being with tremendous piles of cash and intellectual blackmail behind them and yet be thrown out. If they don't appeal, they don't appeal.

Might cloning and designer babies suffer such a fate? It is too early to say, of course, but they could. People's enthusiasm for present-day reproductive technologies is not so unalloyed as their advocates sometimes claim. Although IVF is an exotic technology it is usually carried out in the context of marriage. It is intended to help married men and women, or at least serious partners, to have children together. Thus the technology itself is exotic, but it is aimed at reinforcing the most homely and conventional of all human institutions: the heterosexual, monogamous partnership which leads to the nuclear family. In context, IVF is cosy: in tune with human instincts.

By contrast, the alleged promise of articifial insemination (AI) seems largely unrealised. AI was first used formally in human beings nearly 250 years ago, by the Scottish physician John Hunter. It was offered as a commercial service in the late nineteenth century. Freezing of human sperm became technically straightforward after the 1950s, and so AI became logistically simple: the donor no longer had to be in the next room. With modern marketing (including the Internet) it is easy for virtually any woman to buy sperm from the most accomplished men in the world: with firsts from Stanford in the subject of the mother's choice and gold medals in the Olympic Games (or near enough). Many women proclaim that they would rather live without the encumbrance of men. Many have suggested that they might live like lionesses, in prides, bringing up their children in creches, collectively cared for, consorting with men (if at all) only for social purposes.

So why don't they? Why, instead, do so many intelligent, determined and free-spirited women settle for an average couch-potato, who watches football (so the cliché has it) and reads *Viz*? Perhaps, just perhaps, because society this past few hundred years has been based upon monogamous man–woman partnerships, so this way of life has become the norm. Perhaps too (so some feminists would claim) these monogamous relationships were invented by men for the ultimate convenience of men. If ways of life are purely cultural, then they are subject to change. What is normal in one society, or set of circumstances, may be quite different in another. Perhaps, as men lose their psychological and economic hold over women, more and more women will reject simple heterosexual monogamy in favour of the pride-of-lionesses scenario or any other scenario they may care to adopt. Perhaps, if all these things come to pass, then reproduction by AI will become commonplace, and monogamous heterosexuality with the live-in male as genetic father will seem reactionary, or merely quaint.

But perhaps – this is only a 'perhaps'; but all possibilities ought to be considered, if we want to arrive at the truth – women prefer to live monogamously with men and to bear the children of the men they live with because that is the way they are. Their preference for such a way of life may simply be evolved. If such a predilection were evolved, it would make perfect sense. Men on the whole (or males of any species) are not happy to expend resources on children who are not their own (or not so happy, at any rate); and women want partners to help them raise their children, and know that their partners are more likely to stay faithful (and helpful) when the children are their own. So there are deep evolutionary reasons for heterosexual monogamy. This does not mean that this is the only possible arrangement that human beings can feel comfortable with, for of course we are flexible creatures. Even if heterosexual monogamy was an evolved response and was in this sense 'natural' this would not make it 'right', in any absolute sense (or so says the naturalistic fallacy). It does mean, however, that heterosexual monogamy is what many people, men and women, feel most comfortable with; and what they feel comfortable with, they will practise. IVF, as presently carried out, generally reinforces heterosexual monogamy. AI, though technically much simpler, seems to threaten heterosexual monogamy. Life as a lioness *manqué* may have many theoretical advantages, but women, on the whole, don't really seem to want to live that way; and the technology that could support such a way of life has not caught on. Maybe it will one day. Maybe the news has not yet filtered through. But maybe, too, people will *always* prefer traditional family life and reject any perceived threats to it simply because that's the way people are. 'Rationalists' who proclaim there is a better way have to answer the question 'Why?'

In the same way that people *seem* largely to have eschewed the much-vaunted advantages of AI, so they might also continue to reject cloning and genetic manipulation. They may simply continue to feel that it goes against the grain, and if that is so then all the pressures of the technophiles will not budge them. Of course, there will be a few cloned babies and 'Genrich' children, just as there are a few all-women societies with babies raised in creches. But the idea that such ways of life will become the norm, that sex in humans will purely be for social reasons, is, we may reasonably guess, a nonsense. My caveats of course are speculation, but I feel they are reasonable speculation. I suggest, too, that if people do feel more comfortable with heterosexual monogamy and with babies produced exclusively by sex and without added genes, then it would be positively evil to persuade them otherwise. Whatever the naturalistic fallacy says, the natural instincts and predilections of human beings must be taken seriously. In a secular world it is hard to see what should be taken *more* seriously.

Taken all in all, then, there are grounds for cautious optimism. The fundamental ethical principles summarised by Ramakrishna – personal humility, respect for fellows, and reverence for the universe as a whole – are simple, yet seem robust. First they summarise many centuries of contemplation by serious seekers after truth, and secondly they seem to summarise those aspects of our evolved instincts that have to do with social living. There is such a thing as human nature, and human nature is much more subtle and innately 'moral' than non-biologists (or even many biologists) choose to believe. The naturalistic fallacy does apply: we must use our brains to seek principles of ethics independently of our evolved instincts. Yet we would do well to explore and to respect our instincts, and indeed we ignore them at our peril. For one thing our instincts have evolved to help us to be social beings (teleologically speaking) and in general they have done a very good job. For another, our instincts are *us*, and if ethics are not about us, then what are they about? The free market is with us, is powerful and at present it seems hard to improve on it. But it cannot be relied upon to do what is 'good' (unless, perversely, we define 'good' as what the market is able to produce), so we must be prepared to control it and if necessary to override it. *Because* we are evolved creatures, however – evolved as social beings – our inbuilt instincts should help us to define what we want the market to do and to reject its excesses. We may well continue to feel that the more exotic promises of modern biotechnology *are* excesses. We *can* resist technophilia. To some extent, we have already shown an ability to do so.

The new technologies, taken to extremes, threaten the idea of humanity. We now need to ask as a matter of urgency who we are and what we value about ourselves. It could all be changed, after all – we ourselves could be changed – perhaps by commercial forces that we have allowed to drift beyond our control. If that is not serious, it is hard to see what is.

This book has focused on Gregor Mendel. I have tried to show how modern genetics, the obsession of modern humankind, all flow so naturally from his gloriously simple but far from simplistic ideas. All that has followed since is footnotes. Mendel was born into a rustic, feudal society, but was truly a modern scientist. He was also a cleric. He himself was the most benign of men: courteous, generous, socially conscious. Indeed, he has a great deal to teach us.

Sources and Further Reading

The following is intended as an informal reading list for those who want to get deeper into the subject – and branch out from there.

2. THE PEASANT AND THE SCIENTIST

The definitive modern biography of Mendel is *Gregor Mendel: The First Geneticist* by Vítězslav Orel (Oxford: Oxford University Press, 1996).

3. BREEDERS, SCIENTISTS AND PHILOSOPHERS

See my own *Neanderthals, Bandits and Farmers* (London: Weidenfeld and Nicolson, 1998) and Ernst Mayr's *Towards a New Philosophy of Biology* (Cambridge, MA: Harvard University Press, 1988).

4. FROM MENDEL TO MOLECULES

An excellent general textbook is *Genetics* by Peter J. Russell (third edition, London: HarperCollins, 1992). See also my own *The Engineer in the Garden* (London: Jonathan Cape, 1993) and *The Language of the Genes* by Steve Jones (London: HarperCollins, 1993). Matt Ridley's *Genome: The Autobiography of a Species in 23 Chapters* (London: Fourth Estate, 1999) is also excellent.

328

5. WHAT GENES ARE AND HOW THEY WORK

Molecular Biology of the Cell, edited by Bruce Alberts and others (New York: Garland Publishing,) is very good. Everyone should read *The Double Helix* by James D. Watson (New York: Athenaeum, 1968). *The DNA Story* by James D. Watson and John Tooze (San Francisco: W. H. Freeman, 1981) is a highly entertaining and diverting compendium of papers and articles tracing the elucidation of DNA's structure and function.

6. MENDEL AND DARWIN: NEODARWINISM AND THE SELFISH GENE

The seminal work is of course Charles Darwin's *On the Origin of Species by Means of Natural Selection*, originally published by John Murray in 1859. The Penguin Classics edition dates from 1985; the quote on heredity is on p. 76. Everyone should read *The Selfish Gene* by Richard Dawkins (Oxford: Oxford University Press, 1976), which shows why it is necessary to shift the emphasis from selection of individuals to selection of genes.

Highly recommended modern treatments include *Evolution* by Mark Ridley (Oxford: Blackwell Science, 1996), *Darwin's Dangerous Idea* by Daniel C. Dennett (New York: Simon and Schuster, 1995), and *The Darwinian Paradigm* by Michael Ruse (London: Routledge, 1989). Excellent modern biographies are Janet Browne's *Charles Darwin: Voyaging* (London: Pimlico, 1996) and *Darwin* by Adrian Desmond and James Moore (New York: Warner Books, 1992).

7. 'GENES FOR BEHAVIOUR': THE PROMISE OF EVOLUTIONARY PSYCHOLOGY

The book that started the whole thing off is E. O. Wilson's *Sociobiology: The New Synthesis* (Cambridge, MA: Harvard University Press, 1975). For grand overviews see *Evolutionary Psychology: An Introduction* by Leda Cosmides and John Tooby (London: Weidenfeld and Nicolson, 1999); *Handbook of Evolutionary Psychology*, edited by Charles Crawford and Dennis L. Krebs (Mahwah, NJ: Lawrence Erlbaum, 1998); and, especially recommended, *Human Nature After Darwin* by Janet Radcliffe Richards (Buckingham: Open University, 1999).

See also *Games, Sex and Evolution* by John Maynard Smith (Hemel Hempstead: Harvester, 1988); Helena Cronin's *The Ant and the Peacock: Altruism and Sexual Selection from Darwin to Today* (Cambridge: Cambridge University Press, 1991); Matt Ridley's *The Red Queen* (London: Penguin, 1994); Steven Pinker's *How the Mind Works* (London: Penguin, 1998); Geoffrey Miller's *The Mating Mind* (London: Heinemann, 2000); and *The Truth About Cinderella: A Darwinian View of Parental Love* by Martin Daly and Margo Wilson (London: Weidenfeld and Nicolson, 1998)

8. GENES REARRANGED AND GENES CONSERVED

See my own books, *Food Plants for the Future* (Oxford: Blackwell, 1988) and *Last Animals at the Zoo* (London: Hutchinson, 1991).

9. THE SHAPING OF *HOMO SAPIENS*

Books on modern biotechnologies applied to human beings include *Remaking Eden* by Lee Silver (London: Weidenfeld and Nicolson, 1998) and *The Second Creation: The Age of Biological Control* by Ian Wilmut, Keith Campbell and Colin Tudge (London: Headline, 2000).

10. WHAT SHOULD WE DO WITH ALL THIS POWER?

I find *The Oxford Companion to Philosophy*, edited by Ted Honderich (Oxford: Oxford University Press, 1995), as good a way into moral (and other) philosophy as any. See also Robert Frank's *Passions Within Reason: The Strategic Role of the Emotions* (New York: W. W. Norton, 1988).

Index

331

333